D1599791

NORDEN

AUTHORS

FRIDTJOV ISACHSEN
Professor, University of Oslo

HÅKON MOSBY
Professor, University of Bergen

STEN RUDBERG
Professor, University of Göteborg

CARL CHRISTIAN WALLÉN
Swedish Meteorological and Hydrological Institute, Stockholm

ILMARI HUSTICH
Professor, Swedish School of Economics, Helsinki

GERD ENEQUIST
Professor, University of Uppsala

AXEL SØMME
Professor, Norwegian School of Economics, Bergen

AXEL SCHOU
Professor, University of København

KRISTIAN ANTONSEN
Reader, University of København

HELMER SMEDS †
Professor, University of Helsinki

SIGURDUR THORARINSSON
Museum of National History, Reykjavík

TORE SUND †
Professor, University of Bergen

WERNER WERENSKIOLD †
Professor, University of Oslo

KARL ERIK BERGSTEN
Professor, University of Lund

A GEOGRAPHY OF
NORDEN

DENMARK · FINLAND · ICELAND
NORWAY · SWEDEN

EDITOR
C. Z.

AXEL SØMME

NEW EDITION

HEINEMANN
LONDON MELBOURNE TORONTO

GYLDENDALSKE BOGHANDEL/NORDISK FORLAG
SVENSKA BOKFÖRLAGET/NORSTEDT · BONNIER
AKATEEMINEN KIRJAKAUPPA · AKADEMISKA BOKHANDELN
HEINEMANN EDUCATIONAL BOOKS LTD · LONDON
JOHN WILEY & SONS, INC., NEW YORK

First published in Norway 1960
Second edition 1961
First published in Great Britain 1961
New revised edition 1968

SBN 435 34820 5

The book is set in 10 p. Times Roman type and printed by
J. W. Eides Boktrykkeri A.S - Bergen
The plates are printed by Georg Westermann, Braunschweig,
and the colour maps by Esselte Map Service, Stockholm.
Blocks: K. Heienberg, Bergen. Paper: Saugbrugsforeningen, Halden.

PREFACE

This book was first presented by the national committees of geography of the five Norden countries to their foreign colleagues attending the 19th International Geographical Congress in Stockholm in August 1960. The authors have been in close contact since 1960 in order to maintain the book as a standard work for advanced geography studies abroad. A second edition appeared in 1961 and a German edition in 1967. The present editor has acted as *primus inter pares* for this group since 1957.

Thanks to the similarity of the Scandinavian languages, which permits oral and written communications without risk of misunderstanding, the outlines of each chapter have been extensively discussed between its author and the editor. Physical geography is mainly dealt with in the general chapters, particularly with regard to Finland, Norway and Sweden, which have so much in common, whereas morphology is treated more extensively in the chapters on Denmark and Iceland.

In cultural respects the five Norden countries form a real unity and a book describing the social and cultural achievements of each country would contain a series of repetitions. These topics are, however, not dealt with in any detail in this book.

After some hesitation we decided to treat economic geography by countries in spite of the recent trend towards unification. The present-day economies have developed behind sheltering trade barriers, and a sound appreciation of the present situation has to take into account differing past developments as much as disparities in natural resources.

We have deliberately avoided uniformity in the treatment of each country, hoping by this procedure to emphasize diversities in the landscape and cultural background of Norden. Silviculture has thus been most extensively dealt with for Finland, fishing and water-power development for Norway, and manufacturing industries for Sweden.

To provide comparisons, a chapter on resources and industries throughout Norden has been added, with some tables covering the whole of Norden. Photographs and colour maps form separate sections. The photographs mainly show landscapes and priority has been given to such human features as are peculiar to Norden.

As we are not writing only for English-speaking people, the metric system and national names have been used throughout. Common Scandinavian words used in the text are printed in italics, and are usually given in the singular. A selected bibliography and a place-name index, with some points about Scandinavian geographical terms and a reference list for these words, have been added. Figures for which no bibliographical references are given have been prepared specially for this book. They may be reproduced without the author's permission, but reference should be made to this book and the author's name quoted.

During the editor's frequent visits to Stockholm, Mr. Olof Hedbom, Kartografiska Institutet, has actively cooperated in the preparation of the new colour maps compiled by Professor Gerd Enequist of Uppsala and by State Meteorologist Finn Pedersen of Bergen. Dr. Wolf Tietze of Wolfsburg, the German translator of our book, has suggested modifications for both the German and new English editions. Dr. Margaret Davies of Cardiff has joined us again in preparing the present edition. The editor's main helpers with maps, manuscripts and proofs in Bergen have been Mrs. Johanne Sømme and Mrs. Ellen Torkildsen.

Bergen, April 1968   AXEL SØMME

DENMARK

København kommune, Frederiksberg kommune, 25 counties (19 *amt*, 6 *amtsrådskreds*), totalling 1 020 communes (*kommune*), of which 88 are towns (*købstad*). Ecclesiastical division: 2 038 parishes (*sogn*).

Sjælland:

1–2. København and Frederiksberg kommune, 3. København, 4. Roskilde, 5. Frederiksborg, 6. Holbæk, 7. Sorø, and 8. Præstø amt.

Bornholm:
9. Bornholms amt.
Lolland – Falster:

Fyn:
11. Svendborg, 12. Odense and 13. Assens amt.

Jylland (Jutland):

14. Vejle, 15. Skanderborg, 16. Århus, 17. Randers, 18. Ålborg, 19. Hjørring, 20. Thisted, 21. Viborg, ⁻2. Ringkøbing, 23. Ribe, 24. Haderslev, 25. Åbenrå, 26. Sønderborg, and 27. Tønder amt.
1–13 Øerne (the Islands).
first, the Swedish second; where there are common

FINLAND

9 provinces (*maakunta/landskap*) and 12 counties (*lääni/län*); 545 communes of which 72 are towns (*kaupunkeja/stad, kauppaloita/köping*). Ecclesiastical division: 596 parishes. The Finnish names are given first, the Swedish second; where there are common English names, they are given in brackets.

Provinces:

Varsinais–Suomi/Egentliga Finland (Finland proper)
Ahvenanmaa/Åland
Uusimaa/Nyland
Häme/Tavastland
Satakunta
Savo/Savolax
Karjala/Karelen (Karelia)
Pohjanmaa/Österbotten (Ostrobothnia)
Lappi/Lappland

Counties:

1. Uusimaa/Nyland
2. Turku–Pori/Åbo och Björneborg
3. Häme/Tavastehus
4. Kymi/Kymmene
5. Pohjois–Karjala/Nordkarelen (North Karelia)
6. Mikkeli/St. Michel
7. Kuopio
8. Keski–Suomi/Mellersta Finland (Central Finland)
9. Vaasa/Vasa
10. Oulu/Uleåborg
11. Lappi/Lappland
12. Ahvenanmaa/Åland (special status according to law of 1922)

ICELAND

14 towns (*kaupstaður*) and 16 counties (*sýsla*), and 213 civil parishes (*hreppur*). Cf. Fig. 10.6. The map on p. 7 shows the old division of Iceland.

NORWAY

20 counties (*fylke*); 454 communes (*kommune*), of which 47 are towns (*by*). Ecclesiastical division: 1 069 parishes (*sogn*).

Østlandet (East Norway):
1. Østfold, 2. Akershus, 3. Oslo, 4. Hedmark, 5. Oppland, 6. Buskerud, 7. Vestfold, and 8. Telemark fylke.
Sørlandet:
9. Aust-Agder and 10. Vest-Agder fylke.
Vestlandet (West Norway):
11. Rogaland, 12. Hordaland, 13. Bergen, 14. Sogn og Fjordane, and 15. Møre og Romsdal fylke.
Trøndelag:
16. Sør-Trøndelag and 17. Nord-Trøndelag fylke.
Nord-Norge (North Norway):
18. Nordland, 19. Troms, and 20. Finnmark fylke.
1–17 Sør-Norge (South Norway).

SWEDEN

25 provinces (*landskap*). 24 counties (*län*); 282 *kommunblock*, 900 communes (*kommun*), of which 223 are towns (*stad, köping*). 677 rural districts. Ecclesiastical division: 2 557 parishes (*församling*).

Provinces:	Counties:
Skåne	1. Malmöhus län
	2. Kristianstads län
Blekinge	3. Blekinge län
Halland	4. Hallands län
Småland	5. Kronobergs län
Öland	6. Jönköpings län
	7. Kalmar län
Gotland	8. Gotlands län
Östergötland	9. Östergötlands län
Västergötland	10. Skaraborgs län
Dalsland	11. Älvborgs län
Bohuslän	12. Göteborgs och Bohus län
Södermanland	13. Södermanlands län
Uppland	14. Uppsala län
Västmanland	15. Västmanlands län
	16. Stockholms län
Närke	17. Örebro län
Värmland	18. Värmlands län
Dalarna	19. Kopparbergs län
Gästrikland	20. Gävleborgs län
Hälsingland	
Härjedalen	21. Jämtlands län
Jämtland	
Medelpad	22. Västernorrlands län
Ångermanland	
Västerbotten	23. Västerbottens län
Norrbotten	24. Norrbottens län
Lappland	

The above list has been arranged in a way which facilitates a comparison between the old and the present (right) administrative division.

1 –8 Sydsverige (South Sweden).
9–18 Mellansverige (Central Sweden).
19–24 Nordsverige (North Sweden).

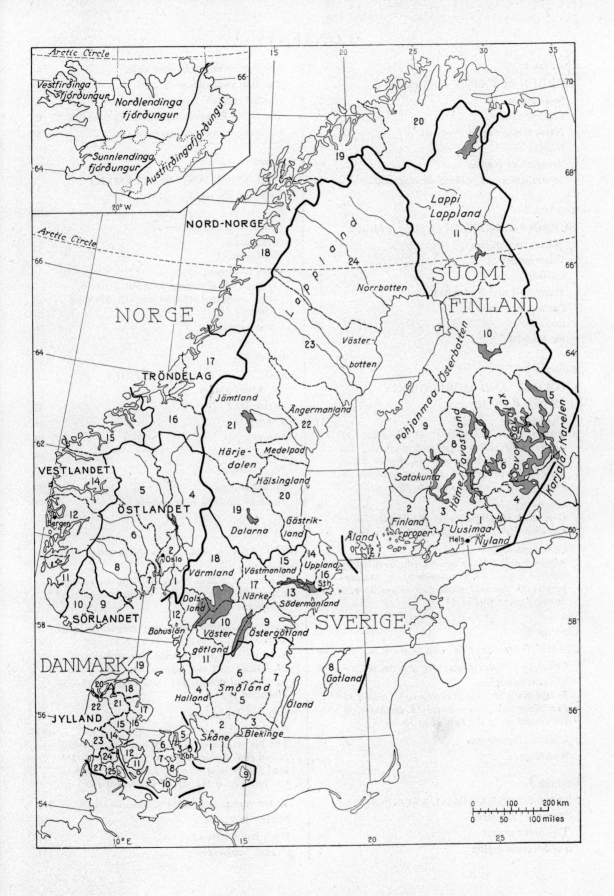

Inset map (Iceland):
Arctic Circle
Vestfirðinga fjórðungur
Norðlendinga fjórðungur
Sunnlendinga fjórðungur
Austfirðingafjórðungur
66
64
20° W

Main map:
Arctic Circle
NORD-NORGE
NORGE
TRÖNDELAG
VESTLANDET
Bergen
ÖSTLANDET
VESTLANDET
SÖRLANDET
DANMARK
JYLLAND
Oslo

SUOMI
FINLAND
Lappi
Lappland
Norrbotten
Väster-botten
Lappland
Ångermanland
Jämtland
Härje-dalen
Medelpad
Hälsingland
Dalarna
Gästrik-land
Pohjanmaa / Österbotten
Häme / Tavastland
Satakunta
Finland proper
Savolax
Karjala / Karelen
Åland
Uusimaa
Hels.
Nyland
Värmland
Västmanland
Uppland
Sth.
Dalsland
Närke
Södermanland
Bohuslän
Väster-götland
Östergötland
SVERIGE
Småland
Halland
Öland
Gotland
Skåne
Blekinge
Kbh
10° E
0   100   200 km
0   50   100 miles

CONTENTS

Administrative divisions pp. 6–7, Photographs between pp. 356 and 357, Selected bibliography p. 334, Place-name index p. 350, Reference list for Scandinavian and Finnish terms p. 353, Colour maps between pp. 358 and 359, Conversion factors p. 354.

Seven colour maps have been retained from the 1960 edition, four new maps have been added (Colour Maps 4, 5, 9 and 10). Two of the older colour maps have been replaced by maps drawn by Georg Westermann Verlag and are included as Figs. 2.1 and 6.1. Of the 165 maps and diagrams included in the 1960 edition, 79 have been retained unaltered, 32 have been slightly altered, and 28 have been redrawn on the basis of more recent statistics. There are 29 new maps. Copyright for the 56 photographs:

A. B. Aeronautic Pl. 12.7
Antikvarisk Topografiska Arkivet Pl. 12.4
Billedcentralen Pl. 11.7, 11.8
The Danish Geodetic Institute Pl. 8.7
Danish Royal Airforce Pl. 8.1, 8.2, 8.4, 8.5, 8.6, 8.8
E. EHLERS Pl. 9.6
K. M. ERIKSEN Pl. 8.3
Finnish Airforces Pl. 9.2, 9.7, 9.9, 9.11
Flygvapnet Pl. 12.6
Försvarsstaben Pl. 12.9
Foto Roos Pl. 9.5
BØRGE FRISTRUP Pl. 8.11, 8.12, 8.13
G. HANNESSON Pl. 10.3
Imatran Voima Osakeyhtiö Pl. 9.1
PÁLL JÓNSSON Pl. 10.5
TH. JÓSEPHSSON Pl. 10.1
Kiirunavaara AB Pl. 12.1, 12.2

Landslaget for Reiselivet i Norge Pl. 11.1
LENNART NILSSON Pl. 12.5, 12.8
GÖSTA NORDIN Pl. 12.11
Nordisk Pressefoto Pl. 8.9
Norsk Hydro Pl. 11.10, 11.11
Norsk Polarinstitutt Pl. 11.13, 11.14
Pietinen Pl. 9.8
G. RASMUSSON Pl. 12.3
T. SAMÚELSSON Pl. 10.2
A. SEIM Pl. 8.10
V. SIGURGEIRSSON Pl. 10.4, 10.6
Svenska Turisttrafikförbundet Pl. 12.10
Teollisuuskuvaus Pl. 9.4
Veljekset Karhumäki Oy Pl. 9.3, 9.10
Widerøes Flyveselskap og Polarfly A/S Pl. 11.2, 11.3,
   11.4, 11.5, 11.6, 11.9, 11.12, 11.15

CHAPTER 1

NORDEN

by Fridtjov Isachsen

THE FIRST North-European land to be explored by navigators from the Mediterranean world may possibly have been the west coast of Denmark. In his Natural History (4, 94–95; 37, 35–36) Pliny the Elder refers to the work of the Greek seafarer Pytheas of Massalia who lived in the days of Alexander the Great. Pytheas' own account of his journey to the North has not survived; and in any case Nordic place names would have occurred in dubious Greek-Latin renderings. Many interpretations of Pliny's names have been proposed. The most recent contributor to this scholarly discussion, Svend Aakjær (København), subjects the 'Pytheas quotations' in Pliny to a close linguistic-geographic scrutiny, and suggests[1] that it is possible to recognize the Proto-Nordic names of two or three localities on the west coast of Jylland. If this is accepted, then Pytheas (Pliny) is the source for the oldest Danish or Nordic place names that have survived in written form.

It is commonly thought that some ethnic and landscape names in the same part of Denmark (Jylland) represent applications or fixations of Germanic tribal names that were well known to Classical Antiquity, e.g. cimbri = Himmerland; teutones = district of Thy; charudes = Hardsyssel; vandili = Vendel or Vendsyssel. The relation between tribal and landscape name may also, in some instances, have been reversed.

Innumerable attempts have been made to decide what part of the Northern Lands Pytheas may have referred to under the enigmatic name of Thule. It is often assumed to have been Iceland, or possibly the Faeroes, or Shetland; others tend to think of the Norwegian coast as the most likely solution of this puzzle.

SCANDINAVIA

In present-day usage, the name Scandinavia denotes the three countries Denmark, Norway and Sweden taken together, i.e. their homelands. It would not be correct to include e.g. the Faeroe Islands, or Spitsbergen, as parts of Scandinavia simply because they are administratively connected with a Scandinavian country. More particularly, Sweden and Norway together are usually designated as the Scandinavian peninsula. This is an unambiguous use of the word. The connections of Finland and Iceland with Scandinavia are discussed below.

The oldest known map which has a representation of the Scandinavian countries is a portolan chart by Giovanni da Carignano of about 1320. The name Scandinavia, though, has come down to us from antiquity and, as used now, is a loan-word of classical-literary derivation. It occurs for the first time in Pliny 4,96 as Scatinavia or Scadinavia (later corrupted into Scandinavia) and is said to be the most noteworthy *(clarissima)* island, of uncertain extent *(inconpertae magnitudinis),* among several others in the immense bay called Codanus, near the peninsula or promontory *(promontorium)* of the Cimbrian people.

Numerous scholars have tried to interpret this name linguistically and to identify it geographically.[2] There seems to be general agreement that *Scadinavia* is a compound word of true Nordic origin, and that the second member *-avia* or *-auia* must correspond to Proto-Nordic *aujo* (Old Norse *ey,*) meaning *island*. Far less convergent, on the other hand, are the suggested interpretations of the first part. Most scholars think that *Scadin-* is derived from the same root that is still recognizable in the Swedish landscape name *Skåne* and the local name *Skanör* at the southern entrance to Øresund. Differing from this, Hjalmar Lindroth maintains[3] an origin from a nucleus *skad-*, meaning darkness, shade, which survives in the Norwegian word *skodde* (mist, fog). This would lead to an interpretation of Scadinavia as the 'Fog Island', or 'Island of Darkness'. Whether this definition is true or not, the ancients seem to have had rather misty notions regarding the Northlands of Europe. Their insular nature, though, was universally realized.

FENNOSCANDIA

A learned name that, although it is of recent origin, has enjoyed wide acceptance, is Fennoscandia. In his Das Antlitz der Erde Eduard Suess refers,[4] erroneously, to 'Sederholm's Fenno-Scandia', interpreted by Suess—also erroneously—as the North-European area of Archaean crystalline rocks. In actual fact, the term was coined in 1898 by the Finnish geologist Wilhelm Ramsay,[5] as is pointed out by J. J. Sederholm[6] himself in his commemoration of Ramsay in 1928. In a paper of 1902, Ramsay[7] explicitly takes exception to Suess' interpretation, saying that Fennoscandia "is not exclusively a geological term", but should be used as a geographical name for "the well defined region which is attached to the rest of Europe only through the isthmian land connections between the Gulf of Finland, Ladoga, Onega, and the White Sea", and whose geological structure and natural environment generally differ entirely from that of the surrounding countries. Already from Ramsay's paper of 1898 it was perfectly clear that he intended the whole of Norway, Sweden and Finland to be linked with the Kola peninsula, the Onega region and Russian Karelia under the new name of Fennoscandia, not excluding from this framework e.g. the Caledonian-folded mountain zone in western Scandinavia, or Skåne. The various parts of this large area have so much in common "with respect to geology and physical geography".

The idea itself is older than the term Fennoscandia. During the latter half of the 19th century, Finnish naturalists were eagerly seeking to define the physical, or 'natural', limits of Finland. In the end, Ramsay contributed the word —after some hesitation between Fennoscandia and Scandofennia—but in 1871 the whole argument had been beautifully expounded by the botanist J. P. Norrlin[8] in his thesis "On the Vegetation of Onega–Karelia and the Eastern Limit of Finland and Scandinavia from the Viewpoint of Natural History".

PHYSICAL FEATURES OF FENNOSCANDIA

A general effect of glaciation in Fennoscandia was the sharpening or rejuvenation of landforms. Countless irregularities were created in all watercourses, and in due time, i.e. mainly since the introduction of the water-driven sawmill about 1520, the utilization of the many water-power sites began. The youthful, broken relief is common to Norway, Sweden and Finland; but the really big hydro-power resources arise only in conjunction with a sufficiently violent macro-relief where great differences of elevation occur together with heavy precipitation. In this respect, Sweden and Norway are in a specially favoured position, sharing between them the mountain zone which some authors[9] would like to call the Scandes, by analogy with the Andes of South America. Norway enjoys the particular 'advantage' of having its highest mountains situated in the southern, most populous half of the country.

In addition to the impact of glaciation, there is a postglacial effect that deserves to be emphasized more than any other. This is the dome-like crustal upwarp that has been going on in Fennoscandia since the Ice Age ended. In the course of this process, extensive areas that were submerged immediately upon ice recession and received their load of marine deposits, were gradually raised above sea level, to form the terrace or plains lowlands so characteristic of many parts of Fennoscandia. Usually, these 'marine', sedimentary lowlands of late- and postglacial formation occur as lobate or patchy indentations around higher ground, leaving the rocky or morainic hills covered by forest and demarcated sharply at a certain, distinct level from the cleared and settled area lower down. This is a recurrent and fundamental motif in the Fennoscandian landscape.

The wider the extent of low-lying land, the larger will be the area affected by any particular amount of uplift of such sedimentary valley- or basin-fillings. The greatest height to which late-glacial marine deposits have been raised is about

300 metres in North Sweden, west of the Gulf of Bothnia, and this is thought to reflect the position of greatest ice thickness in the Würm Ice Age. Crustal movement is still discernible, with a maximum rate of emergence, in this same North Swedish area, of approximately one metre in a hundred years.

The clay plains occupy extensive areas of lowland along the Bothnian coast, in South Finland, and in Central Sweden. At Oslo the 'upper marine limit' is found at c. 200 m, sufficient to give large parts of southeastern Norway the same general character. Peripherally, the ancient marine levels slope down to a zero line which circumscribes Fennoscandia and, furthermore, includes the northern half of Denmark and parts of the East Baltic and White Sea area.

Most of Fennoscandia is occupied by the Archaean Shield of crystalline rocks and offers a rather repellent substratum for soil formation, agriculture and settlement. In Sweden and Norway outcrops of Cambro-Silurian shale and limestone have been preserved in small areas, and, constantly, such favoured patches within the more barren gneissic surroundings have served as nuclei for the subsequent spread of settlement and land clearance. Among these 'Silurian' districts are Västergötland, Östergötland and Närke in Sweden, Ringerike, Toten and Hedemarken in Norway, to name only a few. As some of these lie beyond the limits of late- and postglacial marine sedimentation, they markedly modify the picture of the physical basis for settlement.

NORDEN

Mainly since the First World War, the word Norden (meaning, in all three Scandinavian languages, The North) has been widely used as a name for the small North-European countries taken together, i.e. for Denmark, Finland, Iceland, Norway and Sweden. The living sense of a cultural heritage more or less common to these peoples, and a realization of many common points of interest in the field of international and economic affairs, bring the Norden countries together and create an open-minded attitude towards cultural contact and co-operation in many practical matters.

The most obvious basis for a feeling of kinship is the Scandinavian language community comprising Danish, Norwegian and Swedish.

These languages are, so to speak, interchangeable and are easily understood over their whole area of extension. Their relationship is intimate enough to give the foreigner, who takes the trouble to study one of them, an easy and almost automatic access to the cultural world of all three. This language area would include about 16 million inhabitants. The whole Norden area contains 20 million people. Historically, Icelandic is also a Scandinavian language, but as it has developed rather differently, especially in its phonetic system, while preserving a more archaic grammatical structure, this language could fittingly, together with Faeroese, be said to form a separate, West Nordic, group. Only after special study are the two languages available to Scandinavians, and this applies in particular to Icelandic.

A serious barrier arises from the more isolated position, within Norden, of the Finnish language, which belongs to the Fenno-Ugrian group. On Norden territory, it has a relative only in the language, or rather dialects, of the Lapp minority in the High North. In day-to-day contacts in Finland, the Swedish language frequently serves as an intermediary, a fact which is easily explained by the former importance of Swedish in Finland's public life and, of course, by the actual existence of a sizeable Swedish-speaking minority (350 000) in Finland.

FRONTIERS OF NORDEN

As the word Norden simply denotes a group of states, the geographical extent and delimitation of the Norden region will have to be historically explained.

More or less contingent at the moment of their establishment, frontiers often have their significance greatly increased as the country is later drawn into political focus and more active economic development. This warrants a review of some phases of frontier development, with deliberate emphasis on the little known and almost recent stabilization of boundaries in the sparsely peopled High North.

Although the Norden countries, excepting Finland, look back on a more than millennial existence as distinctive political entities, the consolidation of international boundaries came late in many parts, and occurred gradually. In fact, it was not until the mid-17th century that e.g. the Swedish state secured an outlet on the Kattegat and South Baltic coast. Before that period, Blekinge, Skåne and Halland were Danish provinces, and Bohuslän was part of Norway, so that the territories of the two countries of the Dano-Norwegian monarchy were almost contiguous, leaving a Swedish breathing hole no wider than 15 km near the present city of Göteborg.

In southeastern Norway, the medieval border with Sweden followed expanses of forest land that effectively separated from each other settled areas which, in the east, gravitated towards Lake Vänern and, in the west, towards Oslofjord. On both sides of this frontier, a number of old parish names ending in *mark* (i.e. forest land) are reminiscent of the historical significance of these empty quarters that were later, in the days of lumber export and still more in those of pulp factories, to acquire such high economic value.

Further north, much uncertainty prevailed, and particularly so north of the Trondheim–Jämtland depression. An immense width of useless wasteland, of which the Scandinavian mountain system or 'keel' formed the most conspicuous portion, lay between the scattered Norwegian fjord settlements in the west, and the slowly advancing Swedish pioneer fringe of colonization which was stretching its tentacles westward from the long-settled Bothnian coastal districts.

After lengthy discussion the boundary between Sweden and Norway was agreed upon by treaty in 1751 and marked out on the ground. Today, this is easily the longest unfortified and unguarded frontier separating any two European countries. Since 1809 the northeastern section of the 1751 line has been the boundary between Finland and Norway.

On the 'Subarctic top' or 'cap' of the continent, in Lappland, the definition of the boundary took place, in part, at a still later stage; it was preceded by a long story of competing and sometimes conflicting interests.

In the Middle Ages, the Norwegian domain in Finnmark was extended by means of coastal colonization. The church and fortress at Vardø in the east of Finnmark date from the early years of the 14th century. The fjord and inland areas were the homelands of a scattered and migrant Lapp population that, in the end, had to submit to taxation by two or three masters at the same time, viz. Norwegian, Swedish and Russian. Such tax collecting led to official political pretensions. The gradual northward advance of settlement by all three nations continued. The intricacies of this development have been elucidated by O. A. Johnsen[10] in The Political History of Finnmark.

In the 16th century the Norwegian overlord at Vardø, in addition to governing his own feudal province, had to collect the Crown's taxes in the two Lapp districts called the 'South Mountain' and the 'North Mountain'. South Mountain consisted of the interior of Finnmark, with Enare and Utsjoki added, whereas North Mountain was that part of the Kola peninsula from which the Norwegian authorities collected the Lapp tax, plus, further west, the districts of Petchenga, Pasvik and Neiden. At the same time, Russian representatives, operating from White Sea centres, exercized taxation rights among Lapps in northernmost Norway.

This state of affairs was decisively influenced by the northward and seaward trend of Russian colonization. The first Russian settlement on the north coast of the Kola peninsula occurred in 1524. Russian traders soon established themselves at Kola (Malmis). Norwegian attempts to tax these settlers failed, and the Tsar began to designate Kola as his patrimony. The Lapp tax as such remained a Norwegian interest.

At the close of the century this complicated situation underwent some change. In 1600, the Russians collected their Lapp tax in Finnmark for the last time; and in the winter of 1611/12 the Norwegian administration collected the corresponding final tax from the North Mountain (Kola). The Norwegian rights, however, were not immediately given up, as they were from medieval times associated with wider claims of sovereignty. Incredible though it may sound, the Norwegian administrators of Finnmark, in order to uphold the ancient rights, although no tax was actually obtained, continued their annual 'taxation' journeys to Kola (after 1785 triannually) for two more centuries. And every year the claim was politely rejected by their Russian colleagues in Kola.

After 1611/12 only Neiden, Pasvik, and Petchenga remained as Norwegian-Russian 'common districts', as these areas of mixed taxation were called. Enare district continued as common to Sweden–Russia–Norway, while the other Lapp communities in the South Mountain were common Swedish–Norwegian districts.

This last knot was untied by the boundary agreement of 1751 which laid down the boundary in the interior of Finnmark and transferred Norwegian interests in Enare to Sweden. By the Russian annexations of 1809, Enare ceased to be a common district, and was later, in 1833, joined to Finland.

The Norwegian–Russian common districts were partitioned in 1826. By that time, the Russians had gained a solid foothold in Kola. Among the River-Lapps Russian cultural influence had been strong. By the 1826 treaty, Neiden and part of Pasvik came to Norway, whereas the rest of Pasvik, including, on the western bank of Pasvik river, a 4 sq. kilometres 'outlier' around the Orthodox church at Boris Gleb, plus Petchenga, was attached to Russia. In 1920 Petchenga (Petsamo) and Russian Pasvik were ceded to Finland so that, by a narrow strip of land, the Finnish state gained access to the Barents Sea. This territory was returned to the USSR in 1944.

The various displacements of Finland's eastern border reflect the gradual spread of settlement and, mainly, the changing power balance. The treaty of Nöteborg (1323) roughly outlined a boundary from Systerbäck on the Karelian Isthmus, north- and northwestward across the country to the Gulf of Bothnia.[11] Later, the 'land ridge' was usually regarded as delimiting Finland from East Karelia. Watershed boundaries, though, are of little significance in a plateau country like Finland.

In the Stolbova treaty of 1617, the Swedish king Gustav II Adolf had the boundary drawn across the Karelian Isthmus and Lake Ladoga. After unsuccessful wars, the Swedes, in 1721 and 1743, had to give up the southeastern districts around Viborg and Kexholm, but in 1811 these were reunited with the Grand Duchy, and the old Stolbova boundary existed down to 1940. After the Second World War, the southeastern areas, together with the Salla and Petchenga (Petsamo) districts, were once more annexed by Russia. This produced a population exodus, mainly from the densely inhabited Karelian Isthmus, and was followed by resettlement further west in Finland.

The present Danish–German boundary dates only from 1920. Up to 1864, the Duchies of Schleswig and Holstein were, with a distinctive status, attached to Denmark. After being defeated by the Prusso-Austrian aggression of that year, Denmark had to acquiesce in the annexation of the Duchies, an arrangement that brought the Danish-speaking northern part of Schleswig under Prussian domination. The boundary line of 1920, drawn after a plebiscite, and remaining unchanged after 1945, takes more account of ethnic and national realities.

INTERRELATIONS AND POLITICAL DEVELOPMENT

The insular quality which the ancients attributed to the vaguely known parts that lay towards the Pole, beyond the mainland fringe of Europe, can be said to have validly symbolized a profound historical truth that has continued to manifest itself down through the centuries. For all practical purposes, up to the present day the Scandinavian countries (excepting peninsular Denmark) have remained 'islands', depending, for their intercourse with the rest of Europe, on navigation. In recent years, modern bridges have been built across the Little Belt and a few other straits in the Danish archipelago, but ferry-boats still carry the traffic across the Great Belt and Øresund, and from South Sweden and København to Germany.

The broad isthmus which, between the Bothnian Bay and the Barents Sea, connects Norway–Sweden to the Eurasian block, lies too far north to have played any significant part in the economic and cultural development of Scandinavia, except for the age-long migrations of the Lapps.

The medieval and later Swedish communication with Finland also depended on maritime trade. This traffic gave rise to settlement by Swedish immigrants and the establishment of the Swedish language along portions of the southern and western coasts of Finland. For many centuries, down to 1809, Finland belonged to Sweden. Ecclesiastical development, apart from an initial period of affiliation to the Bremen archdiocese, was similar to that of Sweden, civil affairs were conducted under the same system, and military organization was similar. Such is the historical background that has brought Finland, in spite of the language difference, within the Norden orbit culturally.[12]

For more than four hundred years (1380–1814) Denmark and Norway were united in a common monarchy, with Denmark as the dominant partner. Danish influence in Norway became strong in this period, much like the Swedish influence in Finland, so that administration, army, church organization, written language and intellectual life developed along lines similar to those of Denmark, with a good deal of actual migration between the two countries.

The Napoleonic wars wrought many changes in the political pattern of Norden. Finland, plus a corner of the Swedish province of Västerbotten (i.e. the area east of the Torne River), was ceded to Russia, to form part of the Russian Empire as an autonomous Grand Duchy. This status, which offered some possibilities of home rule and Finnish cultural growth (at least up to the end of the century when a new policy of imperial interference began), was terminated in 1918 by full independence for Finland, recognized by the Soviet Union in 1920.

After the dissolution in 1814 of the Danish-Norwegian kingdom, the Faeroe Islands, Iceland and Greenland remained with Denmark. Norway entered on a 90 year period of loose union with Sweden, an arrangement that by and large respected the autonomous development of Norway. Since 1905 Norway has been an independent kingdom.

The Faeroe Islands constitute, since 1948, "a self-governing community within the State of Denmark", and the Faeroese themselves decide which sections of government they feel financially capable of implementing. Iceland's secession from Denmark took place step by step and terminated in full independence in 1943.

Between Sweden–Finland on the one hand, and Denmark–Norway–Iceland on the other, as a consequence of their divergent traditions, slight differences are noticeable in respect of institutions, social structure and cultural atmosphere. Modern industrial, commercial and social evolution tends to obliterate such shades of difference.

With the exception of Finland, where the trend, however, is similar, the relative numerical importance of the agricultural population has sunk to less than 25 per cent. In most of Norden, economic growth has had to contend with the limitations set by an inhospitable environment, of which the low population density is a striking illustration (Norway 11, Sweden 17, Finland 13, Iceland 2 inhabitants per km² in 1960; lowland Denmark is in a position apart with 109). The northern portions of Norway–Sweden–Finland (together with north European Russia) can be properly viewed as Europe's subarctic 'pioneer fringe' where rapid changes are taking place in our time through modern technology (mining, power development, transportation).

Generally speaking, the Norden countries produce in large quantities a few commodities only, the range of basic resources being somewhat wider in Sweden than in the other four. The variety of processing industries is also greater in Sweden. In several lines of production that depend on the international market, it is difficult for Norden industry to go much beyond semi-processing (e.g. paper pulp, electro-metallurgical products); such branches —like others which supply raw materials proper—are particularly vulnerable in times of economic depression.

The export trade is not large enough to secure payment balance. In the case of Norway especially, shipping, as an international service industry, weighs heavily in the scale and increases the country's susceptibility in periods of economic crisis and political unrest.

The Norden economies are competing, not complementary. For their major commodities, the Norden market, considered as a whole, is grossly inadequate. Although, during the 1960's, the inter-Norden fraction of their total foreign trade has been increasing from 15 to 20 per cent, these five countries belong, by necessity, to a much wider sphere of trade. This is true not only with regard to staple products like pulp, fish and ores, but in the foodstuff trade as well: Denmark's large agricultural surplus can find no adequate outlet in Norway–Sweden–Finland, sparsely populated countries that for various reasons protect their home farmers. Norway, it is true, is seriously deficient in grain for its daily bread, but grain is not an export item from the highly intensive Danish agriculture.

Since 1954, a pooled or common labour market has been functioning, without any revolutionizing effects. The expanding industrial eco-

18

nomy of Sweden has been able to absorb a god deal of foreign labour. The great majority of these foreigners in active employment in Sweden are Norden neighbours, with more Finnish people than Danes and Norwegians taken together. The movement of Finns to Sweden is the most conspicuous feature in the pattern of recent international migrations in Norden.

As a part of a deliberate policy to facilitate contact between the Norden countries, by co-operation in many fields of administration and legislation, the practical significance of state boundaries is also being gradually reduced, and formalities abolished where possible. For citizens of the Norden states, no passports are needed in inter-Norden travel, and no residence permits required. Customs inspection is being simplified by concentrating operations in one post instead of two.

Formerly, the Norden countries used to be active sources of emigration, with a peak movement from Sweden, Denmark and Norway in the 1880's and from Finland in 1901–13. At present, some thousands of emigrants annually leave the Norden countries for overseas, mainly for U.S.A. and Canada, but migration figures are now low, and a state of approximate equilibrium seems to have been attained. To some extent, this may be an outcome of the social security policy which is now pursued, within the framework of the welfare state, by all Norden governments.

NOTES AND REFERENCES

1) SVEND AAKJÆR: Danmarks opdagelse (The Discovery of Denmark). (Nordisk Tidskrift, Stockholm, 1956, p. 219–231; references to earlier literature, p. 219–220). The names in question are the following:
Raunonia (Plinius 4, 94), Cronium — Proto-Nordic *raunanja, *raunja — Danish "hraun", "røn" (bar, spit); most probably the sand bars that shut off the westernmost expanse of Limfjorden in Jylland from the North Sea.
Mentonom-on (37,35) — Proto-Nordic *minthanam, *minthanan — Danish "minne", "minde" (outlet); possibly the historically known seaport of Minde in Nissum Fjord, Jylland.
Abalos, Abalon (37, 35) — historical locality Ålum (Afl-heimr, Avlum) on the narrow Agger peninsula, West Jylland.
2) SCANDINAVIA: references listed in Johs. Brøndum-Nielsen: Gammeldansk Grammatik, vol. II, København 1932, p. 60. — J. SVENNUNG: Scadinavia und Scandia. Lateinisch-nordische Namenstudien (Skrifter utgivna af K. Humanistiska Vetenskapssamfundet i Uppsala, 44,1. Lund 1963).
3) HJALMAR LINDROTH: Är Skåne de gamles Scadinavia? (Namn och Bygd, vol. III, 1915, p. 10–28, part p. 23). — (See also Lindroth in same journal, vol. VI, 1918, p. 104 ff).
4) EDUARD SUESS: Das Antlitz der Erde, vol. III, part 1, Wien 1901, p. 455.
5) WILHELM RAMSAY: Über die geologische Entwicklung der Halbinsel Kola in der Quartärzeit (Fennia, vol. 16, No. 1, Helsingfors 1898, p. 4).
6) J. J. SEDERHOLM: Wilhelm Ramsay (Terra, Helsingfors, vol. 40, 1928, p. 2–3).
7) WILHELM RAMSAY: Om ett sannolikt fynd af kambrisk lera i Viborgs län (Fennia, vol. 19, No. 3, Helsingfors 1902, p. 5).
8) J. P. NORRLIN: Om Onega-Karelens vegetation och Finlands jemte Skandinaviens naturhistoriska gräns i öster (Helsingfors 1871, 132 pp.).
9) The name "Scandes" was proposed, briefly, in 1944 by Erik Ljungner in his paper: Massupphöjningens betydelse för höjdgränser i Skanderna och Alperna (Geographica, Uppsala, vol. 15, p. 119), and later explained in greater detail in his article: Kölen och Skanderna (The Kjöl and the Scandes), in Svensk Geografisk Årsbok, Lund, vol. 24, 1948, p. 190–199.
10) OSCAR ALBERT JOHNSEN: Finmarkens politiske historie (Videnskapsselskapets skrifter, Kristiania, II. Hist-filos. Klasse, 1922, No. 3). Kristiania (Oslo), 1923, 357 pp.
11) HERMAN RICHTER: Geografiens historia i Sverige intill år 1800 (History of Geography in Sweden down to 1800 A.D.). Uppsala, Lychnos-Bibliotek, vol. 17, No. 1, 1959, 287 pp). — A recent discussion of Finland's boundaries, with historical sketch maps, is given by Ragnar Numelin, Finlands statsgeografiska läge (Nordenskiöld-samfundets Tidskrift, Helsingfors, 1959, p. 3–20).
12) In a widely known paper of 1928 (Das geologische Fennoskandia und das geographische Baltoskandia, Geografiska Annaler, Stockholm, vol. X, p. 119–139), Sten De Geer gave, in a series of maps, a synthetic representation of the various features selected by him as constituting the Norden geographic region, taking cultural as well as physical elements into account. The most novel aspect of De Geer's essay was his inclusion of Esthonia and Latvia in a suggested "Baltoscandia", warranted, he felt, by the cultural impact received by these countries during the period of Swedish domination, notably the Protestant faith. In addition, the close relationship between the Esthonian and Finnish languages is emphasized.

CHAPTER 2

SURROUNDING SEAS

by Håkon Mosby

BOTTOM TOPOGRAPHY

THE SEAS surrounding the Norden countries include the Polar Sea, the Barents Sea, the Norwegian Sea including the Greenland Sea,[1] the Denmark Strait, part of the North Atlantic, the North Sea with the Skagerak and the Kattegat, and the Baltic Sea with the Gulf of Bothnia and the Gulf of Finland (Fig. 2.1).

The Polar Sea is poorly known, but soundings have revealed, north of Siberia, a broad Continental Platform where depths of 200 m are found as far out from the coast as 500, 600 or 700 km. The North Polar Basin itself, however, is deep, reaching more than 4 000 m over wide areas, and possibly more than 5 000 m between the Pole and the Bering Strait. A submarine ridge runs from Greenland across the North Pole towards the Siberian Shelf off the mouth of the River Lena. As a result the Polar Basin is divided into two, which will here be called the Spitsbergen Basin and the Beaufort-Siberian Basin. On the basis of the scanty information available, the extension of the two basins has been estimated at about 1.4 and 2.5 million square kilometres at a depth of about 1 500 m (the supposed saddle depth). The shallow shelf sea extends towards the west to the longitudes of Spitsbergen, thus including the Barents Sea between Novaja Zemlya, Spitsbergen og Scandinavia. Depths are here between 100 og 400 m, except in the submarine valley to the northwest of Franz Joseph Land, where depths of more than 600 m are found, and in a depression between Bear Island and the North Cape, not shown in Fig. 2.1, where depths exceed 400 m.

[1] The sea between the east coast of Greenland and a line from the eastern extremity of Iceland to the South Cape of Spitsbergen.

The Polar Basin and the Norwegian Sea are separated by the Nansen Ridge between the north of Spitsbergen and Greenland; its saddle depth until recently has been assumed to be about 1 500 m, but Russian soundings have revealed that it is intersected by a narrow trench, more than 3 000 m deep. The Norwegian Sea is itself separated into two basins by a submarine ridge, the Mohn Ridge, running from Jan Mayen towards the eastnortheast. On both sides depths of more than 3 500 m are found.

The deep waters of the Norwegian Sea are separated from those of the North Atlantic by the Greenland–Iceland Ridge (depth about 600 m), the Faeroe–Iceland Ridge (500 m), and the Wyville–Thomson Ridge between the Faeroes and Scotland. The latter is intersected by the 800 m deep Faeroe Bank Channel.

The North Sea with the Skagerak and the Kattegat, and the Baltic Sea are all shallow, except around the southernmost part of Norway where a submarine valley extends from the Norwegian Sea into the Skagerak; at its deepest part, in the Skagerak, its depth exceeds 700 m. The Baltic Sea is shallow, reaching only to a little more than 200 m, in certain localities near Gotland and Åland. In the Øresund and the Belts the saddle depths are about 35 m.

Table 2.1. *Main surrounding seas.*

	Area	Volume	Mean depth
	mill.km²	mill.km³	m
Arctic Mediterranean	14.1	17.0	1 200
Polar Sea	9.9	12.4	1 300
Barents Sea	1.6	0.5	400
Norwegian Sea	2.6	4.1	1 600
North Sea..............	0.6	0.05	94
Baltic Sea	0.4	0.02	55

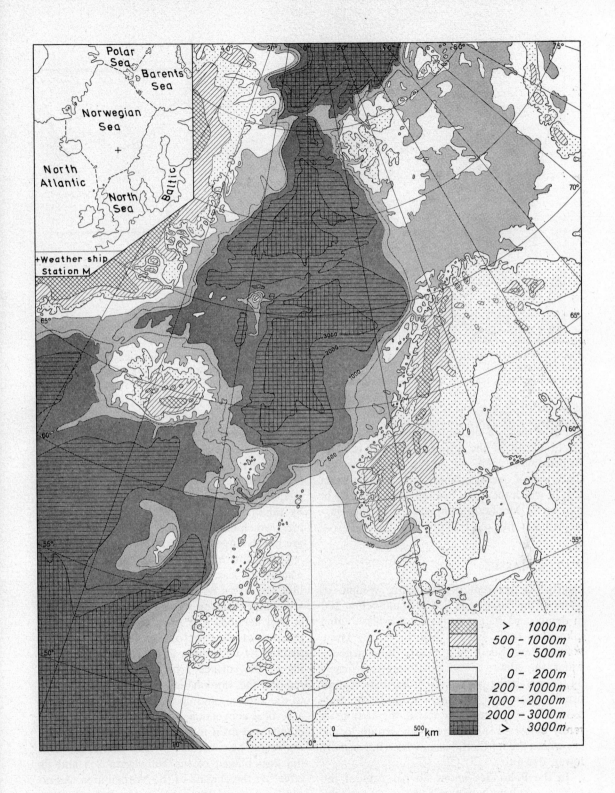

Fig. 2.1. Bathymetric map. Inset map indicates main sea areas.

21

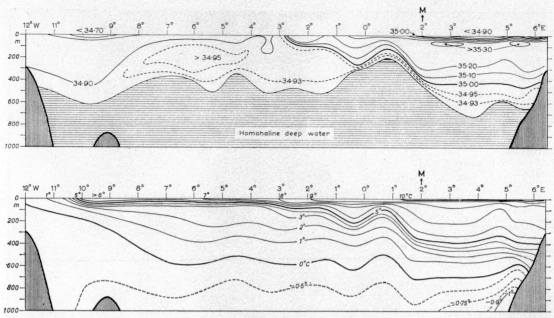

Fig. 2.2. Vertical section at 66°N from 12°W to 6°E. Temperatures in °C in upper diagram, salinity in °/₀₀ in lower. Dark vertical shading: land; horizontal shading: deep water with a salinity of 34.92°/₀₀. The observations were made in July 1935. Although the Weather Ship Station did not operate before 1948, its position has been indicated in the diagram (M).

For a study of the water masses, knowledge of the extent of the different areas is needed. Approximate values of surface areas, of volumes and of average depths are given in Table 2.1, in which the Polar Sea indicates all parts of the Arctic Mediterranean other than the Norwegian Sea and the Barents Sea.

WATER MASSES

Nearly 90 per cent of the entire volume of water of the Norwegian Sea is found below 200 m depth, and 70 per cent or 2.8 million cubic kilometres (mill. km³) is below 600 m. These volumes are filled with nearly homogeneous water, the salinity everywhere being very nearly 34.92 per mille (°/₀₀) and the temperature usually decreasing regularly towards the bottom. The water temperature at the bottom is rarely below –1.00°C, except in certain localities within the northern basin, where it is usually lower, down to –1.20°C.

In the Polar Sea about 80 per cent of the volume is below the 600 m contour; this volume is about five times that of the Norwegian Sea below the same depth. From the data available from the Polar Sea it is known that the salinity of the deep water here is also near 34.92°/₀₀

while the temperature of the deep layers rarely exceeds a lower limit, which is –0.85°C in the Spitsbergen Basin and –0.45°C in the Beaufort-Siberian Basin. Above these layers is an intermediate water of Atlantic origin, characterized by salinities above 35.00°/₀₀ and by temperatures which may be +5°C near Spitsbergen and are hardly anywhere below zero.

From the high values of oxygen content, usually no less than 6.9 cubic centimeter per litre (cc/L) or 84 per cent saturation, it is obvious that the deep water of the Norwegian Sea is well aerated. The process of formation and renewal of the bottom water was first explained by F. Nansen as an effect of the cooling of the surface layer in winter. In certain regions the homohaline water reaches nearly to the surface, and cooling from above sets up a vertical convection, which may reach to great depths and even to the bottom. This process is important also because of the part it plays in the heat budget of the Norwegian Sea and its effect on the climate of the Norden area. As no similar process can occur in the Polar Sea, its bottom and deep water must also have its origin in the Norwegian Sea, from which it flows across the Nansen Ridge into the Spitsbergen Basin.

22

An upper limit of the homohaline deep water of the Norwegian Sea is found at a depth which may vary from less than 200 to more than 800 m. Observations at Weather Ship Station M (66°N, 2°E) have shown changes of more than 300 m in the course of two hours. Nevertheless it appears possible to construct an approximate bathymetric map of this surface, indicating the top of the homohaline water. The dominating feature is a trough running from the Faeroe-Shetland Channel towards the east and continuing towards the north throughout the whole of the eastern part of the Norwegian Sea into the Polar Sea. This trough is filled with Atlantic water and forms a channel through which the Norwegian branch of the Gulf Stream passes from the North Atlantic to the Polar Sea. The approximate horizontal extension is illustrated on Colour Map 7 and may be estimated at nearly 1 mill. km². The greatest depth is about 500 m in the southern part, increasing to 700 m in the north. The total amount of Atlantic water may be roughly estimated at 0.3 mill. km³ or about 7 per cent of the total volume.

The general features of the distribution of temperature and salinity are illustrated in Fig. 2.2 by a vertical section across the Norwegian Sea along the 66th parallel, based on observations made in the summer of 1935. The two parts of the figure, of which the upper shows the distribution of temperature and the lower that of salinity, are extended from the surface only to 1 000 m depth. The true bottom water is, therefore, not shown, its upper limit being at a depth of some 2 000 m or more. The lower curve drawn on the salinity section shows the top of the homohaline deep water. Above this we find in the east, from about 3°W to more than 6°E, the Atlantic water, limited downwards by the 35.00‰ isohaline; it will be seen that in this case the Atlantic water reaches to a maximum depth of about 450 m.

East of longitude 2°E the Atlantic water is seen to be covered by a layer of surface water of lower salinity and of higher temperature. This surface layer occurs in summer only and is due to heating by radiation from sun and sky and to advection of water of low salinity, probably originating in coastal areas. The rapid decrease of temperature (illustrated by Fig. 2.3) and the increase of salinity downwards from the surface water to the Atlantic water gives

a transitional layer of great stability, through which mixing is difficult. Only in autumn and winter is this stratification broken down, the cooling of the surface then setting up a vertical convection. The latter penetrates not only the surface layer, but also the Atlantic water, producing a homogeneous water from the surface until far into the transitional layer between the Atlantic and deep water.

As mentioned, the Atlantic water in the Norwegian Sea is conventionally defined as being water of salinity above 35.00‰. The extreme Atlantic water in the southern area is characterized by temperatures and salinities usually about 9.5°C and 35.42‰. The extreme values are reduced towards the north to about 5.0°C and 34.12‰ respectively north of Spitsbergen. This decrease of the extreme values towards the

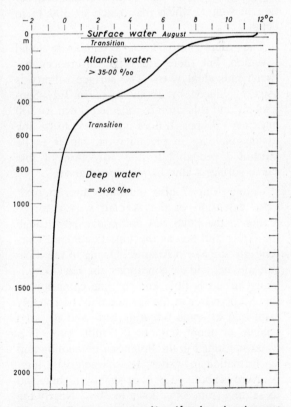

Fig. 2.3. *Temperature distribution in August at 66°N, 2°E.* In summer a layer of surface water covers the Atlantic water; there is a rapid decrease of temperature and increase of salinity downwards through the transitional layer between the two. In winter the surface layer is absorbed by the Atlantic water, which then reaches to the surface. The transitional layer between the Atlantic water and the deep water is permanent throughout the year, but may be found at varying depth.

23

north is very regular, but it can be observed only in summer, because in winter the Atlantic water and the surface water are mixed as a result of the vertical convection.

The numerous data from Weather Ship Station M have shown regular seasonal variations within the Atlantic water. The surface temperature varies from a maximum of between 11 and 13–14° in August to a minimum of 6–7° in March or April. The annual amplitude decreases from an average of 5° at the surface to 1.5° at 100 m, where the maximum is retarded to October–November. Below 300 m no appreciable seasonal variation is found. These variations are due to the heat received in summer by radiation from the sun and sky and to the heat loss by radiation and evaporation in winter. But, as already stated, the whole picture is greatly influenced also by the vertical convection in winter, which may reach to 300 m in depth.

The salinity also shows a regular seasonal variation, but there are great differences between individual years. The surface salinity is usually reduced by about 0.2‰ in July–September, and this drop is reflected down to 100 m or even deeper. It does not appear to be due to any increase in precipitation, but is to be attributed probably to the advection of less saline surface water, as mentioned above.

Colour Map 7 also illustrates the approximate extension of the Arctic water, originating in the Polar Sea and conveyed through the Greenland Sea as the East Greenland Current into the North Atlantic. Owing to the difficult weather and ice conditions, the East Greenland Current is little known. The extension of the Arctic water at the surface may be roughly estimated at some 0.5 mill. km² and its total volume at about 0.05 to 0.1 mill. km³. This water is formed in the Polar Sea by cooling and ice formation in winter. Its characteristic temperature is about −1.8°C or slightly higher, and its salinity from 34‰ down to 30‰. Nearly the same extreme values of temperature and salinity are also found between Iceland and Greenland. But these values are found only in the 'core' of the current. Between the East Greenland and the Atlantic Current an effective mixing takes place, and wide areas are covered by mixed water, often called the Norwegian Sea water, as illustrated by Colour Map 7.

The relatively shallow Barents Sea receives some Atlantic water which branches off from the main current between Norway and Spitsbergen, and also some from the north between Spitsbergen and Franz Joseph Land. The strong cooling in winter and in particular the formation of ice creates a heavy homohaline water, which must be assumed to contribute to the bottom water formation of the Norwegian Sea.

Many of the shallow shelf areas are known to be important fishing grounds. They include the main parts of the North Sea, the waters of which consist mainly of Atlantic water, but are diluted by coastal waters so that the salinity is usually between 35 and 34‰ and sometimes lower, down to 30‰. In cold winters the North Sea water may by cooling become heavy enough to sink down into the above-mentioned submarine valley, the Norwegian 'trench', and bring about a renewal of its bottom water. In the southern Kattegat the salinity is low, about 20‰.

The Baltic is characterized by a surface layer of low salinity; values of 7—8‰ are found in southern and intermediate latitudes, decreasing to 3—4‰ in the northernmost parts of the Gulf of Bothnia. Below this layer is a more saline water of 10—15‰, originating in the Kattegat. Intercommunication is limited to the Sound and the Belts, where the depth hardly exceeds 35 m. Along the bottom an inward current conveys salt to balance the outward transport in the surface current, as will be seen below. As run-off and precipitation in the Baltic are greater than evaporation, Baltic water is conveyed through the Sound, the Kattegat and the Skagerak as the Norwegian Coastal Current. The water masses of this current are gradually being mixed with run-off from rivers and with Atlantic water: but the current continues as a coastal current along the entire Norwegian coast, running inside the Atlantic Current. Its lateral extension varies, usually increasing in spring and summer. Outside and underneath is the Atlantic water, and the mixing zone between the two lies along the continental shelf, and covers most of the banks.

CURRENTS

The general features of the surface current system are shown on Colour Map 7. Dominating features are the Atlantic and the East Greenland Current. The volume transport of the Atlantic Current through the Faeroe–Shetland Channel has been found to vary between wide limits, from 0.6 to 6.5 million cubic metres per second (mill.m³/sec). Similar variations have been found in sections northwestward from Møre, from 1 to 8 mill.m³/sec. But the dynamic computations by which these values have been derived are subject to doubt. Similar computations supported by direct current measurements have given, for the transport of Atlantic water towards the east outside the northern coast of West Spitsbergen, a figure of about 1 mill.m³/sec, but this is based on only one section.

Little is known of the transport of Arctic water by the East Greenland Current. Values of between 1.3 and 1.6 mill.m³/sec have been computed from observations at about 73°N.

On the whole the surface speed of the main current branches is about one half knot, but it is subject to frequent changes, caused by wind. Indications of 'pulsations', especially of the Atlantic Current, have been found; but no method exists by which such variations can be studied with any degree of accuracy.

Colour Map 7 illustrates two major eddies, one in the southern and one in the northern part of the Norwegian Sea. Together with numerous smaller eddies they cover the extensive areas where lateral mixing takes place. The theory of bottom water formation has been very little corroborated by observations until recently, but newer observations indicate an important area of formation within the northern main eddy of anti-clockwise circulation.

As illustrated by the map, at least one branch of the Norwegian Atlantic Current flows into the Barents Sea, and here also two main eddies seem to predominate, one in the eastern and one in the western part of the Sea.

The circulation of the North Sea is also anti-clockwise and is divided into at least two eddies, but these currents are also variable, and so is the Norwegian Coastal Current. In the Baltic the net surplus of water is transported southwards by currents, mainly in the western part of the sea. The average net transport of water from the Baltic has been estimated at 0.016 mill.m³/sec. Apart from this the surface currents of the Baltic Sea are governed by wind.

WATER, SALT AND HEAT BALANCE

The climate of the Norden countries is known to be abnormally mild for their latitudes, and the Norwegian Atlantic Current has long been assumed to be the main cause of this anomaly. Before attempting to evaluate the various factors, let us consider the general problem.

The stratification of the sea is characterized by differences in temperature and salinity. The higher the salinity and the lower the temperature, the greater is the resulting density; and a heavier water will usually be found below a lighter water. Temperature and salinity are conservative characteristics, changing slowly by mixing processes. By the production of typical water masses, contrasts are created in the sea, while mixing processes tend to reduce all contrasts. The resulting average may thus be considered as a balance between renewing and mixing processes.

Physical processes of great importance in this connection are active at the surface of the sea and along the coasts. Heat is received as long- and short-wave radiation from sun and sky, while long-wave outgoing radiation reduces the surface temperature. Considerable amounts of heat are lost by evaporation, since 590 gcal are needed for the transformation of 1 cm³ of water into water vapour, and a layer averaging about 1 m of water evaporates from the oceans every year. But this process is accompanied by a direct transfer of 'sensible' heat from the sea to the atmosphere by convection. This transfer is the main process by which currents influence the air temperature and thus the climate.

Fresh water is added to the surface by precipitation and the salinity of the surface layer is reduced. And fresh water from rivers and brooks, the so-called run-off, dilutes the coastal surface waters. By evaporation, fresh water is removed from the sea, and the salinity of the surface water must increase. In a double sense, therefore, evaporation tends to produce a heavier surface water. Under favourable conditions this may lead to a renewal of the bottom water, as, for instance, in the Red Sea and in the Mediterranean. In high latitudes the net radiation income is low, and the surface is cooled in winter. When sea-ice is formed, only about 5‰ of salt is retained in the ice, while the rest, or nearly 30‰, is transferred to the water immediately below. In some cases this may lead to the production of a water which is heavy enough to sink from the shallow shelf sea to the bottom of the deep ocean basin. This occurs from the Weddell Sea into the Atlantic–Antarctic Ocean or from the Barents Sea into the Norwegian Sea. But in the open deep sea also cooling of the surface may set up a formation of motion of the water particles not only within the Norwegian Sea, but also within the Spitsbergen Basin of the Polar Sea. From basin to basin the temperature of the bottom water increases, being about $-1.0°$ in the Norwegian Sea, $-0.9°$ in the Spitsbergen Basin and $-0.45°$ in the Beaufort-Bering Basin.

Table 2.2. *The Polar Sea balance.*

	Volume transport	Salinity	Temperature	Heat transport
	mill.m^3/sec	$^0/_{00}$	°C	10^{9}kcal/sec
Inflow				
Bering Strait	1.2	32.0	2.1	2.52
Norw. Sea Atl. water	1.4	35.10	3.25	4.55
Norw. Sea bottom water	0.6	34.92	— 0.9	— 0.54
Outflow				
East Greenl. Current	— 2.0	34.0	— 1.8	3.60
Canadian Archipelago	— 1.1	34.0	— 1.8	1.98

ing of the surface may set up a formation of bottom water; most of the bottom water of the Norwegian Sea may be formed in this way, in the area of slow circulation and low stability between Jan Mayen and Spitsbergen.

The heavy Mediterranean water does not only fill the deeper part of the basin, but it flows over the threshold into the Atlantic Ocean, penetrating the Strait of Gibraltar as a salt bottom current. In the east it also creates a bottom current through the Turkish Straits into the Black Sea. In a similar way the deep water of the Norwegian Sea flows over the submarine ridges into the Atlantic and into the North Polar Sea.

Wherever bottom water is formed, the other water layers are, of course, displaced to higher levels. Recent investigations (Mosby 1959) have indicated that in the Norwegian Sea the deep water is in this way moved vertically upwards at an average rate of some 50 m per year. South of the Nansen Ridge the deep water thereby increases in density (weight per unit volume) and flows across the ridge or through the recently discovered trench through it, to renew the bottom water of the Spitsbergen Basin. As a further consequence deep water in this latter basin must flow across the above mentioned Polar Sea Ridge into the Beaufort-Bering Basin. One may thus imagine the bottom water formation in the Norwegian Sea causing a vertical

When a heavier water seeks a level below a lighter water it may have to move over long distances. The distribution of density therefore is a criterion of the movement at any level. On the basis of temperature and salinity observations it is possible by calculations to find the currents in the sea. But as the causes of contrasts in density vary under the influence of meteorological factors, of tidal forces, of internal waves and other factors, many observations are needed to obtain representative mean values of the current. Really long series of direct current measurements in the open sea have only rarely been obtained.

For the study of any limited part of the sea, three basic equations may be obtained by the establishment of the balance sheets on water volume, on salt and on heat content. For the Polar Sea and for the Norwegian Sea (including the Barents Sea) an attempt has been made to evaluate the effects of various factors, using observations, computations and estimates collected from various sources (Mosby 1962). Of the 18 factors considered for the Polar Sea only the ten major ones will be referred here. In Table 2.2 the estimated values of transport by currents are given.

For the water balance a figure of 0.15 should be added due to run-off and precipitation, while about 0.25 must be subtracted due to evaporation and to ice and melting water not included in the estimated currents. From the last column of the table the net amount of heat received is found to be 12.11·10⁹ kcal/sec, and this value is listed in Table 2.3 together with the other heat factors.

Table 2.3. *Heat balance of the Polar Sea.*

	10^9 kcal/sec
Currents	12.11
Radiation	6.80
Ice freezing	3.20
Conduction through ice	— 20.9
Evaporation	— 2.15
Minor factors	0.94

A serious difficulty is due to the variability of the albedo or the reflecting power of the snow-covered ice. As more than 90 per cent of the Polar Sea is covered by ice, this difficulty could, however, be overcome by introducing the heat lost by conduction of heat through the ice-cover itself. It will be seen from the table that 90 per cent of the heat received is lost through the ice.

For the Norwegian Sea, including the Barents Sea, the effects of currents are shown in Table 2.4.

from the ice-free areas (about 2.7 mill.km²). Of the 47·10⁹ kcal/sec about 21·10⁹ kcal/sec or 24.5 kcal/cm²year are transferred to the atmosphere as 'sensible heat'. This would suffice for an increase of the temperature of the atmosphere above the same area by about 0.28°C per day.

For comparison let us consider the results of a study of the data from Weather Ship Station M. By conventional methods an average evaporation of 1221 mm per year is computed here, corresponding to a loss of 72.6 kcal/cm² year as heat of vaporization and 34.5 kcal/cm² year as heat flux to the atmosphere. The latter value would suffice for an increase of the air temperature of 0.39°C per day; the heating of the atmosphere, therefore, is much greater over the Atlantic water than the average heating over the whole of the Norwegian Sea.

The heat loss by conduction through the ice of the Polar Sea was estimated to be –20.9·10⁹ kcal/sec or 6.9 kcal/cm²year. This is less than one third of the amount lost by evaporation from the ice-free areas of the Norwegian Sea, and illustrates the isolating effect of the ice.

Table 2.4. *The Norwegian Sea balance.*

	Volume transport	Sali- nity	Tempe- rature	Heat transport
	mill.m³/sec	$^0/_{00}$	°C	10^9 kcal/sec
Inflow				
East Greenl. Current	2.0	34.0	— 1.8	— 3.6
Atl. water from Atl.	3.6	35.3	8.9	32.0
Outflow				
Atl. water to Polar Sea	— 1.4	35.10	3.25	— 4.55
Bottom water to Polar Sea	— 0.6	34.92	— 0.9	0.54
Arctic water to Atl.	— 3.6	34.0	— 1.8	6.5

Of the originally 23 different factors involved only the dominating 7 are referred to in Table 2.5.

Table 2.5. *Heat balance of the Norwegian Sea.*

Currents	30.9
Radiation	18.0
Evaporation	— 47.0
Minor factors	— 1.9

It is seen that about two thirds of the heat received is due to currents, and that most of the heat is spent in connection with evaporation

The above mentioned surface and sub-surface currents through the Øresund and the Belts have been estimated to transport about 1 000 and 500 km³ per year respectively. As the corresponding average salinities are about 8 and 16‰, it is seen that this transport will balance the total salt content of the Baltic. The net outflow of water is seen to be 500 km³ per year or 0.016 mill.m³/sec; it has therefore been neglected above on the balance sheet of the Norwegian Sea.

The heat balance of the Baltic has been carefully studied by Johnson (1940). For the summer season from 15th March to 15th September he arrives at a net income of 44.5 kcal/cm², which is stored in the water. In winter this heat is lost again, whereby 17.0 kcal/cm² is given off to the air by convection. This is nearly 5 times the estimated amount received by convection from the atmosphere in summer (3.5 kcal/cm²). It will be seen that the net amount of heat given off to the atmosphere of 13.5 kcal/cm²year is about 40 per cent of the corresponding value estimated for the Atlantic water at Weather Ship Station M, and 55% of that estimated for the entire ice-free areas.

SURFACE AND CLIMATE

The above attempt to establish a heat budget for the Norwegian Sea is based on a scanty knowledge of many of the factors involved and should not be considered as much more than an illustration of the order of magnitude. No attempt will be made to elucidate the geographical differences, but some general remarks may be useful.

The total amount of heat received by the sea as radiation at Station M is 55 kcal/cm²year, and the heat loss by radiation is 33 kcal/cm² year. The annual mean of the net radiation received is thus 22 kcal/cm²year; but the monthly mean varies from a maximum of 260 gcal/cm²day in June to −100 gcal/cm²day in December. The annual variation will increase with latitude, but the annual mean value will not vary much. The evaporation varies from a maximum of about 5 mm per day in winter to less than 2 mm per day in summer.

This situation must be expected to be quite different in the areas in the north and west, where surface temperatures are always low. It therefore appears reasonable to expect the heat loss by evaporation and by conduction to the air to be much lower here, while the radiation balance is probably not very different. On the other hand, the net loss of heat will mean a permanent cooling of the water, which will next either be transported out of the region as cold Arctic water, or it may enter into the process of bottom water formation. In the latter case it will be cooled down to −1°C and only again be heated when at some future date it approaches the Atlantic water above.

The above estimated amount of heat of 34 kcal/cm²year lost from the surface to the atmosphere by convectional processes, will directly influence the temperture of the air. It may serve as an illustration of the order of magnitude of the influence of this climatic factor, that the same amount of heat might be obtained by the combustion of a layer of about 3 cm of fuel oil, or of 3·10^{10} tons of fuel oil for the whole area of 1 mill.km² covered by Atlantic water.

If this amount is needed to keep up the positive latitudinal anomaly of the air temperature, one may well expect that in the west and north, where the corresponding value is much lower, the air temperature becomes lower and, especially in winter, conditions become Arctic. This agrees with the distribution of sea ice, as illustrated by the ice borders in Colour Map 11 and on the whole with the well-known strong climatic contrast between the eastern and western part of the Norwegian Sea.

As seen from the preceding section the net loss of heat per unit surface of the Baltic Sea by convection is estimated to be about 40 per cent of that of the Atlantic water of the Norwegian Sea. This may illustrate the relative importance of the Baltic as a climatic factor, and may help in understanding that the effects on the climate of the surrounding lands must be limited.

ICE

The distribution of the ice in the northwestern part of the Norwegian Sea depends also on the East Greenland Current, which carries ice southwards. The striking contrast between these areas in the west and those in the east, with ice-free harbours along the entire Norwegian coast, must be directly ascribed to the Atlantic Current. The formation of ice in the Norwegian fjords, however, is also largely dependent on the amount of brackish surface water present at the time when the cooling sets in. In many fjords the ice-problem therefore is of a purely local nature.

Further information on ice-conditions will be found in Chapters 4, 10 and 12.

PRODUCTIVITY

The term productivity, in the sense 'capacity to produce', is used to indicate the fertility of an ocean region. Primary production is defined as the amount of organic material which by the activity of organisms is synthesized per unit volume or per unit area and per unit time (usually grams of carbon per square metre and day or per per cubic metre and day).

As plants are the only organisms in the sea which can synthesize inorganic substances in significant quantities, the primary production can be measured by the plant production, by adding the amount of organic matter oxidized by the plants and the organic matter secreted by the organisms. When dealing with the open sea, where depths are too great to permit the existence of attached algae, the phytoplankton production equals the plant production.

The zooplankton production is the amount of digested material that is converted into animal protoplasm. Commercial production is the amount of marine products of commercial value. This quantity is usually measured by the products received from the sea, and therefore is no true measure of the fertility, as it depends on the intensity of fishing and on the gear used.

Methods for determination of the primary production by the phytoplankton have been used until recently, when a new technique was introduced using Carbon 14 as a tracer element. This method has been used in Norden waters in the last few years.

The processes of photosynthesis, by which inorganic matter is transformed into organic matter, are largely dependent on light, and as the light intensity decreases rapidly with depth, it appears that the primary or gross production can take place only within the euphotic zone, a surface layer of 80–100 m thickness. But at a certain depth oxygen production equals oxygen utilization; this depth, the compensation depth, will be somewhat different for different species; in our latitudes primary production is limited to a thin surface layer of perhaps 30–50 metres thickness.

However, the gross production naturally depends also on the quantities of nutrient salts present in the water. These substances originate from dead organisms, from the bottom or from the run-off from land. The homohaline deep water of the Norwegian Sea is known to be rich in nutrients; for instance its content of phosphates (P_2O_5) is from 70 to 80 millilitres per litre (mL/L). This is true also of the deep water of the Polar Sea, and the large volumes of deep water thus form an enormous reservoir of nutrients for gross production in these latitudes.

Measurements have shown that a high rate of production is usually found near the boundaries between current systems. Such areas are found 1) between the Atlantic Current and the water from the Irminger Sea, 2) outside the East Greenland Current, 3) on the border between the Labrador Current and the water in the central part of the Davis Strait where values of more than 350 milligrams of carbon per square metre per day (mgC/m^2day) were found (Steemann–Nielsen, 1958). Recent investigations in the Norwegian Sea have also shown similar results (Berge, 1958). Values of more than 400 mgC/m^2day were found within most of the area investigated, i.e. between 64 and 78°N and between 15°E and 0 to 10°W. The highest values amounted to 2000 mgC/m^2day. The distribution of the production capacity in particular, measured at the three different depths, 0, 10 and 20 m, showed a striking resemblance to the distribution of salinity at 20 m depth. Production capacities above $6 \cdot 10^{-7}$ mgC per litre per lux-hour[1] were found between the isohalines for 35.00 and 35.15‰. Within this area the Atlantic water is diluted by admixture of water of Arctic origin. As both of these components are poor in production, it seems that here also the current systems, through the macro-turbulent eddies and possible divergent drifts in the surface layers, bring nutrient-rich, deep water to the surface. Similar effects are found in areas of up-welling, and the above mentioned processes of bottom water formation will clearly help in understanding the results obtained.

Measurements in Danish waters have given values ranging from 6 to 175 gC/m^2year or from 16 to 480 mgC/m^2day, depending on local conditions.

The results from the Norwegian Sea, referred to above, are interesting also from the point of view of commercial production, as the areas of high primary production seem to cover the feeding areas of the Atlantic-Scandinavian herring. Commercial production is treated separately in Chapter 7.

[1]) 1 lux is about 0.00013 gcal/cm/hour.

REFERENCES

BERGE, GRIM: The Primary Production in the Norwegian Sea in June 1954, Measured by an Adapted ^{14}C Technique.—*Cons. Internat. Explor. de la Mer, Rapp. et Proc. Verb.* 144, 1958.

JOHNSON, NILS G.: Östersjöns värmeekonomi.—*Sv. Hydro.biol. Komm., Skr. Hydr.* XV, 1940.
— : Deep Water in the Norwegian Sea.—*Geof. Publ.* Vol. XXI, No. 3, 1959.
— : Water, salt and heat balance of the North Polar Sea and of the Norwegian Sea.—*Geof. Publ.* Vol. XXIV, No. 11, 1962.

NIELSEN, E. STEEMANN: A Survey of Recent Danish Measurements of the Organic Productivity in the Sea.— *Cons. Internat. Explor. de la Mer, Rapp. et Proc. Verb.* 144, 1958.

CHAPTER 3

GEOLOGY AND MORPHOLOGY
by Sten Rudberg

NORWAY, SWEDEN and FINLAND (together with Soviet Karelia and the Kola peninsula) constitute the well-known and well-delimited geographical unit Fennoscandia. In striking contrast to the surrounding parts of Europe the bedrock is of great age, dating from the Archaean era in the central and eastern areas, and from Lower Palaeozoic times in the Caledonian mountain range on the western side of the peninsula. Another contrast is the domination of granites, gneisses and other hard crystalline rocks. A third contrast with surrounding areas—a consequence of the latter—is that horizontally bedded or slightly inclined sedimentary rocks are restricted to small areas in the interior of Fennoscandia and to the central depression of the Baltic and the Bothnian Sea. As continuous areas, such rather undisturbed sedimentary rocks, and sediments belonging to younger geological eras, occur only at the transition to central and eastern Europe, i.e. in Denmark, in the southwestern part of Skåne and in the large islands Öland and Gotland and adjacent parts of the mainland.

Such sediments probably extend under the Baltic, thus strengthening the impression of the Fennoscandian Shield protruding from the younger strata (Colour Map 2). The frontier of the Shield, i.e. the frontier of Fennoscandia, is, in the area discussed, produced by a downbending of the basement, occasionally accompanied by great faults, as, for instance, that following the conspicuous geological boundary in a northwest-southeast direction in Skåne. Great faults are also assumed to be responsible for the Atlantic limits of Fennoscandia. Dependent on such faults are, possibly, a number of longish deeps on the shelf of western Norway.

Iceland, essentially built up of young plateau-basalts, tuffs etc., is in all respects quite different from the rest of Scandinavia. Only in the peripheral faults is there a sort of parallel. These faults, and the great eruptions in Iceland, probably both reflect the great revolutions in the North Atlantic during Tertiary times.

Essential also to the overall picture of Norden are the glacial deposits which more or less cover the whole area, resting directly upon the bedrock.

The stratigraphical *hiatus* between Precambrian basement and unconsolidated Quaternary sediments is among the greatest yet known in the world. It is of overwhelming importance in geological and morphological studies in Fennoscandia. Consequently, the pre-Quaternary rocks and the Quaternary superficial deposits must always be studied separately, and in that way they are discussed here.

THE BEDROCK

Archaean, including Subjotnian and Jotnian

Archaean rocks occupy more than 95 per cent of the area of Finland, about 80 per cent of the area of Sweden, slightly less than 30 per cent in Norway and a small area in Denmark (viz. a part of the island of Bornholm).

Of Archaean rock types, Colour Map 2 distinguishes only between granite, gneiss, schist, etc. In reality there are a large number of different granites, diverging widely in mineral composition and granular size, and in homogeneity. Similarly, the gneisses show wide variations. Large-scale maps with good type differentiation often give a confusing impression.

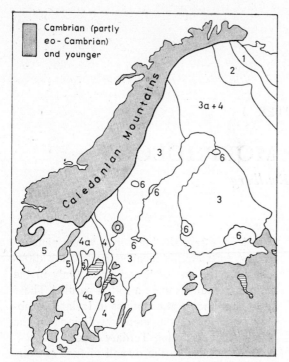

Fig. 3.1 Tectonic regions of Fennoscandia.
1–2. Older orogeneses (saamic, belomoridic), 3. svecofennic, 3a. karelidic, 4. gothic, 4a. pregothic, 5. dalslandic and South-Norwegian, and 6. subjotnian and
jotnian. — After Henning Sørensen: Skandinaviens
grundfjell. Et forsøg på en oversigt. Medd. fra Dansk
Geol. Forening, København, Bd. 14, 1961.

Systematization of the different rock series and
discussion of origins have been facilitated by
the current ideas of the Archaean cycles or
systems, i.e. cycles of rock formation, different
in space and time. Nowadays Scandinavian geologists generally regard these cycles as being
synonymous with phases of mountain building
or orogeny. The rock floor as it now appears is
assumed to show the roots of these old mountain ranges, formed in the same way as younger
and better preserved mountains such as the
Alps. After long periods of degradation deep
sections of the old Archaean ranges have been
revealed, but because of the complicated tectonics of the mountains and tectonic disturbances
after their formation, the rocks in sections now
visible often belonged originally to different
depths. We are fortunate in some cases in being
able to observe only slightly altered supracrustal
rocks, i.e. rocks once formed at the surface of
the earth, such as volcanic and sedimentary
rocks. This is true of the preserved parts of
synclines or of fragments of old overthrust

sheets. But far more frequent are deeper sections of intrusion, of granitization, or the very
deep sections of migmatization (veined gneisses) where there has been melting and/or mobi-
lization of different mineral components.

In Archaean stratigraphy the work must be
carried out step by step; connections over great
distances are impossible, as fossils are totally
lacking (radiometric dating is discussed below).
Hypotheses and opinions are still divergent. A
concept, for long most readily accepted, has
been that of three cycles. These are: the Svecofennic cycle with a dominant east-west strike,
in central Sweden and southern Finland, and
probably in great areas of northern Sweden; the
Gothic cycle with a north-northwest-southsouth-
east strike, in south-western Sweden and southeastern Norway, and the Karelidic cycle with
approximately the same strike in eastern and
northern Finland, northernmost Sweden and
Norway.

Recent mapping, however, and notably modern radiometric dating have produced variations
in the number and age of the cycles. In a recently published paper the suggested cycles,
starting with the oldest one, are: The Pregothic
cycle, the Svecofennic and the Karelidic cycles
(both of about the same age), the Gothic cycle
and the Dalslandic cycle (the two latter closely connected in space and time). Minerals from
Svecofennic rocks are 1 700–2 100 million years
old. The Karelidic rocks have a similar age or
are slightly younger; the Gothic rocks are about
1 400–1 650 million years old or younger, the
Dalslandic about 900–1 100. The dating of the
Pregothic cycle still causes difficulties. The
radiometric methods indicate approximately
the same age as for the Dalslandic/Gothic
rocks, but field evidence makes a far greater age
more probable. Rocks older than the Svecofennic cycle occur on the Kola peninsula according to radiometric datings, and remnants
probably exist in eastern and northern Finland
and in Finnmark (northern Norway)—as they
also do in the Canadian Shield. It should be
noted that the term Archaean nowadays, and
notably in North America, is restricted to rocks
older than 2 500 million years. In that meaning
only few of the Fennoscandian rocks are really
Archaean. As the interpretation of these facts
is not yet clear, it is preferable to treat and
describe the cycles as regional units (Fig. 3.1).

32

In the Svecofennic system the oldest preserved bedrock consists of supracrustal rocks of volcanic origin more or less strongly metamorphosed and to a great extent occurring as so-called leptites. These old volcanic rocks are found in the central Swedish mining district. Probably of the same age are similar rocks in the two North-Swedish mining districts, i.e. the Skellefte area and the Kiruna region. The old supracrustal formation also contains rocks of normal sedimentary origin, such as quartzites, slates, mica schists, conglomerates and limestones. The sediments are generally best preserved in the same regions as the volcanic rocks. As smaller or larger remnants, the old supracrustal rocks, especially schists and slates, are widely distributed in central and northern Sweden and in southwestern Finland. Highly metamorphosed as veined gneisses they are still more widely represented in the same areas. The volcanic and sedimentary rocks are intersected by granites. These often predominate over huge areas mainly in northern Sweden and central Finland. We can distinguish between two generations of granites, the older one forming well-developed rock sequences from acid granites to dark granites, and even to diorites and gabbros. The younger granites are associated with the processes which elsewhere have led to migmatization and the formation of veined gneisses. The younger granites vary only slightly in composition.

The Karelidic rocks are the most obvious feature in the Archaean area of Finland. The roots of the old mountain ranges extend from southeastern Finland to the farthest north, and are dominated by slates, mica schists, quartzites, and by greenstones of different origin. The old supracrustal rocks are often well preserved with original structures such as cross-bedding. Conglomerates, limestones and dolomites occur. Old overthrust sheets can be discerned. The Karelidic formations, which are continued in northern Sweden and northeastern Norway, are accompanied by granites and migmatization as in the Svecofennic system.

The Gothic system exhibits the same general features as the two other systems. Well preserved supracrustal rocks of volcanic and sedimentary origin are found in different localities. Colour Map 2 shows the porphyries of southeastern Sweden (notably in Småland) and also some smaller areas of quartzites and schists. The granites intersecting the supracrustal rocks occupy great areas in the same provinces. The Gothic and/or Dalslandic formations in southwestern Sweden and southeastern Norway appear as monotonous areas of gneisses. They are of varying origin and primary volcanic rocks as well as sediments and granites can be traced. The Pregothic formation occupies areas within the gneiss region of southwestern Sweden, notably in the eastern part.

The Archaean rocks of southern Norway west of Oslofjord cannot yet be correlated with the formations mentioned. Gneissic rocks predominate. Preserved supracrustal rocks of volcanic and sedimentary origin, particularly quartzites (in Telemark) are important, as are intersecting granites. The Egersund field on the south coast has the less common intrusive rock anorthosite which consists almost exclusively of felspar.

Problematic groups of rock are the so-called *Subjotnian* and *Jotnian series,* up to now regarded as of Proterozoic or Algonkian age, but recently proved to be older, probably of Gothic-Dalslandic or partly Svecofennic age, according to radiometric dating. Subjotnian porphyries of varying type, and often of beautiful colours, are well exposed in northern Dalarna, in Härjedalen and in some other localities along the Norwegian border. Of the same age, probably, are the coarse-grained *rapakivi* granites of Finland (rapakivi = decaying stone), and, probably, some similar Swedish granites. The Subjotnian rocks are followed by the red Jotnian sandstones which appear widely in monotonous beds preserved from erosion by downfaulting or protecting sheets of dolerite. The great sandstone areas of northwestern Dalarna and adjacent parts of Norway, and some smaller fields near both coasts of the Bothnian Sea, are particularly noteworthy.

Proterozoic or Algonkian

The Eocambrian series are the only ones nowadays regarded as Proterozoic or Algonkian. Rocks from these series belong for the most part to the Caledonian mountain range and its eastern border regions, and will be discussed below. First in the sequence are the *sparagmite* series of South Norway and Sweden, consisting mainly of sandstones rich in unweathered felspar and lying in beds of varying thickness. Highest in the sequence, monotonous sandstones or quartzites indicate the beginning of the formation of the Caledonian geosyncline. In North Norway slates and dolomites, together with sandstones, are widely distributed. Intercalated between the lower and the higher series, along the eastern margin of the Caledonian mountain range, are tillites (fossil moraines and varved shales) from an Eocambrian Ice Age (or perhaps two in Finnmark). Beyond the Caledonian range Eocambrian sediments occur around Lake Vättern in southern Sweden.

Lower Palaeozoic – Cambro-Silurian

Cambro-Silurian deposits (i.e. Cambrian – Ordovician – Silurian) form the most essential part of the Caledonian mountain range and, in the mainly Archaean areas of Norway and Sweden, are represented in several isolated localities. Although these are usually rather restricted in area, they are of great importance, as many of the most favoured farming districts are based on them. In Norway such deposits occur north and west of Oslofjord and around Lake Mjøsa, and further west on the high plateau of Hardangervidda. In Sweden there are the Cambro-Silurian field stretching diagonally through Skåne, the large islands of Gotland and Öland, a strip on the adjacent mainland, the Cambro-Silurian fields in the provinces of Västergötland, Östergötland, Närke and Dalarna, and a great area around Lake Storsjön in the province of Jämtland. From the latter narrow bands extend south and north along the eastern frontier of the mountain range.

Wherever the contact zone between the Cambrian sediments and the Archaean (or Proterozoic) basement can be studied, the latter proves to have an extremely flat surface, a perfect peneplane, the result of continued post-Archaean degradation. This sub-Cambrian peneplane is very important in many respects. As to deposits, it has often produced equal conditions of sedimentation, and this has been the case particularly for the Cambrian deposits. These generally start with beds of sandstone and are continued as dark alum shales, sometimes rich in bitumen, as in some Swedish areas where oil has been extracted (Västergötland, Närke). But the conditions of sedimentation may vary from place to place even in a shallow sea with a flat bottom. For instance, only slight upwarpings may result in the drying up of wide areas of the sea floor. The Ordovician deposits, formed under these conditions, vary more from place to place. In general limestones are dominant in the east (Öland, Östergötland, Närke, Västergötland, Dalarna and Jämtland) and shales in south (Skåne) and west (central parts of South Norway). The Silurian deposits are essentially limestones in the island of Gotland and some Norwegian areas, but elsewhere occur as shales, especially in Skåne where shales dominate the whole Cambro-Silurian sequence. In southeastern Norway, and in Skåne, Dalarna and Gotland the uppermost Silurian deposits are beds of sandstone which, in Norway, are of great thickness. Here and in Skåne the Cambro-Silurian deposits as a whole are much thicker than in Central Sweden.

The scattered Cambro-Silurian deposits are remnants of an originally more or less continuous cover. Small traces not yet mentioned, for instance swarms of fissures filled with what is probably Cambrian sandstone in southern and central Sweden and the archipelago off southwestern Finland, provide another proof. The reasons for the preservation of the weak Cambro-Silurian deposits vary. They have been downfaulted in Skåne, Närke, Östergötland and Dalarna, downfaulted and folded in the Oslo area, and here, as in Västergötland, they have also been protected by younger lava beds in several areas.

The deposits in the geosynclines of the Caledonian mountain range are in many ways different from those of the shallow seas of the Precambrian areas. Their stratigraphy is difficult to discern because of intense folding, but their thickness must generally be much greater. Rocks of original shale type prove to be the most common in southern central Norway and in the Swedish part of the range, while limestones in northern Norway are more important than they are elsewhere. The sediments are considerably intercalated with intrusive and volcanic rocks, mainly of Ordovician age.

The Caledonian mountain range

The Caledonian range, like other mountain ranges, originated in weak zones in the earth's crust, in geosynclines. They began to be formed roughly 600 million years ago. During continued deepening they were filled with sediments, at first of Eocambrian origin, and later of Cambro-Silurian age. Repeated magma extrusions and intrusions augmented the contents of the geosynclines. The geosynclines were mostly covered by the sea, but some parts may periodically have dried up, resulting in rather special local conditions. Folding took place at different times, the most important being towards the end of the Silurian period or at the transition to the Devonian, more than 300 million years ago. Folding was accompanied by great overthrust movements and metamorphism at greater depths. Long periods of denudation subsequently revealed the deeper sections of the range. As mountain-building stress has in general been directed towards the Archaean foreland in the east and southeast, the mountain range can broadly speaking be divided into longitudinal zones each with characteristic rock, tectonic style and metamorphism.

To the east, in the first zone, are the foreland areas where, locally, the sedimentary cover, but not the Archaean basement, is folded, as in the Cambro-Silurian field of Oslo and in the area of Eocambrian sandstones in Finnmark. In the wide Cambro-Silurian area of Jämtland the sedimentary cover lies in a series of overthrust sheets, but there is no real metamorphism.

In the second zone larger overthrusts are a constant feature in central southern Norway, throughout the Swedish part of the range, and in northernmost Finland and Norway. The complicated system of overthrust sheets or nappes is not yet known in detail. The lowest sheet in the sequence is mostly built up of Eocambrian sparagmites and quartzites, but sometimes slabs of Archaean rock, broken from the basement, have also been overthrust. In northernmost Sweden some nappes are wholly of Archaean rocks. Autochthonous (and para-autochthonous) Cambro-Silurian and Eocambrian sediments of the foreland are covered by these older overthrust rocks. Sometimes the nappes consist of minor nappes, forming imbricate structures. Metamorphism generally increases from east to west. The 'great nappe' consists of rocks from deeper parts of the geosyncline. Cambro-Silurian sediments form the bulk of its rocks, metamorphism is higher—mica schists or phyllites instead of shales and slates—and igneous rocks are important in the form of granites and, not-

ably, basic rocks of different kinds, often altered to gneisses or greenstones. Basic igneous rocks dominate in the high mountains of southern Norway, but their age is still uncertain. In the Swedish part of the range there is usually an eastern area of mica schists (*seve* rocks) and a western one of phyllites (*köli* rocks), in contrast with the usual rule of increasing metamorphism towards the west.

In the third zone, stretching from the Trondheim area through northern Norway up to Tromsø and the Lyngenfjord area, is a still deeper section. The rock types may be similar to those of the second zone, but the folding has generally been stronger. Nappes can no longer be traced. Granite bodies, much more numerous than in the second zone, are sometimes surrounded by aureoles of veined gneiss. Uplifted parts of the old basement have been so altered during the metamorphism that they cannot with certainty be distinguished from granites of Caledonian origin.

The fourth zone, along parts of the Norwegian coast, e.g. between the Sognefjord and the Trondheimsfjord, presents a still deeper section. The mainly gneissic rocks were formerly mapped as Archaean. Many signs, however, point to a partially Caledonian age, e.g. accordance in strike and general structure, and small well-preserved areas of typical Caledonian igneous rocks or schists, such as those in the socalled Bergen arcs. Archaean rocks are probably of great importance within this zone, but because of strong metamorphism and partial melting they resemble true Caledonian rocks ('Caledonized' rocks). The age of some of the igneous rocks, e.g. in Lofoten, is not definitely known.

Upper Palaeozoic – Devonian and Permian systems

After the folding of the Caledonian mountain range Fennoscandia was dominated by degradation, and initially by rapid erosion of the ranges. Evidence for this includes the Devonian deposits on the western coast of Norway and in an isolated locality in the mountains near the Swedish frontier. They consist of thick, mostly folded, beds of conglomerates and sandstones of the Old Red type, and they are freshwater deposits. Marine transgressions do not seem to have occurred over the greater part of

Fennoscandia from Silurian to Quaternary times, and there is a total absence of intervening sediments. The latter fact is of course no proof. It should be noted that the Devonian sediments of the southeast terminate in a cliff on the Latvian coast and partly with a marked slope on the sea floor of the Baltic.

The Permian sediments of the Oslo area are fresh-water deposits. They have made possible the dating of the far more important contemporary igneous rocks of the Oslo region. These igneous rocks occur both as lava beds, as the famous 'rhomb porphyries', and as intrusive rocks in plugs, in chimneys and greater masses. By their extremely great variability in composition they have greatly helped to elucidate the processes of magmatic differentiation. The Oslo area with its underlying Cambro-Silurian deposits was strongly affected by faults during the period of eruption. These faults and eruptions were a pheripherial effect of the Armorican-Hercynian (Variscan) orogeny of central and western Europe. Dykes with 'rhomb porphyries' at greater distances from the Oslo field in the Archaean areas, and dolerite beds in the Cambro-Silurian fields of Västergötland in Sweden, are also thought to be Permian.

Mesozoic

Mesozoic deposits are found in Denmark and on the margins of Fennoscandia, in southernmost Sweden, especially in Skåne, and in a tiny area in northern Norway on the island of Andøy. Triassic rocks include the sandstones and clays of the so-called Kågeröd series in Skåne, and the lower part of its coal-bearing formation. The higher parts of this formation, consisting mostly of sandstones, shale-clays and shales, are of lower Jurassic age. Cretaceous rocks are the most widely distributed Mesozoic deposits in southern Sweden, and they also underlie much of Denmark in the peninsula of Jylland and in the eastern islands. The most common rocks are limestones, but sandstones, sand and clay occur fairly widely. Remnants of Cretaceous deposits in the Archaean areas north of central Skåne indicate a former greater extension. Cretaceous layers also ought to occur on the sea floors of the Skagerak and Kattegat, and in the southern Baltic.

The small downfaulted Andøy field is composed of coal-bearing shales and sandstones of late Jurassic and lower Cretaceous age.

Tertiary deposits

Clays, marls and sands of Tertiary age cover the greater part of Denmark and three small areas in Skåne. The volcanic and tectonic activity of the Tertiary period—the period of the Alpine orogeny—was expressed in Skåne in rejuvenation of great faults, and basaltic necks in the adjacent region. Other possibly Tertiary features are the rhyolitic plug in Lake Mien in Blekinge, the andesitic plug in Lake Dellen in Hälsingland and the dacitic plug in Lake Lappajärvi in southwestern Finland.

The Tertiary period initiates the building of Iceland. The oldest plateau-basalts belong to the Lower Tertiary. Volcanic activity continued throughout the Quaternary period and is still going on (cf. Chapter 10).

GLACIAL DEPOSITS

The whole of Norden was affected by glaciations during the Quaternary period. Glacial deposits are universal there. Colour Map 3 shows the principal features. Norden, including the greater part of Denmark, is wholly dominated by the latest glaciation (Weichsel – Würm), though deposits from earlier glaciations (Saale – Riss) are important in Denmark.

Glaciation

By the lowering of the snow limit at the beginning of the period, glaciers were formed in the high mountains in the western part of the Scandinavian peninsula: cirque glaciers, valley glaciers, plateau glaciers, ice streams, piedmont glaciers and so on. As the snow drift carried great quantities of snow over the range, the culminating points of the ice caps came to be, with increasing glaciation, on the eastern side of the mountain range. Gradually the ice divide moved still further eastwards, possibly to the coast of the Gulf of Bothnia. Altered cyclonic tracks may have contributed to this development.

At the maximum of glaciation, the southern margin of the ice sheets was in central Jylland, in northern Germany, central Poland and in Russia. The maximum ice extension in the west

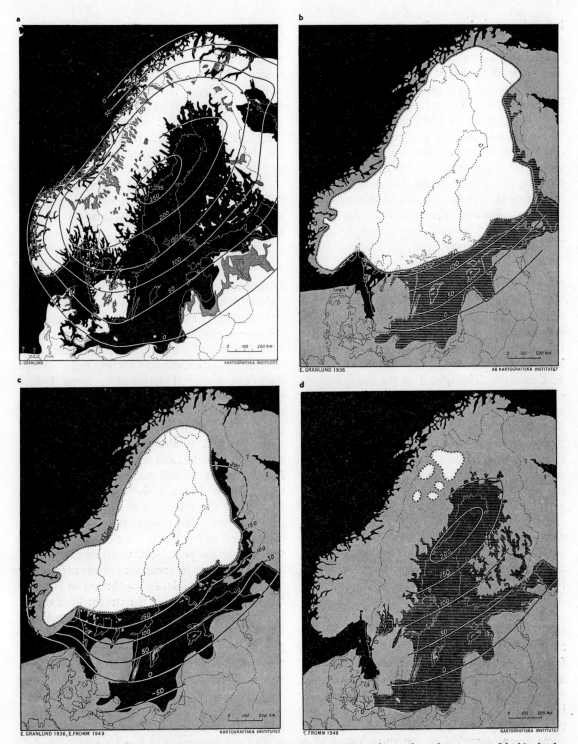

Fig. 3.2. Deglaciation and postglacial uplift. Isobases at 50 m intervals, saltwater sea (black), freshwater lakes (horizontal lines), inland ice (white, map b–d). —a: Highest coastline of the sea and the Baltic Sea. Because of the successive deglaciation and uplift the highest shorelines (usually called the upper marine limit) are not synchronous. — b: Baltic Ice-lake, just before its catastrophic discharge at the northernmost point of Billingen c. 8 000 B.C. — c: Yoldia Sea, c. 7 500 B.C. — d: Ancylus Ice-lake c. 6 500 B.C. Outlet by Svea (S) and Göta (G) rivers, later by Dana (D) river into the Storebælt (Great Belt). Note on all maps the greater extension of the land in the south. It is now thought that the last ice remnants on map d should probably be restricted to the highest parts of north Swedish Lappland.

it not definitely known. It is generally held that the ice calved at the edge of the continental shelf, but recent research suggests that the ice sheet spread further west beyond it. Whether some of the highest peaks protruded as *nunataks* is still uncertain. The refuges postulated by botanists (e.g. along the Norwegian coast) are disputed by geologists and geographers.

As observations of the ice movement (by means of striae, friction cracks, orientation of the long axes of stones etc.) probably relate to late stages in each locality, the striae do not synchronize. However, the pattern of the central ice divide, and its radiating stream lines, are known in broad detail.

Deglaciation

The shrinkage of the ice has been reasonably well elucidated by Scandinavian geologists. The well-known method of measuring the varves of the varved clay has given an absolute chronology whose main dates are well attested by recent research. The retreat of the ice margin is shown on Fig. 3.2. It is obvious that the rate of retreat varied, and that the ice margin must have been stationary in some regions for long periods. Such a stationary line, where the ice margin stayed at least 800 years, passes from southern Norway through Central Sweden to southern Finland. Before and after this stationary period the ice retreat was remarkably swift.

During an ice retreat there is a marked difference between a glacier which terminates in the sea or in a lake, and one in which shrinkage occurs only above water level. In the first case the ice sheet terminates in a cliff, and the retreat of the margin is visibly influenced by calving. In the latter no cliff is formed, the shrinkage of the ice—often dead ice—proceeds as downwasting in situ. Crests and summits are free of ice at an early stage, ice remnants wane in the valleys. Only in the farthest north do conditions seem to have been different. Here the last ice remnants are found in the high mountains, possibly because of some lowering of the snow line at a critical retreat stage, or because of the local environment, e.g. broad, open valleys, which provided easy access to the open sea for valley glaciers draining the remnants of the inland ice.

The ice melted in subaqueous surroundings more than would be imagined from the map of present-day conditions. As is well known, great areas of Norden were depressed below sea level by the weight of the ice masses during the glaciation. Yet the sea level was lower than it now is, because much water was stored in the great glaciers. Because of this double background—isostatic and eustatic—the postglacial uplift of the land, which is still proceeding, has been rather complicated. A good example is the development of the Baltic during three stages: Baltic Ice Lake, Yoldia Sea, Ancylus Lake (Fig. 3.2). This uplift is the last event to bear in mind in describing the Quaternary deposits.

Distribution of morainic deposits

Differences in the thickness of deposits and in the distribution of exposed bedrock are essential features in the landscape which cannot yet be shown satisfactorily in a map. On Colour Map 3 a special symbol for thin morainic cover intermixed with exposed rock has been used to try to give a general picture of the latter. Poorly covered areas are especially common in southern, western and northern Norway, largely regions with a high and steep relief. Much exposed bedrock is also found along the coasts around Stockholm, and still more along the west Swedish coast around and north of Göteborg. Outcropping bedrock is a striking feature throughout the outer fringe of the Fennoscandian skerries. The reasons for the distribution of exposed bedrock are not clear. Marine erosion during the postglacial uplift of the land or mass movement in some very steep area could partly be responsible. In southernmost Norway bare rock occurs where the stream lines of the moving ice diverged. Areas of bare rock are specially common where deep water occurs not too far from the coast. This means that swift ice movement and swift removal of loosened debris was facilitated.

In Norway, Sweden and Finland glacial erosion may have been greater than glacial accumulation. Representative figures for the thickness of moraine cover in Sweden may be as follows: southern Sweden 4–5 m as a mean value, inner northern Sweden (above the upper marine limit) 8–9 m. In Denmark, where glacial accumulation preponderates, the mean value amounts to 50 m. Finnish values are probably similar to those of Sweden.

Types of deposits

A distinctively distributed group of deposits are those in areas which were situated below sea level during the deglaciation, i.e. much of Finland, the central lowlands of Sweden, and an often broad strip of land along the coast of that country, the open areas around Oslofjord and Trondheimsfjord, and a mostly narrow strip of land along the Norwegian and parts of the Danish coasts.

The drift cover in these areas only partly exhibits its characteristic features. Such are the occasionally well-developed drumlins. Such are also the wash-board moraines which occur in series in different parts of the Swedish and Finnish lowlands, and are interpreted as marks of a yearly rhythm in the recession of the ice margin, or more recently, as traces of successive calvings. Larger marginal deposits of detritus which is partly morainic and partly glacifluvial are connected with the great stationary line already mentioned. The early identified *ra* ridges of southern Norway, the middle Swedish end-moraines, and the great *Salpausselkä* of Finland belong to this system. The correlations are still discussed, particularly in the east of Central Sweden.

The glacial streams from the swiftly melting ice masses were heavily loaded, and left important deposits in the landscape. The Scandinavian eskers (oses) are most commonly interpreted as successively deposited delta cones of subglacial melt-water rivers, and eskers above the highest marine limit as tunnel fillings.

The most typical eskers are found in eastern Central Sweden, and in southern and central Finland, where they sometimes stretch in slightly curving courses for more than 300 kilometres, and with their heights of 25–30 m are a striking feature of the otherwise level landscape (see Pl. 12.6). While the typical esker generally follows the direction of the ice movement, there are, in the outer part of Norwegian valleys and in parts of southwestern Sweden, series of conspicuous transverse ridges of glacifluvial deposits. They may sometimes belong to stationary lines associated with terminal moraines like the great 'ra' ridges. Glacifluvial deltas are particularly frequent in association with larger stationary lines or in the valleys just below the upper marine limit. The fine material of the glacial streams, such as clay and silt, is carried away from the mouth to be deposited at a distance, the clay as varved clay in fresh or brackish water.

All deposits were abraded by the sea during the uplift, and were more or less superficially washed, while material of finer grain size was carried away and deposited as layers of sand, silt or clay above the older glacial sediments in lower-lying areas.

Above the upper marine limit conditions can be identical where an ice-dammed lake is formed. Such lakes existed in many places, the best known were dammed between the mountain range and ice remnants farther to the east. The proof lies in terraces, deltas and outflow gorges. Modern thought questions former estimates of the great size of these lakes.

In general, conditions are different above the upper marine limit. Wash-board moraines are absent, but not drumlins, and hummocky moraines in particular are common, both in the high areas of Lappland and in the rolling plains of Denmark and southern Skåne. Eskers are more irregularly shaped, and not as continuous as in subaqueous environments. Outwash plains have recently proved to be rather common in the uplands of North Sweden. They have long been known as a characteristic feature of the landscape of Jylland. In Iceland extensive sandur plains are still forming along the margins of the great glaciers. Examples of melt-water erosion are numerous. Such are the great tunnel valleys of Jylland, formed by great subglacial melt-water streams, and the overflow and lateral drainage channels formed by the melt-waters of the shrinking ice in the highland areas of Norway, Sweden and Finland.

The Quaternary transformation of the landscape has in many respects produced unstable conditions. These result in visible changes and sometimes in swift destruction. Examples include rockslides in the oversteepened sides of the Norwegian fjord valleys, erosion and terrace building in the unconsolidated sediments of the valleys, sometimes accompanied by catastrophic landslides if the material is silt and clay (as along the Göta river in 1950 and 1957), visible silting up of flat coasts in living memory where emergence of land is still important (Bothnian Bay), and effective solifluction and frost weathering in the high mountains. The latter has a special symbol on Colour Map 3. Denmark,

39

with thicker glacial deposits and more extensive remnants from earlier glaciations, is treated in detail in Chapter 8.

GEOMORPHOLOGY

A layer-coloured map shows major features but does not indicate relief details. To show these in part, Colour Map 1 has been constructed; it shows relative relief, i.e. height differences between peak, summit, crest or plateau edge and adjacent sea level, lake shore, valley bottom or plain. Height differences are graded in 9 tints. The map thus shows the real, visible height differences, formed in solid rock or in loose deposits, not height differences within unit sample areas (German *Reliefenergie*).

Altitudes and relative heights

Denmark is a lowland, rising to only 173 metres. But it is not as flat as might be expected and marked plains (relative heights lower than 20 m) are not extensive. Most of the country has a softly rolling character. Relative heights of more than 50 m are frequent and a few of more than 100 m occur (young moraine landscapes, tunnel valleys).

Most of Finland also lies below 200 m. Higher areas are found in central Lappland and on the watersheds along the eastern and northern frontiers. Even here maximum heights rarely exceed 500 or 600 m, except in the narrow northwestern arm of Finland, where summits exceed 1 000 m. As the valleys are only faintly incised, the relief is low. The plains, notably that east of the Bothnian Sea, are the largest in Norden, as are the areas of gently rolling terrain with relative heights of less than 50 m. Relative heights above 100 m are rare in the central part of the country, except around Lake Päijänne and Lake Pielinen. Marked relief, in the slope class 200–400 m, occurs in Lappland in an arc from the Russian to the Norwegian frontier. Only a few isolated Lappland mountains rise as much as 500 m from the plains.

Norway sharply contrasts with Denmark and Finland. High land is dominant; more than half the country lies above 500 m and about a quarter is above 1 000 m. The Scandinavian mountains (the Scandes), the backbone of the peninsula, are continuous except around Trondheimsfjord, where heights fall to about 400–500 m. The highest massifs and summits lie to south-

ward, notably in Jotunheimen (Galdhøpiggen 2 469 m), in Dovre and in the Jostedal glacier area. The highest summits north of Trondheimsfjord exceed 1 900 m.

In the broader southern part of the range there are plateaux with low relief, some hundred metres in relative height, or locally lower. But generally slopes are higher, at least 400 or 500 m. Large areas within the slope classes 700–1 000 m are common over a great deal of Norway; extensive areas with slopes greater than 1 000 m occur, and locally even some with slopes higher than 1 500 m. The combination of great heights with deeply incised valleys and deep penetration by fjords explain the extremely high relief in Hardanger, Sogn, Nordfjord and Sunnmøre and in some northern fjord regions, notably in Lyngen.

Outside the mountain areas slopes are generally in the classes 100–200 m and 200–400 m. Apart from the Oslofjord and Trondheimsfjord areas only narrow strips of coastal lowland occur. These may continue as swarms of islands and skerries, as in the well-known strandflat below the steep western margin of the country. Plains with relative heights of less than 20 m occur in the strandflat area, but are too small to be shown on Colour Map 1.

Sweden has an intermediate position in the Norden relief. The Danish lowland is continued in the wide plains of southern Sweden. These pass as bands of lowland along the coasts and in the north are linked with the great Finnish lowland plains. These coastal lowlands are interrupted only in central Norrland, and they are linked by the Central Swedish Lowland. Some lowlands are well developed plains, e.g. northern Uppland, Öland and Gotland with the adjoining mainland areas, the Lake Vänern plains and the plains in central Östergötland. Otherwise the lowlands are more undulating or hilly, and though relative heights of 100 m are rare, those of 50 m are quite common.

The Central Swedish Lowland separates the South Swedish and North Swedish Highlands. The Southern Highland culminates in a gently rising summit at 378 m. Relative heights of 200 m occur locally around Lake Vättern, but elsewhere they are mainly less than 100 m. The southern part of the South Swedish Highland is a great plain, gradually passing into the southern lowlands. The latter are interrupted

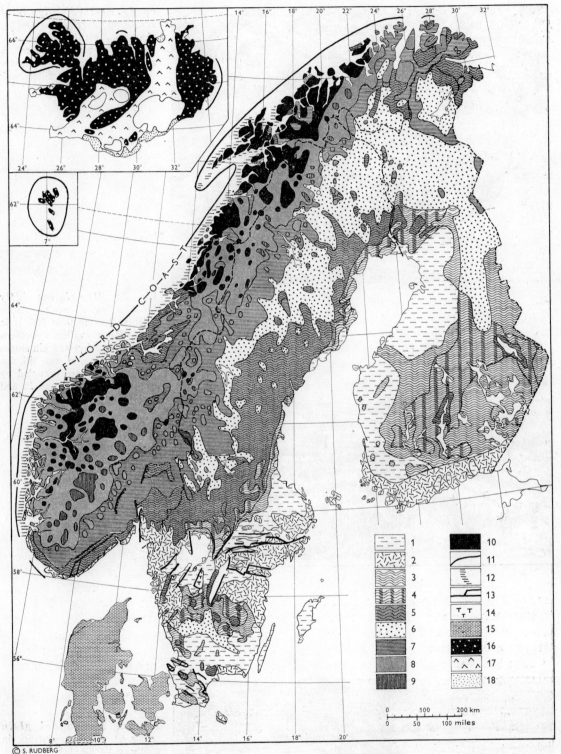

© S. RUDBERG

Fig. 3.3. Morphological type regions. 1. Plain, relative height below 20 m, 2. Fissure-valley landscape: Relief of the Stockholm type, 3–5. Undulating hilly land; 3. Relative height 20–50 m, 4. Relative height 50–100 m, 5. Relative height above 100 m, 6. Monadnock plain, 7. Premontane region, 8–10. Mountain; 8. Fjell in general, 9. Fjell with plateaux, 10. Fjell with alpine relief, 11. Fjord coast, 12. Strandflat, 13. Major fault, 14. Table mountains of Västergötland, 15. Relief essentially due to superficial deposits, 16. Lava plateaux, 17. Young volcanic forms, 18. Sandur plain.

Fig. 3.4. Fissure valley land-scape (type 2) on the Swedish Skagerak coast (Bleket, Island of Tjörn). The barren hills are almost free of glacial deposits, the valley bottoms are filled with clay.

Fig. 3.5. Undulating hilly land (type 5) with relative heights of more than 100 m in Ume River valley, northern Sweden. The forested hill slopes are partly covered with till, the valley bottoms are occupied by fine-grained glacial deposits and partly cultivated.

Fig. 3.6. Monadnock plain (type 6) at Glommersträsk in southeastern Swedish Lappland, about 80 km northwest of Skellefteå. The hill in the centre of the picture rises about 200 m above the plain which is covered with till, bogs or shallow lakes and has few rock outcrops.

Fig. 3.7. Fjell (type 8), partly plateau fjell (type 9) in the upper reaches of the Vindel River, a tributary of the Ume River, northern Sweden, 40–50 km from the Norwegian frontier. The plateaux lie at different levels with varying dissection in and near the main valley.

Fig. 3.8. Fjell with alpine relief (type 10) and cirque glaciers in West Jotunheimen. View from Store Smørstabbtind towards Mt. Soksi and Mt. Storebjørn. This type of relief is often found in western and northern Norway, elsewhere it is restricted to the highest mountains.

Fig. 3.9. The strandflat (type 12), particularly well developed in Helgeland, northern Norway, consists of numerous small, low islands and skerries. A few large erosion remnants protrude sharply from the lowlying strandflat, e.g. Mt. Lovunden (619 m) in the centre, and the peaks of the Træna Islands, on the right.

by higher ridges (horsts) stretching diagonally through Skåne.

The North Swedish Highland is the continuation of the Norwegian highland. The Scandes cross the frontier in northern Dalarna and extend in Sweden to northernmost Lappland in a belt 25–140 km broad. At their southern end heights are lower than in Norway (highest point 1 796 m), but in the north they are higher (2 117 m). As valley floors are rather high, relief is moderate, relative heights are mostly 400 –700 m or even lower. Areas with slopes of more than 1 000 m occur locally, particularly in northern Lappland in the Kebnekaise and Sarek regions. The latter is similar in area to Jotunheimen. East of the Scandes the land slopes gradually seawards. Altitudes are generally 200–500 m, relative heights 100–200 m and locally over 200 m. This vast region, with mountains and adjoining areas of moderate height and relief, is known as the Norrland terrain. The transition zone with the lowland to east and south is mostly well marked (Colour Map 1). As the *Limes Norrlandicus* it is significant in climate, vegetation and settlement.

Iceland is mainly a bowl-shaped highland with coastal mountains and plateaux 500–800 m high in the interior. The ice-capped volcanic areas in the southeast culminate at 2 119 m. Coastal areas with slopes of more than 1 000 m are found in the east and locally in the north. The northwestern peninsula is somewhat lower. The greatest supramarine relative height in Norden is found in Iceland, where the highest peak is situated near the coast. Colour Map 1 shows the interior as an intricate area of rapidly alternating high and low relief.

Morphological type regions

Colour Map 1 gives an incomplete picture of relief features, omitting angle of slope, number of summits and interrelations between relief forms. Relief features are partly shown on the map of morphological type regions (Fig. 3.3), where plains are as on Colour Map 1, but areas in the succeeding lowslope groups have been subdivided.

A special relief type is characterized by a network of narrow intersecting valleys and of broader hollows which may be irregular or may run straight and parallel to each other, giving the landscape an angular pattern. Valleys and hollows are mostly filled with clay or lakes. The higher areas between the depressions are often plain-like. In regions where further dissection has left only isolated hills and hummocks above the clay-covered plains, accordance of summit levels is characteristic, proving that the landscape is a dissected plain. Slopes, mostly in the 20–50 m and 50–100 m groups, are often steep, rising abruptly from the plains or valley floors.

This fissure-valley landscape (type 2 on Fig. 3.3) is typical of southern Finland, of the great archipelago linking southern Finland and eastern Sweden, of the Stockholm area and those adjoining it on the west and south, of the Skagerak coast of Sweden (Fig. 3.4), of smaller areas in southern Norway and in Bornholm. It is here termed relief of the Stockholm type.

Areas with this type of relief in both Finland and Sweden often show a gradual transition to plains and sometimes to gently undulating landscapes. The latter dominate large areas in Finland and Sweden and have been subdivided according to relative height to show regional differentiation. Undulating hilly relief with slopes of 20–50 and 50–100 m (type 3 and 4), with irregular groupings of heights and depressions, and an almost total lack of real valleys, is typical of much of interior Finland and notably the Lake Plateau, of the South Swedish Highland and smaller regions transitional to the Norrland terrain.

Much of the Norrland terrain is mapped as a third type (type 5, Fig. 3.5). Slopes are higher, forms greater and valleys better developed and more continuous, but here, too, the main impression is of an irregular undulating country. This type dominates southern Norrland, but in the north it is restricted to areas near the coast. It is found locally in Finland and is important in southern Norway; slopes are most gentle and regularly aligned valleys are less common.

Monadnock plains, where hills are more widely spaced in true plains, dominate northern Finland and northern Sweden (type 6 and Fig. 3.6). They also occur as a strip of varying width in interior southern Norrland and are sometimes found along watersheds in regions of undulating hilly relief. In Norway monadnock plains of any importance are found only in Finnmark.

From the areas of higher relief we must separate the premontane region (type 7), well

44

developed in interior Norrland and continued in southern Norway. Compared with the regions already described, this has higher altitudes (500 –700 m), greater relative heights (200 m and more), better developed valleys, a coarser valley pattern and in general greater forms. Broad plateau ridges are common, especially in Sweden, where they sometimes widen into plains.

Mountains constitute the regionally dominating relief type in Norway and are important also in Sweden. The word mountain is used here as the equivalent of the Norwegian *fjell* (Swedish *fjäll)*, a word of complex meaning denoting an area of high altitude and high slopes— generally above the timber line. The latter is not, of course, a direct geomorphological factor, but it has been taken into account in constructing Fig. 3.3.

This map distinguishes between three types of mountainous relief. The first is fjell in general, the well-known Scandinavian type, with rounded forms and slopes of medium height (type 8 and Fig. 3.7). The second type is fjell with plateau areas with gently rolling relief, and the third fjell with high and steep relief, with lofty peaks and cirques. The second type has too slight a distribution on the map, because of the small scale. Its most important area is the Hardangervidda, but it is also significant in other parts of southern Norway and in Sweden. The third, alpine relief type, is most strongly developed in western and northern Norway (type 10 and Fig. 3.8). In the interior, and in Sweden, the type is restricted to higher massifs and isolated mountains.

Typical fjord coasts and the *strandflat* (type 12 and Fig. 3.9) are shown by special symbols. True fjords with overdeepened depressions are also found outside the main fjord region.

In Iceland, Fig. 3.3 shows dissected plateau areas, regions of young volcanic forms and *sandur* plains.

Discussion of the morphogenesis

Only Finland, Norway and Sweden are discussed here: Denmark and Iceland are treated in separate chapters. In Denmark most relief features result from superficial deposits, in Iceland they are largely due to recent vulcanism and are true constructional forms.

In Fennoscandia superficial deposits may produce important forms, but for the geomor-

phology as a whole the solid rock and its sculpturing by erosion are far more decisive. Special difficulties in Fennoscandian geomorphology arise from the homogeneity of the Archaean rock areas, the low relief of Finland and parts of Sweden which causes indistinct relations between forms, and the hiatus between the Precambrian and Quaternary, which makes exact geological dating impossible. For these reasons the discussion of morphology is generally concentrated on the following four main topics.

Influence of the bedrock on geomorphology. The Archaean and most of the Proterozoic rocks do not vary much in their resistance to denudation. Hence petrographical differences are not usually distinctly reflected morphologically, but there are exceptions. In the flat interior of Finland the larger monadnocks are often of quartzites or basic rocks of the Karelidic cycle. Basic rocks sometimes produce similar forms in the gneissic regions of western Sweden. The anorthosites of the Egersund region in Norway give rise to an extremely steep and barren landscape. Areas of Subjotnian porphyries in Dalarna are rich in canyon valleys and hills of picturesque form, whereas its Jotnian sandstones form great plains and broad, faintly dissected, plateau-mountains. The role of strike and dip of gneisses is easily seen in the smaller forms of the landscape, e.g. in the shape and distribution of islands and skerries in archipelagoes. Fissures in the bedrock are even more important. The most characteristic features of relief of the Stockholm type are due to fissure systems. It has been proved that a number of such systems are of Precambrian age, but later regenerations may have occurred. The same is true of the great faults shown on Fig. 3.3. Some of these are connected with younger orogenies. Most of the faults of central Sweden are thought to be of Caledonian age, and the Oslofjord faults, and probably some of those of central Sweden, are of Variscan date.

The Caledonian rocks show greater variations in hardness. A number of the highest areas of the Scandes are built of basic rocks, gabbros in Jotunheimen, in the Sulitjelma area and that west of Lyngenfjord, amphibolites in the Kebnekaise and Sarek mountains. Slightly metamorphosed phyllites in the western part of the Swedish Scandes give areas of relatively low altitude and relief, with open valleys which narrow at the transition to the far higher eastern mica-schist areas. Resistant Eocambrian quartzites and sparagmites have sharp relief and narrowing valleys in eastern Norway and in the southern part of the Swedish Scandes. The fronts of overthrust sheets, with their east- and southeast-facing cliffs *(glint)*, are striking features of the eastern side of the Scandes (Colour Map 2).

Outside the Caledonian region, younger sediments, softer than the Archaean rocks, generally result in low relief. Dolerite sheets intruded into Cambro-Silurian layers in Västergötland have produced a quite unique table-mountain or 'mesa' landscape (type 14, Fig. 3.3). The islands of Öland and Gotland (with largely steep slopes along the western coasts) are parts of a mainly submarine cuesta landscape.

The old peneplanes. The sub-Cambrian peneplane, mentioned above, is important in the landscape in spite of its great age. This old surface is perfectly preserved in the immediate surroundings of the Cambro-Silurian remnants, and it is probable that at greater distances from them it can be followed in a more dissected form, judging by the widespread accordance of summit level. Small remnants of Cambro-Silurian sediments in these areas are further proof (Colour Map 2). The probable extension of the sub-Cambrian peneplane cannot for technical reasons be shown on Fig. 3.3. It is found in Sweden around Lake Vänern, along the coast opposite Öland, in parts of Östergötland and northern Uppland, and in adjacent areas of the Stockholm relief type. In Finland it occurs north of the Gulf of Finland and east of the Bothnian Bay (?), in Norway remnants are found in the Hardangervidda area. The sub-Cambrian peneplane is a regenerated one, newly deprived of its sedimentary cover or is still being dissected.

The peneplane in the south of the South Swedish Highland is younger. Its age is uncertain, but it must at least partly be pre-Cretaceous, and regenerated.

Younger denudation surfaces and cycles of erosion. In the Scandes there are fjells with broad and level plateaux which contrast with the deeply incised valleys. A similar sequence of contrasting forms is common in the premontane region. The monadnock plains of northern Sweden have old mature denudation surfaces at different altitudes, separated by steps. Features of this type have been explained as the results of cycles of erosion. This explanation was first advanced for western Norway, where the contrast between level fjell surfaces and fjords or valleys is most striking. It has since proved easier to discern a series of different erosion surfaces on the eastern side of the Scandinavian watershed with well developed premontane region and monadnock plains. That cyclical forms are a common feature is clear from a number of studies, though theories vary as to the number of cycles. A greater number of cycles, giving a system from the mountains to the coast, and only partly influenced by structures, is the hypothesis proposed by the present author in a study of Västerbotten. The age of these erosion surfaces is not yet clear, but it is very probable that the strong rejuvenation of the western Norwegian coast is the result of Tertiary tectonic movements. The angle of slope monadnock plain is very small, similar only to the slope of the flat surfaces developed in savanna climates.

A well-known denudation surface is the Norwegian strandflat, the genesis of which is uncertain. Among the different theories are: a surface of abrasion, a subaerial surface of denudation, a platform caused by glaciers of ice-foot type, a surface of pediment type, caused by lateral erosion of meltwater rivers of former sandur plains. It is probably of complex origin.

Glacial erosion. The last and perhaps the most striking relief-shaping agency in Fennoscandia is glacial erosion. The total effect of glacial transformation of the preglacial landscape cannot yet be stated, as the latter is not yet adequately studied. The highest mountains underwent an initial glaciation of alpine type before the total glaciations. The high plateau generated ice caps and not cirque glaciers.

The morphological result of the initial glaciation can be seen in cirques, preserved in spite of later total glaciations, and in trough valleys. The number and distribution of cirques reflect a glaciation limit (not necessarily synchronous) some 800 or 1 000 m lower than the present one but approximately parallel to it. Thus cirques are both numerous and at low altitudes in the western and northern coastal areas. Sometimes cirque-floors are found near or below sea level, e.g. in the Lofoten Islands. As the cirques are often closely spaced, the landscape is a fretted upland with peaks and horns, with pinnacles (Norwegian *tind*) and arêtes.

At greater distances from the coast and further south and east such markedly alpine morphology is restricted to the highest mountains (e.g. Jotunheimen, parts of Swedish Lappland). Usually the scattered cirques are separated by remnants of the preglacial surface, resulting in the grooved upland typical of the higher parts of the eastern Scandes.

This regional variation in the intensity of glacial erosion is proved by differences in the formation of trough valleys. In the western Scandes ideally shaped U-valleys are numerous, with steep sides and head walls, hanging tributary valleys, and overdeepenings and blocking thresholds cut by interglacial or postglacial notches. The fjords are drowned trough valleys, with overdeepenings of sometimes more than 1 000 m. In the central and eastern Scandes the glacial transformation of the valleys is less complete. Trough valley formation by truncation of spurs, and erosion in the outer curves of valleys can be seen at all stages. Though overdeepening is less than on the western side it is locally important. A parallel to the western fjords is seen in piedmont lakes which occur from northern Lappland to southern Norway.

Trough valleys were partly formed below the inland ice, and this applies also to similar forms in the premontane region and to valleys in areas of undulating hilly relief. In the latter region and over most of Fennoscandia which has low relief, the most important results of glacial erosion are the hollowing out of innumerable lake basins, the swarms of glaciated knobs or roches moutonnées and the perfect adaption of small relief features to structures in areas with the Stockholm relief type. These most typical results of inland-ice erosion can be seen everywhere where superficial deposits are not too thick. Giant roches moutonnées, which may be some hundred metres high, are picturesque features of the somewhat monotonous Archaean landscape.

General tendencies in recent geomorphological studies

Much work has been done on the Quaternary deposits and their landforms. Examples have already been given, but the following may be added. The landforms almost exclusively (with the exception of parts of West Jylland) belong to the last glaciation and its latest phases. In contrast with the situation in Central Europe the forms are normally quite fresh, when not strongly transformed by the abrading sea during the postglacial uplift. For this reason it has been possible to develop new theories, for instance concerning the formation of hummocky moraine landscapes (by squeezing into basalt cavities of the ice), or the deglaciation form sequences in mountain areas with melt-water channels, terraces and glacifluvial deposits (partly subglacial environment).

The locally strong transformation of land forms (notably in unconsolidated deposits) in postglacial time has provided many opportunities for that branch of geomorphology which concentrates on recent morphological processes. Examples are: fluvial erosion and accumulation, shore processes, slope development and mass movement (notably in the periglacial environment of the present). Extensive studies of recent glacier retreat and glacial erosion are also being made.

CHAPTER 4

CLIMATE
by C. C. Wallén

TWO BASIC FACTORS have a decisive influence on climatic conditions in the Norden countries. These are:

a) their position north of 50° lat. N., which means that over the year the radiation from the sun transformed into energy in the lower atmosphere and at the earth's surface is smaller in amount than the energy transmit-

ted to space from the earth's surface and the lower atmosphere. In other words, the annual radiation balance is a negative one.

b) their position on the west coast of the Eurasian continent and around the North Atlantic Ocean and the Baltic Sea.

The annual deficit in radiation balance at latitude 55°N is around 40 000 cal/cm², and

Fig. 4. 1 a. Typical upper air weather situation during the winter (at about 5 000 m) showing zonal circulation with westerly winds over the Atlantic, and northwesterly winds in Scandinavia and central Europe. Isohypses show, in tens of metres, the height of the 500 mb surface. Isotherms in °C. Date 26 February 1949.

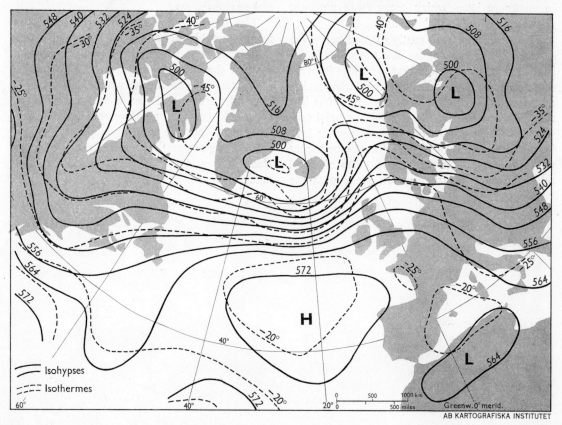

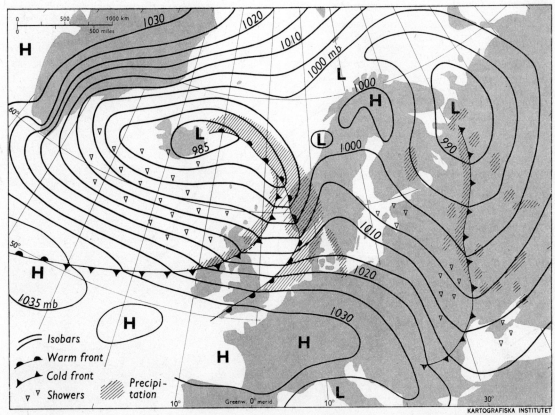

Fig. 4.1 b. The same weather situation at the earth's surface, showing circulation, fronts and air masses over the Atlantic and Western Europe. On this day, 26 February 1949, a typical frontal system with a large precipitation area was invading Scandinavia. A situation like this with strongly westerly winds between a low-pressure system around Iceland and an extended high-pressure system over the Atlantic and central Europe will give high winter temperatures in Scandinavia and Finland with particularly great anomalies on the west coast of Norway. Precipitation is also heavy, particularly on the western slopes of mountains in Norway and south Sweden. In summer a similar situation will give comparatively cool weather with frequent rain in Scandinavia.

at latitude 70°N it is 67 000 cal/cm². These amounts would be much greater if the shortness of the summer and the smaller amount of energy received during the long winters were not compensated to a considerable extent by the comparatively large amount of energy received during the long light nights of summer. Table 4.1 shows the latitude variation in the length of day. At the latitude of Oslo, Stockholm and Helsinki the length of day, including the twilight and dawn, is not less than 22 hours at the summer solstice. In mid-winter, on the other hand, it is only 7¾ hours. In all parts of the northern countries situated north of latitude 60°N the long summer nights, with their good light, are of fundamental importance for the development of vegetation and the possibilities of cultivation.

The deficit in energy is compensated for by energy derived partly from latent heat released by condensation, and partly by horizontal transport (advection) from more southerly latitudes. On the average, precipitation in Norden exceeds evaporation by 200–300 mm a year which means a contribution of some 15 000 cal/cm². All the remainder comes through advection by air and by sea.

Table 4.1. *Variations in day-length*

Lat.	Day-length at summer solstice		Day-length at winter solstice	
	Excl. twilight and dawn	Incl. twilight and dawn	Excl. twilight and dawn	Incl. twilight and dawn
56°	17h 36m	19h 46m	6h 46m	8h 26m
60°	18h 49m	22h 1m	5h 42m	7h 43m
65°	21h 56m	24h	3h 20m	6h 22m
69°	24h	24h	0h	4h 46m

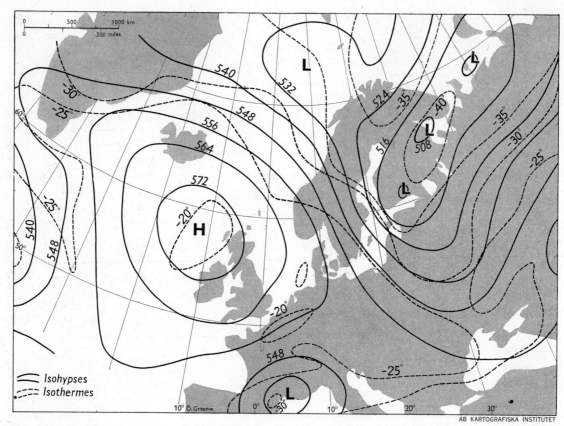

Fig. 4.2 a. Typical upper air weather situation during the winter (at about 5 000 m) showing meridional circulation over the eastern Atlantic and western Europe. Isohypses and isothermes as on Fig. 4.1 a. Date 9 April 1957.

CIRCULATION OF THE ATMOSPHERE AND THE SEA

The most typical features of the circulation of the atmosphere in middle latitudes are a) the prevailing westerly winds both in the upper air and at the earth's surface, b) the middle and high latitude cyclones formed along the Atlantic arctic and polar fronts which develop between the cold air-masses from polar regions in the north and the tropical or milder polar air-masses in the south. At the upper levels a middle-latitude westerly 'jet'-stream, resulting from the north-south temperature contrast, is dominant at about 8 km. This strong westerly current corresponds to the polar front at the surface, and the cyclones formed at the front move with the jet-stream.

In general, the jet-stream and the polar front run northeastwards from the east coast of North America, and the cyclones move most frequently from the Atlantic towards the Scandinavian peninsula, giving predominantly westerly and

southwesterly winds at all seasons. In winter these winds bring a considerable amount of heat both to Iceland and to the countries on the eastern side of the North Atlantic Ocean, which results in large positive temperature anomalies. In summer, on the other hand, they may cause some cooling because of the advection of cool air from the sea.

Although there is usually a strong and steady westerly flow of air at the upper levels over the North Atlantic and northwestern Europe (Fig. 4.1 a) it often happens, and for considerable periods, that this flow breaks down and is replaced by a more meridional circulation. This occurs when deep troughs and strong ridges are formed in the pressure system of the upper air (Fig. 4.2 a). The ridges stop or 'block' the normal westerly flow. Under these conditions warm air moves northwards from southern latitudes along the ridges and cold air flows southwards along the troughs. When this occurs the weather in Norden and over the northern-

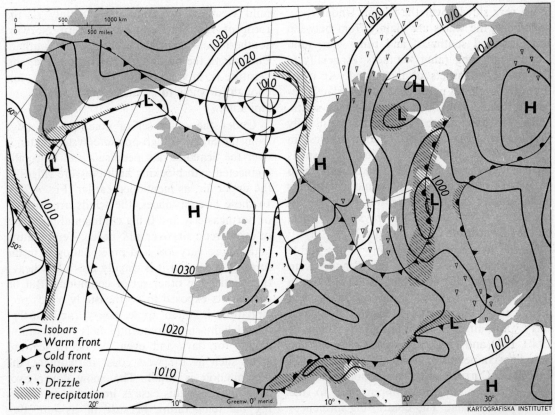

Fig. 4.2 b. *The same weather situation at the earth's surface,* showing circulation, fronts and air masses over the eastern Atlantic and western Europe. In this case of meridional circulation a ridge of high-pressure extends from the South of the British Isles to Iceland. The westerly flow from the Atlantic is blocked and northerly winds carry cold air masses over Scandinavia and Finland. In this case temperature is therefore low and precipitation usually occurs as showers on the east coast of Sweden. With this type of situation in summer temperature is low and weather characterized by high frequency of showers in Scandinavia while weather is fine in Iceland. — When the blocking ridge is situated further to the east over the continent and Scandinavia, the weather is usually cold in winter and warm in summer.

most Atlantic depends entirely on the location of the ridges and troughs.

Although the weather and climate of the Norden countries is, on the whole, influenced mostly by the westerly type of circulation, there is a continuous change from the westerly to the meridional type throughout the year. One or the other of these circulation types may be dominant over periods of several years and may thus give rise to distinct climatic fluctuations from one period to another.

In earlier descriptions of climate it was usual to attribute the positive air-temperature anomalies primarily to the influence of the Gulf Stream. But as the ocean current is a consequence of the prevailing westerly and southwesterly winds, the air movements are the primary cause of the temperature anomalies. The advection of warm water towards northern latitudes, and its warming effect on the air flowing over it, is a secondary factor, but nevertheless it is one of much consequence especially to the winter climate of Norway.

Iceland shows the importance of the westerly circulation in its most pronounced form. Temperatures in southern and western Iceland are, in general, high in winter and low in summer, as compared with those which are normal for the latitude. Precipitation is heavy and the incidence of storms is very high all the year round as a result of the high frequency of cyclones. Variations in the weather depend mainly on the tracks of the cyclones which move eastwards over the North Atlantic. Sometimes these show a marked tendency to curve northwards from positions to the south of Iceland and then to move very slowly over the island. Under these conditions, the winds are mainly from between southeast and southwest and bring very mild winters and cool, rainy summers, especially to the southern districts of the island. At other times the cyclones pass south of the island, between Iceland and Scotland or further south. When this happens the cold arctic air usually flows down from the north and northwest in the rear of the cyclone and brings cold spells especially to the north of the island. In this case easterly or northeasterly winds may prevail for a long time, bringing cold weather to the northern districts. The south then stays fairly warm on the leeward side of the mountains.

Finally it is worth mentioning that a stable winter high-pressure over the Scandinavian peninsula will bring abnormally mild winters to Iceland, because under these conditions the prevailing southerly and southwesterly winds carry warm air over the island. The winters of 1940, 1941 and 1942, which were severe in the Scandinavian peninsula, were all extremely mild in Iceland. Currents in the surrounding seas are also, naturally, of great importance to the weather of Iceland. The contrasting influences of the Gulf Stream and the East Greenland Current sharpen the differences which exist between the west and the east of the island as a result of atmospheric circulation.

Norway and Denmark have, on the whole, a typical maritime climate, while Sweden and Finland have conditions which are transitional between the maritime climate of the Atlantic coastlands and lands which lie further east. Frequent changes of weather, due to cyclonic activity, occur over the whole area, but the maritime influence gradually diminishes towards the east.

Two different sets of conditions are characteristic of Scandinavian winter weather. In the one, winds are westerly or southwesterly and bring in mild polar air or, in exceptional cases, even tropical air: this corresponds to the typical flow at upper levels, as mentioned above (Fig. 4.1 b). Under these conditions, Scandinavia and Finland have high winter temperatures with very great anomalies on the west coast of Norway. Precipitation is heavy, especially on the steep western slopes of the Norwegian mountains, in the western part of Denmark, and on the western side of southern Sweden. Because of the

mild weather, precipitation is mainly in the form of rain in Denmark, western Norway, southern and central Sweden, and southern Finland. In the more northerly regions the temperature is, in spite of the southerly winds, low enough for snow to be the normal form of precipitation.

Under the other set of conditions a ridge from the Siberian high-pressure system extends over the Scandinavian peninsula and is usually connected with blocking high-pressure ridges in the upper air, as mentioned earlier (Fig. 4.2 b). In these circumstances, the winds are easterly or northeasterly and bring continental polar air, or even arctic air, over all Norden. Temperature is therefore very low and precipitation is in the form of snow, but it is usually much less heavy than under the other set of conditions. But on east coasts exposed to northeasterly winds precipitation is often quite heavy; and further inland light snow frequently falls from stratus clouds for days and even weeks. In leeward areas such as the west coast of Norway, the precipitation is small. The snow cover over Scandinavia in this case is important in lowering the temperature because of its reflecting power.

In summer the zonal type of circulation of the upper air brings winds from the North Atlantic Ocean over northwestern Europe. This gives rise to comparatively cool summer weather in all four countries. Owing to strong cyclonic activity, rainfall is usually abundant in the western parts of the countries and increase orographically in mountainous areas. In the rear of the cyclones, cool polar air sometimes moves south from the Arctic Sea. Owing to the contrast between the warm air lying over the land and the cool air at the upper levels, strong vertical currents (convection) are set up and result in frequent showers of rain.

When a high-pressure ridge lies over Scandinavia in summer, the weather will depend very much on the location of the axis of the ridge. In the centre of the high-pressure system the weather is clear, dry and hot. On the east side of the ridge, where the winds are northwesterly, polar air is brought down from the north and frequent showers occur. To the west of the ridge there is much cyclonic activity, and precipitation is heavy, but because the winds are southerly the weather is rather warm.

These weather conditions may also occur in spring and autumn. In late March the influence of the snow cover is still so strong that the presence of a high-pressure system usually produces winter conditions. In May, on the other hand, it may produce very warm weather similar to that of summer. In autumn, a high-pressure system will bring cloudy and foggy weather, with comparatively low temperatures and no precipitation.

A type of weather which is characteristic of the transition period between winter and summer is the so-called 'April weather'. This is caused by a very cold polar or arctic air flowing over Scandinavia and Finland and becoming heated from below by the comparatively warm land surface. As a result convective activity is very strong, and heavy snow or rain showers alternate with short periods of sunshine.

It must be emphasized that the weather which occurs in association with the circulation conditions described above, varies very much with the relief of the land. A particular set of conditions may give quite different weather in the mountains of Norway or western Sweden, from that produced in the lowlands of Denmark, southern Sweden or Finland. Particularly important is the influence of orography on precipitation. Not only is cyclonic precipitation increased orographically, but convective precipitation in summer is also increased as a result of stronger turbulence over a rugged landscape. The orographical increase in precipitation means also an increase in cloudiness and a decrease in the number of sunshine hours. The number of sunshine hours therefore increases gradually from west to east in all four countries.

CLIMATIC CONDITIONS

All the regions of the Norden countries, except the southernmost part of Sweden, most of Denmark, and the coastal area of western Norway belong to the Boreal Forest climatic zone in Köppen's system: in this climatic type the mean temperature of the coldest month is below −3°C and there is a snow cover every year. Some areas in the northernmost parts, particularly the mountainous areas, have a polar climate in which the mean temperature of the warmest month does not reach +10°C.

Temperature

The most typical climatic feature of northwestern Europe is its maritimity, which stands out very clearly on Fig. 4.3. This shows the amplitude between the mean temperature of the coldest month and that of the warmest month, constructed from data derived from 162 stations. The smallest amplitude occurs on the east coast of Iceland where it is only 7.9°; the largest occurs in the inner parts of northern Norrland in Sweden where the maximum figure is 29.1°. The variation in amplitude is mainly longitudinal and is much less affected by latitudinal influences. Very high maritimity is found on the west coasts of Norway and Denmark (amplitude 10–15°); it is smaller, but still very marked, in the Baltic coastlands of Sweden and Finland (16–20°). The Scandinavian mountain range forms a very effective barrier against the influence of the ocean, and marked continentality is therefore found in eastern Norway and in northern and central Sweden, in the lee of the mountains. Where the mountain barrier is low, and the westerly winds come through, the penetration of maritime influence is obvious, as, for instance, to the east of the Storlien pass where Östersund in Sweden shows an amplitude of 22° as compared with 25° at the same latitude in the inner parts of Finland and Sweden. Among other local effects may be noted the influence of the lakes of central Sweden around which the continentality decreases markedly.

Latitudinal position, however, has a marked effect on the mean temperature itself. Whereas København has a mean January temperature of +0.4°, the corresponding figures are lower further north as for example −3.5° for Oslo, −2.5° for Stockholm, −5.4° for Helsinki and +0.3° for Reykjavík. The extreme longitudinal differences within the Norden countries are seen by comparing the January mean temperature of −1.2° in Iceland with the corresponding figure of −15.0° for northern Finland.

The effect of latitude is much smaller in summer, but still quite distinct, especially if we look at the figures for the most maritime parts of Denmark and Norway, and for Iceland. At Esbjerg on the west coast of Denmark the mean temperature for July is +15.7°, at Bergen it is +14.2° and it falls to +11.4° at Tromsø in northern Norway. In the continental parts of

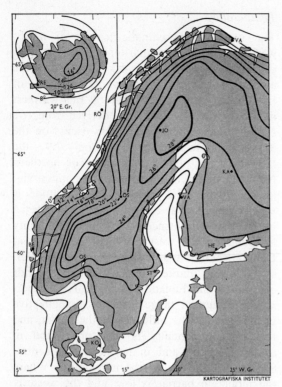
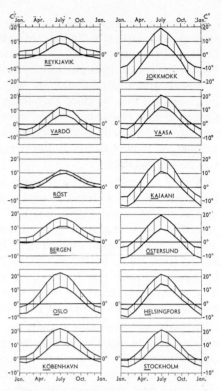

Fig. 4.3. Continentality of climate in Norden. Isolines for the difference between the mean temperature of the coldest and warmest months. For selected stations diagrams are introduced showing the annual variation of monthly means of maximum temperatures. — The remarkably small annual amplitude on the western coasts of Norway indicating extreme maritimity and the gradual increase of continentality towards the east are typical of the climate of Norden.

the region, i.e. in the inner regions of Sweden and Finland the latitudinal effect is much smaller; at Växjö in southern Sweden the mean temperature for July is $+16.5°$ but at Jokkmokk in northern Sweden it is $+14.7°$ and at Sodankylä in northern Finland it is $+13.8°$, which shows that the influence of the long sunny nights compensates in considerable measure for the effect of latitude. The latter effect is reduced in the maritime areas around the Atlantic due to their more windy location and greater amounts of cloud.

The monthly means of maximum and minimum temperatures for selected places are shown in Fig. 4.3. It will be seen that the lowest winter temperatures occur in northern Sweden and in Finland where Karesuando has $-20.0°$ in February. The warmest summers occur in southern Norway where, at Oslo, the mean maximum temperature in July reaches as high as $+22.4°$ although this is partly due to local influences. The inner parts of Sweden also have quite high summer temperatures. Here again

the distance from the sea, and the leeward situation, are more influential than latitude and give the climate continental features. In the south, in Denmark, surrounded as it is by the sea, the maximum temperature in July is lower than that of the continental areas of the Scandinavian peninsula such as southeastern Norway and eastern Sweden.

Temperature conditions in Norden may also be demonstrated by showing the length of the winter and summer seasons. This has been done in Colour Maps 4 and 5 by drawing isolines for number of days with mean temperature below $0°$ (winter) and above $+10°$ (summer). The average number of winter and summer days corresponds roughly to the length of the periods of consecutive days with mean temperatures below $0°$, or above $+10°$. On the same maps values for the mean minimum temperature of the coldest month and the mean maximum of the warmest month are given at selected stations.

In northernmost Finland and Sweden, as well

54

as in the highest parts of the Swedish and Norwegian mountains, the winter lasts for more than seven months (210 days). Its length decreases rapidly in Norway towards the Atlantic so that at the Norwegian west and south coast the duration of real winter is less than 30 days or even nonexistent with the standard definition. In Sweden and Finland there is a slow decrease in the length of winter from north to south, so that it lasts for about four months in the central Swedish lake district (including Stockholm) and for four to five in southern Finland (including Helsinki). In southernmost Sweden and throughout Denmark winter lasts for only about a month. In southern Norway conditions are only slightly different from those in Stockholm with a winter of a little more than four months. In Iceland the duration of winter is less than 30 days on the south and southwest coast. In the north, east, and the interior it may last up to four or five months.

Summer according to the above definition lasts for more than 140 days in Denmark, as well as in narrow bands along the Swedish west coast and the Norwegian south coast. No other regions have summers of that length but the lowlands of southern and western Norway, all Sweden south of the Dalälv and southernmost Finland have summers which last for more than four months. Most other parts of the lands below 500 m have summers of between three and four months. Only in northern Norway, Sweden and Finland do the summers last for only two to three months even at low altitudes. With increasing altitude the summer season in the north decreases rapidly in length, and in the Norwegian and Swedish mountains proper the summers may be as short as a month or less. An area of very short or no summer is also encountered on the Arctic Sea coast of Norway. Summer in the above sense lasts in Iceland for only about two or three months in favourable areas, and it may be even shorter close to the glaciated areas in the interior.

The maps also show isolines for sea surface temperatures of the coldest and warmest month. Winter temperatures below $+4°$ are found in the Baltic, the Kattegat and the inner Skagerak indicating possibilities for sea ice formation. Further west sea surface temperatures are comparatively high due to the Gulf Stream, and stay above $+8°$ north of the Faeroe Islands.

Within a narrow zone off the Norwegian coast there is only a slow decrease in temperature northwards due to the Gulf Stream, and temperature stays between $+5°$ and $+7°$ within this area throughout the winter.

In summer sea surface temperature in the northern Baltic rises to around $+13°$. In the southern Baltic it stays around $+15°$ but is higher in the Kattegat and Skagerak where it averages $+17°$. Westwards, in the Atlantic, it stays lower. It is generally between $+11°$ and $+13°$ north of Scotland and decreases northwards so that between Jan Mayen and north Norway it stays around $+10°$.

Length of vegetative season

One of the best indications of the seasonal variation of temperature is the length of the vegetative season. The length of this season can be broadly defined as the number of days between the date in spring when the daily mean temperature reaches $+3°C$ and the date in autumn when the daily mean again falls to this figure. Table 4.2 gives these dates for various places in the Norden countries, and also the number of days that occur between them. In Denmark and southern Skåne the vegetative season thus defined begins about April 1 and lasts until the beginning of December. In southeastern Norway, central Sweden and southern Finland (around 60°N) the growing season does not begin until the end of April and it does not last beyond the first ten days of November, i.e. it is about two months shorter than it is further south. The beginning of the vegetative season is even longer delayed (by about 10 days) along the Bothnian coasts of Finland and Sweden because of the cooling effect of the Baltic, which produces a similar delay in the fall of temperature in the autumn, so that the length of the season is approximately the same as in southeast Norway, central Sweden and southern Finland.

On the coasts of southwestern Norway the mean daily temperature of $+3°C$ is reached as early as March and lasts until the end of December. Thus the vegetative season in this area is not less than about ten months; only in January and February is the mean temperature below this value. This, of course, is the result of the extreme maritimity of this area. Conditions

Table 4.2. *Temperature, precipitation,*

Stations[2]		January Mean temp.	January Days with frost	April Mean temp.	April Days with frost	July Mean temp.	July Days with frost	October Mean temp.	October Days with frost	Vegetative season[3] 3°—3°	January Precipitation in mm	January Days with prec.	January Hours of sunshine
Fanø	D	+ 0.7	17	+ 5.8	3	+15.7	0	+8.8	1	24.3— 5.12	48	14	—
København	D	+ 0.4	19	+ 5.7	3	+16.7	0	+8.9	0.4	24.3—27.11	36	15	28
Vestervig	D	+ 0.9	17	+ 5.3	4	+15.2	0	+8.4	1	28.3— 5.12	54	19	—
Växjö	S	− 1.8	24	+ 4.6	13	+16.5	0	+6.7	6	5.4— 8.11	39	18	34
Visby	S	± 0.0	20	+ 4.0	9	+16.2	0	+8.0	1	8.4—25.11	43	15	38
Göteborg	S	± 0.0	19	+ 5.9	5	+17.1	0	+8.2	3	26.3—22.11	58	17	56
Stockholm	S	− 2.5	25	+ 3.6	14	+16.9	0	+6.4	4	11.4— 6.11	37	15	32
Oslo	N	− 3.5	28	+ 5.0	11	+17.5	0	+5.9	8	11.4—25.10	44	14	42
Helsinki	F	− 5.4	29	+ 2.9	17	+17.8	0	+5.7	8	16.4— 5.11	54	11	24
Bergen	N	+ 1.7	15	+ 5.7	4	+14.2	0	+7.5	2	17.3— 5.12	221	21	138
Falun	S	− 5.8	29	+ 3.1	20	+16.7	0	+4.7	12	14.4—24.10	32	14	44
Lærdal	N	− 1.1	23	+ 5.7	6	+16.1	0	+5.7	7	29.3— 5.11	57	12	—
Pori	F	− 6.2	—	+ 2.2	—	+16.9	0	+4.4	—		33	13	—
Punkaharju	F	− 9.3	—	+ 1.6	—	+16.9	—	+4.0	—	22.4—21.10	36	19	—
Sveg	S	− 9.9	30	+ 1.0	28	+14.5	1	+1.8	22	25.4— 9.10	27	10	45
Jyväskylä	F	− 8.1	28	+ 1.5	22	+16.2	0	+3.2	8	23.4—16.10	42	10	—
Røros	N	−10.5	31	− 1.5	27	+11.4	1	+0.2	23	7.5—29.9	36	16	37
Härnösand	S	− 5.8	29	+ 1.5	21	+15.5	0	+4.2	11	24.4—22.10	43	14	51
Östersund	S	− 7.9	29	+ 1.0	21	+14.2	0.1	+2.7	13	26.4—13.10	32	14	35
Trondheim	N	− 2.0	26	+ 3.9	13	+14.2	0	+4.8	9	15.4—21.10	78	17	26
Kajaani	F	−10.2	30	+ 0.3	25	+16.3	0	+2.0	14	27.4—10.10	38	10	—
Stensele	S	−11.9	31	− 0.7	28	+14.0	0.1	+0.4	23	4.5— 2.10	26	15	36
Tärnaby	S	−10.6	31	− 1.4	27	+12.4	0.1	+0.2	22	12.5— 1.10	62	20	24
Haparanda	S	−10.3	31	− 1.1	25	+15.5	0	+1.4	17	6.5— 7.10	39	16	28
Sodankylä	F	−12.9	31	− 2.2	27	+14.9	0	−0.7	24	7.5—28.9	29	10	1
Røst	N	+ 1.5	16	+ 2.7	9	+10.8	0	+5.6	2	19.4—18.11	96	24	—
Karesuando	S	−13.8	31	− 4.2	28	+13.0	0	−2.5	25	18.5—24.9	15	15	16
Alta	N	− 7.4	30	− 1.0	25	+12.8	0	+0.6	20	28.4— 3.10	22	9	—
Vardø	N	− 4.8	30	− 1.2	25	+ 8.9	0	+1.7	16	23.5— 2.10	62	17	15
Green Harbour	N	−16.0	31	−13.7	30	+ 5.4	0.9	−6.0	30	21.6—29.8	35	—	—
Reykjavík	I	+ 0.3	20	+ 3.3	15	+11.7	0	+5.0	7	20.5—30.9	92	21	19
Akureyri	I	− 1.1	23	+ 1.6	20	+11.0	1	+3.6	12	—	42	12	6
Holar	I	+ 0.6	18	+ 2.9	15	+11.1	0	+4.6	8	—	204	18	—

are much less favourable in the mountains and valleys of western Norway where local continentality increases rapidly towards the east.

Further north, around the Arctic Circle, the vegetative season starts as early as April in western Norway, but not until about May 20 in the inner parts of northern Sweden and Finland. On the Atlantic coasts the season lasts until October, but in the above-mentioned parts of Sweden and Finland it lasts for only four months, i.e. until the end of September. It is worth emphasizing again that the radiation energy received during the long, light nights of the short vegetative season is of fundamental importance in these northern areas.

In southern Iceland the vegetative season extends from the end of April until the end of October, but in the north of the island it lasts only from the middle of May until the middle of October.

It should also be remembered that the length of the vegetative season depends very much upon height above sea level and decreases by 5 or 6 days for every 100 m increase in altitude. Another feature of climatic interest is the average number of days with minimum temperature below 0°C, which is given for selected stations in the climate table above. In inland districts with great daily amplitude of temperature the risk of damage by frost within the vegetative season as defined above is much greater than in coastal areas.

snow cover and sunshine in Norden.[1]

April			July			October			Year			Beginning and end of snow cover	Stations[2]	
Precipitation in mm	Days with prec.	Hours of sunshine	Precipitation in mm	Days with prec.	Hours of sunshine	Precipitation in mm	Days with prec.	Hours of sunshine	Precipitation in mm	Days with prec.[4]	Hours of sunshine			
39	12	—	58	14	—	84	17	—	687	168	—	—	Fanø	D
38	14	155	59	14	225	49	16	83	533	175	1465	—	København	D
43	14	—	57	13	—	83	19	—	701	192	—	—	Vestervig	D
41	13	200	62	14	290	55	18	106	593	187	1850	—	Växjö	S
36	10	207	50	10	331	49	16	117	513	151	2121	—	Visby	S
46	12	231	69	14	310	75	16	118	738	173	2111	—	Göteborg	S
38	11	194	70	14	274	53	15	99	569	170	1780	—	Stockholm	S
40	10	200	69	13	289	75	14	101	685	155	1842	10.12—20.3	Oslo	N
42	8	173	54	9	293	70	10	80	698	—	—	16.12—20.4	Helsinki	F
111	16	218	109	15	[1]230	220	20	[1]95	1944	221	—	—	Bergen	N
30	11	218	70	15	314	50	15	111	548	163	2021	20.12— 5.4	Falun	S
14	6	—	37	11	—	44	11	—	444	122	—	31.12—18.2	Lærdal	N
33	9	—	57	11	—	66	12	—	—	—	—	—	Pori	F
35	13	—	63	15	—	62	20	—	—	—	—	29.11—26.4	Punkaharju	F
25	9	194	79	15	259	41	11	103	511	135	1754	20.11— 5.5	Sveg	S
35	7	—	59	10	—	59	11	—	635	—	—	—	Jyväskylä	F
18	10	177	61	15	228	33	14	79	449	168	1507	—	Røros	N
38	10	220	49	10	356	70	13	125	631	144	2221	6.12—18.4	Härnösand	S
22	11	204	65	15	294	42	14	98	496	165	1849	10.11— 9.5	Östersund	S
37	13	165	57	15	213	83	18	76	764	188	1405	30.11— 2.4	Trondheim	N
33	7	—	71	11	—	50	11	—	581	—	—	16.11— 1.5	Kajaani	F
24	11	208	67	15	305	43	14	99	503	170	1860	11.11— 7.5	Stensele	S
28	14	182	62	15	260	51	17	90	603	198	1617	27.10— 2.6	Tärnaby	S
33	11	224	48	11	346	58	15	104	532	159	2014	25.11— 3.5	Haparanda	S
30	8	156	65	10	268	51	11	42	520	—	—	30.10—14.5	Sodankylä	F
44	15	—	30	12	—	105	22	—	712	215	—	—	Røst	N
13	11	212	56	14	306	24	13	100	325	165	1794	25.10—20.5	Karesuando	S
15	9	—	38	9	—	25	11	—	298	113	—	4.11— 1.5	Alta	N
35	16	[1]200	38	12	[1]335	62	17	[1]75	573	190	—	31.10—17.5	Vardø	N
28	—	—	16	—	—	28	—	—	—	—	—	23.9—10.6	Green Harbour	N
49	17	135	51	15	181	92	19	74	796	215	1235	11.11—13.4	Reykjavík	I
32	10	109	35	10	145	58	14	49	480	131	966	20.10—27.4	Akureyri	I
110	12	—	95	16	—	169	16	—	1638	183	—	14.11—10.4	Holar	I

[1]) Averages in general for the period 1901–30. For Iceland and Finland values are for the period 1931–50. [2]) The stations are listed from south to north except for Iceland. For location, see Colour Map 6. [3]) Average period with temperatures above 3°C between spring and autumn. The period corresponds roughly to the growing season for grass. [4]) Average number of days with precipitation 0.1 mm and over.

Precipitation

Precipitation is closely related to the atmospheric circulation described in the first section. Because of the prevailing westerly to southwesterly winds, the western parts of the Norden countries receive more precipitation than the eastern parts. Owing to strong cyclonic activity in these areas during the winter the major part of the precipitation falls during that season.

In all parts the amount of precipitation is closely dependent upon height above sea level and distance from the sea. This is particularly the case with the Scandinavian mountains as a whole. While the annual precipitation in Denmark and Finland is between 500 og 1 000 mm, it rises to at least 4 000 mm in the mountain areas north of Nordfjord and south of Bodø in northern Norway, as well as in southern Iceland. Sweden has two areas of high annual precipitation: the western slopes of the highlands of southern Sweden which have amounts of 1 000 mm, and the mountain district on the Norwegian border where the high Sarek massif receives more than 2 000 mm.

The areas of minimum annual precipitation in Iceland lie in the north, in the lee of the glaciers, where the totals are only 300–400 mm. In Norway the driest region lies east of the high mountains of Jotunheimen and has similar amounts. Local variations in precipitation are large for topographical reasons. Even in the western parts there are valleys lying in the lee of mountain peaks where the annual precipitation is as low as 400 mm while in the neighbouring mountains the totals may reach 1 800–2 000 mm.

The dry regions of Sweden are the inner parts of northern Norrland, with 300–400 mm, and the southeastern part of the country, along the Baltic coast, which receives approximately the same amount. On the island of Öland, the low annual precipitation combined with comparatively high evaporation (400 mm) produces a semi-arid climate which is unique in the Norden countries and is accentuated by the presence of permeable limestone. In Denmark and southern Sweden evaporation is in general around 400 mm, but it decreases northwards and westwards, and in the mountain areas of Norway and Sweden it is only 150–250 mm a year.

On the whole Denmark and Finland show small geographical variations in annual precipitation. There is a gradual decrease from about 750 mm in southern Finland to about 500 mm in the north, and from about 700 mm in Jylland to about 500 mm in the eastern islands of Denmark.

In western and northern Norway, where maritimity is pronounced and winter precipitation is predominant, January or October–November are the months of maximum precipitation and spring is the driest season. This is also true of Iceland, apart from some inland areas of low precipitation which receive their monthly maxima in July or August, as do practically all parts of Denmark, Sweden and Finland. Towards the east, as continentality becomes more pronounced, conventional summer precipitation increases in importance in comparison with cyclonic winter precipitation. In these more continental parts of northeastern Europe, February–March are usually the driest months. The monthly totals of precipitation at certain key stations are shown on Colour Map 6.

Snow cover

A snow cover is formed annually in all Norden countries, but it is an irregular phenomenon in Denmark, the southernmost parts of Sweden, and some small areas on the coast of Norway. In the mountains of northern Norway and Sweden the snow cover begins to form as early as the end of September and lasts until the end of May, quite apart of course from the areas above the firn line where the snow cover may last throughout the summer. In southeast Norway, southern Norrland and Finland the snow cover lasts as a rule from the beginning of November until the middle of April. In southern Sweden its duration depends very much upon the relief: in the higher regions it may persist as long as it does in southern Norrland, while in Skåne and Denmark it lasts, on the average, only from the beginning of March.

Sunshine

The distribution of duration of sunshine has very much the inverse pattern of the distribution of precipitation, provided that due allowance is made for the bright summer nights in the northern parts of the Scandinavian peninsula and Finland. The areas of maximum duration, with 2 100 hours a year, are in southeastern Norway, along the coast of Norrland, in northern Finland and southeastern Sweden, together with the islands of Gotland and Öland. The areas of minimum duration include the rainy coastal areas of Trøndelag in Norway and the southwestern slopes of the highlands of southern Sweden which have only 1 400–1 600 hours of sunshine a year. Duration of sunshine in Iceland in general is comparatively short owing to the storminess of the climate. Areas of maximum duration are found in the north in the lee of the mountains and glaciers of southern Iceland.

Ice conditions in the Baltic Sea

The formation of ice along the coasts of the Norden countries is of great geographical significance. Owing to the comparatively warm water of the Atlantic, the formation of ice along the west coasts of Norway and Denmark is not a serious problem, and it is only during abnormally cold winters that ice is formed along the west coast of Sweden and in the Danish Sounds.

In the Baltic Sea and the Gulf of Bothnia the lower salinity extends throughout the water body, and here ice forms every winter. Usually ice starts to form in the northernmost harbours at the beginning of November. At Helsinki and around Stockholm ice usually forms around the turn of the year. It does not form until the beginning of February in the southernmost harbours of Sweden and in the ports of Denmark and it lasts, on the average, for only about a month. The melting of the ice is usually completed in about 80 days so that the northernmost harbours of Finland and Sweden are free by the end of May. The surface water may thus remain frozen from 1–6 months, but owing to the use of ice-breakers, the period during which the ports are closed is much shorter.

It must be emphasized that some winters may deviate considerably from these average conditions. In a severe winter the formation of ice may start about a month earlier, whereas, if the winter is very mild, it may be delayed by no less than twoo or three months. Temperature conditions are, of course, the most important factors in the formation and growth of ice, but for sea trade the influence of wind conditions on the distribution of the ice may be more significant, especially at the end of the winter. Southerwesterly winds are advantageous to Swedish harbours, but disadvantageous to Finnish ports because they often force the ice away from Swedish, but towards the Finnish coasts; northeasterly winds have, of course, the opposite effect.

CLIMATIC FLUCTUATIONS

Most of the local glaciers on the Scandinavian peninsula certainly did not exist during the optimum of the postglacial warm period

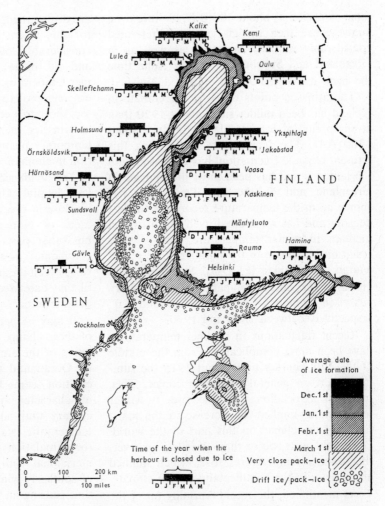

Fig. 4.4. Average extension of ice in the Baltic at different dates during the winter. At selected harbours the mean dates of closing and opening are indicated. — Prepared by B. Rodhe.

(about 4 000–2 000 B.C.) We do not know if there were any glaciers on the Norwegian high mountain plateaux, now covered by Folgefonni, Jostedalsbreen and Svartisen. Glaciers of the same type in Iceland, such as Vatnajökull (with a present maximum depth of 1 000 metres) existed, but were smaller than they now are.

The subsequent deterioration of the climate culminated about 600 B.C., the firn line dropped and the glaciers advanced, in some places to their maximum extension. That climate still exists, even if it has improved somewhat during certain periods, e.g. in the Roman period (A.D. 0–400).

Between the first half of the 18th century and about 1900 the glaciers in most districts in Iceland, Norway and Sweden reached the same extension as about 600 B.C. or were even larger. Since then the glaciers have retreated considerably in these countries as well as in Greenland and Spitsbergen. At the same time the pack ice in the Arctic waters diminished. S. Thorarinsson points out that the climate in Iceland has been milder since about 1920 than at any period of comparable length since about 1200 A.D. The temperature rise during this 'present climatic fluctuation' has increased with the latitudes and has been most pronounced in Greenland and Spitsbergen. This trend has shown up in the temperature records of the last decades and has manifested itself in an overall increase in winter temperature, mainly as a result of a decrease in the number of very cold winters. At Reykjavík, Oslo, Stockholm and Helsinki the mean temperature of January has risen by about 1.5°, 1.0°, 2.0° and 3.0° respectively between 1850 and 1940.

Recent fluctuations in summer temperatures have been more complicated. From the middle of the 19th century until about 1915 the summers were in general becoming cooler. This, taken in association with the rise in winter temperature, implied an increase in the maritimity of the climate in this part of the world. During the next two or three decades, however, the summer temperatures rose, which implied an increase in the continentality of the climate.

As mentioned, the recent warming up of the summers, and of the winters, has been more marked in the northern than in the southern parts of the countries. At Longyearbyen in Spitsbergen the rise in the January mean temperature between 1910 and 1940 was c. 10°, and at Riksgränsen east of Narvik the July temperature increased during the same period from +10.3° to +12.3°. The corresponding increases at København during this period were 1.5° for January and 1.0° for July.

But, while there is hardly any doubt that a distinct climatic 'improvement' had occurred up to about 1940, conditions after that year are more doubtful. There are many indications that the period of warming up has ended as far as the Scandinavian peninsula, Denmark and Finland are concerned; the evidence for Iceland and Spitsbergen is not conclusive. In Stockholm the winter temperature since 1940 has been definitely lower than during earlier decades. Even if the extreme winters of 1940–42

are disregarded, the ten-year overlapping means for this recent period yield values which are considerably lower than those for the twenties and the thirties. The same is true of the summer temperatures, especially those of the northern regions. However, the period since 1940 is too short to permit of a definite conclusion as to whether the decrease in temperatures is a temporary phenomenon or a sustained fluctuation in climate.

The evidence about precipitation is much less definite. Until about 1930 there was an increase in precipitation in the northern coastal areas of Norway and in southwest Sweden, but other parts show very slight changes. In continental areas, such as southeastern Norway, precipitation showed a slight decrease until that date: recent years have not shown any definite trend.

It may be permissible to attempt a summary of these changes in terms of the general circulation of the atmosphere over the North Atlantic Ocean and northwestern Europe. The circulation seems to have become more westerly in character from the middle of the last century until about 1915, when the summer temperature started to rise. Since that date the circulation seems to have become more meridional with an increase in the frequency of southerly winds both in summer and winter, thus causing an increase of temperature in both seasons. Since 1940 the meridional character of circulation has continued, but with more easterly to northeasterly winds in winter and northwesterly winds in summer causing a decrease of temperature in both seasons.

HYDROLOGY

The hydrology of rivers in the Norden countries is best characterized by the annual variation in discharge. Mountain rivers in Norway and Sweden show, in general, similar conditions, while the lowland rivers in southern Norway, central Sweden and Finland show different conditions. The rivers of southern Sweden and Denmark form a third group.

Owing to the precipitation regime and the storage of snow during the winter, the rivers generally have a maximum discharge in spring and a minimum discharge in late winter and during the summer. Mountain rivers in the north show two or even three discharge maxima: one is due to the melting of snow in low forest regions, the second and third are due to melting from snow and glaciers in the highest mountains where melting starts in late spring or during the summer. These maxima are often known as 'home flood', 'mountain flood', and 'high summer flood'.

Further south, only one or two periods of maximum discharge occur, and these are often much less pronounced because of the regulating effects of the lakes, as for instance in central Sweden and Finland. Rivers in southern Norway, Denmark and southwest Sweden may show secondary maxima during the autumn; these are due to the comparatively heavy precipitation in the westerly maritime regions during this season.

It should be added that in western Norway and southern Iceland the large amount of precipitation throughout the year gives rise to a comparatively even discharge curve for most rivers. Maxima may occur in almost any season, although the most common feature in Norway is high water in spring, summer and autumn. The discharge in southern Iceland in the summer is usually lower than that of the winter because of the heavy winter precipitation. The rivers of southern Sweden and Denmark have a lower discharge in summer than in winter because of the comparatively large evaporation that occur during the summer in these more southerly latitudes.

Colour Map 7 has black and white diagrams giving examples representative of different discharge conditions in Norden. The typical late summer maximum of Fykanåga in Norway is due to meltwater from the Svartisen glacier; the curves of the Göta river and Vuoksi are typical of rivers regulated by the storage capacity of great lakes. The rest of the diagrams show conditions which are typical for large adjoining areas of Norden.

Several of the diagrams on Colour Map 7 show both natural and regulated discharge conditions. It should be emphasized that in recent years the rivers of Norden have been increasingly regulated and therefore show annual discharge variations which are quite different from those under natural conditions.

CHAPTER 5

PLANT GEOGRAPHICAL REGIONS
by Ilmari Hustich[1]

NORDEN is in many respects the most favoured
part of the circumpolar arctic and cold-tempe-
rate zone, even though the principal features
of its plant cover are repeated in the North-
Russian, the Siberian and the North-American
Boreal Forest Region and also on the Arctic
coast of the continents. The forest generally
penetrates farther north in Norden than in other
parts of the northern hemisphere, with the exception of the central parts of Siberia. This is a
remarkable and unique exception to the rule
that forest trees reach farther north in a continental area than in coastal areas and is due to
the fact that the Atlantic air masses reaching
northwestern Europe are relatively warm all
the year round. The positive temperature anomaly is largest in winter, but the summer
warmth is sufficient to allow pine forests at
70°18′N in Norway.

In spite of the favourable climate, the flora
and fauna of Norden are poor in species. This
is partly explained by the fact that during the
last glaciation, some 25 000 years ago, practically the whole of the area was covered by the
inland ice, apart from western Jylland and
some isolated 'refuges' whose existence is still
debated by biologists and geologists. Migration
difficulties of the plant and animal world during
and after the glacial period are also a negative
factor to take into account when discussing the
poverty of the flora and fauna.

The major plant-geographical regions are
principally the result of the differences in
climate from north to south. But within these
regions we naturally find considerable hetero-

geneity resulting partly from local climatic
conditions and partly from edaphic and historical factors including the influence of man.
These factors create the plant communities
within the frame largely determined by the
climate. The farther north we are, the greater
are the similarities of the flora and of the plant
communities in a circumpolar direction. Thus
large areas of the arctic region are strikingly
similar with regard to the ecology of the plant
cover. This same feature is characteristic of
the Subarctic region. South of it there is less
uniformity, the plant cover may be very heterogeneous even in localities with a similar climate. The generally more favourable climate of
southern Scandinavia allows for a greater variety
of species and produces several 'levels' in the
forests and also, consequently, greater difficulties of description and classification. It is no mere
chance that plant-sociologists have successfully
established the homogeneity and regularity of
the plant formations on the wide arctic and
alpine heaths with their simple and common
features, while corresponding investigations in
the forests of southern regions are much more

[1] The author gratefully acknowledges the co-operation of
Dr. *Hugo Sjörs*, Stockholm, Dr. *Knut Fægri*, Bergen, and
Dr. *Tyge W. Böcher*, København.

*Fig. 5.1. Plant geographical regions in Nor-
den.* The boundaries are drawn schematically. The
following criteria have been used: The northern pine
forest limit between the Subarctic and the Boreal Coniferous Region (with outliers of pine forest north of it),
the northern oak forest limit between the latter and the
North-European Mixed Forest Region, and, in Sweden,
the southern spruce forest limit between the last-
named region and the North-European Deciduous
Forest Region. The inner parts of the western fjords
of Norway belong to the Mixed Forest Region. The
broken line within the Boreal Coniferous Region suggests a subdivision of the latter. The stipple shows
alpine areas.

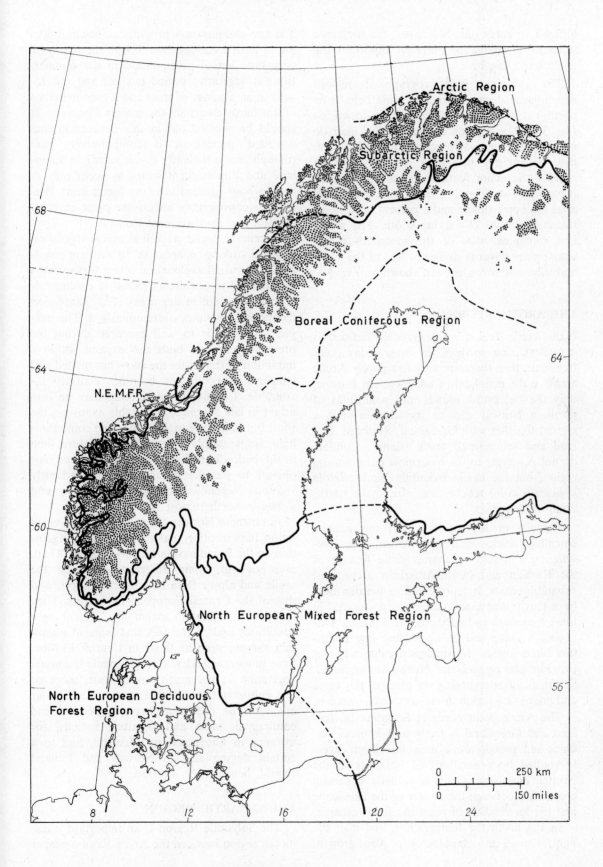

Arctic Region

Subarctic Region

68

Boreal Coniferous Region

64

64

N.E.M.F.R.

60

North European Mixed Forest Region

56

North European Deciduous
Forest Region

0   250 km

0   150 miles

8   12   16   20   24

63

difficult to carry out. Moreover, the increased influence of cultivation plays an important and 'disturbing' role here.

The principal plant-geographical regions which succeed one another in wide belts from north to south, are schematically drawn on Fig. 5.1. The regions shown on the map do not represent a widely accepted classification; they are merely presented here to illustrate roughly the major features in the plant cover. It cannot be sufficiently stressed that the boundaries are approximate and represent only vague transitional belts of varying width. The alpine and subalpine belts of the mountain range, whose plant cover is similar to that of the arctic and subarctic zones, are not shown on Fig. 5.1.

THE ARCTIC REGION

If the Arctic Region is schematically defined as a treeless zone north of the present-day polar tree limit, then there are very few purely Arctic areas on the mainland of northwestern Europe; only the outermost islands and peninsulas of northern Norway can be included in such a region, together with Greenland, Svalbard, Iceland and some small arctic islands. Conifers do not penetrate to the outermost polar coastal region, but the hardy mountain birch *(Betula pubescens* coll.) reaches tree size in the northernmost valleys.

Because of the relief within the narrow so-called arctic zone of Norden, the low-lying, wet tundra, a characteristic feature of the Russian and North-American arctic and subarctic coasts, is represented in Norden only by a partly man-made large 'pseudo-tundra' in inner Finnmark and northernmost Finland. This region is composed of alternating low mountain birch forests and treeless mountain heaths (in Finnish *tunturi,* in Norwegian *fjellhei).* Scientists differ regarding the place of this large and interesting region in the horizontal zonation.

The Arctic plant cover in Scandinavia, Iceland and Greenland is fairly well known. The arctic and 'pseudo-arctic' areas have been eagerly studied by generations of botanists in the Norden countries. There is actually a certain correlation between the beauty of the landscape and the localization of scientific field research.

In the north the temperature, and also the light, is an all-important factor for plant growth.

The late-melting snow provides sufficient moisture in most localities even though there may be very little actual precipitation in the summer. But the vegetative period is short and this results in an absence of trees and a predominance of low hardy dwarf shrubs, mainly *Ericaceae.* It should be pointed out in this connection that so-called permafrost is comparatively rare (though not sufficiently investigated) in Lappland and Finnmark: it seems to occur only in certain bogs *(palsas)* near the forest limit. Permafrost considerably affects the plant cover of Canada and northernmost Eurasia.

In general, arctic, as well as alpine vegetation shows a striking 'adaptation' to extreme conditions. The usual explanation is that leaf surfaces are reduced to counteract excessive cooling, although less than in dry areas. The 'adaptation theory' is sometimes overemphasized. The next year's growth is so well prepared during the previous year that buds can expand within a minimum of time after the snow has melted and temperature conditions become relatively favourable. Locally this vegetation may be luxuriant in late summer; favourable exposure, the short but intense growth period with continuous light, ample supply of mobile soil moisture, lime in the bedrock, and, in some cases, guano, co-operate to produce occasionally a surprisingly vigorous vegetation on some meadows and slopes in northernmost Norway.

In northern Norway the so-called arctic vegetation imperceptibly passes into alpine vegetation on the Scandinavian mountain range. There are, however, some differences between the arctic and alpine flora of northern Europe and that of the Central European mountains. They are due to a certain extent to different light conditions and to the fact that isolated mountain ranges, such as those in Central Europe, have numerous endemic forms, while the arctic vegetation in the north covers wide, more or less unbroken, areas with a more or less similar climate. The difference between oceanic and continental arctic and subarctic regions, for instance in Greenland and Iceland, and to a certain degree also in Norway and Finland should, however, be stressed.

THE SUBARCTIC REGION

The Subarctic Region is an important transitional region between the Arctic Region proper and the Boreal Coniferous Region. The Scandinavian and Finnish Subarctic Regions, partly man-made, constitute a direct continuation of the North-Russian Forest-tundra *(ljesotundra)* and have been drawn as such on recent Russian vegetation maps. It is widely distributed as the low *vidda* of Finnmark and Lappland, north of the forest line proper. In Canada and Alaska there are also similar large transitional belts between the Boreal and Arctic Regions.

The Subarctic Region is the belt limited northwards by the polar limit of the northernmost tree species. In most parts of the circumpolar belt the northernmost trees are conifers which are dominant in the Subarctic Region. In Norden a birch species, viz. *Betula pubescens* coll. grows and even forms forests farther north than any coniferous tree. This makes it difficult to compare the northern boundary of the Subarctic Region of Norden with similar boundaries elsewhere; in Canada and in many parts of northernmost Eurasia the phyto-geographical north boundary of the Subarctic is much clearer. It here coincides with the conifer tree-line. On the south, the Subarctic Region of north-western Europe is very difficult to delimit. Botanists, climatologists, forest-scientists and geographers have different opinions regarding the southern limit. The line indicated on Fig. 5.2 represents an opinion which is not unanimously accepted, but often used.

The Subarctic Region is of varying width, partly depending on the local topography, and partly on the activity of man. The Forest-tundra forms a wide belt in northern Russia and in most of northern Scandinavia, but in northern Norway it occurs as a narrower and less clear belt merging imperceptibly into the Subalpine zone of the Scandinavian mountain range. The subarctic vidda in Finnmark and in northernmost Finland is covered with fascinating forests of low sparse birch over large areas. These low birch forests are a very characteristic feature of Norden; they occur—but not exactly in the same forms—in some parts of Greenland and Iceland, but are not common elsewhere in the circumpolar Subarctic Region.

The northernmost pine forest stands and isolated trees, which spread far into the Subarctic, grow only at well-drained sites with favourable exposure; they are generally remnants of earlier larger pine forests (Fig. 5.3).

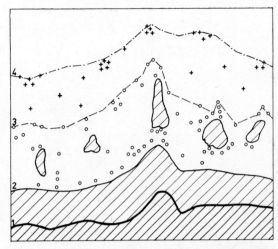

Fig. 5.2. *Forest- and tree lines,* drawn schematically. 1. Economic forest line indicating the northern limit of forestry (a maritime limit is also conceivable). 2. Forest line proper (northern extension of continuous forest). 3. Tree limit. Between the forest line and the tree limit is the Forest-tundra *(ljesotundra)*, the transition from continuous forest to isolated northern forest outposts (circles). 4. Species limit, showing the northernmost occurrence (crosses) of stunted examples or seedlings of the species in question. — After I. Hustich: The Scotch Pine in Northernmost Finland. Acta Botan. Fenn. 42 (1948).

Recently a Swedish geologist (G. Lundquist) has found that the pine stumps lying above the recent pine limit on some mountains are about 6 000 years old. Thees northern occurrences of pine (Scots pine, i.e. *Pinus silvestris*) are another feature characteristic of the Subarctic Region in Norden. The polar forest limit, both on the Kola peninsula and over the greater part of Eurasia and North America, is determined by spruce, i.e. in Norden: *Picea abies (P. excelsa),* and in the Kola peninsula and eastwards: *P. obovata;* there is no distinct taxonomic difference between the two 'species'.

All the phyto-geographical boundaries mentioned above are characterized by a marked lability. At its periphery any species, including the forest-forming tree species, is very sensitive to climatic changes. Earlier 'climatic deteriorations' may have been accentuated by forest cutting and by extended grazing, but they are nevertheless proved beyond doubt. In the last few decades the pine has re-expanded its area northwards and towards the summits of the isolated mountains because of the recent climatic amelioration. This, so far as we know, seems to have reached its peak in the late thirties, but

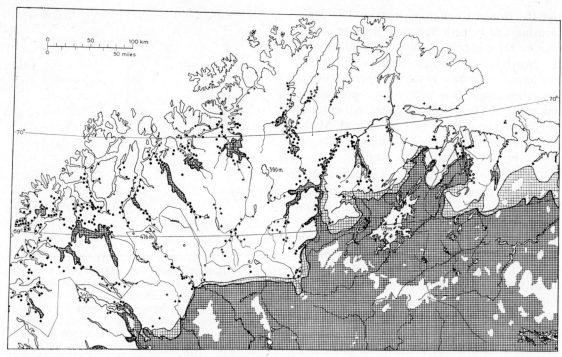

Fig. 5.3. The northern extension of the pine. The darker shading shows more or less close pine forests (which, however, do not always coincide with economically useful forest); the lighter shaded areas show, very roughly, a belt with pine stands and trees among dominant low birch forest. The white areas inside the pine area are alpine regions. Dots indicate isolated stands of pine, circles young pines or pine seedlings beyond the pine tree line and crosses fossil remains of pine. The former Finnish-Russian frontier is shown as a broken line. —
After I. Hustich: On the recent expansion of the Scotch Pine in northern Europe. Fennia 82 (1958).

young pines now occur on mountain slopes which were bare 30–40 years ago.

THE ALPINE AND SUBALPINE BELTS

These are vertical plant zones and occupy vast areas, particularly in mountainous Norway (Fig. 5.1 shows surfaces above 1 000 m). The flora in these zones is similar to that of the Arctic and Subarctic regions described above, though usually more luxuriant, particularly in the Subalpine zone. The lime content of many soils in the Norwegian mountains, together with the high humidity, makes some of the south- and northwest-facing valleys surprisingly rich in species.

From a strictly phyto-geographic point of view it is impossible to separate the Subalpine birch belt from the Subarctic birch zone. The real Arctic region is very narrow in Norden (Fig. 5.1) and contains essentially the same elements as the northern Alpine mountain heaths.

Norden is a rather anomalous section of the large circumpolar belt. This is reflected *inter alia* in the vague phyto-geographical boundaries. In our classifications we should not try to oversimplify the intricate and beautiful mosaic laid down by nature. An interesting feature is that on the isolated fjells east of the high mountain range an Atlantic influence is seen in the Alpine and Subalpine flora. In their main phyto-geographical problems these isolated alpine areas can be compared with the islands off the coast.

THE BOREAL CONIFEROUS REGION

South of the Subarctic Region the vast Boreal Coniferous Region, so typical of northern Europe, begins. It is striking how similar the circumpolar boreal coniferous forests are with regard to their ground vegetation (especially bryophytes and lichens), although the tree species themselves are different in the New and the Old World and, in the latter, different also in northern Europe and eastern Siberia. But it is easy, using the ground vegetation, to point out

66

the great similarities in the forest types or forest ecosystems occurring inside this region in Norden, in Canada, and Siberia.

The Boreal Coniferous Region in Norden is merely a western extension of the large 'taiga' which runs through Eurasia and North America. But nowhere are these boreal coniferous forests so poor in species as in Norden. Here the last glaciation played a double role; firstly it caused a late immigration of vegetation and secondly, particularly in the flatter parts of Finland and northern and central Sweden, it produced similar edaphic conditions over large areas. The results are *inter alia* large monotonous coniferous forests, bogs and fens. These monotonous softwood forests have facilitated forestry and furthered the expansion of the forest industry in Norden. It is easy to understand how Cajander's forest-type theory developed in Norden. According to this theory the productivity of the forests is simply classified with the aid of the ground vegetation (which is used as an indicator of, *inter alia,* the soil quality).

Peatlands play an important role in the Boreal Coniferous Forest Region in Norden; about 30 per cent of the area of Finland and Northern Sweden is covered by bogs and fens of different types. Bogs are the 'poorer' *(Sphagnum)* peatlands, fens (as understood in Norden) the brownmoss-dominated peatlands with a vegetation generally rich in species. Scandinavian bio-geographers have done much work on the age, mechanism, origin, and types of vegetation of the bogs and fens, together with their suitability for different uses (agriculture, forestry, peat as fuel, etc.).

The two predominating species of the Boreal Coniferous Region in northern Europe, Scots Pine and Norway Spruce, react differently on meeting the Atlantic Ocean. The spruce does not penetrate—spontaneously—as far west as does the pine. From this it has been assumed that the spruce, a late postglacial invader, has not yet completed its migration westward. The argument that the present climatic conditions on the western coast of Norway would not suit the spruce is discounted by the simple fact that successful spruce plantings have been made on the Norwegian Atlantic coast even in Troms and Finnmark.

Against the Scandinavian mountain range the comparatively simple and broad homogeneous features of the Boreal Coniferous Region break into a fascinating mosaic which is difficult to represent even on a large-scale map. The imposing fjord coast of western Norway, the surprisingly large and wild mountain plains (Dovre, Hardangervidda) in South Norway cause a distribution of particular plant formations which is largely created by local topography and climatic conditions. Arctic features reach farther south here than elsewhere in Norden, and some of the more or less arctic-alpine plants may even be seen at low levels on the coast with its exceedingly humid and oceanic climate. Thus, luxuriant growth of European oceanic types can be seen on the Norwegian coast close to barren arctic-alpine heaths.

Several attempts have been made to divide the Boreal Coniferous Forest Region into subregions. The very flexible boundary suggested on Fig. 5.1 represents a zone of change of forest types.

NORTH-EUROPEAN MIXED FOREST REGION

This region is not as distinct a regional entity as is the Boreal Coniferous Region. It should be emphasized that even in the Mixed Forest Region up to 75 per cent of the trees are conifers. Further south, other species come in besides the common boreal deciduous trees which are birch *(Betula verrucosa* and *pubescens),* alder *(Alnus incana* and *A. glutinosa),* aspen *(Populus tremula),* mountain ash *(Sorbus aucuparia),* sallow *(Salix caprea)* and bird-cherry *(Prunus padus).* All these reach far north almost to the coniferous forest limit. But in the Mixed Forest Region other deciduous trees also occur more or less regularly, species which are rare or absent in the Boreal Coniferous Region, such as lime or basswood *(Tilia cordata),* maple *(Acer platanoides),* elm *(Ulmus montana, U. effusa),* hazel *(Corylus avellana),* ash *(Fraxinus excelsior),* oak *(Quercus robur)* and endemic species of Sorbus *(S. intermedia, S. hybrida* etc.). In southwestern Scandinavia winter oak *(Quercus petraea)* and beech *(Fagus silvatica)* come in, and in southern Sweden and Denmark hornbeam *(Carpinus betulus).* The latter two, however, are more characteristic of the purely deciduous region mentioned below. Fig. 5.4 shows how far north the different tree species reach in Norden.

In Sweden many of these tree species reach their northern limit within a very narrow belt while in Finland the same tree limits are more widely spaced. This is the result of the differing topography; in Sweden hilly areas meet the plains and in central Sweden form what might be called a 'thermal threshold', which is reflected in the plant world as the 'limes norrlandicus', studied by many Swedish botanists. It should be mentioned that a partly similar limit can also be observed in an even more distinct form in eastern Canada, i.e. the 'limes labradoricus', the result of the climatic influence of the southward extension of Hudson Bay, and of topographic and geological differences at the margin of the Canadian Shield. In Finland, which is flatter, and where the ordinary latitudinal changes of climate are neutralized by the large lake-plateau, the border between the Mixed Forest Region and the Boreal Coniferous Region is much less distinct. The northern limit of the oak is often used as a phyto-geographical boundary, and the Mixed Forest Region is sometimes, particularly in Finland, also called the 'Oak Region', despite the fact that the share of the oak in the forest stands in this region is now only a small fraction. In southern Sweden, particularly in more hilly parts of the interior, there are large areas strongly dominated by coniferous forest within the Mixed Forest Region, but the above-mentioned hardwoods are not entirely absent even there.

The North-European Mixed Forest Region thus reaches from the 'limes norrlandicus' southwards to about the southwestern limit of the spruce (Fig. 5.4). South and southwest of this a northern outpost of the Central- and West-European Deciduous Forest Region reaches Scandinavia and covers the southernmost parts of Sweden and Norway and the whole of Denmark.

THE NORTH-EUROPEAN DECIDUOUS FOREST REGION

This region has not so many tree species as its Central- and West-European equivalent or the Northeast-American Deciduous Forest Region. Yet bio-geographically it is full of interest as marginal regions always are. In the delimitation chosen here it includes a distinctly oceanic area on the southwestern coast of Norway with more frequent and luxuriant yew *(Taxus baccata)* and ivy *(Hedera helix)* than elsewhere in coastal South Scandinavia, and with an occurrence of one evergreen tree, the holly *(Ilex aquifolium)*, and other West-European plants too sensitive to survive the hard winters of much of Norden. The most outstanding feature of the North-European Deciduous Forest Region, however, is probably the beautiful beech forest *(Fagus silvatica)* which adorns the low undulating landscape of Denmark and, to a lesser degree, southernmost Sweden. This region also includes large heather *(Calluna vulgaris)* heaths in Denmark and southern Sweden, which are partly the result of human activity (burning and grazing).

In no other region in Norden has cultivation so extensively influenced plant life. Hardly a square metre of the plant cover in what has been described above as the Deciduous Forest Region represents entirely primeval conditions, except on some exposed parts of the coast with bare rock or sand dunes, and on a few remaining bogs. This also applies to almost the entire Mixed Forest Region.

INFLUENCE OF MAN ON VEGETATION

It would be inappropriate in a short geographical survey of this kind to try to emphasize plant regions only on the basis of the former appearance of the plant world; cultural influence goes back to Neolithic times. And, unfortunately, the knowledge of the development and character of purely natural plant communities seems hardly worthwhile at a time when man is definitely the predominating plant-geographical factor in this part of the world. We shall therefore conclude this survey of the plant-geographical regions by trying to demonstrate the effect of cultivation upon nature in the Norden countries.

In Norden the activity of man and his animals is seen over the whole area, but it is most clearly felt in the regions which have been referred to here as the North-European Mixed Forest and Deciduous Forest Regions where cultivation has been intense, and population is fairly dense. The relation between cultivation and natural vegetation, particularly regarding the present forest vegetation, is complex and it is further complicated by different land-uses in former times as well as by present-day silvicul-

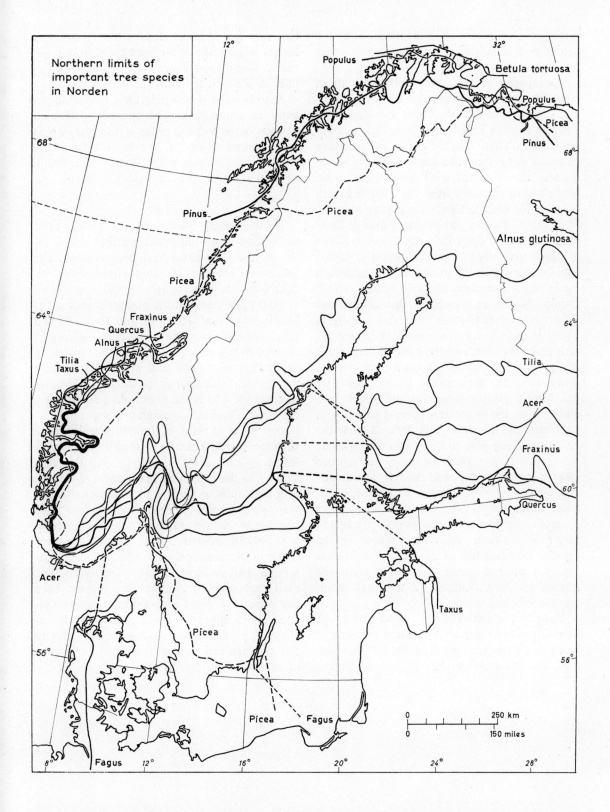

Fig. 5.4. *Northern limits of tree species,* mainly based on Hultén, 1950. Note how, on the Norwegian coast, the boundaries are pressed together in a narrow belt and spread fanlike further east. *Betula tortuosa* (upper right corner), is now usually called *Betula pubescens* coll.

tural measures. Above all, it is influenced by the extent and methods of agriculture and other forms for human activity.

The spread of cultivation which began in Neolithic times penetrated the forest by burning, grazing, etc. and the burnt areas were, as nowadays, often invaded by so-called 'secondary' forests. There was at first mainly primitive extensive agriculture and cattle breeding which needed large areas of open deciduous forests. Maps and descriptions from the 17th and 18th century, for instance, indicate that large areas of Southern Sweden and probably also of Denmark were then open landscapes with patches of deciduous forests larger than those of today. The heather heaths in southern Norden, which are largely a secondary effect of man's activity, should also be mentioned in this connection.

Methods of cultivation have since changed. There is nowadays more concentrated agriculture on better sites, and the cattle do not graze freely in open forests and on semi-natural meadows to the same extent as they formerly did. Timber gives a bigger income than before and this has led to increased forest planning in previously open terrain. The demand from the rapidly growing pulp industry has been greater for spruce timber than for pine, and spruce plantations have replaced mixed woodlands and, especially, birch forest in all Norden countries. Birch forests are, moreover, nowadays succeeded by spruce forests even without any major silvicultural measures. When spruce invades the birch forests the ground vegetation changes; planted spruce forests in Denmark furnish excellent examples of how new plant communities are formed.

The effect of cultivation can also be observed outside the more densely populated portions of Norden. Tillage has spread along the river valleys, and deforestation has been so extensive that very few areas in Norden have coniferous forests which have never been burnt or cut; so-called 'virgin forests' are now limited to insignificant areas in the north.

A recent and penetrating form of human activity in uninhabited and sparsely populated districts is the building of large reservoirs which cover forests and bogs. We know little of the effects of these large water storage schemes on vegetation and on ground water conditions.

*

In this rough sketch of the plant world of Norden some important features which influence the plant cover have been omitted. The successive changes of plant communities inland from the open seashore, the compressed vertical plant zones of the mountain slopes, the locally important effect of the bedrock, and other circumstances, have not been sufficiently stressed in this survey. Vegetation is dynamic in itself. Peat may grow and gradually influence the chemical character of the soil, and lakes may be filled up. The forest grows older and changes character. Natural communities are often replaced by new plant communities which have been more or less clearly created by man or are indirectly caused by his activity. All this contributes to the formation in all parts of Norden of a vegetation so diverse and intricate that our plant-geographical regions mapped above must necessarily remain rather crude abstractions. It is only in order to classify roughly the plant cover of Norden against a wider global background that we have, despite these difficulties, used such regions. And, as has already been suggested, the plant-geographical regions outlined above appear in another, surprisingly unchanged, pattern when we observe the different effects of the regional distribution of the activity of man in our corner of the world.

CHAPTER 6

POPULATION AND SETTLEMENT
by Gerd Enequist

POPULATION

Population and settlement in the Norden countries show striking contrasts from place to place in some ways, but great similarities in other respects. Denmark proper had in 1950 100 inhabitants per km², Finland 12, Iceland 1, Norway 10, and Sweden 16. These averages reveal a striking difference in population density between Denmark on the one hand and the remaining Norden countries on the other. The differences found within each country are still greater.

During the period 1850–1950 the population of Sweden has increased by about 100 per cent, in Norway by 130 per cent, in Iceland by 140 per cent, in Finland by 160 per cent, and in Denmark by more than 200 per cent. Recent figures for population size and density are given in Table 7.1, p. 82.

There is, however, a great difference between the population trend in urban and in rural districts. Denmark, Sweden and Norway, with stagnation or decline in rural population, contrast with Finland, where the non-urban population is still increasing. The urban population in legal cities is 83 per cent of Iceland's population, 50 per cent of Denmark's, 32 per cent in Norway, 38 per cent in Finland, and 53 per cent in Sweden. If non-administrative agglomerations are included the proportions are much higher. For comparison with urban areas in the rest of the world a limit of 1 000 inhabitants has been used on Colour Map 9. With that limit the degree of urbanization is 66 per cent in Denmark, 50 in Finland, 83 in Iceland, 52 in Norway and 67 per cent in Sweden.

Demographic conditions are largely similar in the Norden countries. The age pyramid (Fig. 6.2) shows that Finland and Iceland are distinctive with more children per capita. Birth rates are low, lowest in Sweden and highest in Iceland. Death rates are also low. The West-European trend is most pronounced in Sweden and is discussed in Chapter 12. We cannot expect a marked increase in population in Norden, except in Iceland and Finland (Table 7.1).

Classical physical anthropology recognizes three races in Norden, namely the Nordic Race, the East Baltic Race, and the Lapps. Some alpine influence is found in western Norway and in Denmark. The Nordic Race is characterized by tall stature, long heads, narrow faces, straight nasal bridge profile, and light pigmentation. The East Baltic Race has comparatively low stature, short heads, broad faces and dark pigmentation. Blood group research has shown that a marked eastern influence is found in northern and central Sweden (demonstrated by e.g. the high frequency of blood group B). A West-European influence, demonstrated by a high frequency of blood group 0 and of Rh-negative individuals, is found in southwest Sweden and in Jämtland, Ångermanland, and the coastal area of North Sweden. A Lappish influence (high frequency of blood group A_2) is found in vast areas of northern Sweden, possibly as far south as eastern Dalarna.

Distribution and density

Colour Maps 9 and 10 show the contrast between Denmark and the other Norden countries. Denmark is similar to adjacent parts of

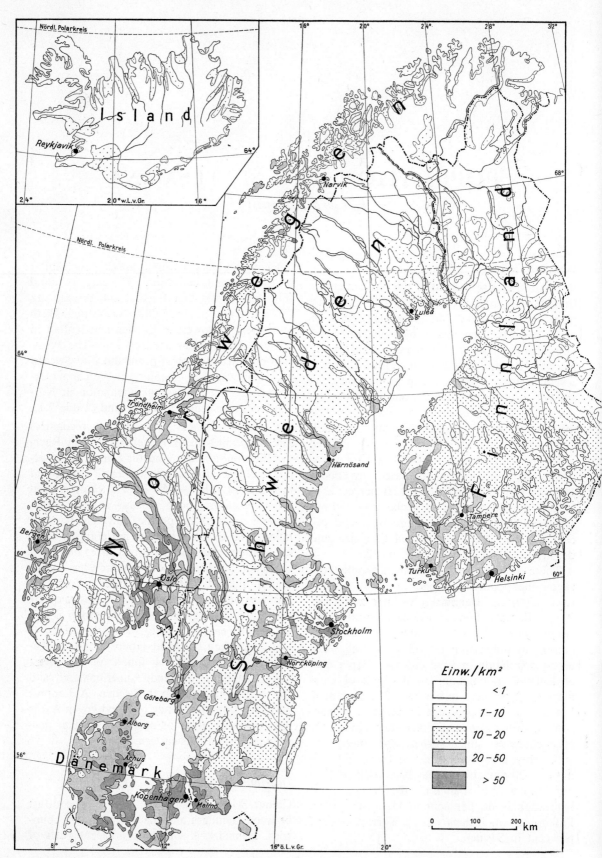

Nördl. Polarkreis

Island

Reykjavik

2|4°   2|0°w.L.v.Gr.   16°

Norwegen

Narvik

Luleå

Trondheim

Härnösand

Nördl. Polarkreis

Bergen

Schweden

Finnland

Tampere

Oslo

Turku

Helsinki

Stockholm

Norrköping

Göteborg

Ålborg

Einw./km²

Dänemark

Århus

< 1

1 - 10

Kopenhagen

Malmö

10 - 20

20 - 50

> 50

0   100   200 km

16° ö.L.v.Gr.   2|0°

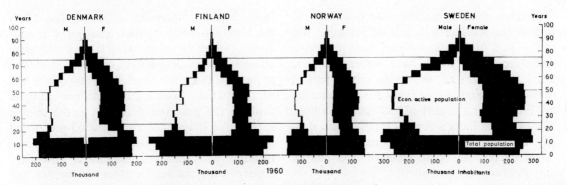

Fig. 6.2. Population 1960 by age and sex.

the European continent in respect of density and distribution patterns. The greatest contrast to this is found in mountainous Norway, where, in large sections, only the coastline and parts of the river valleys are settled and the remainder is uninhabited. A similar contrast is found in northern Sweden and Finland, although it is less sharp, between well settled river valleys and lake basins and sparsely populated intermediate areas. The rest of these two countries and eastern Norway are transition areas with the exception of Skåne which is more like Denmark, and the Central Swedish Lowlands which are distinct from the rest of Central Sweden because of their higher density.

There are several explanations of the distribution patterns which show up clearly on the maps. Physical geography is the dominant influence. The climate becomes more rigorous further north or at higher elevations. In these areas it offers resistance to agricultural settlement. The geological conditions vary markedly. The larger part of Norden consists of ancient crystalline rocks with a thin cover of poor, stony morainic soils. Areas with more recent rocks (Colour Map 2) are best from the agricultural point of view, if the climate is not too severe. The major part of the cultivated land is found below the upper marine limit, but old cultivations occur on moraines at high levels, or on steep slopes in fields which are not fit for modern agricultural techniques. Very important exceptions to this rule are the boulder clays of Denmark and Skåne, which for the

most part were deposited above the upper marine limit but are derived from more recent sedimentary rocks, rich in lime, and therefore most suitable for agriculture.

Because of the possibilities for farming these coastal areas and low-lying plains attract most people. The coasts are the natural location for one of the earliest occupations, fishing, which still plays an important role in coastal settlement, particularly in Norway.

By far the greater proportion of Norden's population is found in low-lying areas. Only Iceland and Norway have steep coasts, and in Norway some settlement has climbed high up the fjord slopes. But most people in Norway, as in Iceland, still live in the lowland, e.g. on the southeastern plains, on the strandflat along the west coast, and in the valleys. Denmark is entirely a lowland, and there other factors have influenced the distribution of population. Sweden and Finland as usual occupy an intermediate position between Denmark and Norway. Here we find settlement at somewhat higher elevation on hills and plateaux in the inner part of the country. Farms are often located on lakeshores or on southward facing slopes of hills to get sun and avoid frost. Their inhabitants work in forestry or have some other subsidiary occupations, and the holdings cannot be maintained solely by the income from farming today. Settlement at high level, even above the tree line in the boundary region between Norway and Sweden, is wholly a survival of earlier settlement.

The density of rural population rarely exceeds 50 per km² (Fig. 6.1). The best agricultural areas have a density of 20 to 50. On the map the coasts, plains and river valleys of Norden stand out as areas of higher density. The lower density of 10 to 20 per km² dominates the rest

Fig. 6.1. Population density 1950. For description of method, see G. Enequist: A Method for Mapping Population Density, *Norsk geogr. Tidsskr.* 17 (1959/60).

of Sweden south of the Norrland boundary, as it does the southwestern half of Finland. The settled part of Norrland (apart from the coast and river valleys which have higher densities) has 1 to 10 per km², as has the settled part of northern Finland. All of inner Norway and inner Iceland has a density of less than 1 per km². Norway often lacks a zone of intermediate density: along the coast and fjords there is a sharp boundary between small areas of high density and wide unpopulated areas.

OCCUPATIONS

Colour Maps 9 and 10 show the population and occupational structure of the Norden countries, the former in rural areas, the latter in urban agglomerations with more than 1 000 inhabitants. On Colour Map 9 black and red dots indicate 1 000 inhabitants in agriculture (incl. forestry and fishing) and manufacturing (incl. mining and building) respectively, open rings 1 000 inhabitants in other industries. The dots may, however, give a misleading picture of the position of agriculture, as forest workers and fishermen are statistically included in the agricultural population. In order to give a better picture of the occupational importance of agriculture, the dot map has been superimposed on a map showing the mean size of agricultural holdings. In areas with medium farm size under 10 ha. the position of agriculture may be considered to be of minor importance.

Denmark is like continental Europe in respect of the distribution of occupations, in that manufacturing is mainly located in the bigger cities. In the other Norden countries, particularly Sweden, the map shows an unusual pattern of manufacturing with many small plants in the rural areas. These plants have not given

rise to agglomerations of, say, more than 2 000 inhabitants because of the character of the industry, which in most cases is very old established (sawmills, ironworks); formerly, more than at present, there were certain advantages in the rural situation. Location close to raw material explains the past and present, e.g. the mining industry of Bergslagen or the wood-processing industries. These are located in respect of raw material and transport conditions (floating). Examples are the Sundsvall area in Sweden and the lower reaches of the Kymi river (Kotka) in Finland, or the water-power sites in the western fjords of Norway. In certain cases urban occupations predominate in remote districts because it has been necessary for additional industries to be added to unprofitable farming. These are small establishments, handicraft and home industries of the type found in the South-Swedish Highlands (glassware industry of eastern Småland). The map shows how the cities influence their surrounding rural areas. This is true particularly of the larger cities like Oslo, København, Helsinki, and Stockholm.

A large number of persons belonging to urban occupations live in small agglomerations with 200–1 000 inhabitants and are included in the rural population on Colour Map 9. The rural area proper also has a fair amount of service industry. As the rural areas are being depopulated these service industries are moving to the agglomerations.

Agriculture is dominant in large parts of Norden, particularly in Denmark and Finland. In some mining areas in central Sweden (Bergslagen) and in wood-processing areas along the Swedish Baltic coast manufacturing is allimportant. In southeastern Norway and in large parts of Sweden agriculture and manufacturing are of equal importance.

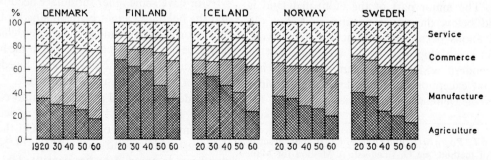

Fig. 6.3. Economically active population by occupations. Agriculture includes forestry and fishing. Manufacture includes mining and construction. Service includes unspecified occupations.

Only a few communes in the Norden countries have more than 75 per cent areally productive population: they are certain fishing communes in Norway, communes with intensive agriculture in Denmark, and remote communes in Finland and Sweden with forestry, some agriculture, and other subsidiary industries.

The connection between agriculture and its subsidiary occupations, forestry and fishing, has always been very strong in Norden, but nowadays it is breaking up. Fishing has always been the most independent of the subsidiary occupations. The number of farmer-fishermen is decreasing and the professional fishermen are becoming a separate, strongly organized group. Agriculture was clearly the main occupation of the Danish farmer at an early stage as it is now. In the other Norden countries, however, agriculture has been and still is closely connected with forestry. There is in general a recession of farming activities from the forest areas, and a consequent depopulation there.

The 'thinning out' of rural population is going on in both densely and sparsely populated areas. The number of farmers and farm workers decreases every year. Modern machinery is extensively used in Norden, and agriculture is carried on by fewer and fewer workers. Some owners of small farms leave them, but their farm land is for the most part used for enlarging the cultivated area of surrounding farms. Cultivated land is generally not abandoned except in Sweden, where it occurs to some extent, particularly in the forest areas. In Denmark it is prohibited by law.

The Lapps

The Lapps (lappish *sabme)* are found in a belt stretching from northern Finland, through Sweden to upper Dalarna, and in Norway from Varanger to Røros. Their areal distribution is widest in Sweden, but most of the Lapps are found in Norway. At the 1950 census there were 2 500 Lapps in Finland, 10 200 in Sweden, and about 1 800 in the Soviet Kola region. For Norway there are no census figures since 1930 when the Lapps numbered 19 100. The 1950 census includes only Lapps in North Norway with Lappish as their home-language, amounting to nearly 9 000.

According to their way of life they are classified as Mountain Lapps, Forest Lapps and Coast Lapps (and in Sweden Fisher Lapps). The first two groups are mainly reindeer-breeders. This Lapp occupation must be regarded as very old, but, on the other hand, nomadism may be of rather late date. Only the Mountain Lapps are nomadic in the sense that they move from the forest region to the mountains or to the Norwegian coast in summer. The whole family formerly took part in these wanderings. Today it is more and more common, particularly in Sweden, for the families to stay in the settled area, while only the herders follow the reindeer. Herding is becoming more extensive, milking is abandoned, and control of the herd is facilitated by the building of long fences between the grazing areas. In 1958 1 842 Norwegian and 3 010 Swedish Lapps still lived by reindeer-husbandry, and in 1960 833 Finnish Lapps lived by it. Swedish law reserves reindeer-husbandry to the Lapps.

Reindeer-husbandry among the Forest Lapps is still extensive and the animals are milked. Where it has been possible the Forest Lapps have adopted a primitive agriculture with a few sheep and cows.

In Norway the great majority of the Lapps live by fishing along the coast and by farming. In Finnmark they have an old tradition of fishing and hunting. In Finland and Sweden Fisher Lapps are found along the rivers and lakes.

RURAL SETTLEMENT

Location

All through our history farms have been located where three conditions are met: availability of soil for grain crops, meadows for hay, and possibilities for grazing. Beside these the household needed forest for fuel, timber and hunting, and it needed water for both people and cattle, and preferably watercourses for fishing.

Maps of the solid geology and superficial deposits of Norway, Sweden and Finland illustrate how the glacially transformed, broken Precambrian surface has created a landscape which is a mosaic of sediments, moraine with forests, swamps, bogs, and lakes. In this type of landscape, which is predominant in Norden, there is usually no great distance between lakes and rivers, so availability of water does not normally determine the general distribution of farms, though it does influence their site. The moraine-covered areas give enough forest for farm needs, but the amount of cultivable land available in Norden is very limited, and it had to be reserved for grain crops, particularly before the heavy clay could be ploughed. The cattle must be stall-fed for several months due to the climate, and large quantities of hay had to be collected from swamps and undrained clayey shores. Summer grazing had to be sought for in the woodland or in the mountains. Thanks to the landscape mosaic, cultivable land, meadows, and woodland needed by individual farms were found close together, but it caused a very wide dispersal of the farms in areas outside the few agricultural plains. On the plains the fine-graded sediments could be used both for arable land and for meadows and grazing. In these areas medieval and later settlement was concentrated in larger villages which were often placed on hillocks because of the need for firm building ground or the scarcity of cultivable land.

No marked changes in the distribution of farmland have occurred during the last hundred years in spite of the introduction of entirely new farming methods. Farmers have ceased to mow their meadows and, for the most part, no longer use the forest area for grazing. These ways of supplying fodder have been replaced by ley farming. Mountains with good grazing conditions are still used for seters (seter, fäbod) with cows during the summer. That is the case particularly in Norway, but only where motorable roads have been provided. Forested moraine and sand areas could earlier be used for cultivation of rye after burn-beating, particularly in Finland. This is not done today, but these methods of cultivation were important for the choice of settlement sites.

Some land has been added through new cultivation and drainage of swamps and lakes. Technical progress has made it possible to plough heavy clays, so a partial shift from sand to clay has taken place. Though important economically, the shift generally has not involved moving of the farmsteads.

Grouping of habitations

Settlement studies frequently stress the difference between Iceland, Norway and western Sweden on one hand and the rest of Norden on the other, in regard to the grouping of habitations. They have suggested that Iceland, Norway and western Sweden originally had only single farms, while the rest of Norden had both villages and single farms. But the position is not so simple as this.

By village (by, landsby) we mean here a group of densely clustered farmsteads. Before the redistribution of land their field parcels were intermingled in common fields, usually so that every farmer had the same number of strips as all other farmers in each field. The strips were not always arranged according to a certain plan, although this was so in the solskifte, in which, as to size, they were proportional to the owner's share of the village, lying in the same order all over the fields. Farm work was organized communally, for example in connection with the use of common land and water, and in deciding the time for sowing, harvesting and grazing on the fields, as well as work on the fences.

There is no doubt that settlement in villages has been practised in Denmark and a large part of Sweden at least since medieval times. In Norway and Iceland on the other hand we find as a rule single farms. They have later been subdivided and thus give the appearance of hamlets. Single farms are also found in Finland and Sweden, where they mainly occur in wooded regions.

The villages were rarely large, compared with much of Europe. At the beginning of the 16th century large villages occurred mainly in Denmark, including Skåne, but only in certain parts of Sweden and Finland. Some of them have possibly originated by grouping together in the Middle Ages what had earlier been smaller groups of farmsteads.

In spite of the dispersal of the villages during the last 200 years it is possible in Norden to reconstruct medieval and even older village forms on the basis of survey maps and remnants on the ground. Non-regular nucleated villages (Haufendorf) occurred over the whole Norden area. Their configuration was mainly dependent on physical features, so that a village may be round, if it is situated on a moraine hillock, or elongated, if it lies along the slope of a ridge or along a watercourse. Such nucleated villages were particularly common in Finland and in parts of Sweden. Sometimes an open space, a sort of green, has developed. After the solskifte

—and the *bolskifte* in Denmark and Skåne— regular village forms are found. In the very regular sun-divided 'row-village' the rectangular building-sites are arranged in a single or double row along a street. The width of each lot was strictly related to the owner's share of the village and functioned as a measure of the width of the strips and their arrangement in the fields. In Skåne and Denmark a wide street often developed into a green *(forte)*.

In Denmark, in Skåne, and in parts of Västergötland this green may be below the fields, and functioned originally as a grazing area. In the rest of Sweden, and in Finland and Norway, the buildings are located higher than the fields as a rule, e.g. on ridge slopes, rock outcrops etc.

A redistribution of land *(skifte)* has taken place in all Norden countries. Generally it had an important effect on the cultural landscape of Finland and Sweden, where it was accompanied by the breaking up of the villages. In reality there are only a few old villages left today in these two countries, except in Dalarna and in Ostrobothnia in central Finland, but the core of an old village is often found as the nucleus of a new agglomeration. Nowadays new clusters of farmsteads and other residences are growing along the roads into a ribbon which often has considerable length and density.

Settlements devoted mainly to fishing occur in some parts of Norden, e.g. in Iceland, in western Sweden and along the outer coast of Norway, particularly in the far north. Most Norwegian fishermen also work farms, but during the big fishing season they may move temporarily to fishing ports and centres for landing and fish-processing where they formerly greatly outnumbered the resident population. Now they usually live on board the fishing vessels.

As a generalization we may state that rural settlement in Norden (excluding Denmark) for the most part is dispersed, if we include not only isolated farms but also small groups of up to ten farmsteads. Larger groups of farmsteads (11 to 50) are rather common, and small agglomerations with more than 50 houses are found. The latter are considered urban in Norden, but from an international standpoint they ought to be classified as non-urban.

Estate, farm, and smallholding

According to the size of holdings and number and size of houses, we may distinguish between estates, farms, and smallholdings. Large landed properties must have been very rare during the Middle Ages. In Denmark and Sweden the nobility, the church and the monasteries created large domains, and castles and manor houses were erected, especially during the 16th and 17th centuries. However, only certain parts of Denmark can be said to have a manorial landscape. The majority of the holdings in Norden are used and owned by the peasantry. Their farmsteads make the landscape distinctive because of the many small buildings, which traditionally are of wood except in Denmark and southern Sweden where brick and half-timbered houses are common.

Smallholders of several kinds were common in Norden. Some of them supplied the estates and farms with labour and had their own small plots close to the home farm, others were real colonists both on the village commons and on land owned by the state. Their houses were considerably simpler than the farmhouses; they have either disappeared nowadays, or are used for other purposes (homes for people in other occupations, summer cottages and so on).

Seasonal settlement

Periodic settlement is common and typical for all Norden countries. The old economy, as far back as we know it in detail, used a number of places in the wide forest areas, in the mountains, and along the coasts for seasonal grazing, hunting, fishing and iron smelting. At those spots people built simple shelters or small huts, particularly if they lived there for some weeks as was the case with the seters. Today they are mostly abandoned or used for other purposes. People in Norden, with its short summer, like to spend some time out in the country, usually on the coast or up in the mountains, and they prefer to have their own summer cottage. Many old fishing cottages and seters are owned by city people, and new summer cottages have been built in such numbers that they give some coast stretches the character of densely settled areas.

In former days forestry workers used seasonal housing. Modern transport facilities now allow them to move daily from their homes in farmstead, village or town.

URBAN SETTLEMENT

The rise of towns in Norden dates from medieval times, only a few small trading towns existed before 1 000 A.D. The town-building impetus was accelerated by the Hanseatic League (Bergen, Visby). Fig. 6.4 illustrates the process by the year of foundation so far as this is known. 80 per cent of Denmark's towns are medieval, but relatively few towns in the other Norden countries were founded before 1580 (Finland 17 per cent, Norway 24 and Sweden 38). Trade was responsible for the foundation of numerous towns, culminating in the mid-17th century. Between 1580 and 1700 34 per cent of Norway's and 26 per cent of Sweden's towns were founded. The number of towns increased considerably during the 18th and 19th centuries, and more were founded in Norway and Finland than in Denmark and Sweden. During the 20th century the number of towns increased as new agglomerations without town status were included among the legal towns. This occurred particularly in Sweden and Finland.

Colour Map 10 shows agglomerations, inclusive of suburbs, with more than 1 000 inhabitants, distributed according to size groups and economic type. The large agglomerations are not adequately shown. København has 1 262 000 inhabitants, Stockholm 1 104 000, Oslo 579 000, Helsinki 537 000 and Reykjavík 144 000 (1960).

The urban population, like the rural, is concentrated on the coasts and on other low-lying areas. Cities, towns, and other agglomerations developed as centres in the more densely populated rural areas. Of equal importance for the situation of cities is the fact that communication was easiest by sea up to the last century. Exchange with overseas countries has always been of the greatest importance for the development of bigger cities. The old Hanseatic cities, such as Bergen and Visby, are examples of cities which have grown on the basis of sea trade. The Norden countries function mainly as an island with regard to foreign trade. Sizable market towns are few in the interiors of the five countries. A number of small agglomerations have sprung up with the development of railways. They have grown fastest if they have been attached to an old settled area, and especially if they have attracted manufacturing.

It is characteristic of Norden that centres for manufacturing, commerce, communications, and administration are often very small (Colour Map 10 and Table 6.1). Except in Iceland 40–50 per cent of the urban agglomerations have less than 2 000 inhabitants. As in other countries with a low population density and dispersed settlement, small agglomerations often have 'central functions'. Consequently the census bureaux in Norden show a remarkable interest in the small settlement nuclei and often consider them urban, a fact which must be noted in making comparisons with corresponding data from the rest of Europe. Several of these small agglomerations differ very little from the surrounding rural areas, but nevertheless function as market centres. In some cases these centres have developed from agricultural or fishing villages and still have a considerable number of people occupied in agriculture, forestry, or fishing. In Sweden and Finland the smallest agglomerations often have a strong forestry element.

The number of towns with more than 50 000 inhabitants is modest (only 32), but their proportion of the total urban population is considerable, in Denmark 62, in Finland 44, in Norway 52, in Iceland 67 and in Sweden 51 per cent. The proportion of the population living in agglomerations between 10 000 and 50 000 inhabitants is similar in all Norden countries (except Iceland)—about 30 per cent. Minor towns with less than 10 000 inhabitants comprise 91 per cent of the total number in Iceland, 83 in Denmark, 83 in Finland, 81 in Norway and 84 in Sweden. The total population in such agglomerations, however, amounts to only 2,5 million inhabitants.

The larger cities naturally are mainly of the same type with strong elements of trade, service and manufacturing. Of the capitals, København and Helsinki have an even distribution of service industry and manufacturing, whereas Stockholm and Oslo are service towns with more than 60 per cent of their total population in the service industries.

As usual the minor towns reflect better than the larger ones the regional differentiation. In Norway market towns are important. Denmark has a predominance of market towns with manufacturing, and Sweden a strong proportion of manufacturing towns. Mixed towns

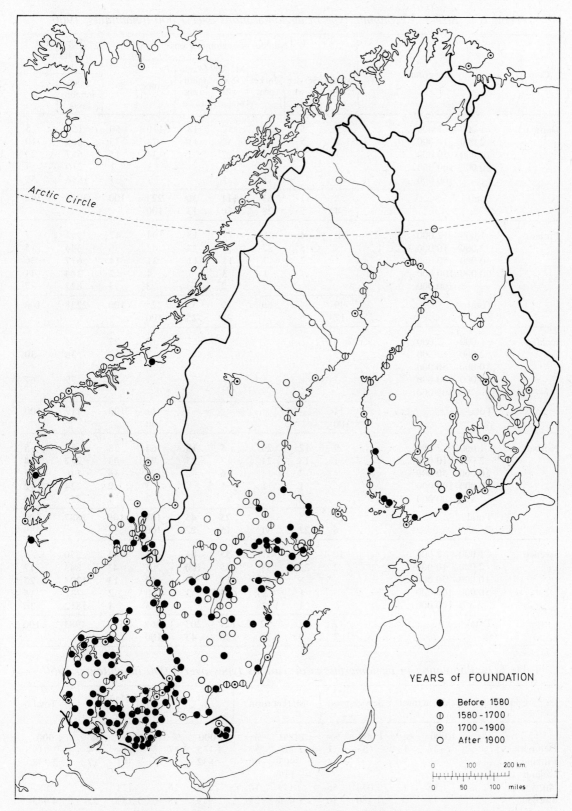

Fig. 6.4. Year of foundation of legal towns existing in 1960 — *købsted* (D), *kaupunkeja* (F), *kaup-staður* (I), *kjøpstad* (N) and *stad* (S).

Arctic Circle

YEARS of FOUNDATION

● Before 1580
◖ 1580 - 1700
◉ 1700 - 1900
○ After 1900

Table 6.1. *Size and economic type of agglomerations over 1 000 inhabitants, 1960*

Country	Size groups	Number of agglomerations							Population in agglomerations	
		Mixed town	Service town	Market town	Market town with manuf.	Manufacturing town	Number	%	1 000 inhabitants	%
Denmark	1 000– 2 000.......	5	5	25	57	18	110	50	154	5
	2 000– 10 000.......	2	5	23	32	11	73	33	302	10
	10 000– 50 000.......	1	1	14	17	1	34	15	697	23
	50 000–100 000.......				3		3	1	210	7
	> 100 000.......			1	2		3	1	1656	55
	Total	8	11	63	111	30	223	100	3019	100
	%	4	5	28	50	13	100			
Finland	1 000– 2 000.......	30	4	38	14	18	104	47	151	7
	2 000– 10 000.......	9	5	22	19	28	83	36	344	15
	10 000– 50 000.......		2	7	11	11	31	14	677	30
	50 000–100 000.......			1	3		4	2	244	11
	> 100 000.......			1	2		3	1	822	37
	Total	39	11	69	49	57	225	100	2238	100
	%	17	5	31	22	25	100			
Iceland	1 000– 2 000.......	3					3	27	4	3
	2 000– 10 000.......	7					7	64	36	30
	10 000– 50 000.......									
	50 000–100 000.......	1					1	9	79	67
	> 100 000.......									
	Total	11					11	100	119	100
	%	100					100			
Norway	1 000– 2 000.......	9	12	20	5	18	64	38	88	5
	2 000– 10 000.......	1	13	21	13	25	73	43	272	14
	10 000– 50 000.......		7	11	6	2	26	16	548	29
	50 000–100 000.......		1	1	1		3	2	224	12
	> 100 000.......		2				2	1	755	40
	Total	10	35	53	25	45	168	100	1887	100
	%	6	21	31	15	27	100			
Sweden	1 000– 2 000.......	10	8	37	55	81	191	41	270	5
	2 000– 10 000.......	2	23	33	45	100	203	43	845	17
	10 000– 50 000.......		8	18	17	19	62	13	1324	27
	50 000–100 000.......		1	2	4	3	10	2	732	15
	> 100 000.......		1	2			3	1	1812	36
	Total	12	41	92	121	203	469	100	4983	100
	%	2	9	20	26	43	100			

Table 6.2. *Population in agglomerations of various types over 1 000 inhabitants, 1960*

Country	Mixed town		Service town		Market town		Market town with manuf.		Manuf. town		Total
	1 000	%	1 000	%	1 000	%	1 000	%	1 000	%	1 000
Denmark	27	1	33	1	1 710	57	1 135	37	114	4	3 019
Finland	65	3	57	3	903	40	832	37	381	17	2 238
Iceland					119						119
Norway	15	1	1 054	56	349	18	298	16	171	9	1 887
Sweden	17	0	1 480	30	1 436	29	919	18	1 131	23	4 983
Norden	124	1	2 624	21	4 517	37	3 184	26	1 797	15	12 246

where areal activities, such as forestry work, may be rather important, are numerous in Finland.

The middle groups (market towns and market towns with manufacturing) are obviously the most numerous, as these agglomerations offer the most varied opportunities to their residents. Denmark particularly has a high proportion of such towns, 78 per cent. Since the two extreme groups, manufacturing towns and service towns, tend to change, as they increase in age and size, to the market town group, the latter group possibly represents a stage of maturity. It is characteristic of Denmark that the towns have reached a high level of balance. That development has been facilitated by the fact that manufacturing in Denmark is not attached to raw materials or power in the rural areas.

Service centres without manufacturing often have special functions, such as the ferry-town of Nyborg. Other towns have a high degree of centrality but a rather low proportion of manufacturing. Typical examples are Tromsø, Östersund and Mariehamn. Like service towns the manufacturing towns must be considered extremes. Small industrial towns in the 1–10 000 category are particularly numerous in Sweden where they comprise 46 per cent of all towns in contrast to 15 per cent in Denmark.

The city plans are rarely medieval, although several cities are of medieval origin. Buildings were mostly wooden in these forested countries, except in Skåne and Denmark, and fires were numerous. For that reason the city plans usually date from more recent centuries. The small town with two-storey houses of wood, often painted in light and pleasant colours, may be considered typical for old Norden cities outside Denmark. In that country the corresponding town consists of comely one- or two-storey houses of half-timber work and brick with tile roofs.

Conurbations of the type found on the European coal fields are lacking in Norden. Where heavy industry occurs, it is mostly found in rural areas and in smaller units. Areas with a single type of industry are of course characterized by its particular buildings. Thus the wood industry areas are distinguished by timber storage heaps, timber yards and acid towers.

CHAPTER 7

RESOURCES AND INDUSTRIES
by Axel Sømme

THE high living standard of Norden cannot be explained by its own natural resources. The Norden countries lack coal deposits of any real importance, but Norway and Sweden have ample water-power and, like Finland, vast forests which provide raw material for manufacturing industries on a world scale. Sweden also has large resources of iron ore, which will be sufficient for her own consumption and for export for many centuries. Denmark has more arable land than any country of equal size, and, in addition, a favourable temperature-precipitation balance; and Iceland and Norway have within their sea territory fishing potentialities which are surpassed by those of few other countries.

The natural resources of Norden are thus bet-

ter than those of many other countries, but the human resources are even more important. A far-reaching equalization of income has occurred during the last few decades, and few countries in the world now show less class differentiation, have fewer labour disputes, and enjoy more political stability.

ARABLE LAND

The resources of arable land are unevenly distributed among the Norden countries. Denmark has two thirds of its land area in arable, Norway only 2½ per cent. Per inhabitant the latter is as poorly endowed as the most industrialized countries of Western Europe. Data for all Nor-

Table 7.1. *Area and population*

| Country | Total area | of which lakes | Population 1960 | | | | Population 1966[4] | | Average annual increase 1950–1960 | |
| | | | Total | Rural[1] | | Urban[3] | Total | Inhab. per km² | Total pop. | Urban pop. |
				Dispersed	Agglomerated[2]					
	1 000 km²	%	1 000	%	%	%	1 000		1 000	1 000
Denmark	43	1.4	4 585	25.9	8.0	66.1	4 779	111	30	38
Faereos	1.4		35				37	26		
Greenland	2 176		33				40			
Finland	337	9.4	4 446	31.1	19.0	49.9	4 626	14	42	56
Iceland	103	0.4	183	19.7	11.1	69.1	189	2	3	4
Norway	324	4.9	3 591	42.8	4.8	52.4	3 738	12	31	41
Svalbard	62		3							
Sweden	450	8.6	7 495	27.2	6.3	66.5	7 773	19	45	99
Total[5]	1 258		20 336	30.5	9.3	60.2	21 114	17	153	241

[1]) Cf. Colour Map 9. [2]) 200—1 000 inhabitants. [3]) Over 1 000 inhabitants. Cf. Colour map 10. [4]) Greenland 1965, Iceland 1964, others 1/1 1966. [5]) Excl. Greenland and Svalbard.

Table 7.2. *Economically active population, 1960*

Country	Total[1]	Primary			Secondary		Tertiary			
		Agri-culture, forestry	Fishing, whaling	Mining	Manu-factu-ring	Con-struc-tion[2]	Com-merce[3]	Sea-trans-port	Other trans-port	Other services
	1 000	%	%	%	%	%	%	%	%	%
Denmark	2 094	16.8	0.7	0.2	28.5	7.8	14.9	1.8	5.4	23.9
Finland	2 033	35.0	0.5	0.3	21.6	9.6	11.6	6.3		15.1
Iceland	72[4]	16.9	7.4	—	25.9	12.7	12.5	8.1		16.5
Norway	1 406	15.6	3.9	0.6	25.5	10.4	13.3	6.1	5.8	18.8
Sweden	3 244	13.5	0.3	0.7	34.2	10.2	13.5	1.2	6.3	20.1

[1]) Males and females, the latter constituting 31, 39, 25, 23, 30% resp. [2]) Incl. electricity, gas and water services. [3]) Incl. banks, insurance etc. [4]) Estimates based on 4 per cent sample, communicated by Hagastofa Islands.

Table 7.3. *Industrial origin of gross domestic product, 1965*

Country	Gross domestic product[1]	Primary				Secondary		Tertiary		
		Agri-culture	Forestry	Fishing, whaling	Mining	Manu-factu-ring	Con-struc-tion	Trans-port	Trade[2]	Other services
	Million $	%	%	%	%	%	%	%	%	%
Denmark	9 710	10	0.2	0.7	0.1	31	9	10	17	22
Finland	7 252	9	9	0.4	0.7	28	10	7	13	23
Norway[3]	7 788	4	2	2	1	27	7	17[4]	20	20
Sweden[5]	15 436	4	4	0		36[6]	8	9	14	25

[1]) At factor cost, i.e. excl. indirect taxes, incl. subsidies. [2]) Incl. banks, insurance etc. [3]) At market prices. [4]) Of this sea transport 64%. [5]) 1964. [6]) Incl. mining.

den countries are given in Table 7.4, the distribution of the arable land is shown on Colour Map 8.

As the major part of the arable land of Sweden, Finland and Norway lies on former seabeds, a map indicating the maximum extension of the lateglacial and postglacial seas gives the best clue to an understanding of the distribution of the arable land. In mountainous Norway these areas are rather limited compared with those of Sweden and Finland, which have a moderate relief and, in the northern part of the Gulf of Bothnia, register a postglacial uplift of 380 m.

The agricultural quality of these marine clays and sands, as well as that of the morainic soils above the upper marine limit, is closely related to the parent rock, the major part of the morainic material being of local derivation. The high quality of the moraine clays of Denmark and Skåne is explained by underlying bedrock which is rich in lime under both the present land surface and the surrounding seas.

In respect of soil and climate Denmark and Skåne form part of Central Europe and their agriculture is similar to that of the Central European plains. A third of the total arable land of Norden is concentrated in Denmark and Skåne. A few degrees further north is Europe's northernmost large agricultural region. It stretches in a west-east belt between 59° and 61°N, from the plains round the Oslofjord through Central Sweden to Southern Finland. A quarter of the arable land in Norden is concentrated here, mainly on marine clays, but there is nothing comparable to the unbroken cultivated plains of Denmark and Skåne. Minor plains, with a fairly high density of farms, alternate with forests which usually occupy more land than the arable fields.

Outside these two areas, Norden agriculture is mainly marginal. Income from the forests

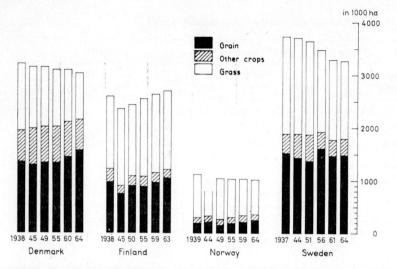

in 1000 ha

Grain
Other crops
Grass

1938 45 49 55 60 64   1938 45 50 55 59 63   1939 44 49 55 59 64   1937 44 51 56 61 64
Denmark   Finland   Norway   Sweden

Fig. 7.1. *Changes in agricultural land* in Denmark, Finland, Norway and Sweden during the last 25 years. Other crops are mainly roots; grass includes rotation grass, permanent grass and natural meadows.

makes a substantial contribution to the cash income of the rural population. In addition, a considerable part of the arable land in these marginal regions is found on better soils in a few, also climatically more favoured, minor areas.

In the marginal regions the earlier system of agriculture may still be carried on, with vast outfields used for hay or grazing. The meadows which are recorded in Table 7.4 are only those which are cut or grazed yearly and manured fairly often. There are no statistical records of the wide grazing areas in the forests, in the mountains and on the coastal heaths. It does not pay to harvest these outfield meadows at the present rate of wages, and vast areas are abandoned each year.

With an arable surface slightly superior to that of Finland, the Danish harvest (in crop units) is three times that of Finland (Table 7.5). The Danish yields of grain are twice as high, viz. 3 200 compared with 1 600 kg/ha. (1953/ 59). Root crops which yield far more than other arable crops, occupy more land in Denmark than in the other Norden countries combined. Yield per livestock unit is higher too (Table 7.6).

The productivity of Danish agriculture is also higher measured in output per man-hour. The Danish plains are well suited to mechanized agriculture, and the farms are larger than in the other Norden countries. Danish agriculture is highly mechanized (107 tractors per 100 holdings over 2 ha.), but the area worked by each tractor is rather low according to international standards (16 ha. per tractor). The corresponding figures for Sweden are 73 tractors and 19 ha.

There is also a marked difference between Norwegian and Swedish agriculture. In Norway 15.6 per cent of the active population is engaged in agriculture, in Sweden only 13.5 per cent (1960). Sweden is self-sufficient in staple food except in years with bad harvests, but Norwegian agriculture provides only 40 per cent of the nation's food. Sweden's more southerly position and the vast plains of Skåne and Central Sweden are the major reasons for the great difference in productivity; the smaller farm units and the more hilly terrain minimize the benefits of mechanization in Norway.

Finland is situated in the same latitudes as North Sweden. The farmed areas are definitely larger (Colour Map 8), and grain occupies five times as much land north of Lat. 62° as in Sweden. Grain for her people still occupies 30 per cent of Finland's grain area, whereas grain for fodder, mainly barley occupies 86 per cent of Denmark's grain fields. Fig. 7.1 shows the differing distribution of the farm land by countries during the past 25 years, and Colour Map 8, inset map, upper left, its distribution in the main agricultural regions. In the far north rotation grass occupies almost all the arable land.

Food production is more costly in Iceland than in other Norden countries; the long grazing season does not compensate for the low summer temperatures.

In all Norden countries animal husbandry ranks first. Its importance in each of them is shown in Table 7.6. Denmark has 1.5 livestock units per hectare of arable land, Sweden only 0.7. Per head of population Denmark's

Table 7.4. *Resources of land, forest and water*

| Country | Land area | Agricultural land 1964 | | | | | Forests [2] | | Rough estimates of | | |
| | | Arable [1] | | | Meadow | Total | Part of land area | Height | Precipitation | Evaporation |
		Total	Part of land area	per inhab.						
	1 000 km²	1 000 km²	%	ha	1 000 km²	1 000 km²	%	m	mm	mm
Denmark[3]	42	27.4	65.2	0.6	3.3	4	10	35	600	350
Finland	305	27.3	9.0	0.6	0.9	218	71	150	550	250
Iceland	100	1.0[4]	1.0	0.5	21.8[5]	0.03	0.03	500	1 900	150
Norway	308	8.5	2.8	0.2	1.7	70	23	500	1 500	250
Sweden	411	33.0	8.0	0.4	5.3	225	55	300	700	300
Total	1 166	96.2[6]	8.3	0.5	11.2[6]	517	44			

[1]) Incl. rotation grass. [2]) Table 7.8 gives lower figures and shows the area in active use. [3]) Excl. Faeroes and Greenland. [4]) Cultivated meadows. [5]) Incl. rough grazing. [6]) Excl. Iceland.

Table 7.5. *Use of arable land, 1959, and Production, 1953–59*

| Country | Arable land | Wheat and Rye | Barley and Oats | Potatoes | Sugar beet [1] | Other root crops | Other crops [2] | Grass | | Production Crop units [4] |
								for hay [3]	for grazing	
	1 000 ha	%	%	%	%	%	%	%	%	Millions
Denmark	2 744	7.6	34.9	3.2	2.0	15.2	13.3[5]	7.7	16.1	119
Finland	2 633	9.2	26.3	3.2	0.6	0.6	5.8	45.0	9.3	35
Iceland	60			1.5		0.3	0.2	88.0	10.0	2
Norway	839	1.2	24.4	6.5		1.8	6.8	52.6	6.7	20
Sweden	3 598	11.4	23.7	3.3	1.4	0.7	16.8[6]	33.0	9.7	79

[1]) For sugar production only. [2]) Incl. fallow. [3]) Incl. silage and grain cut green for fodder. [4]) Fodder value of 100 kg barley. Conversion: 1 crop unit = 100 kg wheat, rye, barley and peas, 120 kg oats, 110 kg mixed grain, 400 kg potatoes, c. 1 000 kg roots, 220—250 kg hay, and 400—500 kg straw. [5]) Of this seeds of grass, pulses, roots etc. occupy 65 000 ha. [6]) Of this oil seeds occupy 85 000 ha.

Table 7.6. *Livestock, 1965 [1]*

| Country | Horses | Cows | Other cattle | Sheep | Pigs | Hens | Livestock (cattle units) 1960 [2] | | | Annual milk yield per cow 1965 |
							Total [3]	Per ha. arable land	Per inhab.	
	Number in millions						Mill. c.u.	c.u.	c.u.	kg.
Denmark	0.1	1.4	1.9	0.1	8.6	20.3	4.1	1.5	0.9	3 946
Finland	0.2	1.1	0.9	0.2	0.6	6.9	1.8	0.7	0.4	3 375
Iceland	0.03	0.04	0.02	0.8	0.0	0.1	0.14	2.4	0.8	2 985
Norway	0.1	0.5	0.6	2.0	0.6	4.6	1.2	1.4	0.3	3 240
Sweden	0.1	1.4	0.9	0.2	1.9	9.1	2.6	0.7	0.3	3 589

[1]) June or July except for Iceland. [2]) Conversion factors: Horses 1.0, cattle 0.8, pigs 0.25 and sheep and goats 0.1. [3]) Incl. goats.

livestock population is three times larger, but even in Sweden three quarters of the total farm income is derived from livestock produce.

In Sweden the area of arable land has been somewhat reduced in recent years and many small and laborious hill farms have been abandoned. In Finland the arable area has increased, new farms having been cleared to accommodate the repatriated Finns from Karelia and to compensate for the arable land lost at the armistice 1944. Icelandic and Norwegian statistics record important areas as potentially cultivable. At present wages and prices it pays only to clear such land to increase existing farms in order to utilize more fully their labour, machinery and farm buildings. The farm population has decreased substantially in all Norden countries since the last war (in 1950–60 by 26 per cent), but they now produce more food with less labour.

FISHING

The fish resources of the vast shelf areas of the North Atlantic gave rise until recently to larger fisheries than those of the North Pacific. As there, the temperate waters are inhabited by a limited number of migratory fishes, mainly cod and herring. At definite seasons immense shoals of these species migrate to their traditional spawning or feeding grounds, and it is easier and cheaper to work such shoals of migratory fishes than the numerous species which occur simultaneously on the fishing grounds of warm seas.

Fig. 7.2 shows the fish catches of the North Atlantic in 1960 distributed according to the division used by the International Council for the Exploration of the Sea (København); Table 7.7 gives the total catch of the more important species for each of the Norden countries with figures for the Faeroe Islands and Greenland also.

Outside the sea boundaries which most countries except the Soviet Union until recently drew three nautical miles outside the outermost headlands and islets not continuously covered by the sea, fishing has been free to everybody. Open bights like Vestfjorden (Lofoten) and Varangerfjorden in North Norway have long been considered national territories. Iceland declared a 12 mile fishing limit some years ago, followed

recently by the Faeroes and Norway. During a transition period fishing rights in the 6–12 miles zone may be allowed by separate treaties to other nations which traditionally fish in these waters.

Iceland ranks next to Norway in fishing among the Norden countries, and Icelandic waters are among the richest in the world. Iceland also has a favourable position midway between the two main consuming regions of the North Atlantic. The catches of fishing vessels of other nations are, however, almost as important as those of Iceland, and the Icelanders need a larger share for themselves. The fisheries are indeed Iceland's sole resource of any real importance, and any reduction by overfishing of the stocks of cod and herring spawning and feeding in Icelandic waters would be fatal for Iceland.

North Norway would also be practically uninhabited without its rich marine resources. Norway ranks second among the fishing nations of Europe (after the Soviet Union) according to weight of catch. In catch value, however, it is surpassed by the United Kingdom, Spain and Italy. A tenth of Norway's total exports are fish products. Cod and herring, the two main species, both spawn in Norwegian territorial waters.

The more distant fishing grounds on the wide shelf area off the Norwegian coast are also a big asset, as the advantages arising from the short distance from home ports largely compensate for the higher transport cost to European and overseas markets. Recently the new, larger Norwegian fishing vessels have joined the international trawling fleet in distant waters, but the Norwegian share of these fisheries is still rather modest, even in the Barents Sea, in spite of the rich Norwegian fisheries off the coast of Finnmark.

The Baltic has rather poor fish resources, whereas the North Sea is exceedingly rich, with herring as the main species. There are usually large catches of herring by Norwegian fishermen in coastal waters. The catches by other nations of haddock, flounder and other demersal species outnumber those of Denmark, Sweden and Norway. Norwegian fishermen take the lead in the new ring net fisheries of herring and mackerel in the North Sea. The Danish fisheries are concentrated in those parts of the North and

Fig. 7.2. *Fish catches of the North Atlantic in 1960*, distributed according to the division used by the International Council for the Exploration of the Sea and specified for each of the Norden countries; all other countries are grouped together. 62°N separates the North Sea and the Norwegian Sea, and 26°E and 73°N the latter from the Barents Sea and the Bjørnøya and Spitsbergen fishing grounds. D=Denmark. F=Faeroes. Fi=Finland. G=Greenland. I=Iceland. N=Norway. S=Sweden. O=Countries outside Norden. — After Sund & Sømme 1962.

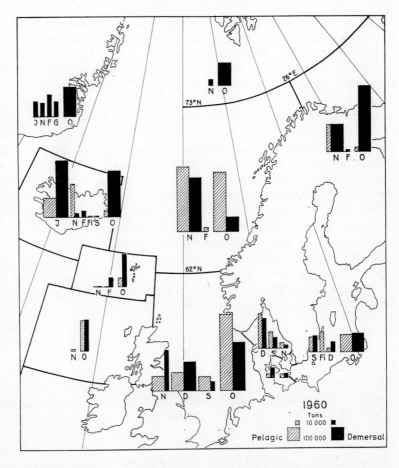

Baltic Seas which adjoin Denmark. More highly priced species, such as flounder and haddock, and the short distance to important foreign markets, account for the high price per kg received by Danish fishermen.

The population of the Faeroe Islands depends entirely on the sea. Foreign vessels take most of the catch in Faeroe waters, and the islands' own fishermen draw larger catches in distant waters, particularly off West Greenland. Many Faeroe fishermen serve on foreign fishing-vessels.

In the Davis Strait hydrographic changes since the late twenties have provided new and important shoals of cod, which are caught by vessels from many different countries. This fishery was at first a summer one. Now it goes on throughout the year from big factory ships. The total catch has increased, but Norden's share of it has decreased.

Whereas conditions for agriculture worsen in more northerly latitudes, it seems that the north-

Table 7.7. *Fish catches, 1965 (Live weight)*

Country	Cod, etc.	Herring etc.	Mackerel and tuna	Halibut, flounder etc.	Red-fish	Salmon and sea trout	Crab, lobster, shrimp, molluscs	Fresh water fish[1]	Others	Total
					1 000 t.					
Denmark	210	350	7	61	138	14	25	4	31[2]	841
Faeroes	109	35	—	0	0	0	0	—	1	145
Finland	0	48	—	—	—	7	—	18	1	74
Iceland	330	762	—	10	38	50	5	—	4	1 199
Norway	637	1 089	159	24	21	220	23	1	106[3]	2 280
Sweden	45	293	13	3	—	1	5	3	2	365
Total	1 331	2 577	179	98	197	292	58	26	145	4 904

[1]) Incl. river eels. [2]) Incl. 26 000 t. unsorted. [3]) Incl. 74 000 t. aquatic plants and picked dogfish 19 000 t.

ern seas are at least as rich as those further south. But the annual yield may vary considerably, mainly owing to the hydrographic conditions in the years during which the fish are maturing. Some year-classes may be practically exterminated whereas others may be exceedingly rich. The herring may even leave its traditional spawning grounds for several decades and appear along other coasts, and this had disastrous consequences for the local fishermen in the pre-motor age. The increasing trawling in areas where immature fish are found, e.g. in the Barents Sea seems to be depleting fish stocks. Here the Lofoten cod is found in its immature form and has its summer feeding grounds when mature. The cod catches in Lofoten have been halved since the mid-1950's.

Scientists agree more or less about protection measures, but it is difficult to reach agreement between governments, e.g. about limitation of net-meshes. In the North Sea overfishing was clearly demonstrated during and after the two world wars when fishing was greatly reduced. The catches during the years following both wars were large and brought in larger fish than those of preceding years. But the limitations agreed upon have not been sufficient to provide real protection. The protective measures which are now being considered by the leading countries are far-reaching and deal with catch quotas and limitations of the size of participating fleets.

The entrance to the White Sea, one of Norway's two traditional hunting grounds for seal, has been closed to Norwegian sealers since the Soviet Union established the 12 mile fishing limit. Since then Norwegian sealing has concentrated on the drift ice off the East Greenland coast; recently Norwegian sealers have also appeared in Newfoundland waters.

After the extinction of the whaling stock of the North Atlantic, Norwegian whaling has been concentrated in the Antarctic. This recent development will be described in Chapter 11. The other Norden countries do not participate in sealing and whaling.

MINERALS

Like the Canadian Shield, the Precambrian areas of Fennoscandia contain numerous and varied mineral resources. This is also true of the Caledonian Mountain Range. The younger

formations which provide coal and oil, occur, apart from Spitsbergen, only in Skåne and Denmark. These deposits of coal, lignite and, in Central Sweden, oil schists which are not exploited at present, give only a meagre contribution to the energy supply of the Norden countries. Occurrences of uranium which are thought to be of commercial value have been found only in Finland and Sweden. In the parts of the North Sea, which according to the mid-line principle are considered to be Danish and Norwegian, gas and oil prospecting has not yet had any success (1967).

Comparative data for mineral resources are compiled only at long intervals, mainly for presentation to international geological congresses. The last one for iron ore puts Sweden second to France in the European list.

The Swedish iron ores occur in the central and northern parts of the country. Those of Central Sweden have been mined for many centuries; they are numerous but small and are almost devoid of phosphorus. This formerly gave Swedish steel an unrivalled quality. At the present rate of production the deposits may last for another hundred years.

The iron ores of North Sweden are concentrated in a few very large deposits in Lappland and are mainly exported. Situated in mountainous areas north of the Polar Circle and far from the sea, their exploitation gave rise to big technical and financial problems. The ores are, however, very rich, with iron contents approaching the possible maximum, and are mainly won from open workings and at reasonable costs. Most of the Lappland ores have a high phosphorus content and had no commercial value before the invention of the Thomas steel converter in the late 19th century. A similar ore body is mined in Central Sweden (Grängesberg).

Norway's iron ore deposits are small compared with those of Sweden, and the iron content is low, requiring concentration before export. But Norway has two deposits (Sør-Varanger, Dunderlandsdal) which are large by European standards, and are both situated close to ice-free fjords and cheap water-power.

The same conditions hold for the Norwegian pyrites deposits. Next to Spain and Italy, Finland and Norway are the largest European producers of pyrites (1967). Copper concentrate production in Finland, Norway and Sweden is chiefly by flotation of cupriferous pyrites ore. The biggest production is from Outukumpu mine in Finland.

Modern geophysical ore-prospecting recently discovered a large new field of mainly sulphide ores in Sweden (Skellefteå) and several important ore deposits in Finland. Iceland's basalts and Tertiary rocks give little hope of future mineral developments.

FOREST RESOURCES

The circumpolar coniferous forest belt between 50° and 65°N stretches across Finland, Sweden and Norway. The 450 000 km² of coniferous forest of Norden constitute half of Europe's coniferous area, if the Soviet Union is excluded. Norden has a strong position in world trade of semi-manufactured forest products.

Finland has three quarters of her land in forests and ranks first in forest area and production per inhabitant, but Sweden has larger forests, and owing to its more southerly situation a larger timber production (Tables 7.4 and 7.8).

In Norway forests occupy only a quarter of the land area. Norway is situated further to the north, a large part of the country lies above the forest limit, and strong winds prevent or reduce growth. Low-yielding forests along the coast and north of the Polar Circle, included in the figures of Table 7.4, have been omitted from Table 7.8 and from Colour Map 8. Nevertheless an annual growth per capita of 3.6 cubic metres gives an important surplus for export, and a sixth of the total value of Norwegian exports is derived from the wood- and wood-processing industries. For Sweden the corresponding figure is c. 30 per cent and for Finland

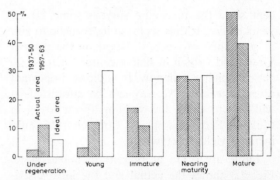

Fig. 7.3. *Actual and ideal 'age' distribution* at the two forest surveys of 1937–50 and 1957–63. The classified forest area is differentiated into the above five *hogstklasser* (cutting classes). According to a rough estimate the ideal age distribution, combined with denser timber stands, will give Norway a total production, incl. bark, of 22.3 million m³ as against 15.0 mill. m³ at the present.

nearly three quarters (1963). Cf. Table 7.13, lower part.

The distribution of tree species varies somewhat. Pine is an inland tree; Finland and Sweden thus have comparatively higher percentages of pine than more maritime Norway, but the spruce is dominant even in Sweden. The differing distributions of tree species have produced different patterns of processing industries. The lumber mills use more pine than spruce, their waste as well as pure timber feeds large sulphate pulp mills; the sulphite and mechanical pulp mills have until recently used spruce exclusively. The differing composition of the export trades is seen in Table 7.13.

Compared with Canada and the Soviet Union, Norden is favoured by its dense network of rivers and lakes suitable for floating. This cheap means of transport was formerly the only way in which the timber could be moved from the forest hinterland to the estuarine processing plants. In the initial stage the short sea journey to the main West-European markets was also very important.

The Norden forests grow more slowly than those of Central Europe, but the quality of the fibres is higher. New techniques have, however, reduced the importance of fibre quality to the processing industries. The management of the Norden forests compares favourably with that of most other countries and can maintain not only sustained but even increased yields. The most recent forest appraisals reveal, e.g. in Norway, an annual increase in yield of one per

Table 7.8. *Forests*

Country	Classified area	Annual growth				
		Total[1]	Pine	Spruce	Deciduous	Per inhab.
	1000 km²	Million m³	%	%	%	m³
Denmark	3.7	2	16	40	44	0.3
Finland	205.0	46	39	37	24	10.3
Norway	57.6	13	24	60	16	3.6
Sweden	222.6	53	37	48	15	7.3

[1] Excl. bark. — After Skogstilgångarne i de nordiska länderna, Svenska Skogsvårdsföreningens Tidskrift 1958, H 3.

cent since the preceding surveys some 20–25 years earlier. It thus seems quite realistic to aim at an annual production, based on the present forest land, which in half a century will be 50 per cent higher than now. In addition, important areas in western Norway can be afforested. It will pay to drain low-yielding forest areas in Finland. Fertilizers spread from aircraft could increase yields everywhere.

Large areas are at present in a bad state. Fig. 7.3 shows the actual and the ideal distribution of the forest land in Norway. Optimal production is obtained when all age-classes occupy equal areas. Until recently old stands occupied almost half of the Norwegian forest area, whereas improved silviculture (more state forests, larger company-owned forests) has produced a better age-distribution in Swedish forests. At present all Norden countries replace old, poorly-stocked stands with young, denser and quicker-growing forests. This change cannot, however, be carried through too quickly because of the risk of a temporary deficit in the supply to the wood-processing industries 25–30 years ahead.

On Colour Map 8 an inset map gives the actual and the approximate optimal production for major regions, and the main map a more detailed picture of the optimal yield, expressed in m³ annual growth (incl. bark) per hectare of forest land. It varies in Sweden from 8.2 m³ per hectare in Skåne to 1.9 m³ in Lappland (averages for the 123 regions on which the map has been based). Similarly, the actual production varies between 7.0 and 1.1 m³ per ha. (averages for the same regions). The highest yields occur usually in regions favoured by good climate and soil where a major part of the land is in arable, but the main producing area lies in a broad zone which stretches northwards from about 60°N on both sides of the Gulf of Bothnia.

By international standards the Norden peoples are liberal users of timber. The widespread supply of electricity and new construction methods will reduce the per capita consumption of sawn timber and fuel, and the increased yield will thus add to the supply of the processing industries. The present trend for further processing of the existing limited timber supply will probably continue. The timber consumption of the sawmills has been fairly con-

stant; the increased fellings have been absorbed by the pulp mills. The pulp is increasingly transformed into paper and, recently, into textile fibres, and the former waste is now used as raw material for valuable chemicals. The Norden wood-processing industries show all signs of developing into chemical industries.

WATER-POWER

Apart from Russia, Norway has the richest water-power resources in Europe. Table 7.4 gives a comparison of the average height above sea level and the average amount of precipitation and evaporation in the Norden countries, and thus indicates theoretical potentialities. On Colour Map 7 the potential water-power resources have been indicated for major regions specially delimited for this study. The electricity production of the existing and planned power plants has been added for each of these regions, and the potentialities have been expressed in kilowatt hours per square km. The map reveals enormous differences between countries and regions. It is, however, difficult to establish comparable figures for water-power potentialities when building costs and conflicting interests concerning water regulation have to be considered. Power schemes which can be realized only at very high cost and with damaging effects on agriculture and other human activities have therefore been omitted.

The former glaciation has considerably increased the heads of water by glacial overdeepening of valleys and fjords, but the numerous lakes, which are also largely due to glacial overdeepening and scouring, or damming, are the biggest asset of the Norden countries. The utilization of their water-power requires comparatively more water-storage than in more temperate countries as precipitation occurs in the form of snow during the long northern winter. At this time, when power requirements are at their peak, only an insignificant part of the precipitation will feed the reservoirs. This applies even to maritime Norway; the major part of the catchment areas is in mountainous regions, and the winter precipitation will not reach the rivers before the snow melts in spring or early summer.

The natural flow varies widely as does the cost of water-storage. Sweden has more lakes—

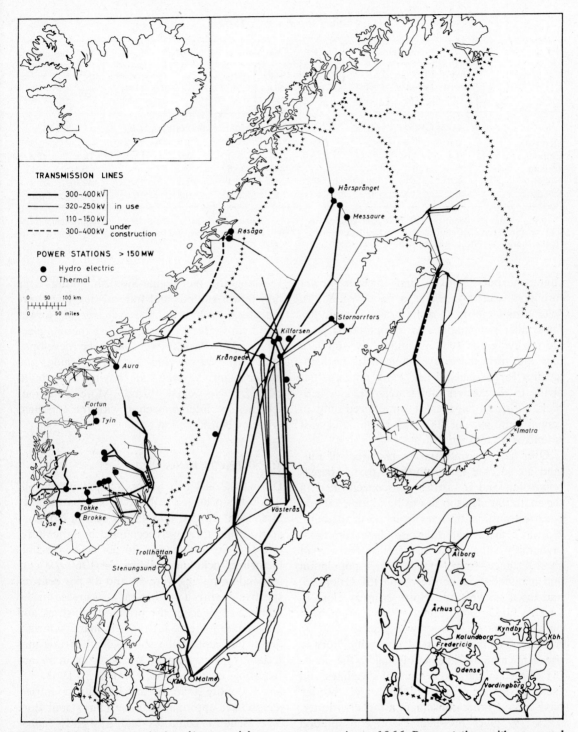

Fig. 7.4. *Major transmission lines and large power stations, 1966.* Power stations with an annual average output of 1 000 million kWh (in Norway in 90 out of 100 years) are named. — Sources: NORDEL, Report 1966 (transmission lines) and the national state power boards (power plants).

and Finland still more—than Norway, but it is easier and cheaper to transform the Norwegian lakes into reservoirs, because the greater number occur in mountains, where the areas sub- merged after dam-building have little or no value as agricultural land or forest. The com- paratively low cost of reservoir-building, com- bined with Norway's strong relief and high pre-

Table 7.9. *Energy, 1965*

Country	Production			Net imports				Total energy aggregate in coal equivalent[1]	Net consumption of electricity	
	Hydro-electricity	Thermal electricity	Coal	Coal	Crude petroleum	Refined oil products	Electricity		Total	In industry[2]
	1 000 GWh[3]		Mill.t.	Mill.t.	Mill.t.	Mill.t.	1 000 GWh	Mill.t.	1 000 GWh	
Denmark	0.0	7.4	—	4.5	3.4	6.7	1.7	20.2	8.1	2.5
Finland	9.4	4.6	—	3.4	2.3	3.0	0.6	12.8	13.4	9.9
Iceland	0.6	0.0	—	0.0	—	0.5	—	0.8	0.5	0.1
Norway	48.9	0.1	0.4	0.8	2.8	2.1	—2.1	13.9	42.0	25.9
Sweden	46.4	2.7	0.1	3.1	3.8	15.0	—0.8	36.8	42.2	26.2

[1]) 1 ton crude petroleum = 1.33 tons coal equivalents; 1 ton refined oil products = 1.5 tons coal equivalents; 1 000 kWh = 0.125 ton coal equivalents. [2]) Incl. transport. [3]) GWh = million kilowatthours. — Sources: UN Yearbook of Trade Statistics, 1965. Nordel: Report 1965 (col. 1, 2, 7, 9 and 10).

cipitation, puts Norway first in water-power resources, with Sweden as a good second. In spite of its larger fresh-water areas, Finland has far smaller potentialities as its numerous lakes are low-lying and shallow, and in the southern part are surrounded by arable land or high-yielding forest. Iceland has larger potentialities owing to its glaciers and water-retaining bedrock, but up to the present has utilized only an insignificant part of its water-power and vast resources of terrestrial heat.

Over half the water-power resources of Finland are located in its northern part, whereas population and industries are concentrated in the south. Sweden too has to build long and expensive transmission lines from north to south. Norway's main waterfalls are, however, more favourably situated, those of East Norway at short distances from Norway's main population and manufacturing centre round the Oslofjord, and those of West and North Norway close to ice-free fjords; large factories have often been built adjacent to these power plants.

Because of the low cost of electricity, Norway uses large amounts in electrolysing, in the smelting of metals and for heating of dwellings and factories by electricity. Finland and Sweden have to give other consumers a higher priority. Table 7.9 gives production and consumption figures.

For many years a small exchange of electricity has occurred between Denmark and Sweden; the latter country supplies hydro-electricity during high water periods and receives from Denmark thermal electricity during periods of low water.

Along the Norwegian-Swedish border large new power stations and transmission lines have recently been built for the exchange of Norwegian hydro-electricity and Swedish thermal electricity. The Pasvik river has been developed jointly by Norway and the Soviet Union, one power plant on each side having been built, both by Norwegian firms. More ambitious schemes for interconnection with the continent is under consideration.

MANUFACTURING

During the last fifty years, a rapid industrialization has occurred in Norden, and particularly after 1920. In that year 45 per cent of Norden's active population were occupied in agriculture, forestry and fishing, and 26 per cent in manufacturing, including building. In 1960 the corresponding figures were 21 and 38 per cent respectively, with a further rapid decrease in the number engaged in the primary industries and a moderate increase for those in manufacturing. Seven per cent of the value added to raw material by processing in West-European manufacturing originated in Norden in 1961, i.e. slightly more than in the Benelux countries, which have approximately the same population. The Benelux countries had a slightly higher share of the employment.

Half the Norden manufacturing is found in Sweden, which in her combined forest and mineral resources has a solidly based economy. Sweden's per capita consumption of steel surpasses even that of U.S. and West Germany. In value added by manufacture per worker employed,

Fig. 7.5. *Manufacturing industries, 1960.* Vertically the diagram shows in million of U.S. $ the value added by manufacture according to the International Standard of Industrial Classification (ISIC), horizontally the distribution by countries. Denmark had 17.3% of the total value added, Finland and Norway 15.5% each and Sweden 51.7%. Since 1960 distributon has not noticeably changed neither by countries nor by industries. Engineering (groups 35–38) increased its share from 34 to 36% in 1960–65, the share of the forest industries (groups 25–27) decreased from 16 to 15%.

4 500 US dollars (1960), Sweden ranks higher than Denmark, Finland and Norway, whose figures are 3 400, 3 100 and 3 800 respectively. Swedish manufacturing thus represents a more advanced stage of industrialization. It also has a higher proportion of industries in groups which require highly skilled man-power (Fig. 7.5). This particular position may partly be explained by the unbroken traditions of her old iron industry. A contributing factor may also have been her possibilities of transforming natural resources into ready capital for building up new industries—in the latter part of the 19th century by felling the virgin forest of northern Sweden, in this century by her large iron ore export.

Sweden accounts for more than a third of the total Norden population, the remainder is fairly even distributed between Denmark, Finland and Norway, and so, too, is the other half of the Norden manufacturing, whether measured in production value or in employment.

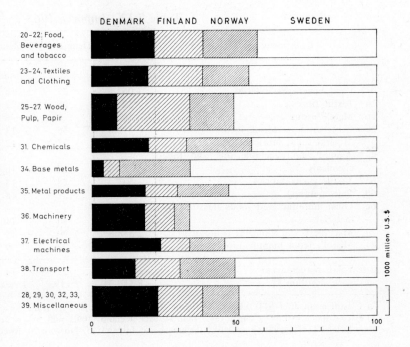

Fig. 7.5 indicates the importance of their main industries for Denmark, Finland, Norway and Sweden. The strong position of engineering (groups 35–38) in Sweden and Denmark and of wood-processing in Finland and Sweden is ob-

Table 7.10. *Manufacturing, 1965*

Country	Number of establishment	Production		Owners, salaried and wage-earners
		Gross value	Value added	
		Million $	Million $	1000
Denmark	6 805[1]	4 516	2 085	412
Finland[1]	6 869	5 006	1 699	405
Iceland[2]	1 246	128	39	15
Norway	9 494	4.557	1 835	348
Sweden	16 595	14 829	6 753	989

[1] 1964. [2] 1960.

Table 7.11. *Persons employed in manufacturing industries, 1960[1]*

Group[2]	Den-mark	Fin-land	Nor-way	Swed-en
	%	%	%	%
20–22 Ford, beverages, tobacco	14.6	11.5	14.2	8.0
23–24 Textiles, footwear etc.	14.8	17.9	13.8	12.4
25–27 Wood, paper and paper products	10.3	24.0	16.5	15.4
31 Chemicals and chemical products	4.1	3.2	6.9	3.6
34 Base metals	0.9	2.3	7.3	7.3
35 Metal products..	6.6	4.9	6.9	6.7
36 Machinery	13.4	9.1	4.0	16.8
37 Electrical machinery	8.8	4.0	4.3	6.8
38 Transport equipment	9.5	9.2	14.5	9.7
28–30, 32, 33, 39 Miscellaneous	17.0	13.9	11.6	13.3
20–39 Total in % ..	100.0	100.0	100.0	100.0
1 000 persons ..	337	374	303	859

[1] Owners, salaried and wage-owners. The percentages for Denmark apply to wage-earners only. [2] Groups as in Fig. 7.5.

Table 7.12. *Imports, 1963*

Commodity group[1]	Norden	Denmark[2]	Finland	Norway	Sweden	Norden
	Million $		thereof in %			%
0–1 Food, beverages, tobacco	1 063.6	27	16	19	38	12.5
2a Textile fibres	123.2	26	22	14	38	1.4
2b Metalliferous ores	102.6	0	6	64	30	1.2
2c Other crude material, inedible[3]	476.0	36	13	18	33	5.6
3 Mineral fuels, lubricants etc.	1 010.2	27	12	16	45	11.9
4–5 Animal and vegetable oils and fats, chemicals	723.7	27	16	19	38	8.5
6a Textile yarns, fabrics	537.5	28	13	17	42	6.3
6b Base metals	463.5	27	18	20	35	5.4
6c Other manufactured goods classified by materials	795.9	30	11	17	42	9.4
7 Machinery and transport equipment ..	2 558.8	20	15	27	38	30.1
8 Miscellaneous manufactured articles ..	620.5	22	9	20	49	7.3
0–9 Total, percentages		25	14	21	40	100
» million $	8 510.2[4]	2 119.2	1 200.8	1 816.6	3 373.4	

[1]) Classification after SITC, Revised (1960). [2]) Denmark proper. Its trade with Faeroes and Greenland is excluded.
[3]) Except fuel. [4]) Incl. group 9 (34.7 mill. $), excl. Iceland (109.5 mill. $). — Total imports 1965: 11 041.9 million $, excl. Iceland (137.2 mill. $), of which Denmark 25, Finland 15, Norway 20, Sweden 40%.

Commodities	Unit	Norden	Denmark	Finland	Norway	Sweden	Norden Mill. $
0							
Grain	Mill. t.	2.2	0.7	0.5	0.6	0.4	162
Fruit and vegetables	»	1.0	0.2	0.1	0.2	0.5	251
Oilseed cake and meal	»	1.4	0.8	0.1	0.2	0.3	115
2							
Oilseed	»	0.8	0.5	0.1	0.1	0.1	88
Round wood	Mill. m³	2.9[1]	0.2	0.9	1.2	0.6	41
Crude fertilizers	Mill. t.	1.0	0.2	0.2	0.2	0.4	30
Salt	»	1.5[1]	0.2	0.3	0.3	0.6	14
Nonferrous ores and concentrates .	»	0.7	0.0	0.0	0.4	0.3	86
3							
Coal	»	8.2	4.0	2.2	0.2	1.8	89
Coke	»	4.2	1.4	0.4	0.8	1.6	92
Crude petroleum	»	8.7	1.8	1.6	2.5	2.8	149
Petroleum products	»	25.6[1]	6.4	2.1	3.3	13.4	680
5							
Manufactured fertilizers	»	2.0	1.1	0.3	0.1	0.5	80
6							
Iron and steel	»	3.3	0.9	0.5	0.7	1.2	468
Other base metals	»	0.4	0.1	0.0	0.1	0.2	225
7							
Motor vehicles	1 000	393[1]	105	53	70	162	575

[1]) Thereof Iceland 24 000 m³ round wood, 0.1 mill. t. salt, 0.4 mill. t. petroleum products and 3 000 motor vehicles.

vious. The most striking fact is, however, the industrialization of Denmark which entirely lacks both power resources and raw materials except for food-processing and the manufacture of cement. The structure of its manufacturing is more like that of highly industrialized Sweden than that of Finland and Norway. The industrialization of the latter countries is more recent and does not yet spread over so many fields. Industry groups in which the raw ma-

Table 7.13. *Exports, 1963*

Commodity group[1]	Norden	Denmark[2]	Finland	Norway	Sweden	Norden
	Million $	thereof in %				%
0–1 Food, beverages, tobacco	1 261.3	76	3	13	8	17.4
2a Wood, lumber, pulp................	1 099.1	1	38	7	54	15.1
2b Metalliferous ores	227.5	1	5	9	85	3.1
2c Other crude material, inedible[3]	254.9	42	10	22	26	3.5
3 Mineral fuels, lubricants etc.	57.3	20	1	53	26	0.8
4–5 Animal and vegetable oils and fats, chemicals	363.0	30	5	34	31	5.0
6a Wood manufactures[4], paper and board	889.2	3	47	12	38	12.2
6b Metals	590.9	4	5	42	49	8.1
6c Other manufactured goods classified by materials	376.7	25	6	14	55	5.2
7 Machinery and transport equipment ..	1 818.8	22	8	8	62	25.0
8 Miscellaneous manufactured articles ..	297.5	41	6	11	42	4.1
0–9 Total, percentages		26	16	15	43	100
» million $	7 269.5[5]	1 869.5	1 142.2	1 070.6	3 187.2	

[1]) Classification after SITC, Revised (1960). [2]) Denmark proper. Its trade with Faeroes and Greenland is excluded.
[3]) Except fuel. [4]) Excl. furniture. [5]) Incl. group 9 (33.3 mill. $), excl. Iceland (94.0 mill. $). — Total exports 1965: 9 111.7 mill. $, excl. Iceland (129.3 mill. $), of which Denmark 25, Finland 16, Norway 16, Sweden 43%.

Commodities	Unit	Norden	Denmark	Finland	Norway	Sweden	Norden Mill. $
0							
Meat	1 000 t.	307	242	2	24	33	190
Butter	»	133	102	16	4	11	129
Cheese	»	117	79	17	14	7	75
Eggs	»	57	39	10	—	8	35
Fish, fresh, chilled or frozen	»	676[1]	{ 216	—	119 }	34	214
Fish, salted, dried or smoked ...	»		{ 1	—	78 }		
2							
Lumber, coniferous	Mill. m³	9.7	0.1	4.6	0.1	4.9	385
Mechanical pulp[2]	Mill. t.	1.1	—	0.2	0.5	0.4	66
Chemical pulp[2]	»	4.9	0.0	1.8	0.3	2.8	582
Iron ores and concentrates	»	22.3	0.1	0.4	1.3	20.5	192
5							
Fertilizers, manufactured	»	1.4	0.0	—	1.4	0.0	50
6							
Newsprint	1 000 t.	1531	—	882	219	430	193
Other paper and board	»	3683	27	1574	426	1656	560
Iron and steel[3]	Mill. t.	1.7	0.1	0.2	0.5	0.9	346
Other base metals[4]	»	0.8	0.0	0.0	0.7	0.1	105

[1]) Thereof Iceland meat 6 000 t. and fish 228 000 t. [2]) Calculated dry weight. [3]) Excl. ferro-alloys. [4]) Incl. ferro-alloys.

terial cost constitutes an important part of the gross value of production tend to be dominant, e.g. wood-processing (both countries) or fertilizers or metals, especially aluminium (Norway). The latter industries (groups 31 and 34) depend on ample supplies of cheap water-power. The recent development of machinery (36) in Finland is also striking.

The textile industries of the Norden countries are small compared with those of the older European manufacturing countries, as are the chemical industries; deposits of salt and coal[1] are lacking, and Norden cannot provide the same facilities for research as the big industrial countries. Other manufacturing groups are very

[1]) Except Svalbard and Skåne (cf. Table 7.9).

95

important, particularly wood-processing. The products of such industries make up a high proportion of the exports of the respective countries, and, put together, an important part of world trade. For example, more than half the chemical pulp entering world trade originates in Norden (1965).

NORDEN'S POSITION IN THE WORLD

Norden's 20 million inhabitants—less than 1 per cent of the world's total—contrast with its share of world manufacturing, shipping and trade. Norden's position in manufacturing has been discussed above. Its contribution to the world's carrying trade is still more important; 15 per cent of the world fleet fly Norden flags; this is mainly due to the strong position of Norwegian shipping. In Europe only Britain, West Germany and France, and in North America the United States can boast of larger shares of world trade. Imports constitute about a quarter of the gross national product in Norden. The high living standard of present-day Scandinavians could not be upheld without this extensive foreign trade, which, however, makes the economy of the Norden welfare states rather vulnerable.

Tables 7.12 and 7.13 show trade by commodity groups and for selected commodities in 1963. Sweden's position in trade is not as dominant as in manufacturing (over 40 per cent of the Norden total). Denmark is a good second (25 per cent). Finland's exports are slightly higher than those of Norway, her imports are much lower.

The differing economic structures of the Norden countries are clearly reflected in their foreign trade. The traditional wood and iron industries still occupy a dominant position. Both wood and metals have, however, been increasingly processed. The exports of newsprint, other papers and board increased in 1957–63 from 2.5 to 5.2 million tons. Exports of iron ores and metals have increased too during the same period, whereas the export of timber and pulp has decreased. The most highly processed commodity groups (7 and 8) have increased their share of the total Norden export trade from 21 to 29 per cent. Imports, however, still surpassed exports in these commodity groups by 55 per cent (1963).

As long as the Norden countries were exporting mainly unprocessed fish, wood and iron, there was little possibility of any trade between them. Their young, growing manufacturing industries have been sheltered behind tariff barriers, with no preferences for the other Norden countries, except during a short period in the 19th century between Norway and Sweden. Danish agricultural export has been, and is still firmly excluded from the other Norden markets.

An attempt a few years ago to establish a Norden customs union for manufactures failed. The EFTA agreement has, however, acted as such, and inter-Norden trade has risen rapidly, imports from 12.5 to 19.2, and exports from 13.7 to 22.5 per cent (1957–65). The two European trade blocks account for 72 per cent of Norden's international trade. The EEC share has been fairly constant during the same period, that of the United Kingdom has declined. The smaller EFTA countries are not very important in Norden's trade, whereas Benelux, France and Italy, as purchasers of Norden goods, equal West Germany, their main supplier (Table 7.14). The growing inter-EFTA trade is thus entirely due to the increased inter-Norden trade.

In order to facilitate comparisons among the Norden countries and between the whole of Norden and the rest of the world, different criteria of economic strength and living standard have been collected in Table 7.15, with figures also for the United States, Britain, West Germany, France, Italy and Japan. Compared with the two former countries Norden has a surprisingly high percentage of its population occupied in primary production, and agriculture, forestry and fishery contribute with 15 per cent to the gross national product, as against 3–4 per cent for the U.S.A. and U.K. Finland especially has a high proportion of its population in agriculture and forestry (Table 7.2), and a low productivity in these industries. They occupy 35 per cent of her active population, but contribute only 18 per cent to her gross national product (Table 7.3). The situation is similar for Norway. This weakness in the Norden economy is, however, counterbalanced by the high productivity of Danish agriculture, Norwegian shipping, and manufacturing in all Norden countries, and results in high national incomes per inhabitant, which for Sweden is surpassed only by that of U.S.A.

Table 7.14. *Imports — Exports, 1965*

	Norden				Denmark		Finland		Iceland		Norway		Sweden	
	Imports		Exports		Imp.	Exp.	Imp.	Exp.	Imp.	Exp.	Imp.	Exp.	Imp.	Exp.
	Mill. $	%	Mill. $	%	%	%	%	%	%	%	%	%	%	%
Norden	2 141	19.2	2 081	22.5	20	21	19	13	23	19	27	25	14	26
United Kingdom ..	1 645	14.7	1 632	17.7	17	23	15	20	14	21	12	18	15	13
Other EFTA countr.	420	3.8	280	3.0	4	4	4	1	1	2	3	2	4	4
West Germany	2 247	20.1	1 318	14.3	22	16	19	11	12	8	16	14	22	14
Other EEC countries	1 621	14.5	1 305	14.1	15	10	13	17	9	12	13	11	16	17
USA	884	7.9	654	7.1	8	8	5	6	13	16	7	9	9	6
Other countries ..	2 214	19.8	1 971	21.3	14	18	25	32	28	22	22	21	20	20
World	11 172	100	9 241	100	100	100	100	100	100	100	100	100	100	100

Table 7.15. *Norden in the world, 1963*

Country	Inhabitants millions	Foreign trade, % of world trade	Commodity imports, % of gross domestic product[1]	Steel consumption, kg per inhab.	National income, $ per inhab.	Food, % of private consumption	Telephones per 100 inhab.	Passenger cars per 100 inhab.	Consumption of electricity kWh per inhab.	Thereof in manufact. industries %
Denmark	4.7	1.2	27	256	1 337	24	27	12.9	1 483	28
Finland	4.5	0.7	21	223	1 040	36	16	6.7	2 603	77
Iceland	0.2	0.1	35	..	1 305	..	26	10.3	3 546	41
Norway	3.7	0.7	32	279	1 176	29	23	9.9	10 761	66
Sweden	7.6	2.1	22	545	1 798	27	40	20.5	5 328	63
Norden	20.7	4.8	25	360	1 413	28	27	13.8	4 798	63
U.S.A.	189.4	15.0	3	540	2 507	21	45	36.3	5 340	51
U.K.	53.8	7.4	16	368	1 258	28	17	14.3	3 226	45
West Germany	55.4	9.5	14	473	1 307	..	14	12.8	2 657	68
France	47.9	5.3	8	326	1 271	31	11	16.3	1 884	68
Italy	50.5	3.3	17	277	701	43	10	7.7	1 413	66
Japan	95.9	3.6	11	258	509	44	9	1.3	1 671	..

[1]) At factor cost.

The above tables are mainly based on annual United Nations' publications: Statistical Yearbook, Yearbook of International Trade Statistics, FAO Production Yearbook and FAO Yearbook of Fishery Statistics, or on the annual statistical yearbooks of Denmark, Finland, Norway and Sweden. Other sources are given below each table. Some tables have been assembled from various sources available to the author, such as 7.3. — Since 1964 current statistics have been given annually in Yearbook of Nordic Statistics, published by The Nordic Council, Stockholm.

CHAPTER 8

DENMARK

by Axel Schou and Kristian Antonsen[1]

INTRODUCTION

In contrast with the other Scandinavian states, Denmark is distinctly an island realm. The peninsula of Jylland and 474 islands form a typical, morainic archipelago with the rocky island of Bornholm and the eight Ertholme detached to eastward. Denmark's size is difficult to state with complete accuracy, because the area is constantly changing owing to the abrasive and constructive forces of the sea and as a consequence of man's reclamation work. On the southwest coast of Jylland, where the tides are important, the shoreline moves in and out with ebb and flow, at places as much as 10 km; this means that in Denmark we must define exactly what is understood by the land area. Here the land is assumed to begin behind the line forming the border of stable terrestrial vegetation. Large islands of sand subject to periodic flooding by the sea, such as Kore Sand in the 'Wadden Sea', are not included in the area, whereas lakes and watercourses are. Lagoons, such as Ringkøbing Fjord, directly connected with the sea, are excluded. The areas of the component parts are:

Peninsula of Jylland	23 792 km²
100 inhabited islands	19 093 »
383 uninhabited islands	47 »
Total area	42 932 km²

The Danish population, 4.8 millions, is not very different in size from that of the other Norden states, but the density is much higher, more than 110 per km². In Sweden, the most densely populated of the other Norden countries, it is only about 17 per km². With regard to the proportions of woodland to cultivated land Denmark also holds a very special position. With 10 per cent wooded and 73 per cent agricultural land the proportions are practically the reverse of those of Fennoscandia.

Position as a land bridge

Denmark forms a land bridge between the Scandinavian peninsula and Central Europe. Over that bridge, plants, animals and people immigrated from the south when the ice-sheets melted away. Since then the land bridge has acted as a line of communication by which European cultural currents came northwards. Moreover, Denmark is situated on one of the main trade routes, the sea route between the Baltic and the North Sea countries; this has been an important factor in the country's commercial development, and has made Copenhagen Free Port one of the great transit ports of Northern Europe. Its situation on the straits connecting the Baltic with the North Sea gives the country a strategic importance in conflicts between Great Powers, a factor which resulted in the German occupation of Denmark during the Second World War.

The situation at the southern border of Scandinavia has involved borderland problems, known elsewhere in Norden only in the east, in Finland. Denmark's present southern frontier was fixed in 1920 after a part of Sønderjylland, which had been under German administration since 1864, was returned to Denmark. It was impossible to draw the frontier line as an absolute national boundary, a Danish minority lives on German territory, and a German one north of the borderline.

These minorities have their separate cultural institutions, schools, churches, associations, as

[1] Physical geography by Axel Schou, human geography by Kristian Antonsen.

98

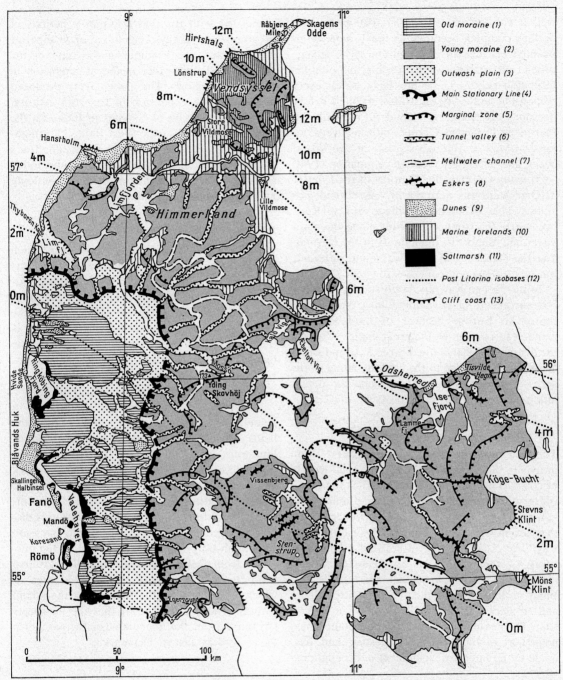

Fig. 8.1. Geomorphological map of the Jylland peninsula and the Danish islands. 1. Old moraine landscape, Saale/Riss-glaciation. Mature relief caused by solifluction and normal erosion. 2. Young moraine landscape, Weichsel/Würm-glaciation. Hilly moraines in the marginal zones, in particular, changing into moraine flats, e.g. in Lolland and northern Fyn. 3. Outwash plain, meltwater deposits from the Weichsel/Würm-glaciation. 4. Main stationary Line during the Weichsel/Würm-glaciation, the most significant physical-geographical and economic-geographical borderline in Denmark. 5. Other significant marginal zones, often forming the glacial series of landscapes (Penck): central depression separated by marginal moraine hills from the distally-placed outwash plains. 6. Tunnel valleys, with long lakes and bogs in depressions. 7. Meltwater channels. 8. Eskers. 9. Dune landscapes: coastal dunes and continental dunes. 10. Marine forelands: beach ridge plains, barred foreland, and true raised sea-floor: Yoldia-plateau (left) and post-Yoldia coastal plains (right). 11. Saltmarsh. 12. Isobases for the relative uplift of land since the Litorina/Tapes-transgressions of the Neolithic period. 13. Cliff coast. — Compilation based on the geomorphological map of Geodætisk Institut, edited by Axel Schou, and maps of Danmarks Geologiske Undersøgelse.

well as political representation. The whole borderland-complex becomes so much more complicated because all combinations of language, official citizenship, national feeling, and political affiliation occur. These are facts which every responsible authority must have in mind before decisions are taken. It should be remembered that many Danes, as German citizens, were obliged to fight as German soldiers in two World Wars, and during the German occupation (1940 –45) many Germans living north of the frontier as Danish citizens were put in very difficult positions. Thus in a frontier village such as Rudbøl, where the frontier line runs along the main street, the fate of the inhabitants of the German and the Danish road-sides was quite different, but had serious consequences for both sides.

In the air age Kastrup Airport at København has succeeded in developing into one of the busiest in Europe because of its favourable position in relation to the great circles between the densely populated towns of U.S.A. and western Europe, and also to the corresponding circle across the North Pole to Japan and the population agglomerations of East Asia.

The archipelago nature of Denmark
The land border with West Germany is 67.7 km in length, but the sea boundary, the total length of coast, is more than 7 400 km. Thus the Danish territory is a much dissected land mass, and sea and land are as intimately connected as they are in the coastal regions of western Norway. The circumference of a circular land territory of the same area as Denmark would measure 742 km. The actual coastline is ten times as long as this theoretical shortest line, and no place in Denmark lies more than 52 km from the nearest coast. This circumstance has helped to mould Denmark's destiny and has made for an intense development of occupations associated with the sea. Denmark's periods of greatness have always been based upon superior naval power, for example in the time of the Vikings and during her medieval expansion in the Baltic region. The same factor produced her mercantile expansion in the 16th century, and the foundation of colonies in India, on the Guinea coast and in the West Indies. Throughout the 17th century there was flourishing trade with adventurous voyages to China, and today Denmark has important fisheries, shipbuilding and shipowning companies.

Physio-geographical significance
It is not only its archipelago character which gives Denmark a distinctive stamp; relief features and soil also contrast with analogous features of the other Scandinavian states. The huge deposits of moraine-material which built up the Danish hilly and hummocky relief, as well as the vast outwash plains, are consequences of the fact that Denmark is an area of glacial accumulation, whereas the other Scandinavian states as a whole are characterized by glacial erosion.

The boulder content of the moraines is a guide to the origin of the ice flow and to the lands over which it passed. Many rocks, such as limestone, were plucked out and carried along, but as these rocks extend widely under Denmark and neighbouring countries they do not provide much indication as a rule. More useful as indicator boulders are rocks whose outcrop is distant and more limited. The principal ones are the rhomb-porphyry of the Oslo region, the porphyry from Dalarna and the so-called Østersø (Baltic) quartz porphyry, the original area of which is the floor of the Baltic near the Åland Islands. They make it clear that the ice-sheets advanced from the Scandinavian regions north of, as well as east of Denmark.

GEOLOGICAL STRUCTURE AND PALAEO-GEOGRAPHICAL PATTERNS

Solid geology of Bornholm
In the north of Bornholm, which forms part of the Fennoscandian Marginal Zone, the old highly metamorphosed rocks, the granites, lie high and are delimited by faults as are the horsts in Skåne. They are the result of granitization of Precambrian formations. The granite massif is interspersed with fissures filled with consolidated magma masses—dykes of pegmatite or diabase. In South Bornholm the granite is

overlain by Cambrian, Ordovician, Gothlandian and Rhaet-Lias sediments (Fig. 8.2).

In the Ice Age Bornholm was entirely covered by the ice cap which by its abrasion carved the granite into roches moutonnées of all dimensions, from very small ones to the huge dome of Hammerknuden on the northwest coast.

Solid geology of Jylland and the Islands

Below this part of Denmark are rocks similar to those of Skåne and adjoining parts of Central Europe: a mosaic of dislocated sediments, chiefly limestone, sandstone and argillaceous shale. Knowledge of the geological structure is due especially to borings made for water-supply purposes and for oil investigation. The latter have gone down to 4 000 metres.

In Denmark Precambrian granite and gneiss are everywhere concealed under thick deposits of younger rocks. In Fyn (Funen), for instance, the granite is first encountered at a depth of about 900 m; in North Jylland, at Frederikshavn, at 1 275 m and in central Jylland it is assumed to lie deeper than 5 000 m. The overlying sediments were formed over a period of more than 200 million years by deposition in the post-Permian depression, the 'North Sea Basin', which extended between the Fennoscandian Shield on the east, the Caledonian foldchain on the northwest and the Variscan fold zone on the south. Denmark's sedimentary rocks were deposited in the eastern part of this extensive basin (Fig. 8.3).

Permian red sandstones and shales (Rotliegendes) are evidence of a desert landscape and salt lakes. There are also traces of the vulcanism which is manifested in the Oslo region by the rhomb-porphyry layers. In the closing phases of the Permian (Zechstein) a shallow sea lay where Denmark is now. In the dry climate the North Sea Basin gradually became a complex of lagoons and salt pans, which are responsible for the thick salt deposits found both in Jylland and in Lolland.

Arid desert conditions continued in the Early Triassic (Buntsandstein), changing later to marine (Muschelkalk), but in the Upper Triassic were replaced by deserts with mud sheets and salt lakes like those known today in arid regions. In the Jurassic a silting sea covered Denmark. The Cretaceous sea whose beach

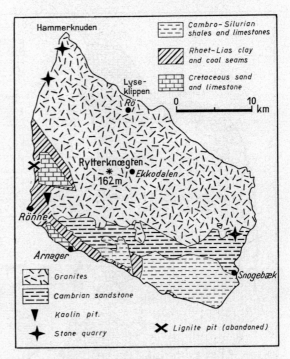

Fig. 8.2. *Solid geology of Bornholm* and important mining localities. Over much of North Bornholm the Quaternary deposits are so thin that the surface relief is conditioned by the glacially eroded granite. — After Schou in K. M. Jensen, Vor Klode, København, 1953.

sediments have been found in Central Europe (Elbsandstein), lay over Denmark, and calcium-shelled organisms sedimented while the warm climate favoured coral reef formation and calcareous deposition such as that known today around the Bahamas. The uppermost Cretaceous, the Danian formation, has limestone rocks formed by the disintegration and rebedding of material from older Cretaceous sediments, and reefs composed partly of coral and partly of bryozoa.

Tertiary sediments were deposited partly in the sea and partly in the local coastal regions, where, in deltas and beach swamps, lignite beds formed between sand strata. Beds of volcanic ash bear witness to the activity of the volcanoes which then were active in Skåne. The folding of the Alpine chains caused secondary dislocations of the earth's crust which gave rise to regions of great relief energy. The consequent acceleration of both erosion and sedimentation may be the explanation of the thick Tertiary series of clay and sand.

101

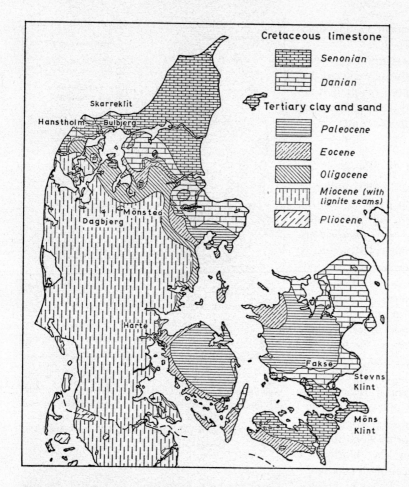

Fig. 8.3. Solid geology of the Jylland peninsula and the Danish islands. — After Theodor Sorgenfrei og Ole Berthelsen: Geologi og Vandboring. Danm. geol. Unders. III. Række. No. 31. København 1954.

Cretaceous limestone

Senonian

Danian

Tertiary clay and sand

Paleocene

Eocene

Oligocene

Miocene (with lignite seams)

Pliocene

The Quaternary glacial periods

The deposits of the last three of these have been found in Denmark. The plant associations of the bog deposits and the molluscan fauna of the marine sediments provide unmistakable evidence.

Glacial activity, especially in the last two glaciations, was significant in modelling Denmark's surface. The sediments of the Riss or Saale glaciation dominate the superficial deposits in southwest Jylland. In the Würm or Weichsel glaciation, the final Ice Age, the ice covered only northern and eastern Denmark as far as the Main Stationary Line through Jylland. Here Würm moraines form the surface layers, but glacifluvial rivers transported sand and gravel out over the lowest parts of West Jylland too (Fig. 8.1).

Stratigraphy

Fig. 8.3 shows that the pre-Quaternary sediments lie with the old sediments in the north

and east, and the youngest sediments in the southwest of the country. The strata dip from north and east to the southwest. After the strata had been planed off horizontally by the ice-sheets, the pattern of the underlying rocks appears in concentric belts around a centre to the southwest of Denmark. The irregularities in the contours of these belts are due partly to the building up of salt domes, especially in the Limfjord area. Under the pressure of the overlying sediments the Permian salt layers behaved like a plastic mass which was sometimes forced up right through the overlying rocks, up to the base of the Quaternary. Locally the underground strata outcrop at the coasts in cliffs such as Stevns Klint in East Sjælland (Figs. 8.1 and 8.11).

Exploitation

The Bornholm granites are used for building and paving stones and as road metal. Kaolin survives here and there notwithstanding glacial abrasion. The sediments of South Bornholm are all more or less useful. The Rhaet-Lias clay is used in Bornholm's potteries and brick works.

In Jylland and the Islands Cretaceous sediments are widely distributed and thick (over 700 m at Harte in East Jylland); but in the pre-Cretaceous beds only the salt has been used as yet. The Senonian limestone predominates. In the Limfjord district, where the chalk lies high and where the overlying glacial deposits are thin, the chalk is quarried on a large scale and used in the cement industry, for lime-burning and for fertilizing. The Danian limestones vary a great deal; the bryozoan limestone exposed in Stevns Klint is interbedded with layers of flint which are so resistant that they overhang the Senonian limestone base. Boulders of bryozoan limestone occur in many places in the glacial strata and are used in limeburning. In earlier times the bryozoan limestone was sawn out to make building stone, as witness the churches in the vicinity of Stevns Klint. Danian limestone was already being mined in the Middle Ages in Jylland at Dagbjerg near Viborg, where the underground galleries can still be seen. Modern mining, both opencast and subterranean, is proceeding at Mønsted close by. The Danian limestone which lies under the Sound and the København area is much fissured in its upper sections. This facilitates a rapid groundwater movement and gives København a constant and plentiful, though hard, water supply. The coral limestone is quarried at Fakse in South Sjælland; it is a porous type that is excellent for lime-burning, while the harder varities are employed for building stone. The incoherent, friable part of the Fakse limestone is used, together with asphalt, for road surfacing.

The Tertiary sediments include *moler,* which is composed of diatom shells and therefore has a low specific gravity and is very porous. It is used for light-weight bricks and insulating materials. Finally, the 'brown coal' (lignite) of west Jylland was mined on an unusual scale for industry and domestic heating during the Second World War when supplies of foreign fuels failed. It is still being extensively worked, but solely as a raw material for the large thermal power stations in Jylland and Fyn.

THE DANISH LANDSCAPES

GLACIAL LANDSCAPES

The hill islands of West Jylland

In the last glaciation the ice failed to cover the whole of Denmark; it stopped short at the Main Stationary Line (Fig. 8.1). As a consequence, West Jylland south and west of that line lay throughout the period like an arctic landscape beyond the ice margin. Thus the ancient moraine landscapes of the Riss/Saale glaciation were subjected to a radical transformation. During this long period the hill islands lay unglaciated, thousands of years before the other Danish landscape materialized. The lakes disappeared as a result of sedimentation, drainage and infilling by organic matter, and the watercourses reached their depth limits.

Running water, rain, snow, frost, wind and gravity in unison have transformed the original glacial landscape into the present-day old moraine landscape, the oldest of all Danish landscapes. It must be remembered too, that the old moraine landscapes were particularly exposed to the special arctic surface-modifying processes, notably solifluction, when periglacial conditions existed. The result is that the hill islands, as these landscapes are called, present in their gentle configuration a contrast to the pronounced relief of the young moraine landscapes, for instance those of East Jylland. A description of the hill islands is best put in the form of a negative count of their landscape elements. Old moraine landscapes lack tunnel valleys, marginal moraines, lakes, very hilly areas and undrained depressions, in fact all the elements which make up the morphological character of the usual moraine landscape. The relief is not morainic but that of a mature normally eroded surface, and only their deposits prove that these are landscapes built up of glacial drift.

The size of the hill islands varies considerably, from 2000 km² to isolated hummocks with a surface of a few hundred m². These 'islands' may rise out of the outwash plains with a slope so gradual that topographically their limits are vague; at other places erosion slopes make them rise sharply out of the plains.

Outwash plains

Between the hill islands the enormous plane surfaces of the outwash plains seem to be quite flat, but in reality they are very faintly dipping gravel and sand cones with their apices along the Main Stationary Line (Fig. 8.1). The slope varies in the different parts of the plain; it is greatest near the apex and decreases outwards. In the middle of the plains the gradient is 1:700, in the outer parts it is 1:1 000. These are the tremendous deposits of the meltwater rivers —the sandy areas of the extensive inland deltas—formed beyond the ice margin in the final glaciation, and wholly analogous to the Icelandic sandur south of Vatnajökull in our own day.

In many places the borderline between outwash plain and young moraine landscape is formed by terminal moraine mounds or terminal moraine landscapes, clearly delimited as higher ridges along the highest parts of the plain. In a number of places the landscapes are typical glacial series corresponding to the Penck system, for instance in Odsherred, West Sjælland (Figs. 8.4, 8.5 and 8.6), in the south of the Djursland peninsula on the east coast of Jylland, and in the western Limfjord area, e.g. in Lemvig. There, and at many other places, one encounters the classical glacial landscape succession: central depression, which may often be covered by the sea and appear as a bay; the enormous marginal moraine, and outside this the widespread surface of the outwash plain.

However, the transition from moraine landscape to outwash plain may be quite different. There is a reversal of these relief details in places where relatively large meltwater deposits were laid down, but there were only very small moraines. Here the outwash plain may lie at a higher level than the adjoining parts of the moraine landscape. The border consists of a slope, caused by a slide of outwash sand after the supporting glacier wall—or dead ice—melted away. In many other localities the transition from terminal moraine landscape to outwash plain is devoid of distinct relief characters.

The greater part of the Main Stationary Line of the Würm/Weichsel glaciation, along its north to south section from Viborg to the frontier, lacks the features that are characteristic of the Penck series. But its distinctive soils are not to be mistaken. Different crops grow on them: barley, wheat and sugar beet in the young moraine landscapes, rye, potatoes and kohlrabi on the sands of the outwash plains.

The flat surface of the outwash plains is dissected by valleys; because of the changes in drainage since the formation of the outwash plains, and as a consequence of the altered levels, they are often valleys within valleys, the younger valleys having cut down into the older ones. There have been other modifications of the original outwash plain surface. There are some examples of outwash plains with dead-ice relief. The originally flat surface of the plains is broken by circular hollows, formed by subsidence when masses of dead ice melted. These hollows may be filled by lakes or bogs.

Colonization of the heaths of Jylland

The outwash plains have been radically altered by cultivation during the past century. Heathed moor once reigned supreme in a very thinly populated region, with more dense settlement only in the river valleys where the farms lay in rows utilizing the grazing land of the broad valley bottoms. Nowadays the fields are spread over the fluvial plains too and the landscape is crossed by strips of plantation which act as windbreaks. In other places large conifer plantations dominate the landscape. In contrast with East Jylland the highways run perfectly straight for scores of kilometres, evidence of the flat surface which makes the curves and bends of roads in the hilly country unnecessary.

Young moraine landscapes

Where the ice covered the land in the last glacial period, i.e. in the regions north and east of the Main Stationary Line, we find moraine landscapes with much sharper relief than those of the hill islands of western Jylland. Among the young moraine landscapes is the highest point in Denmark, Yding Skovhøj, 173 m. These are the areas which have been exposed for only a relatively short time, i.e. since the last remnant of ice-cap melted about 12 000 years ago. Surface forms capable of being described as original are rare, however. In this densely populated, long tilled land the hand of man is perceptible in the transformation of the landscape: ploughing has smoothed out the small irregularities of the surface and the original harshness

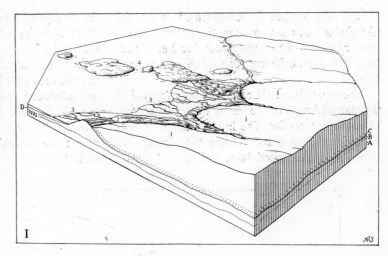

Fig. 8.4. Glacial stage (I). During an advance of the ice cap in the last glacial period the lobes of the ice margin (1) pushed the frontal moraine material forward as enormous marginal moraines (2) which form the skeleton of the landscape structure in Odsherred (cf. Fig. 8.1). The meltwater rivers rushing out of the glacier gates, built up fluvial plains (3) of gravel and sand ahead of the ice front. Out in the sea are islands (4), built of moraine deposits from earlier ice advances.—A. Preglacial (Tertiary) deposits. B. Moraine. C. Ground moraine. D. Meltwater deposits.—Block edges 30×38 km.— After Schou 1949 a, p. 7 A.

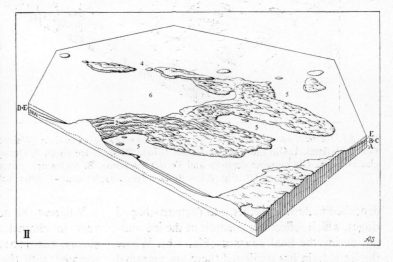

Fig. 8.5. Stone Age transgression (Litorina stage) (II). The ice disappeared, leaving newly-formed moraine landscapes and outwash plains whose relief reflected their genesis in an ice-marginal zone. The central depressions (5) on the site of the former ice lobes were inundated by the sea during the Stone-Age transgressions. The outwash plains farthest west form the floor of the shallow Sejerø bay (6). The islands off the north coast are attacked by the sea. Central depression, morainic hill country and outwash plain collectively represent the glacial series of landscape forms according to Penck's system.—A. Preglacial deposits. B–C. Moraine. D. Meltwater deposits. E. Sea-bed deposits. — After Schou 1949 a, p. 7 B.

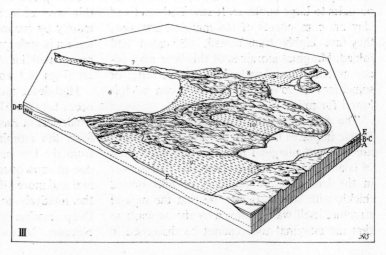

Fig. 8.6. Present stage (III). The eroding and sedimenting actions of the sea combined with the emergence of the land (4 to 5 metres) and man's efforts at reclamation are responsible for the present shape of Odsherred. The creation of marine forelands (7–10) welded the island remnants together, partly into Sjællands Odde (7), the peninsula of Northwest Sjælland, and partly into the garland-shaped north coast (8). The reclamation of Lammefjord (9) created 50 km^2 of farmland, where the surface is as much as 4 m below sea level and is protected by embankments. Sidingefjord (10) is another embanked area.—A. Preglacial deposits. B–C. Moraine. D. Meltwater deposits. E. Sea-bed deposits. — After Schou 1949 a, p. 7 C.

of the hill shapes is ameliorated after the ploughshare has cut through the ground thousands of times. The young moraine landscapes have two quite different forms: hill country and flats.

The moraine hill country was formed in the marginal zone of the ice by the accumulation of moraine material. The largest ranges of hills were formed in places where the glaciers, in their advance, pushed large volumes of earlier the topographical features but merely by the great quantity of stones in the surface. The material of these marginal moraines is widely used industrially. Gravel pits are often dug into the mounds and large quantities of road metal are produced from the boulders. Shallow hollows in the hill sides, remnants of abandoned gravel pits, are often characteristic, and in places the mounds have been removed in their entirety.

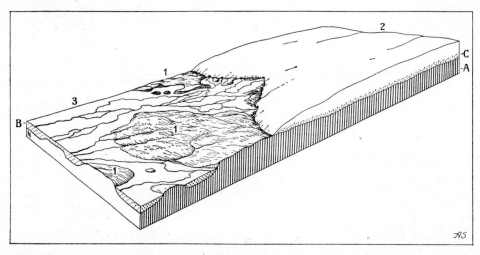

Fig. 8.7. Landscape development during the last glaciation (Weichsel/Würm) at the Main Stationary Line in Jylland. 1. Old moraine landscapes (Saale/Riss). 2. Ice sheet. 3. Outwash plains of the Weichsel/Würm-glaciation. A. Old moraine deposits and Tertiary deposits. B. Meltwater gravel and sand. C. Moraine of the last ice sheet. Cf. Fig. 8.1.—Block edges 20×50 km. — After Schou 1949 a, p. 6 A.

deposited material together into rampart-shaped ridges, which reflect the position of the ice margin during the final advance (Fig. 8.6). Where the ice margin has oscillated there are marginal moraine or parallel hill moraines. The material is composed of grains of all sizes from clay particles to large boulders. If stratified sand and clay are components of the marginal moraine, they are highly transformed, dislocated and folded. Marginal moraines of this type may occur as hills some hundred of metres long, or sometimes as rows of hills which can be followed for miles.

The washing of the material may be so effective in places that only the largest grain sizes are left; and marginal moraines are often built of coarse gravel and large boulders and appear in the landscape in the form of hills dotted thickly with stones. It may be that the mound structure itself was destroyed by the outwash so that the marginal zone cannot be discerned in

Whereas the soil of hilly moraine land may vary in character and be gravelly, sandy or clayey, the moraine flats are essentially associated with the distribution of boulder clay. Under these smoothly undulating flats is an ice-eroded plane surface which was covered by a thin layer of moraine when the ice disappeared, mainly by evaporation. In Lolland this form of terrain is widespread, the areas between København, Roskilde and Køge in Sjælland are similar (Figs. 8.1 and 8.14).

High-level moraine flats, moraine plateaux, occur between Horsens and Kolding and around Fredericia in East Jylland. In its original surface form the moraine plateau is indistinguishable from the low moraine flat; that it is distinct is due to subsequent alterations produced by normal and more effective fluvial erosion caused by the relatively low depth limit on the plateau. Deep erosion gullies intersect these moraine plateaux. In some cases the erosion phase is relatively young and the plateau is cut only here and there at the edge. In others the process is more advanced, the retrogressive erosion of the streams having disintegrated the plateau surface.

On account of their fertile soil and their flat surface, the moraine flats are the best farmlands in the country. The highest quality of agricultural soil is to be found on them. If they were not the first regions to be tilled in Denmark, it was doubtless because the heavy clayey soil was

of man's work in the form of embankments or ramparts. These eskers often lie in flat landscapes and therefore are in marked contrast to their surroundings.

Eskers consist of stratified sand and gravel deposited in running water between walls of ice. In some eskers these horizontal or slightly dipping beds make up the greater part and are covered with a thin layer of moraine. In other eskers there is a core of boulder clay enveloped

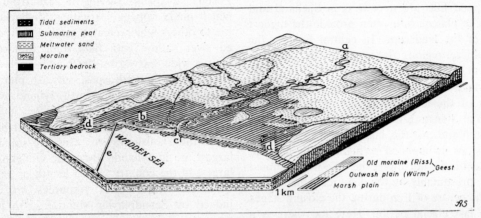

Fig. 8.8. Danish marsh plain and geest landscape, Southwest Jylland. a. River Bredå. b. Old course of Bredå. c. Ballum sluice, present outlet of Bredå. d. Dyke. e. Rømø embankment. — Block edges 12×20 km. — After Schou 1949 a, p. 16 A.

more difficult to cultivate with primitive implements than the lighter sandy soils, which were preferred by the earliest farmers. Another important reason is that often it was only by means of drainage operations, which require a good deal of technical skill, that these low flats were transformed into the ideal farmland they now are.

Special features of the glacial landscapes

The meltwater deposits have left their mark in forms other than outwash plains, although the latter are easily the most dominant form of deposition of glacifluvial material. They have also built up landscape forms that differ fundamentally from the plains. Among these are the elongated hills known as eskers which occur within the area last glaciated, and are common in the Danish Islands. They usually lie at right angles to lines where the ice was stationary. Solitary eskers, and also whole chains of them, often lie along peculiar, winding courses; for considerable distances the height is so remarkably uniform that the observer is apt to think

in meltwater deposits in which the bedding is vertical, a structure bearing evidence of thrusts after the material was laid down.

Stratified drift deposited in flowing water makes up a hill type which differs considerably from the esker in shape. These are kames, a modification of which occurs in Denmark with the name hat-shaped hill. The structure of their stratified sand and gravel reveals that these were formed by deposition in water and, as in the case of the eskers, their steep walls must be taken to be ice-contact slopes. Some of these hills rise as much as 30 m over the moraine flat. As the layers dip steeply or may even be vertical and represent a thickness of several hundred metres, they were probably fill material in deep isolated ice crevasses, in contrast to eskers, which are subglacial river-bed sediments.

The types of landscapes resulting from the deposits of stagnant meltwater, the ice-lake sediments, consisting of clay and fine sand, are neither geologically nor morphologically the same as the types described above, although transitional forms do occur.

107

Flat-topped hills, which are to be found in all parts of the country, vary in size from 100 m to 4 km in diameter and have steep sides and a flat top, 5 to 20 m above the surrounding country. The material forming them is stratified clay, originally deposited as a floor sediment in lake basins in the dead ice. Because of its finely washed state the clay is very suitable for brick-making. Almost everywhere these hills have been extensively worked, and the larger plateaux are often surrounded by brickworks. Such flat-topped hills are numerous in Sjælland and Fyn. The plateau hills often provide the highest point of the landscape. In central Fyn, in the Vissenbjerg region, flat-topped hills occur in different levels.

Ice-lake deposits also formed during the retreat of the ice. The largest of these basin-flats is at Stenstrup in the southeast of Fyn. On the south and east this lake bottom, 5×7 km in dimensions, is bounded by higher, hilly ground, whereas on the northwest the lake was dammed by ice, presumably by the dead ice which occupied the centre of Fyn during the closing stages of the last glacial period. Here too there is a large brick-making industry, based upon the easily accessible deposits of fine clay.

Moraine hills can be classified according to their shape and direction. The marginal moraine hill has its longitudinal axis parallel to the ice margin, another type, the drumlin, has its longitudinal axis conforming to the movement-direction of the ice. The ground-plan of these drumlins is very eccentrically elliptic. The surface is smooth with a gradual fall on all sides. Often the drumlins are grouped and have the same longitudinal orientation, or they may lie in lines. They vary in length from a few hundred metres to a kilometre, and some are even longer. Their shape and orientation make it clear that drumlins formed in conjunction with living, moving ice. Presumably the material was deposited under the ice and then the latter's movement smoothed and distributed it in the same direction.

Another characteristic Danish moraine terrain is the hummocky moraine landscape with many small hills devoid of any particular longitudinal direction; they lie in unsystematic groups and the many undrained depressions are likewise irregular in their placing. This remarkable moraine landscape was formed in conjunc-

tion with melting masses of dead ice, and the hummocky surface is a direct consequence of the irregular accumulation of the moraine in the ice. When the ice melted, the material sank and was deposited on the spot, and there was no subsequent planing off. Lumps of dead ice may have caused the hollows.

WATERCOURSES AND VALLEY LANDSCAPES

Postglacial rivers, varying in size from those which made rain gullies with a V-shaped profile to others which created mature flat-bottomed river valleys with flats some hundreds of metres wide, carved up the higher parts of the young moraine landscapes, outwash plains and lateglacial plateaux in North Jylland without altering their main outlines.

Compared with those of the rest of Scandinavia the Danish watercourses are small. The largest are in Jylland, where the Gudenå is the largest in the country with a length of 158 km. Thus the water-power resources are small, judged by Scandinavian standards. In former times the relative importance of water-power was much greater. In the Middle Ages and until quite recently water-power was utilized for flour milling and other purposes. The possibility of obtaining water-power was a vital factor in the localization of the first industrial plants.

Subglacial tunnel valleys, cut under the ice by the tremendous meltwater rivers of the glacial period, contrast sharply with the recent valleys. The dimensions vary. The large ones are a mile wide; the easterly, lowest parts of these tunnel valleys are submerged and form the East Jylland fjords. The surrounding glacial landscape often lies 100 m above the valley bottom, and very steep slopes, often timbered, lie along the valleys and fjord sides. Often the slopes have slipped, but just as often they are precipitous where the stream at the bottom has been able to remove the talus, or where the depth and currents in the fjord have prevented any accumulation of the material falling from the slopes. Rainwater erosion has grooved the slopes, but these gullies seldom extend back beyond a belt a kilometre wide from the fjord. On the other hand the plateau is cut up a good deal in this belt; in places the valleys are so close together that the parts of the intervening surface are reduced to narrow remnants or have disappeared altogether, the valley sides then meet in ridges or 'false hills'.

In tunnel valleys the longitudinal profiles are uneven, hollows with lake or bog depressions alternating with higher moraine thresholds. In places where the underlying ground offered little resistance, the water flowing under pressure in tunnels under the ice was able to remove large portions of it. The well-known lake districts of central and east Jylland, e.g. the Silkeborg lakes, are also tunnel phenomena, for these elongated lakes fill basins so formed. They presumably held lumps of dead ice in the melting period so that they were not filled up with meltwater sand, but with ground water. As tunnel valleys produce elongated depressions, the lakes often ribbon out along the valley and several may lie in a chain.

The direction of these tunnel valleys was determined principally by the direction in which the ice moved, because sub-glacial tunnels parallel with that movement could continue to exist in the living ice, whereas transversal fissures would sooner or later close up during the movement. The tunnel valleys are important in siting, for they determined the situation of East Jylland's coastal towns.

Extra-marginal meltwater valleys formed by the mighty rivers of the melting period run along the ice margin, unlike the tunnel valleys which lie at right angles to it. At many places, for instance in East Jylland, there are extensive valley landscapes where the two valley systems cross, as in the Mossø, and Salten Langsø region. The Gudenå runs through both meltwater valleys and tunnel valleys, which cause and explain the many changes of direction in its flow. The large valley systems which in former times were extensive swamp regions, have long formed natural borders. Present-day county, district and parish boundaries still follow the rivers in the broad valley bottoms which, by regulation and drainage, have been transformed into farm land and pastures. In many places the railway lay-out also conforms to the pattern of the valleys. The gravel terraces of the valley sides are naturally-levelled flats suitable for track laying, and the gravel deposits of the valley can be used as track ballast.

MARINE FORELANDS

About one tenth of Denmark's surface was built up by marine sedimentation. These forelands are low, flat tracts and are best developed in North Jylland. According to the manner in which the marine foreland was formed it is possible to distinguish between four types: beach ridge plains, barred foreland, true raised sea floor and marsh plain.

The beach ridge plains, composed of gravel and pebbles, occur in localities exposed to great wave activity and where beach-drifting material is abundant. They are unsuitable for cultivation; but when a covering of vegetation has developed over them they can become pastures; at many places, however, they form heather-clad beach heaths which nowadays are being used for recreation. Gravel and stone workings also give these areas commercial possibilities in this age of concrete (Fig. 8.9).

Barred forelands occur where bays, cut off from the sea by spits, gradually become

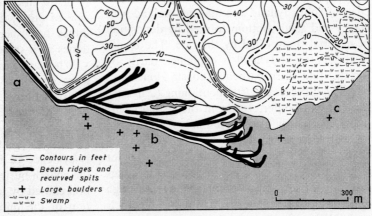

Fig. 8.9. Marine foreland formation and bay-closing stages, Begtrup bay, Djursland peninsula, East Jylland. Contours at five foot intervals. The 15 foot contour corresponds to the shoreline of the Litorina Sea; uplifted moraine cliffs rise from it. — a. Bay totally closed by formation of beach-ridge plain and barred foreland. b. Mature bay-closing stage, a complex of recurved spits is under development. c. Early stage of bay closing. Large boulders have been washed out of the moraine during the Litorina transgressions. — After Schou 1959.

overgrown. The use made of these tracts varies greatly according to their stage of development. The immature forms, characterized by thickets of reeds, are of little use except for wildfowl shooting. The mature forms may be excellent farming soil when the groundwater level has been suitably regulated by draining and ditching, and when the danger of inundation is ruled out either by marine deposits forming natural barriers or by human agency. The latter has been widely employed in Denmark; in most cases the embankments have been easy to build, the natural barrier system merely needing slight prolongation or reinforcement at exposed spots.

True raised sea floor occurs especially along the shores of Limfjord, a strange, flat landscape almost devoid of relief, with meadows and drainage ditches and a border of reed swamp out against the fjord. In parts of these flats, where drainage is difficult because of the slight elevation above sea level, the soil is swampy. The two largest continuous stretches of bog in Denmark, Store and Lille Vildmose, lie upon such an old, uplifted Stone-Age sea floor. They are high bogs, wet and difficult to approach in the marginal zone but with metre-thick peat layers built so high above the general level that desiccation has finally inhibited the growth of bog plants, with the result that the central parts are heather-covered. These large peat deposits are now used for horticultural peat and as fuel reserves, and drainage will convert the bogs into pasture lands.

Salt marsh plain is found along the west coast of South Jylland as a marine foreland with clayey and sandy bottom formed by deposition of material transported by the tide. The extent of the marsh in Jylland is explained partly by the fact that these particular coasts alone have any tidal difference worth mentioning (2 m near the German border, 1.5 m in the Esbjerg harbour), and partly by the presence of flat tracts, i.e. outwash plains, over whose westerly parts the marine clay could be deposited. The outer marsh, where accretion is still proceeding, takes the form of low-lying beach meadows through which wind the widely ramified net of channels and tidal creeks. Protected by sea dykes from destruction by salt-water and storm floods lies the cultivated marsh, a flat land characterized by straight drainage ditches and rectangular fields. Cattle fattening on the marsh belongs to the history of Danish cattle breeding. Nowadays there seems to be an increasing tendency to exploit the marsh by mixed farming.

DUNE LANDSCAPES

In Denmark these cover no more than 1.6 per cent of the total area; they are the natural landscapes that offer most resistance to cultivation. The dunes are natural enclaves in a land otherwise largely tamed. As they are formed of beach sand, dried by the wind and blown inland, the dune landscapes in Denmark are distinctly western in distribution. There is a practically unbroken belt of dunes from Skagen to the peninsula of Skallingen outside Esbjerg, continuing on the seaward side of the North Sea islands (Fig. 8.1). Their distribution is a result of the frequency of westerly winds and the great breadth of the North Sea shore at low water in conjunction with the heavy transport of sand along the coast.

Littoral dune rows. With the constant addition of sand the embryo dunes merge and, as their natural habit is to lie parallel with the shoreline, they grow into a continuous row of littoral dunes above the high-water mark. In places, as outside Tisvilde Hegn in North Sjælland, there is a single distinct row; elsewhere, as on the west coast, there are several older rows of dunes. In the dune belt farther from the sea, where the supply of sand is small and the wind velocities lower than at the coast, the sand-retaining properties of the vegetation dominate the wind action, and the plant community of the littoral dunes is replaced by a succession of other, denser kinds. The young 'white' dunes have been succeeded by mature 'grey' dunes with smoothly domed outlines.

When gales tear the dune vegetation to shreds, large masses of sand may move inland before the pressure of the wind. Sand-flight disasters have laid waste large areas in former times, as for instance in the Tisvilde district, where the sand-flight plantation known as Tisvilde Hegn is evidence of it. At Skagen in North Jylland the church buried in the sand recalls the destruction caused by former storms. Nowadays migration of the dunes has been completely halted except at one place, Råbjerg Mile in North Jylland, which is still moving five to eight metres eastwards every year.

Parabola dunes. Many small blow-outs will often combine into single, large ones, the erosive force of the wind being concentrated locally because some of the blow-out ravines will accommodate greater masses of air and make passage easier for them. The deflation works downwards and may sometimes remove metre-thick layers of the original surface of the land. Parabola dunes are most common in West Jylland. The path of the wandering dune forms a smooth deflation plane, flanked by long rows of dunes, lying parallel to the prevalent wind direction. The entire system is parabola-shaped in plan with its axis in the wind direction and its opening facing the wind.

In the old dune landscapes deflation plains form at a level governed by the groundwater, and here and there in dry periods, deflation may create shallow hollows which become water-filled in wet periods, forming shallow deflation lakes. The landscape is transformed into a conglomeration of stable dunes, deflation plains and newly-formed white wandering dunes. The so-called inland sands on the outwash plains are inland dunes formed from the sand and gravel of the fluvial plains.

GRANITE LANDSCAPES

These are found only in Bornholm, where there is Denmark's solitary outcrop of Precambrian. The entire granite region passed through a process of upheaval between fault lines, whose principal direction is seen in the trend of the present coastline northwest–southeast and north–south. This horst was land surface for a long period, and it was finally modelled by ice erosion. The granite area is high, the highest point, Rytterknægten, being 165 m above sea level.

For long periods this granite land was exposed to the active forces of erosion. Weathering loosened the outer layer of granite. Streams inland and waves at the coast removed the loose soil, and finally ice-sheets eroded the granite land into its present form.

Surface irregularities were smoothed off and in many places there are polished granite surfaces with distinct striae which demonstrate that the direction of the ice movement was mainly from east to west. In many parts of Bornholm the moraine cover is so thin that cultivation is impossible. Here we find a landscape with roches moutonnées and erratics: isolated blocks of granite left behind by the ice, occasionally poised so insecurely that they can be rocked. A rough cover of heather, juniper and birch adds to the individuality of the landscape.

Joint valleys were formed when the ice removed the friable parts of the granite massif. The joint valleys often have precipitous and vertical walls with talus at the foot. The valleys often contain pools or chains of pools of elongated form. In many cases they are overgrown and are now bogs. The direction of the streams is generally determined by that of the joint valleys. In size, these valleys vary from a few metres in width to large ones like Ekkodalen, which is 60 m broad.

The scenery of North Bornholm is quite different from that of the other Danish islands, and for this reason it is a very popular holiday area.

COASTAL FEATURES

SHORELINE DEVELOPMENT

Denmark's curious shape is the result of a combination of many different forces. The subterranean dislocations which are so characteristic of Central Europe have also helped to give Denmark her form. Prominent land masses like the peninsulas of Stevns on the east coast of Sjælland and Djursland on the east coast of Jylland are horst formations of the bedrock where resistant Cretaceous sediments withstood erosion by the ice sheets. The same applies to coastal projections like Bulbjerg at the northwest corner of Jylland, where the Danian limestone has put up a respectable resistance to the waves of the North Sea. The stack known as Skarreklit off the coast of northwest Jylland is evidence that the land was once larger. The situation of the island of Bornholm was also determined by underground dislocation. The directions of the fault lines in Bornholm correspond with those of Skåne.

Nevertheless, Denmark's outline is mainly governed by the surface relief created by moraine deposits of the Würm glaciation (Figs. 8.4,

8.5 and 8.6). Where these moraines are of considerable thickness, as in northwestern Sjælland and on the south coast of the Djursland peninsula, they form projections on the coastline; elsewhere, where glacial erosion hollowed out central depressions, the latter appear as round bays, as in the cases of Køge Bugt (Sjælland), and Kalø Vig and Ebeltoft Vig (Jylland).

Another factor of much influence on the formation of the coastline is postglacial changes of sea level. These changes are of a complicated the sea are decisive in shaping Denmark (Fig. 8.10). On exposed coasts large amounts of land have been gradually broken down. Their materials have been graded according to grain size, and the fine-graded sediments were usually precipitated in still water at greater depths, whilst gravel and pebbles accumulated nearer the coast and formed marine forelands, i.e. coastal plains, at many places.

The coastline has acquired new shapes whose directions are determined, above all, by the

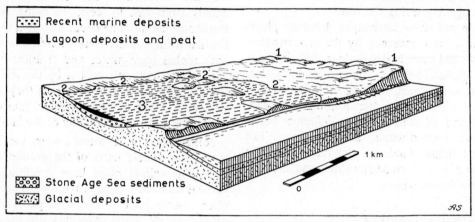

Fig. 8.10. Danish moraine coast, North Sjælland. Old stage of coastline simplification. Cliffs in glacial deposits alternating with coastal plains.—1. Terminal moraine of the last glacial period at right angles to the present shoreline, now protected by groins. 2. Raised moraine coast of the Stone Age (Litorina) Sea. 3. Raised barred foreland and beach-ridge plains. — After Schou 1956, p. 416.

character. Since the Ice Age the land mass on which Denmark is situated has been raised. This isostatic upheaval is at present small compared with that occurring in northern Sweden. Calculations based upon sea level observations show that it amounts to about 1 mm per annum. The zero-isobase of this upheaval runs through Denmark (Fig. 8.1). In the southern parts of the country a similar submergence rate has been found. The eustatic level-changes of the ocean surface caused by melting since the Ice Age, and calculated at about 120–140 m, are a further complication. Emergence and transgression took place within the same period, each process predominating at various times, and causing variations in the coastlines and extent of Denmark. In periods of upheaval Denmark was larger, as in the postglacial Continental Period (Fig. 3.2 d, p. 37), whereas submergence periods are reflected in transgressions of the Litorina Sea in the Stone Age (Fig. 8.5).

The disintegrating and depositing activities of directions of the wave fronts and the extent of the sea surface on which the wind can develop waves. As the size of the waves also depends on the depth of the water, the extent of shallow-water areas is crucial.

A strong tendency towards simplification is characteristic of shoreline development in Denmark. The coast of North Sjælland shows on a map as a straight line. The sea has cut cliffs through all earlier hills and has occupied intermediate bays (Fig. 8.10). The present direction of this coast, southwest-northeast, is due not to the initial relief but to the constantly working forces of the sea. The west coast of Jylland is a similar north-south straight line from Thyborøn to Blåvands Huk because of the work of the sea.

This shoreline simplification is an outcome of nature's establishment of conditions of balance: marine agencies produce a shape which offers them least opposition. Glacial deposits offer slight resistance to wave attack, and mature stages in the simplification process will be

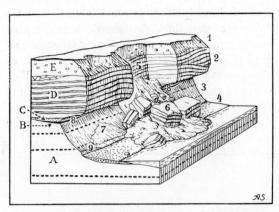

Fig. 8.11. Limestone cliff, Stevns Klint, East Sjælland. 1. Slope of boulder clay. 2. Precipice of overhanging limestone. 3. Undercutting of cliff by wave action. 4. Beach with flint pebbles. 5. Fault niche after fall of limestone. 6. Screes of limestone and moraine. 7. Screes of limestone. 8. Bed of clay. 9. Wave-cut notch. — A. Senonian limestone with concretions of black flint. B. Clay, sedimented in shallow basins in the surface of the Senonian limestone. C. Cerithium limestone. Upper limit: an abrasion plain. D. Danian limestone, Bryozoan, with continuous beds of grey flint. Upper layer locally transformed into breccia by ice pressure. Upper limit: glacier-scratched plane with striae. E. Moraine.—Block edges 30×70 m. — After Schou 1949 a, 30 B.

reached at all exposed localities. On the other hand, initial stages of morainic coasts may be observed at the head of many inlets and fjords, and the entire sequence of coastal simplification can be observed along the Danish morainic coasts.

Coast protection and land reclamation

In this densely populated country the hand of enterprising man has wrought many changes in the landscape, not least in shaping the coastline. Attempts are being made to preserve the land where marine attack threatens to destroy farming areas, land is also being reclaimed from the sea. The former process is responsible for the many groins (Fig. 8.10) which characterize numerous coastal stretches, for example the Limfjord spits north and south of Thyborøn Channel.

Reclamation has mostly been carried out where it has been relatively easy to build embankments which close off shallow fjords across their narrow inlets. The most extensive operation of this kind was on the Lammefjord, Sjælland (Fig. 8.6). Fifty square kilometres of land

have been reclaimed there by building an embankment across the fjord mouth. A ring-canal collects the surface water from the surrounding hills. At the lowest spots the fields lie 4 m below the water level of Isefjord. Other important reclamations are in Rødby Fjord in Lolland, bays in the Limfjord area, and in Odense Fjord on the island of Fyn.

Land reclamation, based on recent research, has been started in the tidal area known as the Wadden Sea (Vadehavet) in Southwest Jylland. There, the fine-grained ooze deposited twice a day is reclaimed by digging ditches at right angles to the direction of the tidal flow. The ooze sedimented in the ditches is excavated at yearly intervals and spread over the intervening tidal area. When the flats are sufficiently high vegetation appears and in time they are diked and protected by sea walls from destruction by storm floods (Fig. 8.8). A new tract of land of this kind is called *kog*.

TYPES OF COAST

Cliff coasts

Even though Denmark's area is relatively small, a large number of different types of coast are represented. In North Bornholm (Fig. 8.2) there are rocky coasts with all the usual features such as skerries, stacks and caves carved out of the high granite mass. At Møn, Stevns and Bulbjerg are cliff coasts (Fig. 8.11) carved in the limestone rocks which are the bedrock of the greater part of Denmark. In most places, however, the coasts are formed of glacial deposits, boulder clay and sand (Fig. 8.10).

The many different cliff forms are due partly to structure: the varying powers of cohesion of the argillaceous and arenaceous rocks, and partly to the constant alternation of these two rocks. There is another, co-ordinate, factor however, viz. the phase of cliff development (Fig. 8.12). Thus combinations of structural forms and phases of development result in the many kinds of cliffs which, combined with the various types of flat shores, produce a very variable and highly individual coastline. Old forms occur when the entire cliff is covered with screes from top to bottom.

Shore profiles with two cliffs, a recent one in course of formation and an old, uplifted one, of Litorina Age, are very common in Denmark

8

113

north of the zero-isobase for the post-Litorina uplift (Fig. 8.10). The variations are numerous, due partly to regional variations in the present-day uplift and partly to the character of the active marine forces. In Vendsyssel there are two raised coastlines: the cliff coast of the Litorina Sea and, higher up, that of the Yoldia Sea (Fig. 8.13).

that offshore breaker action expends itself far from the shoreline. An almost uninterrupted marsh zone borders the southwest coast of Jylland (Fig. 8.8). It is the lowest western part of the outwash plains which lie under the shallow water of the Wadden Sea. Only this part of the Danish coastland has a significant tidal range. On the whole the surface of the Danish tidal

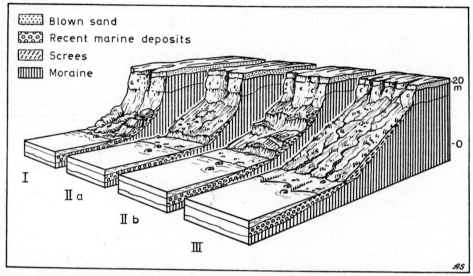

Fig. 8.12. Moraine cliffs. Stages in the development of the profile. I. Initial stage. Vertical precipice and screes. II a. Young stage. Retreating precipice and increasing scree slopes with abrasion undercutting in cliff foot. II b. Young stage. Slide terraces in the scree. III. Mature stage. Wave erosion eliminated after development of a stable beach caused by beach drifting or groin building. Old stages occur in which the scree slope from the beach to the top of the former cliff is covered with vegetation. — After Schou: Danske Klintekyster. Natur og Museum. Århus 1957.

Flat coasts

However, there are many coasts of a less dramatic character than these cliff coasts. Most Danish coasts have flat shores: these are of two types that are essentially different.

Beach-ridge shore is found where the breaker zone reaches in to the shoreline; on this a beach is built up of gravel and sand from beach-drift along the shore (Fig. 8.9). The size of the beach will vary with the difference between high and lower water. Ridges of stones, pebbles or sand, built up under storm conditions along the shoreline, are significant features of this flat shore type. Along the North Sea it is often several hundred metres, while on the Baltic shores it is mostly only a few metres.

Marsh-land shore occurs in very sheltered places, e.g. in the inner parts of fjords and bays or where the slope of the sea floor is so slight

areas is in equilibrium and there is no general elevation through sedimentation. Sea level changes caused by wind pressure are more important there.

TYPES OF HARBOURS

The extensive and sinuous coastline produces many natural harbours. The deep fjords of East Jylland afford shelter from gales and bring ships far inland. At the head of each of these inlets a town has grown. In most places the depth of the fjords has also permitted deep-draught vessels to navigate up to the old harbours, but the many river mouths used as medieval harbours had to be abandoned when ships became too large. In places where deep channels close to the shore make navigation possible, where adjacent islands provide shelter, and where the currents are such as to prevent silting, the harbour potentialities are particularly good. This is the case in the strait between Amager Island and Sjælland where the port of København has developed. The original harbour lay in the lee of Slotsholmen, the present site of Gammelstrand. The deeps in the Wadden Sea similarly determined shipping routes in that area. The channel of Grådyb, be-

built to lead migrating sand away from the harbour entrance. The island harbours, on the other hand, are connected with the mainland by a bridge which permits material migration between the shoreline and the harbour. The coast of West Jylland, with heavy wave action and enormous migration of material, makes piers expensive and harbour works very diffi-

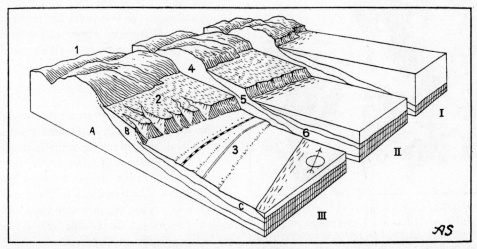

Fig. 8.13. Danish moraine landscape with coastal plains and raised shorelines, Vendsyssel, North Jylland. I. Lateglacial stage. The Yoldia Sea washing along the moraine landscape. II. Stone-Age stage during the Litorina transgressions. III. Present stage.—A. Moraine. B. Lateglacial marine deposits. C. Postglacial marine deposits.—1. Hilly moraine landscape. 2. Lateglacial plateau. 3. Postglacial and recent coastal plain with road and railway. 4. Raised cliff shoreline of the lateglacial sea. 5. Cliffs of the Litorina period. 6. Present shoreline. Block edges 1×2.8 km. — After Schou 1956, p. 419.

tween Skallingen and Fanø, determined the site of Esbjerg when export of farm produce necessitated a large-scale port on the west coast of Jylland.

If ports are needed in localities where the physical conditions are absent, artificial ports of various types are built: pier harbours, for instance Skagen, Hundested, and island harbours, a type peculiar to Denmark, such as Rungsted north of København, Arnager and Snogebæk in Bornholm. These harbours are designed especially for beach-drifting coasts. The sand-proof piers of the pier harbours are

cult, but fish ports and ports of refuge have had to be built here. Hirtshals harbour was sited on a projection where beach-drifting is relatively small. In a similar locality a harbour is at present being constructed at Hanstholm. The west coast port of Thyborøn was built on the channel connecting Limfjord with the North Sea.

The construction of fishing ports in the late 19th and early 20th century has been decisive in changing Danish fishing from the coastal type, aiming at supplying the home market, to large-scale fishing whose catch is mostly exported or landed abroad.

SOILS

Soil development

Because the surface of Denmark is composed of deposits from two distinct glaciations and of lateglacial and postglacial marine sediments, and as blown sand is uppermost in many lo-

calities, the soil types vary considerably from place to place. The character of the soil is also influenced by the quantity and nature of the humus and by climatic factors, notably precipitation which, varying widely both in areal

115

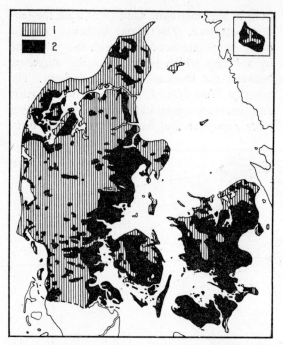

Fig. 8.14. *Distribution pattern of clayey and sandy soils* in Denmark. 1. Preponderantly sand, 2. Preponderantly clay. For different origin of the initial soil materials, cf. Fig. 8.1. — After Bornebusch and Milthers 1935.

and seasonal distribution, complicates the pattern over quite short distances. Centuries of tillage, varying locally in its intensity, bring a time factor into the picture. At many places on the Danish islands the soil has been tilled since the Neolithic period, whereas on the outwash plains of West Jylland cultivation dates from the latter half of the 19th century. The picture is actually not so simple as this because the outwash plains had been previously tilled, but farming was abandoned there in the Early Iron Age.

The character of the moraine is subject to considerable variation locally, according to the proportions of gravel, sand and clay in it (Fig. 8.14). In the unweathered state the calcium content, so vital for farming, is high in consequence of glacial erosion of the underlying limestone beds. Nine tenths of Denmark's surface consist of these glacial deposits, its fertility varying from almost sterile morainic gravel to rich boulder clay.

Strictly speaking, these morainic deposits are not the best natural soil for farming, but proper cultivation, supply of missing elements and regulation of the water-table by drainage have raised the quality, with the result that the yield

per hectare is as high as anywhere. The large quantities of boulders in Danish field walls are evidence of diligent clearance by countless generations to secure the best possible surfaces for cultivation. Where meltwater sand covers large tracts, as for instance in West Jylland, effective soil improvement has diminished the once wide difference between the fertility of these regions and that of the rest of Denmark, but there will never be complete uniformity of fertility. East Denmark, where clayey soils predominate, still leads in crop yields per unit of area.

Podsols

Climate has the greatest effect on the character of the soil. As a result of Denmark's relatively high rainfall and moderate temperatures, leaching of the soluble substances in the upper soil layers, podsolization, is becoming a problem. Precipitation is heaviest in southwestern Jylland where sandy soils are best developed and biological factors are favourable; this is the most podsolized region in Denmark.

In sandy places, such as the outwash plains and the ancient moraine landscapes of the Riss-Saale glaciation, the roots of heath plants are so dense that the activities of earthworms are inhibited. Vegetable matter does not break down into humus but accumulates in a peaty mass, 'sour humus', which, despite its high content of organic matter, contains little soluble and easily accessible nutriment for plants (Fig. 8.15). The percolating water contains humic acid which

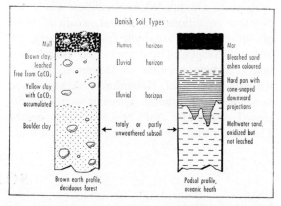

Fig. 8.15. *Typical Danish soil profiles.* The left-hand column shows a profile common to the east of the Main Stationary Line, and that on the right a podsol profile found west of it in Jylland. (For totaly, read totally.) — After Schou 1949 a, Text and Photographs, p. 46.

seeps down and dissolves both iron and lime salts so that the upper layer becomes leached and turns into a poor soil, *blegsand* (bleached, ash-coloured sand), consisting chiefly of insoluble grains of quartz. In the subsoil the percolating water precipitates the dissolved salts again, cementing the soil particles into a dark brown sandstone, hard pan or iron pan. The bleached sand is sterile and the iron pan may prevent water circulation, so that it becomes waterlogged in rainy periods and desert-like in droughts.

Podsols are limited in Denmark to the areas south and west of the Main Stationary Line through Jylland, so far as major occurrences are concerned. Minor patches occur in east Denmark in sandy areas exposed to desiccation. Podsolization is now being counteracted by deep ploughing, which breaks up the hard pan. The soil can be made good by marling and regular draining.

The heather moors which once ran unbroken across the horizon are now mostly chequered with fields and conifer plantations. Straight highways have replaced the sandy tracks along which ox-drawn carts used to rock across the heather. It should be stressed that heaths are not the primary vegetation cover; remnants of oak thickets and several other clues, such as many traces of earlier cultivation, show that heather is the secondary cover of the outwash plains. Heather moors result from biotic influences and cannot be assumed to be a relict of a tundra cover.

Brown forest soils

In East Denmark, that is to say to the east of the Main Stationary Line and of the clayey areas north of it, the usual type is brown forest soil. The surface layer is mull with a neutral or slightly acid reaction, a granular structure useful for cultivation as is its water-binding property. Under the mull the percolating water has a high oxygen content because of the porosity and high carbon dioxide content of the mull resulting from very active oxidization in that layer. The oxygen causes the formation of reddish-yellow ferrous compounds in the upper clay and sand strata, and the carbon-dioxide-rich water dissolves the lime salts. This it does to such an extent that lime has to be added in the form of marl or powdered chalk. The

groundwater becomes very rich in calcium, good for drinking, but because of its hardness it causes much scaling and wastage of soap. The brown forest soil occurs in areas whose natural vegetation is temperate deciduous forest. Here the supply of organic matter at leaf-fall is abundant and biological decomposition is rapid, especially through the medium of bacterial activity. Soil ventilation is promoted by earthworms. The brown forest soil of Danish farms is eloquent of rational cultivation, of copious applications of stable manure and fertilizers and also of crop rotation, and therefore must be regarded as a distinctly man-made phenomenon.

Other soils

The soil of the low marine forelands is often of a sandy, gravelly character and is unsuitable for ploughing, so that these areas are often left in pasture. The groundwater in some of these localities contains salt which further detracts from their usefulness. Sulphur and iron compounds may also be troublesome.

With the help of modern soil-research most Danish soils can be improved so much that, even if they are useless for agriculture, they can be afforested. Dune soils resist improvement but are planted with conifers to protect adjacent cultivated land from destruction by sand drift. Sand dunes are stabilized by planting them with marram grass *(Psamma arenaria)* and with mountain pine *(Pinus montana)*.

Water economy

Annual precipitation varies from 450 to 800 mm, and ensures adequate water content of the agricultural soil. The problem is the wide seasonal variation of precipitation (Fig. 8.17).

In Denmark the soil water economy varies with the alterations in balance throughout the year between precipitation and evaporation, run-off along watercourses and downward percolation. The latter takes place mainly in winter. In summer, evaporation is so great that small watercourses shrink considerably and in the relatively rainless early summer months the soil may become so dry that it inhibits growth and photosynthesis. In strong winds there is a risk of aeolian erosion, especially of sandy soils. Planting of sheltering hedgerows is a counter measure, but field spraying with pumped-up groundwater is more effective, though because of the expense it has not yet been widely adopted. Of greater importance is the meadow irrigation practised along some Jylland streams. On the other hand, in winter and spring, reduced evaporation produces waterlogged fields, temporary small lakes and ponds which may hold up spring farm work and thus reduce the crop yield. This danger is being effectively counteracted and drainage of the lowlands represents a very large investment of labour and capital, about a quarter of the agricultural area being well drained artificially. As a consequence of all methods of soil improvement farmland now covers three quarters of Denmark, and high yields per hectare are possible for many crops.

CLIMATE AND VEGETATION

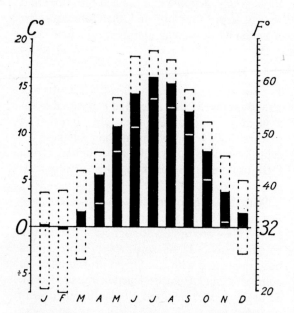

Fig. 8.16. Yearly variation of air temperature. Black column: mean monthly temperature. White column above: highest mean monthly temperature since 1874. White column beneath or white line through the black column: lowest mean monthly temperature since 1874. The variations are considerable. The weather of Denmark is complex. Oceanic and continental weather types interchange as a result of a situation in a region where air masses of different physical structures are constantly in conflict. — After Schou in K. M. Jensen (edit.), Vor Klode I, København 1953.

Denmark's unusual climate is a direct consequence of its situation in the west wind belt of the north temperate zone on the west side of Eurasia. That Denmark faces the North Sea, and is not open to the Atlantic is another vital factor: Denmark has not so typical a maritime climate as e.g. the British Isles. On the other hand, the ameliorating influence of the Baltic Sea is such that Denmark does not have the continental climate of East Europe. Exceptionally, when winter ice closes the Baltic and it ceases to act as a thermal reservoir, masses of cold air from the east may spread over Denmark and cause an 'ice winter'. This occurs in about five winters per century. In the first of the three ice winters 1939–42, a temperature of –31°C was measured, the lowest ever recorded in Denmark. Conversely, summer high pressure systems over Scandinavia keep out the cool westerlies, and high temperatures are recorded. The highest air temperature measured under such conditions is 35.8°C. However, ice winters and heat waves are rare; more moderate temperatures are the general rule.

Temperature and precipitation

The annual temperature range is given on Fig. 8.16 which also shows that deviations from mean values are very great because different types of air masses constantly succeed one another over Denmark. The precipitation diagram (Fig. 8.17) shows that rain falls all the year round, and that in this respect too, annual variations may be considerable. Winter precipitation is relatively small, but this is of little significance biologically as the water requirements of plants are small in that period. What is more serious is that the spring months are also dry. In that period crops grow vigorously because of rising temperatures, and a dry May or June reduce the crop yield considerably. The wettest months are August and October, which is regrettable from an agricultural point of view. When the grain is ripening in August large quantities of water are unnecessary, and at harvest time they are directly harmful; indeed sometimes they are disastrous. On the other hand root crops thrive in a wet autumn.

Rain is mainly cyclonic. The mean annual precipitation in Denmark is 60 cm, varying from about 80 cm in Southwest Jylland to about 40 cm on Sprogø in the Great Belt. The lowlands around the Great Belt have low precipitation; they lie in the rainshadow of the frequent west winds which drop their moisture over Jylland and Fyn and become still drier on sinking over the Great Belt.

Although Denmark is small in extent there are typical regional climatic differences, above all between the coast and the interior owing to marine influences. The coldest month on the west coast has an average temperature of 0.5°C, but the interior of Bornholm has less than −1°C. Summer temperatures also show that continentality increases towards the east. The temperature at the west coast is then 15°C whereas the southeast of the country has over 17°C. The length of the frost-free period also varies regionally. On an average the last night-frost on the west coast is on April 3rd, whereas inland in Jylland it is as late as May 19th. The first night-frost of autumn comes about September 28th in the interior of Jylland but not until November 27th in the sea-girt Ertholme east of Bornholm in the Baltic.

Phytogeography

Phytogeographically Denmark is also a borderland. Her position in the north temperate climatic zone, with a mean temperature above 10°C for more than 4½ months of the year (Fig. 8.16) means that deciduous forest is the natural vegetation, but that the country lies close to the border of the coniferous belt. Some localities in central Jylland have a mean temperature approaching that of the coniferous region; and spruce plantations thrive. On the other hand, natural deciduous woods of beech, oak, elm and linden are to be found almost everywhere. The woodlands which cover 10 per cent of Denmark's area were practically all planted and are in the care of foresters. The deciduous woods have beech as the dominant tree, and the conifer woods introduced spruces and pines.

Denmark's forest history is being elucidated by means of detail analyses of plant pollen recovered from the peat bogs. After the waning of the ice the country's first vegetation cover was the hardy plants familiar to us from Arctic tundras. The first trees to immigrate were the birch, the hazel and the aspen. As the climate improved the spruce took the lead and in the

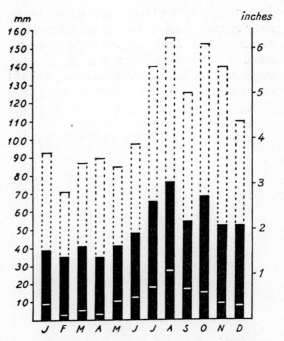

Fig. 8.17. *Yearly variation of precipitation.* Black column: mean monthly precipitation. White column: extreme monthly maximum precipitation value since 1874. White line: extreme minimum since 1874. —The precipitation varies more than the temperature. Humid and dry summers alternate as do winters with heavy snowfall and those with no snow. Heavy rain during the harvest period often troubles the farmers but can be overcome by means of combines whose use normally makes it possible to harvest quickly on dry days. Dry springs may also retard growth. — After Schou, see Fig. 8.16.

continental period the country was covered by enormous pine forests, which in the warm period of the Stone Age gave place to the mixed oak forest. In that ancient forest were the isolated clearings which initiated cultivation and led to the present complete reversal of proportions of forest and tilled soil. With the change to a cool and rainy climate about 500 B.C. the beech attained supremacy and it has remained the naturally dominant woodland tree.

Other widespread plant associations include dune vegetation, in which marram grass, sand sedge, crowberry, creeping willow, buckthorn etc. are adapted to the extreme conditions of the unstable blown-sand regions. Heather moor was formerly widespread on the podsolized outwash plains but is also found on the sandy, steep slopes of the morainic hill country and, in special varities, on the gravelly beach-ridge plains and in the granite terrain. Bogs are of two main types: fens or lowland bogs occur widely in the many undrained depressions of the young moraine landscapes, while extensive high bogs are found on waterlogged flats such as the emerged Stone Age sea floor of North Jylland. Dunes, moors and bogs together cover 8 per cent of the country's area. Finally, mention must be made of the marine vegetation: the green, submarine meadows of grass wrack in the inner waters, brown seaweeds farther out and red algae in the deep waters.

SETTLEMENT AND POPULATION

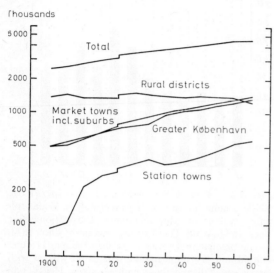

Fig. 8.18. Population, 1901–60, totals and numbers according to type of settlement (semi-logarithmic scale).

Introduction

It is assumed that the first settlement of Denmark took place shortly after the retreat of the last ice sheet. The country has been inhabited ever since—originally by food gatherers and hunters, later by pastoralists and soil tillers. Even in the Neolithic, agriculture was the principal occupation, and by the beginning of historical times the essentials of Denmark's settlement were already complete. The villages were scattered about the country, roads connected large and small settlements, whilst regular communications beyond what are now the borders were established.

The names of the villages as a rule make it possible to make a fairly reliable estimate of their ages. The earliest types have names ending in -inge, and these towns can probably be dated to about the beginning of the Christian era. Later periods were characterized by expansion, when new land came under the plough and new villages were founded. The latest type of name (with the suffix -torp) originated in the period 1000–1200 A.D. Naturally, there were changes in the settlement of the country after that time, but the original pattern is still clear.

Once the country had been wholly occupied, several centuries passed without much change. From 1300 to 1800 the population remained fairly constant at about one million. In that period the rural population decreased whereas the towns grew. The great change as regards both form of settlement and population trends came round about the year 1800. The transfer of the land to free ownership from copyhold and the consequent dispersal from the villages completely altered the character of the rural settlement. At the 1801 census the population numbered about one million, with a tenth living in København (Copenhagen) and a tenth in the provincial towns. In 1960 the population had grown to 4½ millions, with 1.3 million living within the boundaries of Greater København, and 1.4 million in the provincial towns; in other words, in the course of those 150 years the urban share of the population had grown from 20 to nearly 60 per cent. The rapid development of the towns was made possible chiefly by the growth of industry; increased trade and the expansion of communications also did their share.

Manufacturing industry and crafts, including construction, are now the largest of the productive occupations. In 1960 34 per cent of Denmark's active population were occupied in these trades as against 16 per cent in farming, market-gardening, forestry and fishing. A comparison with other European countries shows that Denmark is in a transition phase industrially. The proportionately low degree of industrialization may presumably be attributed both to favourable natural pre-conditions for agriculture and to an unfavourable starting-point for industry, caused by the almost total dearth of industrial raw materials and sources of energy.

120

Villages and farms

Throughout the greater part of the country the nucleated village was the common form of settlement until agrarian reforms began towards the close of the 18th century. Open-field farming was gradually done away with and the strips were consolidated, each farmer receiving one or more lots. As a result, some of the farm buildings were moved out to their own lands, which meant a reduction in the size of such villages. Prior to the agricultural reforms isolated farms were rather rare. The landscape is now characterized by dispersed farms, distances between the farmsteads are relatively small, and large, continuous farmlands devoid of settlement occur only when the natural circumstances are of a special nature (for example extremely low-lying land) or within the domains of a manor.

Even now the villages have functions that are common to the parish, they process certain farm products and are the site of dairies, grain and feeding-stuff businesses, smithies and machine workshops, and they often have farm machinery depots which undertake cultivation and harvest work for the farmers. The villages also have their retail shops and other more ordinary service businesses. Cultural institutions—church, school, assembly rooms—are also found in the villages as a rule.

Towns

The Danish towns are of widely different origin, age and importance. The majority date from the Middle Ages; very few are older, and still fewer are less than a hundred years old. Manufacturing industry is predominant in only a small number of the provincial towns, and, apart from København, practically all Danish towns have retained their character of trade centres, most of them being intimately associated with their hinterland, some with export trade and a few with transport business as important supplements. If we consider the initial factors that determined the location of the towns, as well as the natural factors, it is possible to single out several characteristic groups of towns.

The ford towns are a special type, common in East Jylland but also found in other parts of the country. Originally these towns were situated at the head of their fjords, at the river mouth. Their longitudinal dimension lay across the watercourse, where the main street was laid upon a natural or artificial elevation leading to the ford, and afterwards to the bridge across the river. Very often the ford towns have important subsidiary occupations such as transport or fishery. When a ford town began to grow, the main valley with the river and its water meadows were usually unsuitable for building purposes, and the town therefore spread along the slopes and up the hillsides, where the highways ran. Typical examples of towns of this type are Kolding, Vejle, Randers and Hobro.

The deliberately planned towns, Fredericia (founded 1650), a fortress town, and Esbjerg (1868), a seaport, are less common. In contrast with the ford towns, where the situation facilitates landward transport, Fredericia and Esbjerg stand on a spit and an outward curve of the coast respectively. Esbjerg is in the neighbourhood of two ancient ford towns, Ribe (south) and Varde (north), but has far surpassed them in size and importance.

A third type of town developed in close association with ferry communications between the islands. The ferry towns were fortified for many years, more or less effectively, a fact that emphasizes the importance of the ferry routes. Helsingør (Elsinore) is perhaps the most handsome example of this group, but it also had the special function of collecting the Sound dues, which were enforced from 1429 until 1857. Since their foundation Korsør and Nyborg have retained their position as transport towns, their harbours are still their nuclei. As a ferry terminal Middelfart (Little Belt) was once almost as important as the last two towns, and Kalundborg has also played a similar role; it is still a ferry terminal linked with Århus.

Other towns have religious and administrative foundations. Odense and Viborg were important religious centres before the coming of Christianity, and the episcopal sees afterwards centred there served to consolidate them. Today Odense has an industrial and mercantile influence far beyond its significance in ecclesiastical and civil administration, but this is by no means true of all towns of this type. In Viborg religious and public institutions still dominate the town, and the same applies to Ringkøbing, Ribe and Thisted. Such towns are often important educational centres, with grammar-schools and teachers' colleges.

121

Quite distinct from these types are towns devoted exclusively or mainly to residential purposes; there are retail shops and local craftsmen, but usually hardly any industry. Towns of this type are often suburban in character or predilectively inhabited by people living on their pensions or private means.

Tourist centres and seaside resorts are similarly devoid of industrial and commercial activity. Along the coast of North Sjælland there is a line of urban settlements of this kind; elsewhere in the country they are frequented only during a very short period in summer.

The railways have had no small influence as town builders. Quite a number of townships only began to expand vigorously after the railway had reached them, e.g. Esbjerg, Herning and Brønderslev.

The appearance of the railway also engendered an entirely new form of settlement, the station town. The great improvement in transport possibilities attracted certain trades to the stations from both villages and towns.

Occupationally the station town closely resembles the small provincial town. The chief occupation is trading, at times closely followed by industry but rarely exceeded by it, and always in conjunction with handicrafts.

The railways, and in some cases new harbours have given most towns access to large markets both at home and abroad, but it is still true of many towns that the greater part of their commercial life is based upon selling to and buying from a rather small hinterland.

One special type of modern settlement is the large fishery town found particularly on the west coast of Jylland, the largest being Hirtshals, Thyborøn, Hvide Sande and Esbjerg. Fishing, trading in and preparing fish, as well as the building of boats and manufacture of fishing gear, make these towns very specialized settlements. The building of new, large harbours has made increased fishery possible and is the reason for the growth of these towns. There are some older fishing towns along the coasts of the Kattegat, including Skagen, Frederikshavn, Kerteminde and Hundested.

Distribution and occupations

Of the total population of 4.8 millions, more than 3 millions now live in some form of urban settlement. Of these 3 millions, nearly 2 live on the Islands, including 1.5 million in Greater København alone. Although the importance of København extends beyond Sjælland and therefore no direct comparison is possible with the more local functions of the provincial towns, the fact remains that the Islands as a whole have a greater share of the urban population than Jylland. Within the counties of Jylland, too, there are still very great variations in the proportion of the urban population, despite the many recently founded towns of central and western Jylland.

The movement from country to town has been of great significance in the growth of the towns; for a long time it was either beneficial to the rural districts or at any rate it had little effect on their normal functions. But more recently a number of rural communes have suffered considerable population losses with a consequent weakening economically and socially. Roughly speaking there now remains only one large 'immigration' region in Denmark: the suburbs of København. High migration percentages are recorded chiefly in the Islands, comprising practically the entire region beyond København's outermost environs. To this should be added the northern part of Jylland.

The urban community of København is very large in proportion to the size of Denmark, comprising more than 40 per cent of all those employed in the country's urban occupations. This proportion dominates the distribution pattern of urban occupations.

In the Islands (excluding Greater København) 11 per cent of the total population are employed in agriculture as against 32 per cent occupied in the urban trades. In East Jylland the difference between the two percentages is even bigger because the region is rather intensively urbanized. In North and West Jylland the proportion employed in agriculture is about half of those working in urban occupations.

The greater industrialization of East Jylland, as compared with that of North and West Jylland, provides a partly parallel situation to the dominating position of the metropolitan area compared with Sjælland, Lolland and Falster. Similar differences are observable in the distribution of other characteristic urban occupations such as trading and transport.

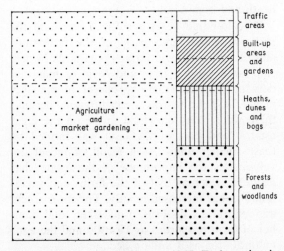

Fig. 8.19. Use of total area, 1965. Each section is divided into two by a horizontal broken line, the lower part in each representing Jylland, the upper one the Islands. Farming and market gardening utilize 73% of the country's surface.

AGRICULTURE

By international standards Danish agriculture is highly developed, even though agriculture no longer holds the same dominating position among the country's occupations as it did up to a decade or two ago. Denmark must now be described as a farming and industrial country. In 1960 only 16 per cent of the population were employed in agriculture. If all those employed in processing, transporting or trading farm produce and raw materials are included, the share is somewhat larger. The significance of agriculture in the total economy is most clearly manifested in the sphere of foreign trade where, in spite of the recent rise in industrial exports, farm produce is still by far the biggest item, comprising just under half of its proceeds.

Denmark does not possess any natural advantages for agriculture which are not equalled or even surpassed by other countries, apart from easy access to Europe's two big food-consuming countries, highly industrialized Britain and Germany. Denmark's role as a main supplier of high-quality food is predominantly due to the organization and spirit of Danish farmers. It has been vital that Danish agriculture has long been geared to foreign markets and is accustomed to react to new situations

and consider them from the viewpoints of both producer and consumer. Changes in demand are studied in relation to future patterns of production. Another very important feature has been the co-operative movement among the farmers which has accelerated the implementation of the results of research, the widespread use of consultants, and an effective organization of the processing and marketing of agricultural produce. Danish agriculture, 'more dependent on foreign markets than on the home market, is thus a dynamic factor in the life of the nation, in contrast to several other European countries where agriculture is a depressed industry.

Of the land area of Denmark proper, about 42 000 km², slightly more than 27 000 km² or 65 per cent, was arable land in 1965. In Europe, the Netherlands is the only other country with so large a part of its area devoted to agriculture and with a similar cultivation intensity and size of farming population. In other

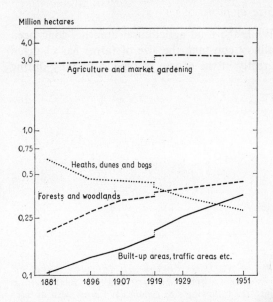

Fig. 8.20. Use of total area, 1881–1951 (semi-logarithmic scale). The agricultural area (incl. market gardening) was constant throughout the period, *i.e.* about 3 million ha. Heath, dune and bog areas decreased from 0.6 mill. to less than 0.3 mill. ha. Wood and planted areas rose from 0.2 to about 0.5 mill. ha. Buildings, communications etc. occupy a steadily increasing share of the area; the absolute increase within this period is considerable, from 0.1 to 0.4 mill. ha. The two figures for 1919 are caused by the return of Sønderjylland to Denmark.

countries only small parts can compare with Denmark in this respect. The remaining third of the land area is used as follows: Permanent pastures and meadows occupy 8 per cent, woods and plantations 11 per cent, heaths and bogs just under 7 per cent, whilst 9 per cent comprises built-up areas, roads, railways and the like (Fig. 8.19). During the past hundred years part of the agricultural area has been taken for buildings, roads, railways, ports etc., but so far it has been compensated for, more or less, by previously uncultivated land coming under the plough (Fig. 8.20). It is this 'inner colonization' that has made it possible for industrialization to spread with small loss of cultivable land resources. Growing population, continued industrialization, higher standards of living, better means of transport and new forms of housing will involve a rapid increase in urban areas. Even if this change is not particularly great in point of area, it will be perceptible because, as a general rule, it will affect fertile and well cultivated land.

Size of farms

While the total agricultural area has long been almost constant, the size of farms has changed greatly in the course of time, especially during the past half century. This is chiefly the result of a deliberate land policy, contributing factors being increased cultivation and reclamation of heath and bog.

Two hundred years ago the Crown and the manors owned large parts of the farmlands, and the characteristic farm—as regards ownership—was the big farm and royal or manorial domain. Viewed from the aspect of management, the position was quite different, because there were many copyhold farms on the great estates, and part of the land was farmed by these smaller units. As a result of recent developments the importance of the estates has declined, whereas that of the farms and smallholdings has increased greatly. The most recent agricultural census (1960) gives the total number of farm properties as 194 000 and the agricultural area as 3 million hectares.

The distribution according to size is fairly even, but with a distinct maximum for the medium-sized farms (Fig. 8.21). Compared with most countries in Western Europe the share of the large landed estates in Denmark is rather small, about 10 per cent against 25 to 40 per cent elsewhere, e.g. in Germany. The typical Danish farm is one with an area of between 10 and 30 ha.; in that group there are about 81 000 farms whose land comprises about 45 per cent of all the agricultural area.

Another characteristic group is the smallholdings. These are usually properties of less than 10 ha. but large enough to provide the proprietor with his municipal occupation. Because of differences in the quality of the soil and in the local possibilities of laying out farms of suitable size, the smallholdings vary considerably. The establishment of smallholdings was encouraged by the State (1899 and 1919 Acts), originally on account of labour shortages in the rural areas, and later more for political reasons. Altogether about 27 000 smallholdings resulted from these acts; in addition, a number of small farms were awarded extra land.

There is a close relation between quality of soil and farm size. On the outwash plains of western and central Jylland with their sandy soil the area of the individual farm is large, no matter to what group it belongs; in direct contrast is the best morainic soil of the Islands, where the farms are much below the national average for their particular group.

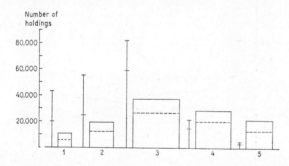

Fig. 8.21. Distribution of farming area according to sizes of farms, 1956. Subdivision is into the following size groups: 1. Farms with an area of 0.55–5 ha. 2. 5–10 ha. 3. 10–30 ha. 4. 30–60 ha. 5. Over 60 ha. A vertical line indicates the number of farms in each group; a horizontal line shows the number of farms in the Islands (upper part) and in Jylland (lower part). The squares represent the total area of the farms within each of the 5 groups. The broken lines indicate the division between the Islands and Jylland, the shares of the Islands being above. — The predominating farm size is 10–30 ha., forming 40% of the total number and 45% of the total area; the preponderance of this type is greatest in Jylland.

124

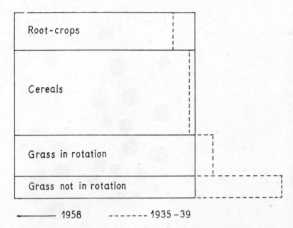

Root-crops	
Cereals	
Grass in rotation	
Grass not in rotation	

——— 1958   ------- 1935–39

Fig. 8.22. Distribution of farming area by crops, 1958 and 1935–39. The square represents the total agricultural area and the subdivision (continuous horizontal lines) by crops 1958. The broken lines show the average size of the areas 1935–39. The root-crop area rose by 13%, the cereal area by 3%, rotation grass fell by 8% and permanent grass by 32% between the pre-war period and 1958. Cf. Fig. 7.1, p. 84.

Soil and climate

Natural conditions are on the whole favourable for farming in respect of terrain, soil and climate. Over most of the country the configuration of the ground permits the growing of crops of all kinds; the exceptions are the steep slopes and hills in the marginal moraine areas, the glacifluvial valleysides and the ancient shore lines. Low-lying areas at the coasts, such as saltings and some marshy regions, are also of limited usefulness. In earlier centuries ill-drained land was not farmed, but in the course of time various forms of water control greatly reduced the areas in which over-abundant water chronically or temporarily represented an obstacle to farming.

In the Islands and East and North Jylland the improved soil consists mainly of weathered moraine deposits with a varying content of clay, sand and gravel but without the large and medium-sized stones which the farmers have removed from the fields in the course of the centuries. It also contains a large proportion of organic substances or the products of their putrefactive processes, and finally, a quantity of salts of external origin, such as those applied in artificial fertilizers. Part of the lime content is original, part is the result of marling.

A subdivision of Denmark into agro-geographical regions will largely reflect variations of soil, because climatic differences are relatively small. Precipitation, however, is greater in the western part of Denmark than elsewhere in the country. The effects of this difference are reduced because in West Jylland the farmlands are generally sandy and therefore unable to hold the water so near to the surface as the clayey soils in other parts of Denmark. Moreover, strong winds are more prevalent in the west than in the east, with the result that notwithstanding the greater precipitation, dessication phenomena are much more widespread near the North Sea coast. However, water is nearly always within reach of the roots of cultivated plants, and exceptionally low yields as a consequence of water shortage are almost wholly confined to a few particularly exposed areas.

Seasonal variations in precipitation are not unconditionally favourable; for instance there is the slight rainfall in the spring months when more abundant moisture would be preferable for the early and rapid growth of the crops; and the heavy rainfall in August coincides with the harvesting of the grain. As a general rule there is a relatively long frost-free period.

CROPS

Grain crops usually occupy 55–57 per cent of the total agricultural area. The areas under grass comprise fields in rotation and permanent pastures; together they cover about 30 per cent of the agricultural area. Third place among the principal crops is held by roots, including all forms of beet and potatoes; in 1966 root crops occupied 13 per cent of the area (Fig. 8.22).

The use to which the farmland is put varies considerably from one part of the country to another; root and grass areas are relatively largest in Jylland, whereas cereals and seed crops are relatively largest in the islands.

As a natural consequence of the paramount importance of animal husbandry in Danish agriculture, fodder crops dominate not only the total vegetable output but also the grain crops.

Cereals

Of the current cereals, wheat is the most sensitive to both soil and climate. The highest yield per hectare is obtained where the soil is suitably clayey without being heavy. Thus the natural

125

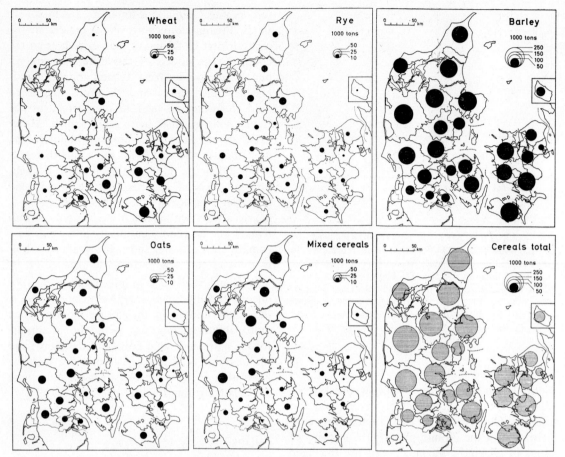

Fig. 8.23. Cereal crops, 1963 (by counties in tons). The total grain crop corresponded in 1966 to 58 million crop units (one c. u. equals the feed value of 100 kg barley).

prerequisites of extensive wheat growing are to be found in the moraine lands. The greater part of the wheat output comes from western and southern Jylland and from Fyn and East Jylland. Winter wheat is mainly grown; as a general rule spring wheat has such a low yield that it is unable to compete with other grain crops. The wheat harvest fluctuates between 400 000 and 550 000 tons, in 1966 it was 400 000 tons.

Even on very sandy or acid soil rye gives a satisfactory yield and under these circumstances is often the best crop. The greater part of the rye output comes from West and North Jylland. In recent years the annual harvest of rye has fluctuated between 250 000 and 400 000 tons, in 1966 it was 140 000. Contrasting distributions of cereals are shown on Fig. 8.23.

Barley is Denmark's chief cereal crop and represents about two thirds of the total grain harvest. In former days it was mostly grown on the heavier soils, like wheat, but during the last war

the farmers were compelled by the shortage of imported feeding-stuffs to put more land under barley. The movement was accelerated in the post-war years, being furthered by the use of new varieties and increased application of artificial manures. The barley crops have increased almost continuously, and in 1966 amounted to 4.2 million tons. The greater part of the barley is used as fodder, especially for pigs; smaller quantities are used in the production of grits or are employed industrially, especially by the breweries. Malting barley is grown on such a wide scale that a certain amount is exported.

Oats are hardy, thrive even on very sandy soil, and are resistant to wet summers; they are grown especially in West, Central and North Jylland. However, oats are no longer cultivated so widely, principally because of a relatively low feed value and the gradual displacement of horses for traction. The area under oats, which before the war was about 375 000 ha., had fal-

126

len by 1966 to about 200 000 ha., the lowest figure ever recorded. In that year the output was about 860 000 tons, of which only a small quantity is used for human food in the form of groats, the remainder being consumed as fodder.

The four principal cereals are mostly grown separately, but a mixed crop of barley and oats is also sown. Its advantage lies in its usefulness as a kind of insurance, because variations in the weather which may retard the growth of one cereal, or reduce its yield, will not affect the other or may even promote its growth. Mixed barley-oats areas are most common in West and North Jylland and have changed little during the past twenty years; in 1966 there was a harvest of about 400 000 tons, all of which was used for fodder.

Cereal crops supply almost the whole home production of the concentrates used in animal husbandry and are for that reason grown in spite of their relatively low yields compared to roots. As an average for the whole country the total yield was calculated at about 49 crop units per hectare for the period 1960–66. The difference in the yield of the three crop groups is very considerable, for on the whole the cereal crops, together with grass and green fodder, gave the same yield, between 42 and 46 crop units per hectare, whereas the root crops gave about 80 units. Both climate and soil are more favourable for the cultivation of roots, which, because of their long growing period, can utilize the comparatively high autumn temperatures. The cultivation of feeding-stuffs with a high protein content is either impossible or results in only a small yield; as a consequence, the best fodder combination is obtained by the home production of coarse feed (grass and roots) and carbohydrate-containing concentrates (cereals). The protein-containing concentrates (oilseeds) have to be imported.

Roots

Root-crop growing began to increase with the rising importance of animal husbandry towards the close of the last century. Since then the increase in areas and yields of roots has been a steady one, interrupted only occasionally. As in the case of cereal crops, most of the roots harvested are used for fodder. Earliest introduced of the roots now grown were turnips, fol-

lowed by mangolds, kohlrabi and lastly fodder beet. The dry matter content of roots varies between 9 per cent and 24 per cent. Most of the dry matter is carbo-hydrates, barely one tenth being protein. This applies solely to the root, which up to a few decades ago was the only part of the plant used. Nowadays the top is also in wide use, being a valuable supplement to feeding-stuffs on account of its high protein content.

The turnip is not grown much nowadays, its principal areas being in West and North Jylland where it gives a relatively good yield on the sandy soils and in smaller areas whose early autumn frosts make them unsuitable for roots with a longer growing period.

The mangold is grown rather more than the turnip. Its cultivation reached its peak in the 1920's. This root, which contains 12–13 per cent of solids, will thrive only on clayey soil, and it develops best when there is ample summer warmth. It is grown mostly in southern Sjælland and in Fyn.

Kohlrabi is the chief root crop. It does well on most soils, and thrives on sandy and acid soils unsuitable for other roots. But it also needs ample rainfall and is therefore a very suitable crop throughout most of Jylland. The growth period is long and kohlrabi is fairly frost-resistant. This is an advantage, because lifting of kohlrabi can be postponed without risk until the greater part of the autumn work is over. Kohlrabi predominates almost everywhere in Jylland, but is less important in the Islands, because there the farmers can grow other more productive roots.

The fodder sugar beet, a cross between sugar beet and mangold, has gradually displaced the mangold, because it has a higher nutritive value and yet requires no better growth conditions. The fodder sugar beet has therefore become the most important root crop everywhere in the Islands. In Jylland it covers a wider area in the east than in the rest of the peninsula. One third of the country's root-crop area is used for fodder sugar beet.

Originally an industrial raw material, the sugar beet is now extensively grown for fodder, but neither area nor yield reach the same level as those of the industrial sugar beet. The latter is mainly grown in the islands of Lolland and Falster, in southern and western Sjælland, in

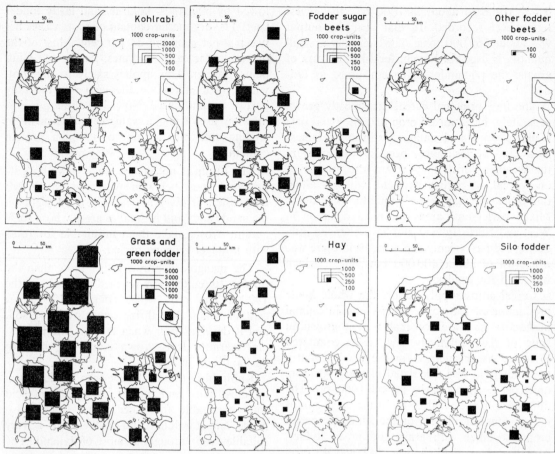

Fig. 8.24. Fodder crops 1963 (by counties in crop units). Fodder sugar beet include sugar beets used for fodder; other fodder beets include mangold and turnip. The quantities indicated are for roots only. Root tops are included in grass and green fodder, half in fresh grass and green fodder, and half in silo fodder. The fodder value of grass (mainly from grazing) and green fodder in 1966 was 49 million crop units, or approximately 85 per cent of the total cereal crops.

Møn and in Fyn. Sugar beet for fodder is mainly grown in Jylland.

The pre-condition for this widespread root growing is a large cattle population, devoted principally to the production of milk. Without consistent improvement of soils of widely varying quality root crops could not have attained their present importance, and it would not have been possible to alter the composition of the fodder by replacing imported concentrates with home-grown feeding-stuffs.

The only other root crop of any importance is the potato. Sandy soil is favourable for its cultivation as the field work is lighter than on clayey soil. Thus the potato is mainly grown in Central and West Jylland and in Himmerland; in the Islands, northeastern Sjælland alone grows any large quantity. Cultivation is mainly for three purposes, edible potatoes, industrial

potatoes for the manufacture of alcohol and potato flour, and fodder potatoes which are chiefly fed to pigs. Many varieties are grown, the edible ones for their flavour, and industrial potatoes with an eye to the highest possible starch content. Early potatoes are produced, partly by market gardeners, for the specially high price obtainable for them.

Grass

The remainder of the agricultural area, forming one third of the total, is devoted to grass and green fodder. The greater part of the grass area is sown in regular crop rotation, and almost all the remainder has been improved by mixing in special plants. It is usual to sow with a mixture of grasses and legumes, the principal ones being rye-grass, timothy, meadow fescue and clover. The lifetime of the stand is very important

128

when selecting the plants, for some only yield well for a year or two (e.g. red clover), whereas others grow well for many years (e.g. white clover). Normally grass and green fodder contribute about 30 per cent of the total vegetable output. The greater part is grazed, a minor quantity is used as silage, and an even smaller part as hay.

The rational utilization of grazing potentialities, and of grass and green fodder, was the most recent phase in modern Danish agriculture. The expansion of the area under the plough took place at the expense of the permanent pastures, a development which has not yet come to an end. This can be seen from a comparison between their present areas and those in existence just before the Second World War. During this short period the total area of permanent grass and meadows has decreased by 300 000 ha. The Danish climate is not particularly suitable for grass growing: compared with most dairying countries the growing period is much shorter; this applies to both European and overseas countries. In addition, precipitation is rather inadequate; spring rainfall is usually low, whereas the ample supplies of summer rain make the pastures relatively good in the late summer and autumn. Low-lying areas are usually suitable for pastures, and provided the rainfall is well distributed, the greater ability of clayey soil to retain water will often favour its utilization for grass, whereas sandy soils will be unsuitable for the purpose. To some extent the distribution of grass is a result of these factors, but not wholly, because practically all farms, regardless of suitability, will have to keep a certain minimal area under grass. The grass areas are relatively largest in Jylland,

where 35 per cent of the agricultural area is so used, whereas the corresponding share in the Islands is 17 per cent. Both terrain and soil have contributed to this difference.

Of other crops, mention may be made of seeds of beet as well as of grass and clover. Most of the seed-growing areas are in the Islands, especially southern Sjælland; seed-growing in Jylland is practically confined to the east. Industrial crops apart from these mentioned, chicory roots, mustard and flax, are insignificant.

ANIMAL HUSBANDRY

In the closing decades of the 19th century Danish agriculture changed over from preponderantly vegetable to preponderantly animal production, and there has since been an inclination to consider the latter line as stable, even if marketing difficulties or unfavourable prices have been experienced from time to time. At present about 85 per cent of the vegetable production is used in animal husbandry. But no branch of husbandry is developed as an isolated activity, and arable farming, dairy production and pig breeding are combined to ensure the highest possible output.

In this century milk production has been the most important part of Danish animal husbandry, but more and more weight is now being attached to meat production. Not only are herds bred for meat, but many dairy cows are slaughtered sooner for beef.

The cow population is dominated by the two national breeds, the Black and White Danish and the Red Danish dairy breeds, which

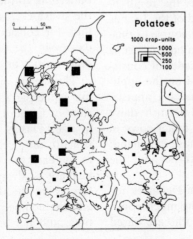
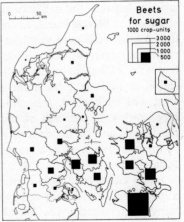

Fig. 8.25. Potatoes and industrial sugar beet crops, 1963 (by counties in crop units). Potatoes are grown chiefly on the sandy soil of North and West Jylland. Of the total potato crop 90% is grown in Jylland. Maribo county predominates for sugar beet, 52 per cent of the total crop came from that county alone, and 41% from other counties in the Islands.

in 1966 represented 77 per cent of all dairy cows. Two other breeds, both originally raised in other countries, are also of some importance. They are Jersey and Shorthorn cattle, which in 1966 formed 16 and 1 per cent respectively of the dairy herds.

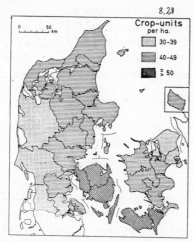

Fig. 8.26. Area yield in crop units, 1963, (averages). The map shows, for each county, the total yield measured in crop units per ha. For the Islands the average is 55, for Jylland 49 and for the whole country 51 crop units per ha.

The Danish Black and White milch cows are confined to Jylland. Originally this breed was dominant all over that part of the country, but is now losing ground. Its former popularity was due to its robustness and hardiness, which enabled it to thrive even in areas where grass was poor and weather an obstacle to dairy farming. With the better conditions nowadays for milch cows the Black and White breed has been unable to compete with the Red variety, to which it has proved inferior in many districts.

The Red Danish dairy cow is the result of crossing between the native breed of the Islands and the Red Slesvig breed. In the course of time these crossbreeds have acquired a homogeneous racial character, the result of decades of consistent work of improvement, based on the application of uniform criteria for judging appearance and milk yield. The Red Danish dairy breed forms 67 per cent of the milch cows in the Islands and 42 per cent of those in Jylland; in other words it is dominant throughout the country.

Jersey cattle have been kept in Denmark for a long time, but without achieving much popularity until recently. The Shorthorns are based upon imported stud animals, chiefly British; animals of this breed are kept mostly for beef and were originally found only on the coastal marshes of western Jylland from the Varde district down to the border.

Jylland has about 75 per cent of the total cattle population; but, as in the Islands, there are marked variations in density. If the intensity of cattle breeding is measured by relating the herd to the size of the agricultural area, the result is an average of 110 head of cattle per 100 ha. (1966) for the whole country. On this basis the cattle density is lowest in the Islands; it is particularly low in the vicinity of København and in Lolland and Falster, where large sections of the agricultural area are devoted to market gardening and industrial sugar beet. The islands east of the Great Belt all have a lower cattle density than the average for the whole country, whereas Fyn's density is above the national average, a fact which also applies to most of Jylland. There the highest densities are found in the central and northwestern parts of Jylland, and the lowest in the south and west of Sønderjylland (Fig. 8.27).

The total milk output is now about 5.4 million tons a year. The average yield per milch cow varies between 3 400 and 3 600 kg per annum, but there are very considerable fluctuations, and cows with an annual milk yield of over 10 000 kg are not uncommon.

Most of the milk produced is used for butter making, though the amount has decreased slightly and is now 60 per cent of the total milk output. Cheese-making consumes 15 per cent. These are the two principal products of the dairies, which return the skimmed milk and the buttermilk to the farmers who use them to feed the livestock, especially the pigs. Most of the milk for consumption is distributed by special dairies in the towns which receive milk from other dairies or direct from farmers.

The second most important Danish farm animal is the pig. Contrasting with the almost constant cattle herd, the pig herd fluctuates rapidly in size. This is because the life of the porker is short and because it is a fairly simple matter to increase the number of sows. Thus a rapid increase is always possible, the regulating factors being the demand in the buyer countries and the competition from other supplier countries, and not least the relation of the cost of

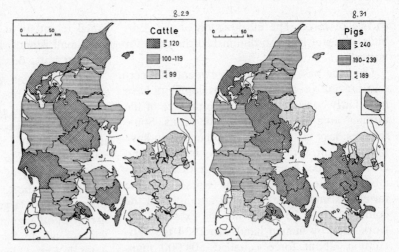

Fig. 8.27. Cattle and pigs in relation to farming area, 1963. The maps show the number of head of cattle and of pigs per 100 ha. of agricultural land in each county. 26% of the cattle are in the Islands, 74% in Jylland. 67% of the pigs are in Jylland.

fodder (especially cereals) to the market price. The pig population decreased very heavily during the last war, but since then it has increased almost continuously and is now about 8.5 millions, as against 3.2 mill. in 1935–39. The output of pork and bacon fluctuated similarly, in 1935–39 it was 342 000 tons, in 1966 790 000 tons.

The usual composition of the pig feed comprises grain, potatoes, sometimes sugar beet, skimmed milk and whey, the principle being to utilize the best feeds that can be derived from the local crops, combined with the milk returned from the dairies. As in the case of the cattle, there are very large variations in the density of the pig population. The raising of special crops explains some of these differences, others are connected with particularly large fodder-crop areas.

The present Danish country breed is the product of crossing the Danish with the Yorkshire pig. By selecting the best animals for breeding it has been possible to obtain the maximum amount of meat suitable for bacon manufacturing, a quality that is generally in great demand, and maturity has been hastened.

As the last important sector of animal husbandry comes poultry farming. There has been some change in the relative values of egg production and meat production. Although the stock of hens is now about 25 per cent lower than before the war, the output of eggs is nearly at the same level. As might be expected, a relatively large part of the poultry is kept on the small farms; for example, farms of less than 10 ha., representing only 15 per cent of the total agricultural area, have 36 per cent of the poultry. The poultry stock has been improved along the same lines as the other domestic animals as regards selection of breeders. A number of ducks and geese are kept, as well as a small, but growing, number of turkeys.

Sheep, now totalling c. 18 000 were once important in some areas, e.g. West Jylland. They were already decreasing in numbers in the late 19th century.

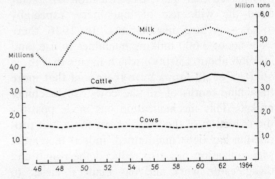

Fig. 8.28. Cattle and dairy cow totals (July counts) *and milk output* 1946–64. The annual milk production in 1950 reached the pre-war level (over 5 mill. tons) and since then has shown only small fluctuations.

MECHANIZATION

Horses numbered 45 000 in 1966, representing less than half of the 1948 total. The use of horses was already on the wane in the years between the two wars, but nevertheless most of the farm work was still being done by horses only a few years ago. Tractors are now in wide use, in 1966 there were 166 000 of them, compared with 4 400 in 1944. It is reckoned that 80 per cent of all the farms now use tractors, either

131

private or hired. The introduction of the combine-harvester has also diminished the need for horses.

Over the past 25 years it is evident that certain aspects of agricultural development have been fairly constant, for example the size of the farming area and the number of farms. Some features have changed slowly, others again have fluctuated in various directions, but the total change has not been of great significance.

One single element in the working of the farms has undergone a radical alteration in the course of these 25 years, i.e. the extent of the work done by human hands. In 1934 the agricultural labour force equalled 504 000 man-years, by 1966 it had declined to 198 000. As the farmers, their wives and young children comprised almost the same numbers at both times, the whole decrease was among the employed workers. The number of these workers has been reduced to less than half in the last quarter century. The decline in the labour force has been met partly by the increased use of tractors. Other mechanical installations have also played their part; electrification has facilitated the wide use of machinery, especially milking-machine installations. In 1936 there were about 3 600 milking machines in use, and in 1966 about 150 000, which means that three quarters of all farms have them and that more than nine tenths of all the cows are machine-milked. This mechanization has made possible the reduction of the farm labour force, but production has been maintained, indeed increased. Mechanization has also reduced the rough and disagreeable work and has made it easier to cope with farm work which has necessarily to be done outside normal working hours.

MARKET GARDENING AND FRUIT GROWING

The area used for market gardening and fruit growing has increased considerably in the present century; in 1907 it was 5 400 hectares, in 1935 10 200 ha., and at the last agricultural census in 1966 30 000 ha. It is distributed very unevenly over the country, 21 per cent of the area being in Jylland, 38 per cent in Fyn and 41 per cent in the other islands. Market gardening occupies large areas around København, Odense and Århus. There are also smaller areas devoted to intensive fruit growing on both large and small islands, more especially in the southernmost parts of the country.

The principal vegetables grown are white cabbage, red cabbage, carrots, onions and leeks. Since the war the growing of summer vegetables in particular has been on the increase. Denmark is self-supporting, as far as most of the ordinary vegetables are concerned, but there is some import, especially of those whose season in Denmark is too short, such as tomatoes and cauliflowers. The largest vegetable-canning plants are in those regions where market gardens are widespread, in Sjælland: København and Slagelse, in Fyn: Odense and Svendborg.

In 1955 the number of fruit trees was 4.5 million, of which 3.8 million were apples. In recent years the commercial apple crops have fluctuated between 80 and 100 million kg. A similar quantity is grown in private gardens. For some years now Denmark has had an export trade in apples, particularly to the Scandinavian countries and to Eastern Europe.

FORESTRY

The forested area represents 11 per cent of the whole land surface, corresponding to 147 000 hectares in the islands and 326 000 ha. in Jylland. In the Islands deciduous trees predominate, occupying two thirds of the forested area. Both in the Islands and in Jylland beech is the principle deciduous tree, with oak coming next. Conifer woods in Jylland cover three quarters of the forested area, and both there and in the Islands spruce is the most important tree. Second in order of importance among the conifers is the mountain pine, which is almost confined to Jylland. A considerable part of the woodland area is practically useless for cultivation, for instance the plantations of West Jylland are on very sandy soil.

From time immemorial the State has owned much forest land, and the area has been extended by the planting of dunes. The State is now the owner of over 120 000 ha. of woodland and plantations, corresponding to a quarter of the total wooded areas. These State woods as a rule are large, continuous ones where rational forestry is possible, whereas more than a third of the privately owned woodland is split up into small units. In recent years total fellings have been round about 2 million m³, thereof timber 1.5 mill. m³.

FISHERIES

Denmark's long coastlines and the abundance of fish in the surrounding waters have been very favourable to the development of the fishing industry. Fish-bones and oyster shells found in Mesolithic deposits are clear evidence that the sea contributed largely to food supplies from the beginning. In the early Middle Ages the herring fisheries in the Sound were of first importance in the country's economy. Autumn herrings were exported via the great herring markets to Western Europe. When the herring shoals fell away towards the close of the 15th century, new grounds began to be fished, especially off Jylland, but this time mainly for the supply of the home market. The lack of harbours and poor facilities for fish transport to other parts of the country hindered developments for a long time; boats were small, gear light and distance to the market long. As a consequence the fisheries were mostly of a local character for the supply of a local market.

The vital change set in round about the year 1880 with the introduction of seaworthy decked boats which made possible effective deep-sea fishing. Another epoc-making event was the invention of better fishing gear, especially the 'Danish seine'; the use of motors both for propulsion and for hauling the seines was another important development.

The most important fisheries are in the North Sea and the Skagerak, whereas the Kattegat, the waters of the Belts and the Baltic are of secondary importance. For example, in 1965 the North Sea landings totalled 480 000 tons, valued at 280 million Danish kroner; in the Skagerak the corresponding figures were 145 000 tons and 82 mill. kr. The landings in the other areas mentioned had values of 40 and 80 mill. kr. respectively. Altogether the fisheries earned 570 mill. kr.

The North Sea fishery comprises firstly flatfish, which are caught in the western North Sea and mainly taken fresh direct to Britain, second come various small fish (herring, sprats, etc.) which are used for oil and fish meal production. The landings from the Skagerak include cod. The Belts and the fjords produce large quantities of eel, and the Baltic is fished for salmon; both are valuable fish.

The new harbour works of the past 75 years have been of inestimable value to the deep-sea fishery, as have the railways. Esbjerg was planned as an export centre for dairy produce, and it is now the home of a large part of the fishing fleet. There are now several important fishing ports on the west coast of Jylland, e.g. Hvide Sande, Thyborøn and Hirtshals, and on the east coast Skagen and Frederikshavn are the main ports. All have fish auction marts, as well as good transport services by rail or lorry. There are also shipyards and repair shops. In many cases these towns also have a subsidiary industry, such as fish canning or oil and fish meal production.

INDUSTRY

General background

The prototypes of Denmark's industries appeared in the 17th century when the State, in accordance with the mercantile system, tried to foster industries and, especially, textiles. Broadly speaking, however, these endeavours were abortive and the change-over to free trade around the year 1800 resulted in the diminution of industrial output.

There was a slight revival towards the middle of the 19th century, but it was only in the last

quarter of this century that industrialization really began. The employment of mechanical power was an important factor in the rate of industrial growth and also in its localization; for example, electrification, as achieved in the first quarter of the present century, caused its dispersal.

Agricultural produce, and especially the products of animal husbandry, was originally very important in industrial development. This was not only because animal products provided raw materials, but also because simultaneously with the change from cereal to animal production there was a greatly increased demand for cultivating and dairying machinery and implements. In addition, there was a vigorous increase in the demand of the prospering farmers for machine-made products to replace things which had previously been made by handicraft and cottage industries. Nowadays, however, this interplay between agriculture and industry is much less important.

There is no doubt that the lack of natural raw materials in Denmark was the main reason why industrialization started so late in comparison with other countries. Energy resources are of poor quality and small, and this alone explains the lack of industrial incentive. The same applies to ores, timber, and to raw materials for textiles and the chemical industries, of which very modest quantities are available. Only agricultural produce and minerals for the production of building materials occur in such quantities that they can sustain a modern industry without the addition of much imported material.

The use of clay and lime in the manufacture of building materials started early and flourished as other industries developed. Agricultural prosperity and the needs of the increasing herds meant that large supplies of materials were required for new farm buildings. At the same time the towns grew rapidly.

Denmark's position on the North Sea facilitates the supply of raw materials and fuel, so that in many spheres she is able to compete with other countries in Western Europe. The configuration of the coasts has favoured the development of towns either on the coast or linked to it by short and cheap transport (Fig. 8.29). Transport costs between overseas producers of raw materials and Danish consumers are thus lower than in most countries in Western Europe.

The large quantities of goods carried to and from Denmark have favoured the development of the shipping industry, and with it, a large shipbuilding industry. The fishing and subsidiary industries are similarly favoured by the country's situation.

Another important factor must be mentioned, i.e. man-power. From the beginning of the 19th century the population began to rise rapidly as a result of improved hygiene and the rising standard of living. By the middle of the century migration from country to town had already begun, a movement which increased considerably as a result of the subsequent reorganization of agriculture and increase in mechanization. As a consequence the growing industries have scarcely ever been short of labour. This has led to the present industrial structure, in which more weight is attached to the manufacturing of highly specialized products than elsewhere.

Foodstuffs, tobacco and beverages

The foodstuffs industry is one of the largest industrial groups in Denmark, the high value of the product is due to the prices of the raw materials used, and not so much to the processing. Much the greater part of the agricultural production is resold to the home market or for export either unprocessed (milk, eggs, meat) or in semi-manufactured form, e.g. butter and bacon. The highly processed farm produce like canned goods, sugar and beer goes chiefly to the home market and, owing to the latter's limited size, forms but a small part of the total production of foodstuffs.

The dairies deal with practically the entire output of milk; they vary considerably in size, the largest being the household-supply dairies, especially those in København. The dairies are scattered fairly evenly over the whole country, almost every parish having one. The necessity for short transport from producer to dairy is the background of this location, because the great majority used to be supplied with their milk by horse-drawn vehicles. In recent years the use of motor-driven vehicles, as well as more economic operation of the dairies, has led to the closing down of some of them, but their number is still very high compared with that of other dairy countries. Some of the dairies are designed solely for producing a single commodity such as liquid milk or cheese, but the great majority have a mixed output with butter as the principal item of manufacture.

The pig slaughter-houses are chiefly situated in the towns, and are spread fairly regularly over the country; very few are more than 30 kilometres apart. They vary greatly in size, as do the areas which they serve, and the pig herds.

The chief product of the pig slaughter-houses

is bacon, most of which is exported, principally to Britain; the main ports of shipment are Ålborg, Århus, Esbjerg and København. In addition they supply fresh pork, most of which is sold on the home market. The production of cooked meats and canned meats is carried on partly at the pig slaughter-houses and partly at factories not directly connected with them financially. As some of the meat products are perishable, the hinterland supplied by each factory is restricted to a rather small area. This industrial branch is best developed in København, followed by Odense, Kolding, Randers and Ringsted (central Sjælland).

Fruit, vegetables and fish are also canned. These plants are usually situated near their raw materials, the fruit- and vegetable-canning industry being in København, Fyn and south Sjælland, whereas the fish-canning industry is important at the fishing ports, especially at Skagen and Esbjerg, but also in København.

Milling, one of the country's earliest industries, completely changed its character in the past hundred years. There was formerly a very large number of mills, each supplying a rather small local area, but now their total is much smaller, and the old-fashioned water-mills as well as the majority of the windmills have disappeared, as a consequence of the introduction of the steam-engine and later of electricity.

The old-established Danish sugar industry was first based upon imported raw sugar, chiefly from the Danish tropical colonies of those days. From about 1800 the sugar refineries decreased rapidly and after the mid-19th century they were insignificant. Nowadays the sugar industry is based solely upon home-grown sugar beet. At the present time there are nine sugar factories and two refineries. All the factories are situated in those areas where sugar beet growing was originally considered to be most favoured by soil conditions. In Lolland and Falster there are five, and four are in the southern part of the other islands.

The sugar factories are rather large establishments; in order to transport the very considerable quantities of beet from the growers to the factories special rail tracks were laid at many places, but they are falling into disuse because of competition by motor-lorries. As the sugar factories also need very large quantities of fuel, their total transport requirements are heavy,

and therefore proximity to the beet-growing areas and easy access to sea transport have been essential factors in their location.

The manufacture of margarine began in the 1880's and the number of factories rose quickly until the 1920's. Since then there has been a reduction, partly by closing small plants and partly by mergers. Some of the large firms also co-operate closely, making it possible to have joint production and distribution.

From the employment angle the breweries are the second largest branch in the foodstuffs and beverage industry. After a period with a very large number of breweries the highly developed technique and highly standardized products of the large breweries have brought about a heavy reduction in number. The two largest breweries are situated in København, and supply almost 90 per cent of the total output; those next in order of size are at Odense, Århus and Randers. Exports of beer are quite important and at present represent about 10 per cent of the output.

The manufacture of spirit, *akvavit,* and yeast is carried on at five factories, all owned by a single concessionary company. A process of concentration began 150 years ago and was completed by the State concession of 1923. In that period the number of distilleries fell from about 2 500 in the year 1800 to the present two. The preconditions of this development were partly that the improved technique required larger units, and partly the declining consumption of akvavit and the rapidly rising use of alcohol in industries. Spirit and akvavit are now made at Ålborg, Hobro (north of Randers) and København, and yeast at Randers and Slagelse (Sjælland). The raw materials of the distilleries are molasses, potatoes, grain and sugar beet.

The largest branch within the foodstuffs and beverages group is the tobacco industry. Cigarette manufacture is mainly by large firms, which are mostly in København. Cigars are still partly made by hand in both large and small establishments. The manufacture of cigarillos and pipe tobacco is mainly mechanical, the small factories provide only a minor part of the output. Distributed according to hands employed and turnover, the largest factories are situated in København, Ålborg and Horsens.

135

Textiles and clothing

It is characteristic of the Danish textile industry that the average size of mill is rather small compared with that found in other West-European countries. The domestic market is small and therefore provides no chance for special establishments to expand greatly.

The cotton spinning mills mostly produce loom and hosiery yarns for the home textile factories; there is very little production of other yarns. The mills are at Vejle. After many vain attempts to establish cotton mills, dating back to before 1800, the oldest of the present mills was started at Vejle in 1892.

There is a fair number of cotton and silk weaving mills. The largest are in København, Grenå, Ålborg, Fredericia, Vejle, Herning and Helsingør, these towns having more than 75 per cent of the total number of workers in this branch. Their production comprises all usual cotton and silk piece-goods for clothing, furnishing and technical purposes, whereas their production of specialities is smaller; this applies to fashion goods, for which the small size of the market limits the selling possibilities.

The wool industry originated in a generally widespread domestic craft; it did not develop definitely into an industry until the 19th century. At first, water-power was widely used for processing the wool, and it is for that reason that many of the present cloth mills are situated near watercourses.

In its present form the hosiery industry is much later than the other branches of textile manufacturing. In former times the making of hosiery everywhere formed part of the work of the home, supplies being supplemented by purchase on only a small scale. Many of these purchases were made from the Hammerum district, i.e. the area around Herning in Central Jylland, where the small returns from farming together with an ancient royal privilege, granting free trade throughout the country, provided an especially good foundation for domestic industry. It was that industry which developed into what today is the hosiery district around Herning; the area houses more than a third of the country's hosiery workers, and very nearly half of the production value of the hosiery industry comes from it. Moreover, a fair number of the establishments outside the area are direct offshoots of Hammerum's industry or were founded by people who migrated from there. The hosiery industry is the branch of the textile industry that has flourished best in the post-war years; it is almost supreme in the home market, but has also been able to work up quite a considerable export trade.

The first clothing factories began in København, presumably as a result of narrow market considerations, and most of the establishments today are still in København and the largest towns. The industry is characterized by the use of many special machines and by carefully planned production. As a consequence the employment of workers at home, which was a widespread custom right up to the outbreak of the last war, has been largely discontinued. As the industry employs much female labour it competes with the textile industry in that respect, so that the one often excludes the other as at Ålborg and Vejle, where textile manufacture is alone in the field.

It is usual to find the clothing industry in the more central parts of the towns; until quite recently this applied to København and it can also be seen in the larger provincial towns such as Odense and Århus. The association of this industry with the populous parts of the towns is presumably connected with the former employment of home workers. In recent times there has been a movement away from the town centres, because more space is required for the new methods of factory production. One result is to be seen at København, where one area has been set aside as a 'ready-made town' at quite a distance from the town-centre.

Chemical industries

The chemical industry developed partly to meet the needs of agriculture and partly for the supply of the Danish market with consumer goods. Very few establishments in the Danish chemical industry can be described as really large.

Fertilizer production is concentrated on three superphosphate factories, two in Jylland (Fredericia and Nørresundby) and one in Sjælland (Kalundborg). Nitrogenous fertilizers are produced in Grenå. The oil mills (Århus and København) also operate in close association with agriculture. It is true that the oilseed crop in Denmark is very small, but the oil mills also supply cattle-cake made from the extraction residues of imported oilseeds and thus make an important contribution to the farmers' supplies of concentrates. Oil seed is sold to the margarine, soap and paint industries. The large mills are partially designed with an eye to export, a diminishing part of their business.

Soap and paint factories use chiefly home-produced fats for their bases, together with imported essences, essential oils, colours and the like. Both branches had formerly a large number of small plants which are now concentrated in few and large ones. The soap industry works solely for the home market, whereas much of the paint produced is exported. Most of the plants are located within the metropolitan area, but there are important factories at Århus, Odense, Køge (south of København) and Esbjerg.

The rubber industry comprises only a few establishments, of which the largest are at Køge, Helsingør and København. Their production comprises practically everything normally made of rubber except motor-car tyres and inner tubes. The industry is now large enough to supply the home market with consumer goods and most technical products.

One section of the chemical industry has branched out separately, namely pharmaceutical products. These include insulin, penicillin, sulphanamides and other synthetically manufactured substances. Insulin production is based on the use of pig pancreas, supplied by the bacon factories which refrigerate them and forward them to the insulin manufacturers. Other establishments make subsidiary materials for agriculture such as protective chemicals for plants.

Brick, cement and glass

The Danish rocks and superficial deposits are rich in materials needed by the building industry. The principal section of this industry is brick-making, whose labour force represents a third of the total mineral-processing industry. The largest brickworks are in northeastern Sjælland, in Fyn and on Flensborg Fjord. With few exceptions the brickworks are situated outside the towns; for example, of those supplying the metropolis the nearest is 20 km away from the city centre, and the location is similar for many other towns. In the course of time every form of clay has been utilized, but stoneless varieties are preferred. Those mostly employed nowadays are types of morainic clay and ice-lake clay, though marine clay is also used at some places. Ice-lake clay deposits are responsibe for the large brick output at Stenstrup in the south of Fyn and at Egernsund on Flensborg Fjord. Marketing considerations are most obvious in northeastern Sjælland, where the many brickworks supply København and its environs.

There are five cement works, three of them being at Ålborg, the fourth on Mariager Fjord south of Ålborg, and the fifth southwest of København. The raw materials, clay and chalk, are present in large quantities and easily accessible; and the five works all have coastal location and easy supply of fuel. By virtue of its location and good supplies of raw materials the cement industry has been able to develop rapidly, it supplies the entire home market and also has large exports.

The glassworks as well as the porcelain and earthenware factories were originally based partly on raw materials of domestic origin. These are not of such great importance today but determined the location of the establishments. The glass goods include bottles and household articles, while the greater part of the production at the porcelain works consists of household utensils and certain forms of technical porcelain. Both industries manufacture art products.

Foundries and engineering works

The iron and metal industry includes a number of different branches of production which together form the principal industrial group in the country and employ about a third of the total industrial labour force. Throughout the past century the most important branch of this foundry has been the combination of iron foundries and engineering works.

The number of iron and steel works proper is limited. The five existing plants employ about 1 700 hands, the greater part at the steel rolling-mills at Frederiksværk (northeast Sjælland); from scrap and some pig-iron the latter produce steel and rolled articles in the form of sections, bar iron and plates.

Foundries and engineering works are so intermingled that it is hard to distinguish them. The beginning of the engineering industry resulted from the more general adoption of the steam-engine from about the middle of the 19th century. The subsequent mechanization of existing industries and the growth of new industries, which took place towards the close of that century, all caused a rapid growth in engineering. The range of customers was extended by the agricultural demand for machines for cultivating and reaping as well as for dairies and slaughter-houses. Later came other new products such as cement machinery, machine-tools, cranes and lifts. And as at the same time electricity really became widespread, a great need for electrical machinery arose together with an increased use of machines in general.

These changes in demand and consequently in production caused a heterogeneous development of the different sectors of the engineering industry. After the Second World War specialization has continued and most of the engineering industry is supplying both the home market and a growing demand from foreign countries. The Danish engineering industry has not been able to compete in the international market in articles based on mass production. With no possibilities of a low-priced production the greatest importance has been attached to goods of high quality. In contrast to big industrial countries Danish machinery exports comprise many mechanical units of individual character.

Most of the foundries and engineering works are located in København, Odense and Århus, but practically every town in the country has one or more representatives of these branches. On the other hand there are hardly any foundries in the station towns, where a number of the smaller engineering works are located. Presumably this difference of distribution is connected with the time when the branches originated, and should be seen in relation to the genesis of the towns concerned. As some of the smaller establishments are engaged in a combination of production and service in the form of repairs, it is natural for their market area to be purely local. In contrast, the large plants in København and the bigger towns have a nation-wide, and some even a world-wide, market.

Being directly contributory to the electrification of trade and industry, and indeed of life in general, the cable works, electro-mechanical factories and radio factories have had a rapid development. Denmark is not so thoroughly electrified as Norway and Sweden, or quite on a level with the industrial countries of Western Europe; but electrification has such great economic advantages that it is still rapidly proceeding. The electrical industry developed late, and accordingly is not so widely dispersed as several other branches; today it is found mainly in København, Århus and Odense.

Shipbuilding

Denmark's situation and the consequent importance of maritime transport, as well as the activities of Danish shipowners in the international carrying trade, have fostered the shipbuilding industry. The shipyards sell their ships at home or abroad, and for several years ships have been the biggest single item among the industrial exports. Most of the new ships come from seven yards, which are situated in København, Helsingør, Nakskov, Odense, Ålborg and Frederikshavn, whereas the other yards are chiefly occupied with repairs. The growth of the shipbuilding industry in the present century has been greatly influenced by two factors. One is the vigorous expansion of Danish shipowning, and the other is the increasing use of diesel motors in ocean-going vessels. (The majority of the yards are owned or controlled by shipowners.) The first ocean-going diesel-propelled ship, the Selandia, was designed and launched from a København yard in 1912. The advantage obtained from this early start has been maintained by the frequent introduction of new designs. The shipyards are large customers of many branches of Danish industry, for instance for ships' equipment with auxiliary motors, refrigerating machinery, heating plant, ventilating and electricity installations, all of which are mostly supplied by Danish concerns.

Other industries

Automobiles are imported either complete or in parts for assembly in København. The body-makers operate largely with imported semi-manufactures such as motors and chassis, from which they build up lorries, buses and special vehicles. Bicycles are made chiefly of imported parts, though a few factories, for instance in København and Horsens, make their own frames.

Native wood accounts for half the output of the wood-working industry, the plants employ-

138

ing imported woods are in København and a few seaports. The furniture factories are spread fairly even over the entire country, though the largest is in København; dispersal was caused by the cost of carriage of such bulky goods.

As a consequence of Denmark's small forested area, paper manufacturing is based on pulp imported from Sweden and Finland, though extensive use is made of waste cardboard and paper, a process which has gradually attained such dimensions that a new paper mill in the metropolitan area employs this material almost exclusively. Production mostly comprises printing and writing paper as well as wrapping paper and cardboard. The paper-making industry is one of the oldest in Denmark: the oldest mill started in the 16th century.

The printing industry has branches in every town, but it is mostly concentrated in København which has the big daily newspapers, most of the weekly press and the largest publishers' printing works.

REGIONAL DIVERSITY

Some evaluation of the extent of industrialization in various towns can be made by using a location index, as seen from Fig. 8.29, which shows the numbers employed in industry as a proportion of the local population. The resulting percentage is converted into an index with the average percentage of all localities put at 1. Accordingly, localities with a location index of over 1 will be more industrialized than the average.

Only eight towns, including Odense, Vejle, Helsingør, Nakskov, Herning and Frederiksværk, stand out by reason of very intensive industrialization. These towns are dominated by a single industry, four by large plants involved in the iron and steel industry. Because the country's present occupational structure shows an industrialization that is not yet particularly intense, these towns are exceptions to the normal type of Danish industrial towns.

The second type of industrialized town, i.e. that with well diversified industry, is represented first and foremost by København. Other towns of the same kind are Næstved, Fredericia, Horsens and Grenå.

Consequently it is within these two groups of towns, which have a location index of over 1,

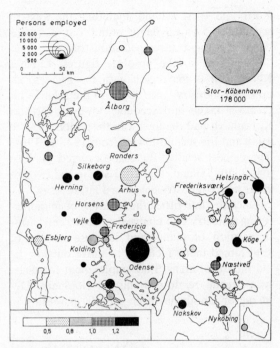

Fig. 8.29. *Location-index of manufacturing industry*, 1960. Calculations based on percentages of inhabitants occupied in industry. Average of all localities shown equals 1. Scale (lower inset left) shows the location-index. The circles are proportionate in area to the number of persons occupied in industry. Upper right inset represents Stor-København (Greater Copenhagen). — After Antonsen 1964.

that we find much the greater part of Danish industry; in 1960 they had about 75 per cent of the total number of workers. In the post-war period these towns on an average have had a greater relative growth in numbers of industrial workers than all the towns as a whole.

One group of towns on the edge of the industrial areas comes rather close to them in degree of industrialization and in fact, in structure, is rather similar. Towns of this kind are e.g. Århus, Ålborg, Randers and Nykøbing (Falster).

In the fourth group are many of Denmark's trading towns, including Esbjerg and most of the Sjælland towns.

The group of towns with a very low degree of industrialization is mainly found in the northern and western parts of Jylland, i.e. Thisted, Skive, Lemvig, Ringkøbing and Tønder. In the rest of the country there are only two towns of this type, i.e. Skanderborg and Nyborg.

It is evident that the east coast of Jylland, Fyn and northeastern Sjælland have much more industry than the rest of the country. Parts of

139

North and West Jylland, including the western section of Sønderjylland, stand out as areas which are under-developed industrially.

According to the absolute figures, Greater København is the region with the greatest increase in industry since 1938. If the relative increase is taken into account, however, Greater København had the lowest in the period 1938 to 1948 and the second-lowest from 1948 to 1960. The highest relative increase occurred in West and South Jylland, that is to say in the two regions where industry developed latest.

Since the late fifties the location of manufacturing industry has changed considerably. Modernization of plants and increase in size of firm forced many factories to move outside the old industrial areas. Full employment for nearly a decade reinforced this development. Demand for labour has been rapidly increasing in the towns—especially in København, while a certain reserve of manpower existed in rural areas.

Labour-intensive industries, including some which are low-wage industries, moved to smaller towns and to rural districts. Here they successfully competed with agriculture in the demand for labour. Most textiles and ready-made garments, trades formerly dominated by København, are now produced in Jylland.

Recently the rapid increase in the service industries has added to the already existing shortage of labour. Manufacturing industry in København and the bigger towns has consequently lost ground. In spite of a national increase in manufacturing these changes resulted in a relative decline, later followed by a fall in the absolute size of manufacturing in the København area.

COMMUNICATIONS AND TRADE

Because of its lay-out, Denmark relies on many forms of transport. Shipping has been favoured as the settlement pattern is dominated by coastal towns near or on readily navigable waters. The deeply indented coastlines lessen the distance between the interior and navigable water. As a rule, however, overland routes are quicker than those by sea, connections are more frequent, and they therefore carry the greater share of the passenger traffic. Modern developments in motorization, highways and bridge-building have also added to the importance of the overland routes.

Roads and railways

Several of Denmark's main roads date back to antiquity; among them is the *Hærvej* which runs southwards from Viborg towards Slesvig; parts of it are still included in the main north-south road in eastern Jylland. There are now about 2 300 kilometres of main roads connecting the largest towns and running to frontier crossings and frontier ports; secondary roads, totalling about 6 200 km, run between the towns and the most densely populated parts of their hinterland. Local traffic in rural areas proceeds along 47 600 km of by-roads, in addition to which there are the street networks of the towns, amounting to about 4 400 km.

The main purpose of the Danish highway system has not changed much during the last two hundred years. The network of course has been extended in keeping with the increase of population and dispersal of settlement, but it still serves towns and villages whose mutual relations have changed little since the network was established. The East Jylland highway linked the towns and was carried across fords, it kept to the least hilly parts of the terrain and had many twists and turns. In spite of improvements and minor changes the basic pattern is unchanged and will remain so until connections are made with the new European main road system.

The good quality of Danish roads and the people's high standard of living meant that motorization began early; in the 1920's Denmark was one of the three most highly motorized European countries. The crisis of the 1930's, and above all the Second World War, caused a serious interruption; the number of motor vehicles has begun to increase again only in the past few years. In 1966 there were 1 060 000 motor vehicles in the country, of which 243 000 were lorries and delivery vans.

Denmark has about 3 900 kilometres of railways, of which 2 450 are run by the State, the remainder being the property of private com-

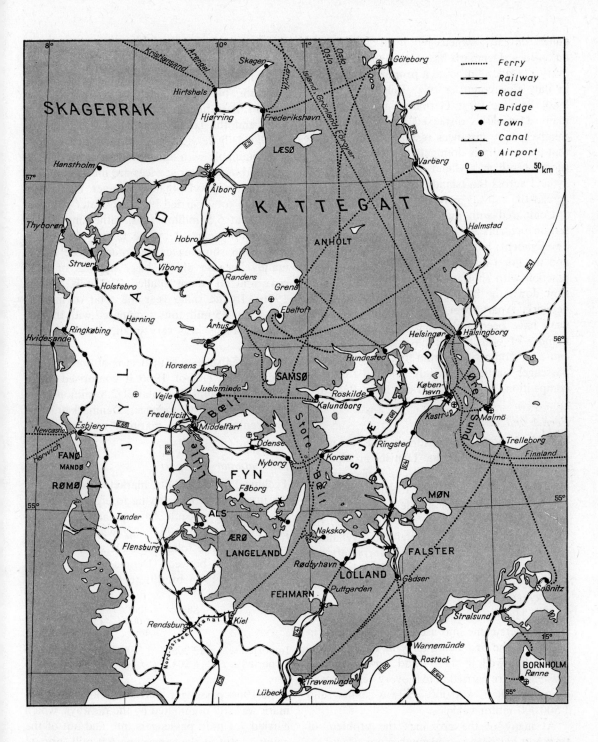

Fig. 8.30. Communications in Denmark and Danish waters, 1967. The crossing by the new ferry, opened in 1963, between Rødbyhavn on Lolland and Puttgarden on Fehmarn in West Germany takes only about 45 minutes. This connection is now by far the most important route between the continent and Norway, Sweden and Sjælland, used by nearly all international trains and many motor vehicles. The old bridge crossing Lille Bælt, linking Fyn and Jylland, has become too narrow for the increasing traffic. A new bridge close to the old one is under construction and will be finished in a few years. — The possibility of building bridges and/or tunnels crossing Store Bælt and Øresund has been discussed for many years, but decisions have not yet been taken.

panies largely owned by local government authorities. Denmark has 93 km of railways to every 1 000 km² of area, a proportion exceeded in only five countries, viz. Belgium, Switzerland, Britain, West Germany and East Germany. Denmark's dispersed land area and the relatively long distances resulting from the fact that the country is dominated by two main axes (north–south in Jylland and east–west from Jylland across the Islands to København), have spread the railway network widely.

Compared with many countries the Danish terrain presents no great difficulties to railway development; but the low cost of sea transport and the good quality of the highways, in conjunction with shortage of capital, combined to slow down the laying out of a denser railway network. Apart from local lines no new railways have been built since 1928, and a large number of branch lines have been closed because of competition from road traffic. Rail passenger traffic has mainly suffered from this competition, but goods traffic is also affected.

Ferries and bridges

The highly indented coastlines and the many inhabited islands in the Danish archipelago made widespread ferry services a necessity at an early date. The growing intensity of traffic and technical progress has led of late to the building of bridges to replace the ferries, but the main traffic between Sjælland and Jylland is still completely dependent on the ferry services. The principal ferry crossings in the inland network are the two routes across the Great Belt, viz. Korsør–Nyborg for railway traffic, and, nearby, Halskov–Knudshoved for highway traffic. Steamers came into use in the Great Belt in 1828, and the first steam-ferry in 1883; motor-ferries followed in 1927, and now 7 million passengers are carried across every year, as well as more than 400 000 railway units and 1 500 000 motor vehicles.

At many of the crossings the problem of transport has been solved much more effectively by the construction of big bridges. The Little Belt Bridge (1 178 m) has spanned the gap between Fyn and East Jylland. The Storstrøm Bridge (3 200 m), linking Falster and Sjælland, and the bridges across Limfjord in northern Jylland have brought the peripheral areas closer to the centre of the country. Cf. Fig. 8.30.

Sea transport

Denmark's land transport system is well developed in relation to its size and dismembered structure, but home-water routes are still important. Passengers are carried between København and the large towns of East Jylland by regular daily services; less frequent connections are obtainable with almost all the seaports. But regular home-water services are much more important for goods than passenger traffic. In 1966 the total carried by home-water shipping was about 5.5 million tons, rather more than the quantity carried by the railways.

Foreign shipping carries much more cargo, mainly because of the large imports of coal, coke and oil (these totalled 17.3 mill. tons in 1966). In the same year the total of imports was about 25 mill. tons. Compared with this the export tonnage was very small, about 5.2 mill. tons.

The Danish merchant fleet is of considerable size. At the end of 1966 it comprised 1 226 vessels representing a total of 2.8 million gross tons. As regards tonnage, Denmark ranked fourteenth among the maritime nations.

International transport

Technical developments, market conditions and the interest taken in serving foreign markets as efficiently as possible have meant that transport by land, especially by highways, is of rising importance. The following table shows the tonnage carried between Denmark and foreign countries in 1966 by different means of transport:

	Ship 1 000 tons	Rail 1 000 tons	Road 1 000 tons	Total 1 000 tons
Imported ..	22 909	1 538	1 229	25 676
Exported ..	5 205	680	2 648	8 533

In 1966 passenger traffic to and from Denmark was still dominated by the railways, which carried 7.4 mill. passengers into and out of the country. But at the same time 6.9 mill. private cars passed the frontier, of which only 1.5 mill. were registered in Denmark. In addition 0.7 mill. persons travelled by bus and 3.1 mill. by air (both including transit).

Finally, mention should be made of the air traffic. Kastrup Airport near København is an important transit station for inter-European and inter-continental flights. Interior airlines are few owing to the effective competition of shipping and railways.

The transport business is an important section of the country's economic life; in 1960 it employed 7.5 per cent of the economically active population, or about half the total agricultural labour. Because of the very considerable earnings in foreign exchange, especially by Danish ships in foreign trade, the transport business is also very important in Denmark's balance of payments. Earnings of shipping cover the greater part of the deficit on the balance of trade.

FOREIGN TRADE

Denmark has a large foreign trade in relation to her total population; this indeed is a necessity for a small country with few natural resources if she is to prosper and maintain a high standard of living. For both imports and exports the turnover per capita is much higher than it was before the war, even at constant prices. This growth is a logical consequence of continued industrialization, which presupposes increased imports of raw materials and fuel and higher exports of finished industrial goods. The composition of Denmark's foreign trade has changed considerably during the past thirty years. In the 1920's manufactured goods predominated on the import side and exports comprised agricultural produce almost exclusively. In the 1930's the imports of raw materials increased while those of finished goods were reduced; but in this period agricultural produce still dominated the exports. During the first post-war years, when there was a world scarcity of raw materials, farm products maintained their share of the exports, but in the early 1950's and particularly after 1955, industrial products gained ground at the expense of farm produce. During the past few years agricultural produce represents about a third of the total export value, whereas industrial goods are responsible for about 55 per cent, the remainder being such things as fresh fish and ships which are changing hands.

The composition of imports has also changed. Raw materials for agriculture have decreased, the use of foreign feeds having fallen off considerably, whereas the application of imported fertilizers has increased somewhat. Measured

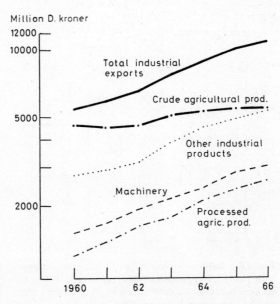

Fig. 8.31. *Distribution of exports according to commodity groups, 1960–66* (semi-logarithmic scale). The export value in current prices.

in absolute quantities imports of finished consumer goods and raw materials for industrial processing, and especially energy raw materials (coal, coke, petrol and oil) have increased in the years since the war. This development is explained by the rising standard of living and the consequent increased consumption, and also industry's growing use of raw materials for both the home market and for export.

Among Denmark's trading partners Britain is still the principal buyer of Danish export commodities and supplier of her imports. But Britain's role is no longer so dominating as it was before the war; in particular her importance as a buyer country has diminished considerably, because British imports of Danish agricultural produce have dropped in consequence of increasing production in Britain. Trade with West Germany has greatly increased and this country is now Denmark's second largest trading partner. Trade with the other Scandinavian countries is very important, especially with Sweden. Other European countries which supply Denmark's imports are the Netherlands, Belgium and France, but exports to these countries are only small. In recent years it has been possible to build up a considerable trade with U.S.A. Besides these main trading partners Denmark has commercial relations with a large number

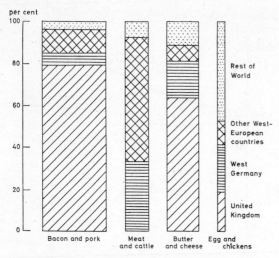

Fig. 8.32. Composition of agricultural exports and their geographical distribution, 1966. The column breadths are determined by each group's share of the agricultural exports, totalling 4 555 million Danish kroner, of which 57% went to Britain and 15% to West Germany.

of countries all over the world, a trade that is based upon constantly increasing industrial exports and the sales abroad of fully processed agricultural produce in the form of canned foods. Figs. 8.32 and 8.33 show the present distribution of exports.

In the past decade agricultural exports have stagnated, and indeed have slightly fallen at times, whereas industrial exports have grown. Agricultural exports are very sensitive to competition with the output of state-subsidized farmers in the most important buyer countries, and consumption of foodstuffs in Western Europe has not increased at the same rate as the increase in incomes. As state support for farmers in other countries can scarcely be expected to decrease much in the future, it is not likely that Denmark's agricultural exports can be expanded to any great degree. Consequently the expansive sector of her foreign trade will be the industrial exports.

Agriculture's share in the total income has fallen off in relation to the pre-war years and has continued to fall throughout the post-war period; farming, forestry, market garden-

ing and fishery now correspond to less than 11 per cent of the gross domestic product. Industry, handicrafts, building and construction activities and public works cover at present about 40 per cent of the gross domestic product, a share that is slightly higher than before the war. Shipping, other forms of transport, commerce, banking, insurance, etc. amount to about 27 per cent altogether of the total income, and the last 22 per cent represents personal services, house rents and public services. Cf. Table 7.2, p. 83.

The development which has occurred during the post-war years is an expression of the change in the structure of the Danish economy. The result is that not only has agriculture's share of the national income diminished, but the service industries have become increasingly important. Internationally, such a development is typical of nations which have reached a similar stage of development.

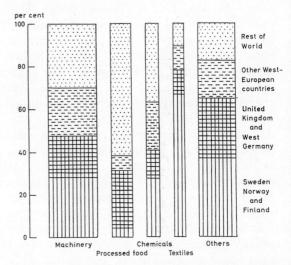

Fig. 8.33. Composition of industrial exports and their geographical distribution, 1966. The exports, excl. ships, are subdivided into 5 groups. The column breadths are determined by each group's share of the industrial exports, which go to many more countries than the agricultural products. Sweden, Norway and Finland buy 30%, Britain and West Germany 22%, other West-European countries 18%; and other countries 30% of Denmark's industrial exports, totalling 8 148 million Danish kroner.

The largest of the islands are Streymoy (373 km²) and Eysturoy (286 km²); and, like most of the Faeroes, they are elongated in shape with a distinctly NW–SE longitudinal axis. The same direction is repeated, not only in the narrow straits which divide them, but also in the shore-lines of many fjords and coves. It is also charac-teristic of many of the concavities of the land surface: main valleys, lakes and lake-chains. In the variation of the heights, too, this direc-tion holds good, for as a whole the highest land is in the northwestern parts of the islands. The group is a vestige of a once large continuous land area split up along fissures which lie north-west–southeast.

Geological structure

The principal element is the basaltic strata, lying almost horizontally, varying in thickness from 10 to 30 m (max. 70 m) and having a total thickness of about 3 000 m. The strata ex-tend for many kilometres, and can often be correlated from island to island. Every basaltic stratum was formed by a volcanic eruption and thus corresponds to a sheet of lava. The erup-tions seem to have taken place over a long period in the last Cretaceous and the early Ter-tiary.

The black or grey basalts are intercalated with beds of tuff having an average thickness of under one metre. These tuffs are of brick-like consistency and colour and are formed of hard-ened volcanic ash, compressed and burnt by the overlying lava.

In certain localities, on Suðuroy for instance, there are coal seams between shale and clay ironstone. The coal is lignite and the seams are under a metre in thickness. The Tertiary fossils place the eruption periods chronologically, and the very occurrence of such organic sediments —like the finds of plant remains in the tuff strata—is evidence of periods with a possibility of organic life between the eruptions.

After the basalt sheets were laid down the whole mass became fissured even in Tertiary times; subsequent pressure equalizations were localized to these fissures, with the result that simple fissures developed into fissure zones in

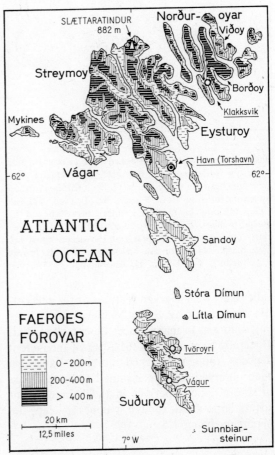

Fig. 8.34. *Hypsometric map of the Faeroes.* The Faeroes are a part of the North-Atlantic basalt region. Originally the islands were one whole mass, but are now converted into an archipelago by the action of erosive forces. In contrast with the rest of Denmark, where the surface forms are characterized by glacial deposits, the Faeroes are a typical glacial erosion region.

which the rock was split into thin lamellae. Masses of molten matter from the magma after-wards passed into these fissure zones and soli-dified as dykes, whilst other masses intruded and solidified as sills between the basalt strata. In both cases contraction after cooling caused the regular jointing that is so characteristic of basalt, resulting in columnar structures. The dykes are sometimes up to 10 m thick, while the intrusive rocks may be up to 50 m thick.

In the Glacial Age the Faeroes were a sepa-rate glaciated area and the elements of glacial erosion, cirques, roches moutonnées and glacier

145

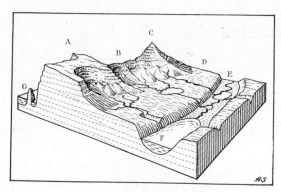

Fig. 8.35. Landscape types of the Faeroes. A. Basalt plateau with biscuit-board topography formed by cirque valley erosion. B. Arête, sharp-ridged crest *(kambur)* between two cirques. C. Peak *(tindur)* formed by cirque erosion from 3 sides. D. Terrace, old flat valley bottom. E. U-shaped valley overdeepened by glacial erosion. F. Fjord, transgressed part of the glecially eroded valley. G. Stack at the ocean coast (cf. Fig. 8.36). — After Axel Schou in K. M. Jensen (edit.), Vor Klode, II. København 1955.

valleys, are very marked features of the present-day landscape (Fig. 8.35). Moraines are usually only thin and in many places absent altogether. Generally they occur in the form of incoherent deposits, though hardened moraines have also been observed and are assumed to be evidence of several glacial periods in the Faeroes. Peat covers large areas, though it is never deep, the maximum being 1.5 m.

Coast types

Almost everywhere the ocean coasts of the Faeroes are of steep rock (Fig. 8.36). Vertical cliffs often rise to dizzy heights. The rock wall off Enniberg, on northern Vidoy, rises straight up 725 m above the sea—undoubtedly one of the highest cliffs in the world, if not the highest. The energy of the ocean waves comes unabated in to the coasts in most places; and, because the depth of water is sufficiently great close in, the breaker effect is extremely violent. Beach ridges thrown up to a height of 32 m and the removal of blocks of 15 tons at that height during an onshore gale bear witness to the extraordinary force of the breakers.

In joint zones disintegration proceeds more rapidly and caves are formed. Waves pressed into the caves during storms also erode the roofs and extend them upwards to considerable heights; the roofs may sometimes be brought

down by this means. On the other hand, solid resistant areas jut out and form more or less prominent features. Where joint fissures cut into the coast, marine erosion at their base, and fluvial erosion above, often combine to form narrow ravines of a type which in the Faeroes is called *gjógv*. The same type may also be formed by erosion in basalt dykes if the intrusive basalt is less resistant than the surrounding rocks. There are also examples of the reverse, the intrusive basalt being more resistant and projecting as a ridge. These processes mould the characteristically irregular, much indented coast line with its skerries, i.e. land remnants in all stages of disintegration.

The basalt strata, which, as a result of undermining, break off in large fragments along almost vertical cleavage planes, stand out on the cliff face like steep walls. The tuff beds, which crumble more easily, form the talus-covered slopes. Where intrusive rocks appear in the walls the latter often have the characteristic columnar structure.

The fowling cliffs, for which the Faeroes are famous, are conditioned by the stepped structure of some of the mountains, the ledges forming the nesting places of the innumerable fowl breeding on the cliff. It is these steps that make it possible for people to move about on the cliff face (Fig. 8.36).

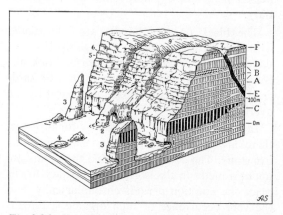

Fig. 8.36. Faeroe ocean coast. 1. Wave-cut cave. 2. Marine arch. 3. Stack. 4. Skerry, residual land. 5. Wall, caused by hard lava beds. 6. Sloping talus, caused by disintegrating tuff beds. 7. Cleft left by disintegration of eruptive dyke. 8. Fissure from joint-zone. 9. Ice-eroded, partly moraine-covered surface. A. Basalt bed. B. Tuff deposits. C. Intrusive mass. D. Coal seam between argillaceous schist. E. Basalt dyke. F. Moraine. — Block edges: 250×450 m. — After Schou 1949 a, p. 23.

The fjord coasts (Fig. 8.35) differ characteristically from the ocean coasts. Inside these deep fjords there is shelter from the ocean waves which, out towards the Atlantic, are so violent in the breaker zone that landing is impossible, often for several months at a time. The shape of the profile is also altered in the fjords where the foot of the mountains is not subjected to constant disintegration by wave attack. Here the shelves may be widened to extensive smoothly inclined slopes where grazing and cultivation are possible, or even building on the flat surfaces. The quiet waters inside the fjords favour landing, and this is where the population has settled.

Mountain landscape

At many places in the valleys erosion by glaciers resulted in the same U-shaped troughs as in other mountainous landscapes once covered by ice, with waterfalls at the transition from plateau flat to glacially deepened valley bottom. Remnants of the old preglacial valley bottom are observable at many places in the form of terrace flats at a height of 200–300 m. Morphologically they correspond to old erosion surfaces in Britain but are usually much flatter.

In shape the mountains are characterized by their stratified composition which is responsible for the stepped structure and flat tops to be seen everywhere, and also by the glacial erosion of the final ice period, visible in the u-shaped valleys and the cirques *(botn)* of the mountain sides. Deep adjoining cirques are often separated by sharp ridges or *kambur* (arêtes). Where the erosion has come from three or more sides there may be peaks of the Matterhorn type, in the Faeroes called *tindur*. The highest point in the Faeroes, Slættaretindur, reaches 882 m above the sea (Fig. 8.34).

Climate and natural vegetation

The climate is typically oceanic with but little difference between the seasons. January has a mean temperature of 3.2°C and July 10.8°C. The air is always very moist, and precipitation is heavy, 159 cm per annum distributed over 280 days. Days with fog are very frequent, storms and high winds common. Table mountains, ridges and peaks are often hidden by fog and wet mist. To a great extent the natural vegetation, shrubs, grassy heaths and bogs, is governed by the natural conditions, but cultural factors are also active. For example, the large flocks of sheep prevent the growth of trees and high bushes so that there is no real woodland— woody plants are represented by low heather and willow bushes. It is a harsh climate making cereal-growing almost impossible, but favourable to grass which in turn is the basis of the sheep-farming. The wretched climatic conditions compel the population to turn to the great fish resources of the sea to compensate for the scanty yield of the land.

POPULATION AND OCCUPATIONS

The Faeroe Islands were colonized about the year 800 by Norwegian Vikings and they were part of Norway until the beginning of the 17th century, when they became connected with Denmark administratively. Under the Peace of 1814, when the union between Norway and Denmark was dissolved, the Faeroes remained as part of Denmark. Simultaneously the last remnants of Faeroese self-government were abolished, not to be revived until 1948. Since then the Islands have been largely autonomous, with self-government in occupational and cultural matters, a revenue authority, local government body and, moreover, the Faeroese flag is recognized and Faeroese is the mother tongue. It is an independent language, occupying a place between Norwegian and Icelandic and, because Danish was the official language, it developed only very little into a written language.

The Faeroese population totalled 37 000 in 1966, giving an average density of 25 per km², twice that of Norway. Towns and villages are separated by large uninhabited areas. The configuration of the land has resulted in settlement wherever it was possible in the fjords simultaneously to cultivate the soil and find landing places. The largest town is Havn (Tórshavn), 9 700 inhabitants, in the southeast of Streymoy.

Originally farming was the principal occupation and it continued to be so well into the 19th century; now slightly more than 5 per cent of the active population are solely employed in agriculture. There is very little arable farming. The land with the best quality and situation, the *indmark* (infield), representing 3 per cent of

147

the total area of the islands, is devoted chiefly to grass (90 per cent), and most of the remainder to potatoes. Very small areas are under 6-rowed barley, turnips and green vegetables. The uncultivated land, the *udmark,* is used for sheep which graze all the year round. Very little wool is produced and it is of poor quality, whereas mutton is an important item of the diet. The total sheep population is about 70 000, of which half are slaughtered each year. There are about 2 500 cattle, and the milk output per cow is low (a third of the Danish average). No pigs are kept, but there is some poultry.

The farms are very small and each holding may be in several dispersed pieces. As a rule the freeholders have the smallest lots, because the copyhold farms have not been subdivided to the same extent.

Fishing is the all-important occupation of the Faeroese. In early days is was confined to open boats fishing in coastal waters, and what was caught was mostly consumed locally fresh or dried. Larger decked boats were not adopted until towards the end of the 19th century, and in the course of time some have had a motor installed. During World War II the Faeroes were occupied by Britain and supplied her with large quantities of fish. The increased incomes were largely spent on modernizing the fishing fleet, which now comprises cutters and an increasing number of trawlers.

Most of the fisheries around the Faeroes are, and have long been, in British hands. Thus Faeroese sea-going craft are usually far away and take their heaviest catches in Greenland and Icelandic waters. Fishing ports have been established in Greenland as bases for Faeroese fishermen, e.g. Færingerhavn, south of Godthåb.

The greater part of the catch consists of cod from West Greenland which is mainly salted. Flounders and other demersal fish are caught near the coast and taken directly to the market. The salted and split cod mostly goes to the Mediterranean countries and to South America. The fresh and frozen fish is sold almost exclusively to Britain.

Whaling is of some significance. Pilot whales *(Globiocephalus melas)* are often encountered in Faeroese waters, especially in late summer, when they are driven by boats to certain localities and killed close to the shore. Every available boat takes part in these exciting hunts, and the catch is divided into carefully apportioned quantities between the hunters and the people onshore. The meat and some of the blubber are used for food, and oil is extracted from the remaining blubber.

GREENLAND

PHYSICAL GEOGRAPHY

The most northerly point of Greenland, Kap Morris Jesup, is in latitude 83°39′ north, the southernmost, Kap Farvel (Cape Farewell), in latitude 59°46′ north. The north-south length is thus about 2 600 km, equal to that from the north coast of Scandinavia to Switzerland. The most easterly point, Nordostrundingen, is in longitude 11°39′ west, and Cape Alexander is in longtitude 73°08′ west. The total area is 2 175 600 km², of which 1 700 000 km² is covered by the ice cap. The ice-free land consists of a coastal strip which is nowhere more than 200 km wide, an archipelago of skerries and a number of mountains, nunataks, which protrude through the thinner margins of the ice cap (Fig. 8.37). The ice-free area is 341 700 km², but of this the north coast and most of the east coast are uninhabitable and almost inaccessible frigid wastes. The inhabited area is about 150 000 km², and lies mainly in the southern two thirds of the west coast (Fig. 8.38).

In physical geography Greenland's place is determined by the island's situation on the continental shelf of North America and by its climatic relationship to the Arctic area. Politically Greenland is an integral part of the Danish realm.

Prior to World War II Greenland was justifiably regarded as a particularly remote region, because there were few means of communications which could cope with the rigorous Arctic conditions. It was further accentuated by the common use of world maps on Mercator's projection which grossly misrepresented the size and situation of Greenland. The Mercator map concealed what modern polar projections reveal, that the Arctic Ocean is an Arctic Mediterranean, in which Greenland occupies a central position between North America and Asia: i.e. between the Western and Eastern Worlds. Great circle routes between the world's two main concentrations of population run through the Arctic region across Greenland, which thus acquires potentialities as a central point in the intercontinental network of airlines. These possibilities were first recognized by the Californian route of SAS (Scandinavian Airlines System) which crosses Greenland and uses Søndre Strømfjord airfield to refuel (Fig. 8.38).

Greenland has great politico-geographical importance as long as the clash of interests continues between the Great Powers. NATO's strategic defence system has the easternmost extension of the DEW (Distant Early Warning) line system in East Greenland.

Currents and ice formation

The Greenland waters are the meeting place of very varying bodies of water, a fact which is important climatically, and consequently affects both fishing and trade. A tremendous current, the East Greenland Current, runs southward between Nordostrundingen and Vestspitsbergen. At the southern tip of Greenland this cold current meets a branch of the warm Gulf Stream, the Irminger Current, which turns west near Iceland. The cold and warm waters blend and, in the form of the West Greenland Drift, move northward along the west coast of Greenland. Off Godthåb the Drift flows westwards on encountering the banks off the coast. This body of water is Atlantic in character, though varying a good deal, and is of great importance to the fisheries of West Greenland.

Access to Greenland by sea is wholly dependent upon the locally and seasonally highly variable ice situation. Two main groups of sea ice occur: 1) fjord and bay ice, and 2) drifting ice (pack ice). Icebergs form in summer when glacier tongues on reaching the sea become waterborne and break off, or when the floating ice barriers of the ice cap calve. Some icebergs may tower up as much as 100 m and all will have 40–70 per cent submerged. As a consequence, all glaciers debouching into the sea have a vertical front, with heights up to about 50 m. Icebergs will often be stranded in shallows near the shore, to float again when re-

duced by melting. About 5 per cent are large enough to resist melting, and ocean currents carry them south to Newfoundland, where they finally melt on encountering the warm water of the Gulf Stream. These drifting icebergs may be a serious danger on the North Atlantic shipping route and efforts are being made to eliminate it by means of an extensive warning system. Icebergs have been encountered as much as 240 nautical miles southeast of Kap Farvel. Most of the bergs come from Greenland's west coast, where many glaciers are highly productive. There are also productive glaciers on the east coast.

The pack ice forms as winter ice on the coasts of Greenland and also on the surface in the Arctic Ocean. The polar pack ice may be four or five years old and three to five metres thick before it breaks up. Currents cause pressure ridges of much greater thickness.

The East Greenland Current carries pack ice southwards and this ice, called *storis* in Greenland, blockades the east coast during the greater part of the year. Off the south coast, where the belt of drift ice in May–June may be 100 nautical miles wide, the storis current turns northwards along the west coast. The pack ice current increases in winter; it reaches its maximum in October at Scoresby Sound on the east coast, in January at Kap Farvel and in February at Julianehåb on the west coast. It may reach Godthåb in May, but not regularly. In July the pack ice along the southwest coast decreases and may have disappeared altogether by August.

If sea routes are difficult, and wholly impossible along certain parts of the coasts for long periods in the year, aviation possibilities over Greenland are definitely favourable. All doubt as to the suitability of the Arctic air regions for traffic has been removed by the air services which SAS has maintained regularly since 1954 over Greenland to California and over the polar basin to Japan. Flights in the Arctic, which before World War II were accomplished only by adventurous explorers in specially equipped planes, are now run daily by five different companies.

Ice landscapes

The Greenland landscape pattern is governed partly by the geological structures, the Green-

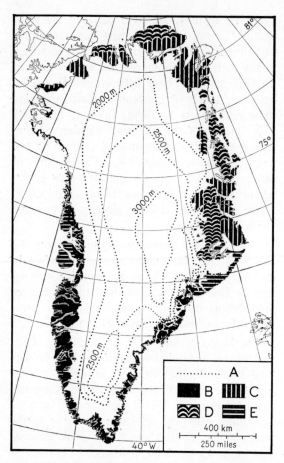

Fig. 8.37. Greenland. Ice-free area and ice cap.
A. Contours of the ice cap surface. B.–E. Ice-free land:
B. Gneiss-granite bedrock, C. Sedimentary bedrock, D.
Folding zone, and E. Tertiary basalt.

land Shield and the accumulated sedimentary rocks overlying it, and partly by the action of Quaternary ice coupled with the late and post-glacial changes of sea level. The recent land-scape-forming agencies, weathering, normal erosion, glacial erosion and marine abrasion, have made no changes in the general configuration.

The Greenland land mass under the ice cap may be described as a basin-shaped mountain massif of glacial-age phase. The bottom of this basin is under the northern part of the ice cap and lies at 250 m below sea level. The low central regions are completely covered by the mile-thick mass of the ice cap which, in the form of valley glaciers, glides out through depressions in the coastal mountains to the low land or into the fjords. At places devoid of coastal mountains, glaciers slide bodily along a broad front into the sea. The 100 km wide Humboldt Gla-

cier is the largest, and in Melville Bay the ice cap forms a tall, vertical wall of ice in the sea for a distance of 300 km. The marginal mountains are highest in East Greenland, where Gunnbjørns Fjeld reaches 3 700 m (Fig. 8.38).

The ice cap covers by far the greater part, more than four fifths, of Greenland's surface and represents an eighth of the world's total ice sheets. The highest point of the ice cap is not at the middle but out towards the east. West of Scoresby Sound the greatest height has been measured at 3 300 metres. The greatest thickness is about 2 000 m, and the average thickness is calculated at 1 515 m by means of a large number of measurements made by seismic soundings. In 1966 a group of American scientists succeeded for the first time in boring through the inland ice, measuring a thickness of 1 500 m in the Thule region, thus verifying the previous seismic soundings there. The ice cap is not a vestigal part of the last Ice Age; it is recent and the result of present-day climatic conditions, which, in turn, it strongly influences because of its size.

The precipitation of the central area is about one metre of snow per annum, which corresponds to an annual growth of 30–40 cm of ice. This increment is offset by loss of material by melting, evaporation and the formation of icebergs. The movement of some of the valley glaciers is very rapid, for example, a rate of 31 m per 24 hours has been found in Upernavik glacier. The height of the snow line is 1 200 m in South Greenland, 700 m on Disko Island and 320 m at Kap York in North Greenland. In the continental parts of North Greenland, e.g. in parts of Peary Land, it is 900 m.

Isolated glaciation occurs here and there in the rim mountains where precipitation is heavy, whereas the most northerly parts, where the low humidity of the cold air causes slight precipitation, for instance in Peary Island, have only small ice sheets and may be characterized as Arctic desert.

The surface of the ice cap is in the form of two domes of ice. The southern one (Fig. 8.37) has a summit level of 2 800 m, and the greater northern one reaches a height of 3 300 m above sea level. As the highest parts are situated east of the centre of the ice cap where the precipitation is small, and as there seems to be no relationship between the ice cap surface and the substratum relief, the explanation of these topographical features must be sought elsewhere. The outflow of the ice is easier to westward where subglacial valleys conduct ice streams to the shore. This fact could provide the key to the problem. Perhaps climatic conditions in the period when the ice cap was formed initially, as individual glaciers of the piedmont type welded together, have to be taken under consideration when working on this problem. The ice surface is flat, but formed in long, low undulations. The powdered snow on the surface is swept together locally into drifts by strong winds, or it is blown along and forms sastrugi patterns with furrow structures.

Since World War II scientific work on the ice cap has made great advances thanks to new glaciological methods and new forms of communication. Caterpillar 'cats' of various types, such as the 'weasel' and 'sno-cat', make it possible to transport large quantities of material and personnel. Radio-technical communication between base and expedition teams, and electronic navigation make for increased safety. 'Jato', jet-assisted take-off, makes it possible for even large types of planes to start from the snow carpet, and supplies can be carried in over the ice cap and delivered, either by parachute or simply by throwing them overboard.

The marginal zone of the ice cap differs considerably from the inner parts by its sharper gradients and by its zone of crevasses and icefalls, which may make penetration extremely difficult. Snow-bridges concealing the crevasses present elements of great danger.

Solid geology and landscapes

The Greenland Shield, like the Canadian Shield on the west and the Fennoscandian Shield on the east, is made up chiefly of gneisses and granites. These rocks are basal in the Precambrian fold-mountain systems. In their higher zones certain sections of less completely metamorphosed rocks such as quartzites and shales remain. All the Precambrian mountain systems have undergone peneplanation, and in places younger Precambrian sedimentary rocks have been deposited on this sub-Cambrian peneplane. Such are the Thule formation's conglomerates, sandstones and dolomite. Formations built of palaeozoic, mesozoic and cainozoic

sedimentary rocks are also important. The Caledonian folding produced simple folding, overthrust folds and metamorphism of the initial sedimentary rocks that were affected by it, *inter alia* in East Greenland. The presence of tillite suggests that there was an ice age 500 million years ago; the Tertiary strata are evidence of a warm temperate climate prior to the Quaternary ice ages. Some igneous rocks form significant landscape features, for example Tertiary plateau-basalt, which occurs in the middle of both west and east coasts (Fig. 8.37).

On all these rocks the landscape-moulding agencies, first and foremost glacial erosion, created the Greenland types of terrain whose heterogenous relief is the result of the varying resistance of the rocks and of the locally varying strength of the eroding forces.

Roches moutonnées relief is largely predominant in the gneiss-granite area. In conjunction with striations, these rounded rocks reveal the direction of the last ice flow. Selective glacial erosion accounts for the wealth of lakes in this terrain. The lower parts of the glacial-eroded land appear in partly submerged forms as skerries. There the form-complex of the surface is increased by the abrasion terraces resulting from wave action. The southern half of the west coast has a distinct strandflat, a low, hummocky border of land contrasting conspicuously with the high mountain landscape behind it and continuing into the skerries. At many places isolated steep-walled high mountains, the so-called *umanaq* mountains, rise above the low coastal landscape. Similar terrace flats have been observed on the continental shelf off the coast, presumably formed under the lower water level in the Ice Age. Judging from the abrasion and accumulation terraces the shoreline has lain at varying levels, with a height variation of about 200 m, the result of Ice Age and postglacial eustatic and isostatic changes.

Alpine forms of mountains with arêtes between the cirques and steep peaks occur in the highest areas, especially in East Greenland. These rugged forms, the result of frost shattering and nevé erosion, contrast strongly with the rounded outlines of the glacier-abraded mountains. These high regions were never covered by ice and are believed to have been possible refuges for a part of the Greenland flora during the ice ages. Within the inner part of the rim mountains there are still nunataks of similar character.

Plateau landscapes are formed where surface layers of basalt or sediments lie horizontally. Such table mountains are present in all erosion stages, gully-scarred at the edges and with scree cones of all dimensions. In places the basalt areas may be so dissected by erosion that cirques, crests and peaks similar to those of the Faeroes result.

The great valley systems were originally shaped by normal erosion and the erosional pattern is often governed by joints. Their present form is due to much deeper cutting by glacial erosion. Their cross-sections are U-shaped and through glacial plucking the longitudinal profile is irregular, depressions alternating with thresholds.

The outer, submerged parts of the valley systems form the enormous fjord complexes that are so characteristic of Greenland. The varying depths and the barrier effect of the thresholds often isolate water masses and produce great variation in fishing possibilities.

Outwash plains like the Icelandic sandur, built up of meltwater deposits, act as fill in the bottoms of the valleys. In a land where aviation is important, and where flat ground is otherwise rare, the outwash plains are valuable for laying out airports, e.g. Søndre Strømfjord.

Moraines of all types, lateral, medial and terminal, occur locally at all glaciers, but large moraine landscapes are rare. Arc-shaped systems of terminal moraines sometimes form local landscapes opposite the glacier snout, a result of the present glacier regression which is due to recent amelioration of climate. Extensive moraine landscapes are uncommon because the great ice-age moraine accumulations occurred at levels now submerged by the sea. These masses of material now form banks on the continental shelf, banks which often strand the icebergs. Along the southwest coast these banks are now important as fishing grounds.

Temperature and precipitation

Greenland has an arctic climate, but as a result of the island's great extent from north to south there are important local differences. In South Greenland the climate is Subarctic. In sheltered localities inside the fjords are birch woods, dwarf birch and willow shrub, evidence of the proximity of the timber line which is generally regarded as the boundary of the Arctic and corresponds to areas with a mean temperature in the warmest month of 10°C. At Ivigtut the July average is 9.9°, and February −7.9°. Otherwise the west coast up to Disko Island has an Arctic climate with mean temperatures for the warmest month between 5° and 10°C, e.g. Godthåb, July 6.5°, February −10.1°C. More to the north there is true Polar climate, e.g. Upernavik July 4.9°, February −23.2°.

The annual precipitation decreases rapidly from south to north, e.g. Ivigtut 113 cm, Upernavik 23 cm. There is a maritime type of climate in the coastlands and a continental one in the inner parts of the fjords, where, notwithstanding the proximity of the ice cap, the summers are much warmer than at the coast. Føhn winds from the ice cap are an integral part of the Greenland weather complex.

The ice cap has its own climate, with mean temperatures for all months below zero, varying with height and mainly determined by the special conditions applicable to the ice: insolation and radiation, changes of heat content during melting and freezing, etc. Formerly it was considered that there was constant high pressure over the ice cap owing to rapid cooling of the air above it. Recent observations show that cyclones pass over Greenland. The Greenland weather conditions are of great importance in forecasting weather over the North Atlantic, and thus over Northwest Europe. Greenland's dimensions, severe winter climate and difficult traffic conditions, combined with the special difficulties for long-wave radio communication in the Polar region, have all required large resources of man-power and capital to establish and maintain this internationally important work.

Flora and fauna

As in other Arctic regions the vegetation is adapted to the extreme conditions: the long dark period and the short bright summer with long days. There is also adaptation to the perma-frost and abnormal soil conditions. Southward facing slopes, the so-called urteli, often have a short but hectic flowering of plants. The many waterlogged flats have cotton-grass and other bog plants, but otherwise the surface is sparsely covered with a carpet of mosses, lichens and dwarf shrubs, and in the more continental inner fjords with Arctic grass-steppe.

The higher fauna is dominated by marine forms. Of the 31 species of mammals 22 (6 species of seal and 16 of whales) live in the sea, and the pack-ice habitat of the polar bear is also marine. Terrestrial mammals such as the musk ox, polar wolf, mountain hare and arctic fox represent very special structural adaptations to their Greenland environment. The caribou is hunted in certain localities. Bird life is rich, with 60 breeding species and still more visiting birds, cliff birds being typical. Fishes are extremely numerous with a hundred species, several of which, including cod, are represented in large numbers and are of great economic importance, as are halibut and salmon. The deep-sea shrimp *Pandalus borealis* is also caught. Lower forms of freshwater life are common, one feature being the enormous swarms of mosquitoes in summer.

HUMAN GEOGRAPHY

Settlement of Greenland probably occurred at a rather late stage in history. European colonization began about 1 000 A.D. with the arrival of Norsemen from Iceland. Eskimo immigration is believed to have started in northern Greenland about 2 000 B.C. The Norsemen settled on the mildest part of Greenland's west coast where they could practise the economy then existing in Iceland, viz. animal husbandry supplemented by cultivation and hunting.

Connections with other parts of Norden diminished when the expansionist pressure from that civilization had spent itself. The Norse colonists succumbed to climatic deterioration and were displaced by Eskimos penetrating southwards. Numerous finds suggest that there was a gradual decline in vital food supplies, which ultimately led to a physical degeneration of the population. Today, ruins of farms, hamlets and churches are the only relics of this medieval outpost of Europe in the northwest. With its loss, Europe also lost the knowledge of the continent west of the Atlantic Ocean. When Europeans returned to Greenland about the year 1600, the remnants of the Norse colonies had succumbed a century ago. Archaeologists have given us an unforgetable impression of this medieval struggle against overwhelming forces

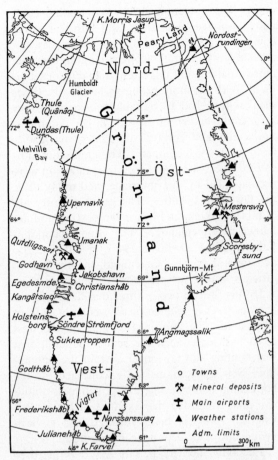

Fig. 8.38. *Greenland, distribution of population, airports, mines/mineral deposits and meteorological stations.*

of nature and unsurmountable distances. Depicted by tools, ruins and graves, it is one of the most pathetic chapters in Scandinavian history.

The Eskimo population, which superseded the Norsemen, had an entirely different economic pattern based on the hunting of marine mammals, notably seals. Meat and blubber were the dominant elements of the diet, blubber was used for heating, and skins were used for clothing, houses and boats. The Eskimos settled along almost the whole coastline of Greenland, but even they could not withstand the rigours of the climate when hunting failed; remains of settlements abandoned several hundred years ago have thus been found in many places. Settlements were gradually concentrated on the west coast with only a few remaining to eastward.

Modern Danish colonization began in 1721. Danish policy tried to preserve the Eskimo economy. The government-operated trading company supplied fire arms and other hunting equipment and received a share of the catches, especially skins and blubber. Hunting became more efficient, and this led to a change in settlement. With the more primitive hunting methods the Eskimos had to be widely dispersed; now they could gather in slightly larger communities, trade and receive supplies more readily from the Danish company. The gradual modifications in economy and social organization were accompanied by intermarriage, and today there are few pure Eskimos. The great majority are of mixed Eskimo and European descent and are known as Greenlanders. The Greenland population totalled 39 600 in 1965, including 3 200 persons not born in Greenland, mainly Danish officials, public servants and technicians.

During the last two or three decades there has been a decisive change in the economic life of Greenland. The improved climate on the west coast has so reduced the seal population that seal hunting can no longer sustain the population. New occupations are encouraged, as the population is increasing, and government initiative aims at raising the standard of living. Private enterprise is being fostered and government control of economic life reduced.

Economic activity in Greenland is in three main categories, the first and most important being the occupations pursued by the Greenlanders themselves without direct public intervention. The second comprises the activities of the government-operated trading company and government-sponsored construction and investment in distributive trades, transport, building and public installations. The third activity, mining, is of very little significance to the Greenland population; most of it is carried out by Danes and the products are exported.

Fishing is by far the most important of the indigenous industries, followed by hunting and farming. The output is almost sufficient to cover the local consumption of meat and fat. In addition to the local consumption of fish and fish products Greenland supplies about 35 000 tons annually for processing and export by the trading company. Fish accounts for about 80 per cent of the Greenlanders' total earnings from commodity sales; the corresponding figure for seal hunting is about 8 per cent (skins and meat), for sheep rearing 5 per cent, while the balance is distributed over many small items, such as skins and feathers.

Most of the fishing by Greenlanders is along the centre of the west coast and mainly in the fjords there. The fishing banks in Davis Strait are too distant for the Greenlanders' small boats, and these waters are fished by vessels from several European countries. Godthåb, Frederikshåb and Sukkertoppen are important fishing centres, but fishing also occurs along the entire coast south of Disko Bay. Most of the seals are caught in the northern districts of Umanak and Upernavik. Sheep rearing is centered around Julianehåb where the Greenlanders use the same pastureland as the medieval Norse settlers.

Valuable minerals are not very common in Greenland. Until synthetic cryolite came into use, Ivigtut mine in south-west Greenland was the main supplier of the world aluminium industry. The mines are now nearing exhaustion. In East Greenland a large lead deposit at Mestersvig was mined for a short period. Cretaceous coal is still mined near Qutdligssat on Disko Island.

The modernization of Greenland's economic life and living conditions has led to radical changes in the pattern of settlement. There is constant migration to the larger communities, notably to the biggest town, Godthåb, with 3 300 inhabitants, which is the administrative centre. Almost two thirds of the population now live in the towns to which they are attracted by production, trade and transport activities, by better housing standards and richer community life. Natural conditions in Greenland and the great distances to be overcome will make it possibe to equip fully only a small number of communities. A further concentration of the population is thus probable.

The language spoken in Greenland is the Eskimo language, but it has absorbed many new words, especially from Danish. The main language in the schools is the Eskimo language; only a small part of the teaching is in Danish. For their advanced education, both in practical and theoretical subjects, many Greenlanders go to Denmark. Books and newspapers are published in the Eskimo language and regular radio broadcasts are made in it. Legally Greenland is a part of Denmark with representation in its parliament and local self-government.

CHAPTER 9

FINLAND

by Helmer Smeds[1]

INTRODUCTION

Finland holds a special position among the Norden countries, lying as it does on both the northern and eastern margins of Norden. It has by far the longest common frontier with an extra-Norden state, and it is also, and this fact cannot be overstressed, the most poleward-situated Norden country: "the Republic Farthest North".

The northern tip of Finland reaches a trifle beyond 70°N. Norway protrudes farther into the Arctic, and Sweden almost as far, but the southern limit of Norway lies at about 58°N and that of Sweden at about 55°N, whereas the Finnish territory reaches southwards only to about 60°N. Hence the bulk of Finland lies much more polewards than that of Norway and Sweden. Broadly a quarter of the area of Finland (and roughly a third of its latitudinal extension) lies north of the Arctic Circle. No other state in the world has such a markedly northern position, and no other region in the world situated so far polewards has been so densely populated and so fully developed by man as Finland. Norway has more inhabitants north of the polar circle, but they depend mainly—in contrast with the inhabitants of northern Finland—directly or indirectly on the resources of the sea.

The average population density of Finland is 14 per km², as against 5.5, 6.4 and 2.5 for the corresponding latitudinal belts of Sweden, Norway and that part of European Russia which lies west of the White Sea. Its arable area is much greater than that of the corres-

ponding parts of neighbouring states: roughly 2.7 million hectares as compared with 730 000 for Sweden, 510 000 for Norway and 920 000 for U.S.S.R. in the latitudinal belt 60°–70°N.

Outside Europe, areas in the same zone are practically devoid of cultivated land, e.g. in Alaska, Greenland and northernmost Siberia. Correspondingly towns which act as local service centres or manufacture local raw materials are much bigger in Finland than those in the same latitudes in Sweden or Norway: Oulu with 81 000, Kemi with 30 000 and Rovaniemi with 27 000 inhabitants in 1967 at respectively 65°, 66° and 67°N have no counterparts in corresponding parts of the neighbouring Norden countries, apart from the recently mushrooming iron-manufacturing Swedish town of Luleå at about 66°N. The Swedish mining city of Kiruna and its Norwegian port Narvik, due south and north of 68°N respectively, are bigger than any urban centre in northernmost Finland, but their role is national rather than regional, and even, in a sense, international.

Pioneering

The principal reason why Finland is more densely settled and extensively cultivated than corresponding parts of Sweden and Norway seems simply to be that the human effort here has been greater and the natural resources have thus been utilized to a higher degree. Finland has been forced to make such an extensive use of these resources because it lies wholly north of 60°N and lacks the climatically and edaphically more favoured regions possessed by Sweden and, to a lesser degree, Norway.

Physical factors explain the relatively dense settlement and extensive arable lands of Fin-

[1] Professor Smeds died in 1967 and Paul Fogelberg, Department of Geography, University of Hensinki, has seen the new version through the press.

155

land (see below), but ultimately one is brought back to purely human factors to explain the phenomenon of this strongly developed country close to and overlapping into the Arctic. The population density of an area, its carrying capacity, depends mainly not on its natural resources, but on the inhabitants' ability to make use of those resources. For example, before the coming of the white man, the North American continent supported about a million nomadic Indians. The area which later became Finland was inhabited before the arrival of our ancestors by a thin, probably very thin, settlement of nomadic hunters, the Lapps, whose number can hardly have been much higher than 10 000. The incoming of the ancestors of the present population was, in a sense, as significant and as dramatic as the coming of the American pioneers though, because it happened more than a thousand years earlier, we do not know its details.

Among the Norden peoples the Finnish one is, and has perhaps always been, foremost in pioneering, a clearer of forests and wrestler with stones and boulders. When the Swedish kings wanted to settle and cultivate the forests of their realm they often sent for Finnish colonists, *kirvesmän* (axemen, i.e. wood cutters) as they are called in the 16th century tax registers. Because of this deliberate colonization, extensive districts of Sweden from below 60°N northwards are known as *Finnskogar* (Finn forests). Finnskogar are also found on the Norwegian side of the frontier. The Finnish settlements in northernmost Sweden and northernmost Norway are signs of another pioneering activity which, continuing until the 19th century, has created a Finnish minority in these regions.

The drive northwards into the forests is as typical a Finnish phenomenon as the challenge of the sea has been typically Norwegian, and pioneering is a major formative feature of the Finnish character. There is a special word in Finnish, *sisu,* denoting a resolute determination to finish a given task however hard it be. Sisu has been fostered by pioneering work continuing for centuries in unusually hard conditions.

Physical features

The physical advantages bestowed on Finland as compared with northern Sweden and north-

ern Norway, are all caused by a single factor, the lowland character of the country. The mean altitude of Finland is, according to two pre-war computations, about 150 m above sea level. About two thirds of the area lie below 200 m, whereas the mean altitudes of the corresponding parts of Sweden and Norway are c. 350 m and c. 700 m. This means that the adiabatic range, averaging about 0.5° per 100 m, gives with similar air masses, an advantage of about 1°C compared with Sweden, and one of about 3°C compared with Norway. In fact, in practically the whole of Finland altitude does not limit cultivation of grain crops, as it does for considerable areas in Norway and Sweden. This advantage is even more noticeable in the wider extension of the forested area.

Up to c. 67°N almost the whole area of Finland with the excepton of the eastern border region and part of the central lake plateau, lies below the upper marine limit, i.e. has been covered by postglacial phases of the Baltic Sea. Below this line, fine-graded sediments well suited to cultivation are to be found. This does not mean that these good agricultural soils are uniformly and amply spread over the whole area formerly covered by postglacial seas (or lakes), as will be shown later, but it does give an advantage over Sweden and Norway. Its level land surface gives Finland an asset which they largely lack (Colour Map 1).

Marchland position

Finland is not only a marchland against the North, it is also an outpost against the eastern world. This does not imply only a history of frequent wars and frontier displacements, but also a marked isolation and retarding of cultural development, since new cultural ideas and new economic trends have usually filtered in slowly from the west. A Finnish scholar has aptly compared Finland with a medieval urban courtyard house whose sole communication with the outer world was through the narrow entrance to the street (i.e. for Finland, the Baltic Sea). Linguistic isolation regarding both west and east probably accentuated this blind-alley position. Ethnic contrasts and differences in degree of evolution explain a certain awe for Finnish witchcraft formerly felt by the other Norden nations. It is comparable to the Finnish pioneer's fear of Lappish sorcerers and witches when the two peoples met in the heart of the territory which is now Finland, and of which numerous traditions survive.

Finland has always tended to lag behind in development. Transocean emigration, industrialization, rural depopulation and other phenomena which have transformed the European landscape, have always entered Finland some decades later than the rest of Norden. This is not entirely a disadvantage, and is temporarily overcome by great leaps forward as has often been the case in Finland. The burden of costly readjustments made necessary by technical progress has therefore not weighed as heavily on Finland's economy as on that of her western neighbours. And a development by leaps and bounds has sometimes brought Finland not only abreast of her Norden contemporaries, but occasionally ahead of them, e.g. in political development (women's voting rights and one-chamber-system as early as 1906) as well as in some cultural and economic features (architecture, co-operative organizations).

The serious political consequences of the marchland position in relation to Russia have to some extent been counterbalanced by the economic advantages of this situation, accentuated by the common rail-gauge of Russia and Finland, and by the proximity of a great consumers' market close to the eastern border (St. Petersburg–Leningrad). To this market considerable quantities of Finnish butter have been exported, as has a large amount of iron and iron products from works in eastern Finland which used bog-iron as raw material in the mid-19th century. It should also be emphasized that the long eastern frontier has not always been a barrier, but at times a line of cultural contact. Finnish words relating to the Christian faith, for example cross, bible and priest, are of Russian origin. The extension of the Orthodox faith, has, however, encompassed only a relatively narrow frontier zone north of Lake Ladoga, of which merely the northernmost tip is now within the borders of Finland. Numerous orthodox churches with their characteristic cupolae in both towns and villages in eastern Finland, many of them erected by post-war refugees from the same area, remind the thoughtful spectator of an eastern cultural influence dating back to the very dawn of Finnish history.

Regional diversity

Unlike the other Norden states Finland is a country where distinct regional contrasts are seldom met with. It is a monotonous land, monotonous because of the uniformity of its climate and the continuous serene greenness of its coniferous forest cover (relieved only by the pale grey hue of its birch forests, but very rarely by the deep verdure of broad-leaved deciduous trees), monotonous even by the uniformity of its economy and its cultural landscape. Its foreign trade, to a degree unmatched by any other Norden country, even Denmark, has been founded on one main asset, its great coniferous forests.

Regional contrasts exist, as is only natural for a country which extends over 10 degrees of latitude and 12 degrees of longitude, but it calls for a keen and trained eye to be aware of them, since limits between geographical regions tend to be vague. The main regional divide follows roughly the limit between regions 1–5 and 6–8 on Fig. 9.2. Northeast of it is a very thinly settled area of forests and bogs and, far up in the north, barren fells. Southwest of the divide is a fairly well settled and well developed area with a network of towns, railways and manufacturing centres. These two divisions, of approximately the same size, have been called by J. G. Granö Unsettled Finland and Settled Finland, Nature and Culture Finland on Fig. 9.2. The difference is primarily caused by contrasts in climate (note e.g. line of 180 days with snow cover) and soils, the first area lying predominantly above, and the second predominantly below the upper marine limit, but historical factors are also important.

Farthest southwest and broadly limited by a line between the outlets of the Kokemäki (Kokemäenjoki) and Kymi rivers lies 1) the Southwestern Core Region of Finland, comprising half of the country's inhabitants, most of its towns, its largest manufacturing industries and its most intensive agriculture. This region includes the historical province of Finland proper (see p. 7).

Extensive clay plains (cf. Fig. 9.3) with a relatively high density of farms are found south of the Näsijärvi, Roine and Päijänne lakes (cf. Fig. 9.5). Lines of towns lie along the railway between Helsinki and Tampere and along the Kymi river between Kotka and Lahti, and Finland's most important ports lie along the country's most accessible coast (cf. Colour Map 10). Concentration of population in the southwestern core region continually increases as urbanization proceeds.

Apart from this southwestern core-region, which in itself is highly diversified, four major geographical regions can be discerned in the southwestern half of the country: 2) the interior Lake Region, to which for practical reasons may be added the more or less lakeless coastland region east of the Kymi river, 3) Southern Ostrobothnia, a rich agricultural region with large, level, cultivated fields in the interior, and narrower and more stony but intensively cultivated fields at the coast, 4) Suomenselkä, a mostly level watershed region, with extensive forests and bogs, which extends from

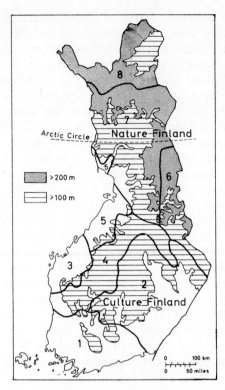

Fig. 9.2. *Geographical regions.* For explanation see text. For Finland's administrative divisions, see pages 6–7.

the coast north of Pori northnortheast to Lake Oulu and 5) Central and Northern Ostrobothnia, a discontinuous region, comprising a southern larger area from Kokkala to Oulu and a smaller northern sub-region covering the Kemi and Tornio valley plains. Although this region lies more to the north, it has more extensive arable lands than the Suomenselkä region, and parts of it, e.g. the Oulu plain, strike quite a 'southern' note.

In the northeastern half, three geographical regions can with somewhat greater difficulty be distinguished: 6) The Eastern Border Region (North Karelia – Kainuu – Kuusamo), from 62°30′ to about 66°, an upland region with settlements on hills and lake shores, 7) South-Central Lappland or Peräpohjola (the Far North), a forested region with extensive bogs and settlement only along the rivers, and 8) the Fell-Lappland, an area of forest-tundra (see p. 65) which, however, also includes forested lands, such as the pine forest south and east of Lake Inari.

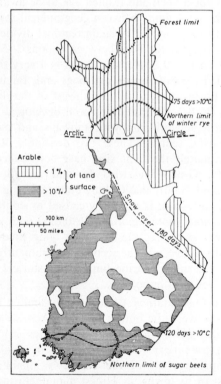

Fig. 9.1. *Some significant limits in Finland.* — Length of thermic summer according to Kolkki, Meteorologisches Jahrbuch für Finnland, Band 50, Teil 1 – 1950. Helsinki 1960. Northern limit of general cultivation of winter rye and northern limit of general cultivation of sugar beet, after Linkola, Suomen mantieteen käsikirja, 1937. Duration of continuous snow cover 1892–1941, computed after Simojoki, Fennia 70, (1947).

NATURAL FRAME

BEDROCK AND MORPHOLOGICAL FEATURES

As already mentioned Finland is for the most part a lowland; one third of its area lies below 100 m, two thirds below 200 m and almost nine tenths below 300 m. Situated in the more sheltered east-central part of the Fennoscandian Shield, its rigid bedrock has resisted the orogenic forces which gave rise to the Caledonian folded mountain chain in the western part of the Shield during the early Palaeozoic. Finland also lacks the great faults, upwarpings and downwarpings, which created horsts and grabens at the southern and western edges of the Shield during the Alpine orogeny. Rocks of periods later than the Precambrian are almost completely lacking (see Colour Map 2).

The surface of the bedrock is strikingly even. Vertical differences exceeding 200 m are, with the exception of northern Finland, very rare, and those of less than 20 m are, on the contrary, common (Colour Map 1). The uniformity of the land surface finds an expression in the almost identical heights of the surfaces of the famous thousand lakes of the country: Saimaa 76.1, Kallavesi 81.6, Päijänne 78.3, Näsijärvi 94.9, Pielinen 93.6, Keitele 99.3 m above sea level (Fig. 9.5). This level rock surface of southern Finland is usually thought to be an age-old erosion surface, which is widely developed beyond the borders of Finland.

Even though the rock plain is extremely level, smaller elevations are numerous. Often arranged in a regular pattern, they give the land surface a distinctive imprint in different parts of Finland. Thus the ridges and depressions of the Svecofennic and Karelidic zones (Fig. 3.1, p. 32) often follow the strike of the schists, in the southern part of the Karelidic zone to such an extent that the local population differentiate between journeys 'across' (i.e. W–E) and 'along' (i.e. N–S) the country. Geological structure is clearly discernible in the configuration of the shorelines and the lakes. Examples include the southwestern archipelago with its W–E running shorelines and Lake Päijänne, where bays and peninsulas conform to the pattern of fractures and faults. The miniature relief within the rapakivi areas is to a large extent

pre-determined by uncommonly distinct cleavage-surfaces of that rock. The most striking correspondence between tectonic structure and morphology is furnished by the Oulu plain and the Pori-Kokemäki plain, both absolutely level, and both with a foundation, buried underneath quaternary deposits, of horizontally bedded sedimentary rocks (Fig. 9.3).

The reaction of the rigid bedrock to the orogenic forces from the west and the south has largely been one of fracturing rather than folding. The land surface has a distinct fracture pattern, forming in many places an irregular fault-mosaic. The latter is the basic factor in the intricate network of land and water surfaces which is the distinctive feature of the two most characteristic Finnish landscapes, the interior

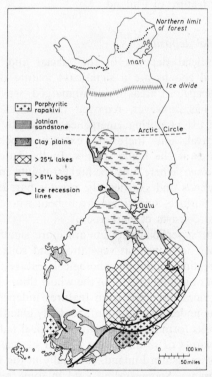

Fig. 9.3. Main physical features. Lake covered surface according to Renquist, Fennia 72 (1952). Surfaces in bogs according to Ilvessalo 1948. Heavy black arcs in the south mark halts in the recession of the ice margin. Eskers lie at right angles to these arcs (cf. Colour Map 3). The horizontally bedded Jotnian sandstone produces extremely level plains, whereas the rapakivi sheets, because of angular faulting, produce highly uneven surfaces.

region of the thousand lakes and the outer one of the skerry guard.

The Alpine orogeny was expressed not only in a rejuvenation of the old fracture pattern, but also in an upwarping of extensive areas. As a result a somewhat higher rim along the eastern frontier, broadening to the north, encircles the lower southwestern part of the country. Further north downfaulting has produced the Inari lowland basin. Some steep-sided valleys have been cut in the highland rim by rejuvenated fluviatile erosion, as for example the Koitere Valley south of Pielinen. On the whole fresh erosional forms are insignificant. The same is true of the traces of glacial erosion in Finland, which is understandable because the ice was moving over level lowlands. The main erosional result of the inland ice was a removal of loose deposits and rock debris from faults and fractures. Thus the fracture pattern of the bedrock was revealed as the most distinctive morphological feature of Finland.

Glacial deposits

Superficial deposits of the glacial and postglacial epochs are a significant feature of the landscape. In areas once submerged, wave action has, however, removed these areas to a large extent during emergence caused by land upheaval, and there are extensive rock exposures at the higher points. In the outer archipelago, where only the highest points emerge as islands and skerries, the greater part of the land surface, sometimes throughout whole parishes, consists of bare rock.

The superficial deposits are more significant in their influence on vegetation and soils than in creating major morphological features. The cover of glacial drift is on the whole thin. Usually it does not itself form features independent of the underlying rock surface. Only glacifluvial deposits form important morphological patterns

Swarms of drumlins are typical of scattered areas in eastern Finland, especially in the north (Kuusamo, Suomussalmi), and in some regions in the southwest, e.g. the centre and south of the main island of Åland. A more rare landscape is that created by closely set parallel low moraine ridges running transverse to the ice flow: such a washboard pattern is found e.g. in the Vaasa archipelago and in southern Lappland (Pudasjärvi).

Great marginal formations, composed of both till and glacifluvial material, are typical of Finland. The two *Salpausselkä* ridges running parallel and about 25 km apart, are unmatched in length and height by any other corresponding marginal moraines in Norden. At some points they are made up exclusively of glacifluvial material, or have a quite unsignificant core of till. At other points patches of till are buried in thick layers of stratified sand and gravel. At Lahti the Salpausselkä ridges have a curious 'knee', which marks the conjunction point of two ice lobes. The Finnish name, meaning damming-up ridge, is a misnomer. It was coined in the mid-19th century, when it was thought that these gravel ridges dam up the interior lakes. In reality the lakes lie behind rock thresholds. Other ridges, Jaamankangas in the east (near Joensuu) and Hämeenkangas in the west (west of Tampere) also mark stillstands of the ice margin.

Eskers are characteristic of Finland (cf. p. 39 and Pl. 9.11). The highest eskers, which rise to 60 m above their surroundings, are found in the southwest. Lakes with limpid water, *valkeajärvi* (white lake), often fill hollows created by the melting of isolated dead-ice blocks or stranded icebergs.

The postglacial uplift is a factor of foremost geographical importance. At first it was rapid, perhaps as much as 10 m per century. The present rate of elevation is 40 cm at the southern coast, and about 1 m along the western coast near Vaasa. Because of the lowland character of the country the land area added in this way has been, and is still, much greater than in Sweden. It is estimated that the area of Finland increases by about a thousand square kilometres per century.

Variations in uplift have affected the inland waters of Finland. During the first postglacial stages deep bays which opened northwards took the place of the present big lakes. Later these bays were shut off from the sea, but still had northwards outlets. By differential uplift their basins were tilted southwards with subsequent flooding of the southern and recession on the northern shore, until finally they successively flooded the southern thresholds and new southernt outlets were formed, first for Näsijärvi, then for Päijänne and last for Saimaa. As a result relatively large clay areas were exposed on their northern sides, especially around northern Kallavesi and northern Pielisjärvi. Sometimes man has helped to create southern outlets, as for example in digging a canal through Jaamankangas from Lake Höytiäinen to Pyhäselkä in 1859 with the result that the level of the lake fell by 9.5 m, and 153 km² of fertile lakebed were exposed. Similarly in 1830, an artificial outlet made between Lake Längelmävesi and Roine, southeast of Tampere, caused a fall of 2 m in the level of Lake Längelmävesi and a gain of 23 km² from the lake-bed.

The distribution of postglacial fine-graded sediments, clay, silt and loam below the upper marine limit, is one of the most important geographical factors in Finland. The extension of clay areas within the large region which was covered by postglacial lakes and seas is, however, very uneven. It seems that the rapid retreat of the shoreline during early postglacial times did not offer opportunities for a more thorough outwash of the morainic drift. The somewhat higher areas of the interior thus possess only small clay and fine-graded deposits apart from lake-bed deposits in ephemeral ice-dammed lakes along the eastern border of the ice sheet, and from silt and sand deposits on the sides of eskers. The most extensive clay and sand plains are found 1) in the southwest, inland from the coast in a belt between the rivers Kymi and Kokemäki, south- and westwards of the Salpausselkä ridges, 2) in a triangular area on the west coast in Southern Ostrobothnia, which like the first area has a very level land surface, and 3) along the rivers further north, especially south of the Oulu river, and along the rivers Kemi and Tornio. Between Kokkola and Oulu esker sand has been spread over the clay by marine abrasion. Active dunes occur at the shore, and fossil ones well inland.

CLIMATE

Despite her easterly situation the climate of Finland is much influenced by cyclones and is akin to that of her western neighbours, especially northern Sweden. In normal years Köppen's Dfc (boreal, humid) climate prevails throughout the country, but during warmer years southern Finland has a Dfb regime with 4 months with a mean temperature above 10°C. Similarly the southwest may sometimes have a Cfb regime with a mild winter, no monthly average being below —3°C.

Regional contrasts are not marked, neither in temperature nor in rainfall. Southern Finland has a mean July temperature of 17–18°C, central Finland one of 16°C, and Lappland one of 14–15°C. Winter temperature contrasts are sharper, the February mean averaging –4°C in Åland, but –19°C in the 'arm' of Lappland (between Norway and Sweden) with altitudes of 500 to 1 300 m.

The climatic advantages of South, as compared with North Finland, are best expressed in the length of certain temperature periods. The length of the growing season (total of days between the mean temperature's passing of 5°C in spring and autumn) is 175 days at the south coast, against 120 in Lappland; the length of the grazing period 160 and 110 days respectively, and the amount of effective temperature during the growing season, all temperatures below 5°C being eliminated, is 1 300°C in southern Finland as against only 600°C in northernmost Lappland (Fig. 9.4 f–h). The duration of snow cover is only 80–140 days in the southwest, but in the Lappland arm 220–250 days. The depth of the snow cover averages only 20 cm on the Åland Islands, but in the region of maximal snow cover east of Lake Oulu it averages more than 80 cm (Fig. 9.4 i).

The annual rainfall averages 750 mm in the south, where the western end of Salpausselkä is considered to have an orographical effect on the precipitation, but is only 400–450 mm in westernmost Lappland, which lies in the rainshadow of the Scandinavian mountains. On the whole the western coastland is somewhat drier than the eastern interior. The heaviest rainfall is in August, but there is a tendency towards a later, secondary precipitation maximum in the sea-influenced southwest, and towards a somewhat earlier one in the more continentally-influenced northern interior. The spring is dry, especially along the coast. Cf. Table 4.2, p. 49, and Colour Map 6.

HYDROGRAPHY

Finland is literally a country of thousands of lakes. Their actual number in present-day Finland is shown on the 1 : 400 000 map as 55 000.

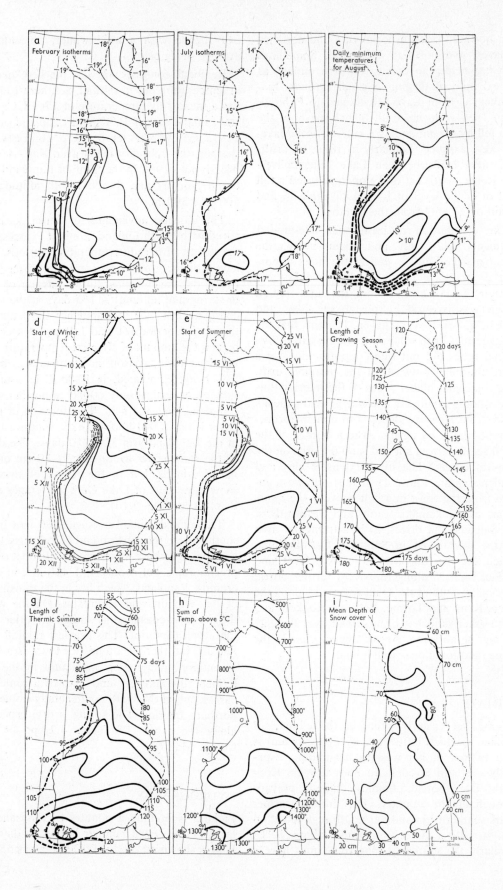

The distribution of lakes is, however, very uneven. The Lake Region, and especially Mikkeli county, situated entirely within its borders, has about a quarter of its area covered by lakes, but Central Lappland, southern Ostrobothnia and southwestern Finland contain extensive areas without, or with only insignificant, lakes. H. Renquist (1952) estimated that a quarter of the country has a percentage of lakes below 5, another quarter from 5–10, a third from 10 –20 and the fourth, more than 20 per cent. Compared with the other Norden states and with most countries the inland water area is enormous. The shoreline of the lakes is highly irregular. In

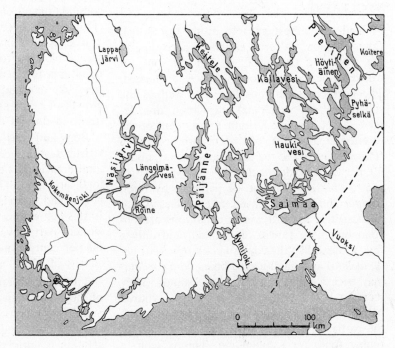

Fig. 9.5. Rivers and lakes; joki = river; järvi = lake; vesi = water, lake.

theory each inhabitant could have 100 m of fresh-water shore at his disposal.

It is often assumed that the majority of Finnish lakes are moraine-dammed. This, however, is not the case. They originate, with some exceptions such as the dead-ice ponds of the Valkeajärvi type mentioned above, in declivities of the bedrock, and lake regions are therefore regions with a highly fractured bedrock. This is apparent on closer inspection of the courses of the lake shorelines, which tend to follow certain dominating faultline directions, notably the NW–SE line.

Fig. 9.4. Climatic features. a. February isotherms, b. July isotherms, c. Mean daily minimum temperature for August, d. Average date of first winter day (diurnal mean temperature 0°C or less), e. Average date of first summer day (diurnal mean temperature 10°C or more), f. Length of the growing season (average number of consecutive days with mean temperature above 5°C), g. Length of thermic summer (number of consecutive days with mean temperature above 10°C), h. Amount of effective temperature during the growing season in day-degrees, temperatures below 5°C eliminated, i. Average depth of snow cover 1892–1941 in cm. — Averages 1921–50 if not otherwise stated. a–h from Kolkki 1959 (cf. Fig. 9.1), i from J. Keränen & V. V. Korhonen in Suomi (1952).

Central Lappland may owe its scarcity of lakes to the thick cover of weathered rock which drapes the bedrock at the quaternary ice divide. The paucity of lakes in other areas is assumed to have been caused, e.g. in Ostrobothnia, by an old drainage pattern which was unaffected by glaciation and postglacial uplift.

As in other newly emerged landscapes the drainage pattern is immature, and bifurcations are not uncommon. The total of lakes decreases through silting and through erosion of enclosing gravel or rock barriers. Man has frequently assisted in drainage of lakes. During the last 50 years 500 lakes have been drained and 509 km² of former lake-beds transformed into land.

The lakes are shallow; the mean depth varies from 5 to 20 m. Only one lake has a maximum depth of over 100 m, whereas Sweden has 10 and Norway 35 lakes with a depth exceeding 100 m. As a result the total water volume of the lakes is small, and, because they lie at low levels, their water-power potential is insignificant compared with that of Sweden and Norway with much smaller percentages of lake surface. The total volume of the 17 biggest Finnish lakes is roughly equal to the water-body of Lake Vänern, and the waters of all the Finnish lakes would hardly fill the basin of Lake Onega.

163

VEGETATION

Finland lies almost entirely inside the Boreal Forest Region. Its forest coverage, according to the survey of 1951–53, is 218 740 km², of which 30 per cent is more or less water-logged. The northern coniferous forest as well as the subarctic (and subalpine) vegetation are described in Chapter 5. About 55 per cent of the forested area consists of forests with Scots pine *(Pinus silvestris)* as the dominant species, about 30 per cent is dominated by Norway spruce *(Picea abies)* and about 14 per cent by birch *(Betula* spp.). Broadleaved tree species which are sensitive to hard winter conditions are uncommon in the forests of Finland, and only a few of them, like the common oak *(Quercus pedunculata)* and small-leaved lime *(Tilia cordata)* may occasionally appear in pure stands. They seem to be restricted to edaphically favoured habitats, and were therefore affected more by the earliest clearances than by later felling of timber (oak) for shipbuilding. This is seen in

common names of settlements like *Niini* or *Lind* (Finnish and Swedish for lime tree), and *Tammi* or *Ek* (oak). Nineteenth-century botanists discerned eleven 'grove centres'. A grove was defined as a forest of predominantly broadleaved trees like oak and lime with a luxuriant undergrowth of herbs and grasses. Such groves often occurred on soil derived from limestone.

Bogs and fens are among the most characteristic features of the vegetation cover. Their total area is 97 420 km², or 32 per cent of the total land area. They are most extensive in the north, and especially between 64° and 67°N. In this belt extensive areas, especially in the flat western part, have a swamp land percentage of 60 per cent or more; individual parishes may consist of 80 per cent of bogs and fens.

There are several more or less distinct types of bogs and fens. The two main types are ombrotroph bogs, dependent on precipitation and dew only, and minerotroph bogs whose vegetation is enriched by ground water from the surrounding area. In the forest surveys, however, four main categories, based upon vegetation, are used. They are: 1) pine bog *(räme)* with a thin cover of stunted pines, a thick undershrub vegetation of among others dwarf birch *(Betula nana),* and a thick layer of bog moss *(Sphagnum* spp.), 2) spruce (or birch) bog *(korpi)* with usually a thick tree cover of spruce and /or birch, and an undergrowth of shrubs, sedges *(Carex* spp.), and often ferns, 3) open treeless Sphagnum bog *(neva),* mostly very wet, with sedges on a thick layer of peat, and 4) open fen *(letto)* with a richer limestone bedrock. The 1951–53 forest survey classifies 41.7 per cent of the swampland area as räme, 21.0 per cent as korpi, 25.0 as neva, 2.9 as letto and 9.4 as *turvekangas,* i.e. drained bogs with forest vegetation.

Usually räme, korpi, neva and letto are intermixed, and form peatland complexes. In the south and along the western coast up to 63°N the raised bog complex (hochmoor) is supreme. Its most distinctive features are a high flat centre, mainly covered by neva and räme, rising from low margins.

In the north water-logged sedge bog *(aapa)* predominates. This is concave in profile and has a less regular outline than the raised bog. In Lappland it has a special form characterized by peat banks running at right angles to the water

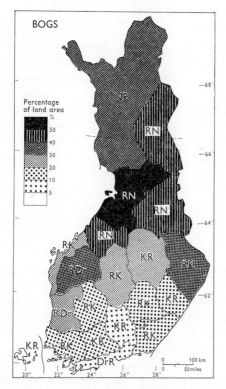

Fig. 9.6. Bogs, types and distribution, according to the 1951–53 forest survey. The hatching indicates the bog area of the forest board districts as a percentage of their land surface, the capital letters the dominate types of bog in each district: R = räme, K = korpi, N = neva, Dr = drained bogs.

flow. They are most important for the crossing of these large bog units. In the furthest north the aapa bog complex is replaced by the mound bog unit. The mounds *(palsa),* as well as the above-mentioned peat banks, are created by melting and regelation. The mounds are up to 7 m high and contain permanent ice bodies.

In the character of their peat layers Finnish bogs differ greatly from those of Western Europe. The peat layer is often thin, often not more than 0.5–1.5 m, seldom exceeds 6–8 m, and consists mainly of undecayed raw peat, well humified brown or black peat being rather exceptional. For this reason few Finnish peatland areas are suitable for peat-cutting for heating purposes. The rows of peat pits with accompanying drying-frames, a familiar sight on Finnish bogs, produce peat for litter and for horticultural uses.

The main factor in bog formation is bad drainage. The generally level land surface, aided in some areas by an impermeable soil cover, produces inadequate drainage. In northern Finland large amounts of surface water freed by the spring thaw may stay on the surface until midsummer, and this too encourages the spread of moss *(Sphagnum* spp.) producing peat.

Whether bogs and swamps have developed on former forest land, or by overgrowing of lakes, has been much discussed. It was first thought that most Finnish bogs and swamps had developed on former forests. More recent research has made it more probable that a large part, maybe the major part, of Finnish peatlands formed at an early stage on emerging seabeds or on land freed by melting of the quaternary inland ice. Water-logging of forest land, however, is important, especially where the natural drainage is disturbed and impeded by differential land uplift. Forest fires which cause the groundwater level to rise are another factor favouring water-logging of forest land.

POPULATION AND SETTLEMENT

THE PEOPLING OF FINLAND

As a whole, Finland was settled much later than the other Norden states. The detailed picture of the extent of settlement in the mid-16th century presented by the 'land books' of Gustaf Vasa, reveals that even at that time the whole northern half of the country and the interior northwards from 62°N remained unsettled. The littoral bias of this settlement pattern and its focusing on the fertile clay-lands of the southwest it noteworthy. Of the 125 medieval parishes of Finland only 18 are situated north of the Kokemäki river and only 6 east of the Kymi river, and about two fifths of the total are closely concentrated in three small regions which have been continuously settled since prehistoric times (Fig. 9.7), viz. the main island of Åland with 6 parishes, the inner coast region of Finland Proper with 20 parishes, and the Satakunta-Häme region along the Kokemäki river and the lake-lowland of southwest Häme, where there were 27 parishes. Outside this pioneer frontier were the nomadic Lapps. The unsettled area was also used by the Finns as a hunting and fishing ground.

The Lapps of the interior seem to have been driven away from their fishing waters and hunting grounds during the 16th and 17th centuries. Nevertheless, at the beginning of the latter a scatter of Lapps existed in Southern Ostrobothnia, witnessed *inter alia* by the fact that Lapp herders took care of domesticated reindeer herds on islands outside Vaasa. A route used by wild reindeer herds led there from the north, and wild reindeer were commonly hunted in the frontier region between Ostrobothnia and Satakunta up to the mid-18th century. Another wild reindeer track followed the eastern margin of the Lake Region to Saimaa, and here, too, wild reindeer existed up to the end of the 18th century. Both routes seem to have been fringed by Lapp settlements.

The northward push of Finnish settlers since 1550, with subsequent expulsion or absorption of the Lapps, can easily be followed in historical documents. The first Finnish settlements were founded on Lake Oulu in 1550.

By the mid-18th century the first settlements had been founded on glacifluvial deposits along Ivalojoki and Lemmenjoki, close to their outlet in Lake Inari. By about 1800 the Finnish colonists *(lantalaiset* or dung men as they were and are called by the Lapps) had reached the water divide on Maanselkä (68°N). Today only an insignificant remnant of the old Finnish Lappmark exists, mainly in Utsjoki parish north of Lake Inari, the only predominantly Lapp parish in Finland. There is a lesser remnant in the Lappland arm, in Enontekiö, but the total of pure Lapps in Finland was only 1 312 in 1960, a decrease of 60 per cent since 1950.

Swedes and Finns

Swedish colonization of the south and west coasts of Finland may partly be contemporary with the first Finnish settlement. The Swedish settlers too had direct contact with the Lappish population, as witnessed by place names and traditions. Swedish colonization brought about christianization of parts of Finland and gained strength when the country was brought within the realm of the Swedish kings. A Finnish historian has stressed the fact that Swedish settlement reaches farthest inland in two places, on

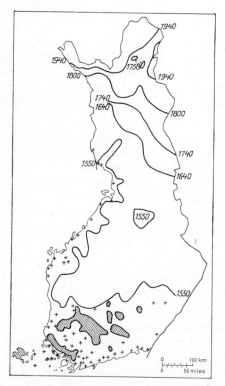

Fig. 9.7. *Advance of permanent agricultural settlement*. Shaded areas: the first regions to be densely settled. Crosses mark sites of medieval churches (except those in the shaded areas). Continuous lines indicate boundaries between settled and unsettled areas. Mainly after Eino Jutikkala in Suomi (1952).

the Kymi river in the east, and on the small river Perhonjoki, debouching at Kokkola in the north, both thought to coincide with an old Swedish-Russian frontier. At first there was also Swedish settlement east of Kymi along the coast to Viipuri and north of Kokemäki along the coast, but the former was already fennicized by about 1400 and the latter after 1600. The language frontier has remained relatively stable with occasional fennicization or swedicization of isolated settlements of both groups or of minority groups in bilingual communities.

In 1960 the Swedish-speaking population of Finland was about 331 000, or 7.4 per cent of the total population. In 1880 the percentage was 14.3, and it has been assumed that during the 18th century it must have reached 20 per cent. The relative decrease is primarily due to the fact that the coastal regions soon became fully settled, and no empty land was available for further settlement. It may also be worth noting that the areas where Swedish predominates lie outside the industrialized districts at the mouths of the big rivers. Furthermore emigration has always taken a greater toll among the Swedes of Finland than among their Finnish compatriots. The decrease is also due to the fact that the Swedish-speaking population experienced the so-called vital revolution earlier than the Finnish. The awakening of national feeling in the late 19th century also led to the emphasis on Finnish as the nation's tongue. Many Swedish-speaking intellectuals started to speak Finnish, and took a Finnish name. Urbanization has led to the fennicization of former Swedish parishes around the Finnish capital (Fig. 9.8).

The pioneer fringe

The occupation of new land by forest clearances and by founding of new settlements inside and outside the settled part of Finland since 1550 is reflected in the steady increase of the population total. This can easily be followed from the first census in 1749 to the end of the 19th century. Afterwards industrialization and subsequent urbanization become the main factors behind the population increase as seen from the table below.

Population growth in Finland, 1749–1967.

1749	420 000	1879	2 000 000
1808	900 000	1908	3 000 000
1843	1 500 000	1967	4 650 000

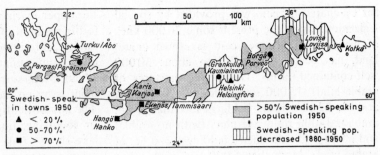

Fig. 9.8. Retreat of the linguistic border in Nyland 1880–1950. — Helsinki is in a region which up to 1905 had a preaominantly Swedish-speaking population; old Swedish names of villages like Kårböle, Konungsböle, Mellungsby, Sottungsby date from the Dark Ages. Even the name Helsinki (Helsinge) points to a Swedish origin (Helsingland). — After Klövekorn 1960.

Pioneering activity has never stopped in Finland, and there is accordingly a continuing expansion of settlement and subsequent increase of population in the northeastern part of the country, which now has about a tenth of Finland's population, but in 1650 was practically empty. In 1750 it had about 1 per cent and even in 1880 only about 4 per cent of the country's total population. The parishes which in 1936 became the administrative county of Lappland had only 40 000 inhabitants in 1880, whereas the county today has about 200 000. This push northwards is in many ways comparable to the American push westwards, although there are many differences. The main one is that the undeveloped potential of northern Finland is small, and will soon be fully utilized. A continued move northwards of the population is therefore improbable.

RURAL SETTLEMENT

By the *storskifte,* carried out in Finland as in Sweden after 1757 (see p. 304), pioneering and the spread of settlement was greatly promoted. The true strength of a nation was deemed to be its total population, and every means of increasing this was attempted, including establishment of settlements, farms and crofts in the hitherto unsettled wilderness, and subdivision of existing farms. The 19th century is thus a period of great expansion of settlement in Finland. The subdivision of farms went on steadily, although in 1841 it was laid down that holdings must be large enough to sustain four adults (in 1852 this number was increased to five). The former county of Viipuri was, however, exempt, and here subdivision of farms greatly exceeded that in other parts of Finland. The number registered increased as follows: 1895 128 500, 1915 207 200, 1924 332 100, 1930 481 000, and 1953 774 000.

The extension of rural settlement was greatly facilitated by the subdivision between the farmers of common pastures and forests, which dates from the end of the 18th century. Hitherto settlement or land clearance on the common village (or parish) land had been prohibited unless all the farmers of the village agreed. After the pastures and forests were divided the owners could reclaim their new lands as they wished, and a great pioneering activity, focused on the former common lands, followed. It was partly carried out by the younger sons of the farmer either by full rights to the new land, or by only temporary right to it *(torp,* see p.   ), the reclaimed area returning to the farm on the death of the reclaimer.

When the forest and common pasture were subdivided, a restricted amount of land was allocated to each holding. At first this was 600–1 200 *tunnland* (1 tld is slightly more than 0.4 ha. or 1 acre) per *mantal* (an old land-tax unit, corresponding originally to one holding). In many villages and parishes there thus accumulated a surplus of land, which was reserved for the Crown *(kronans överloppsjord),* except in Åland and in Viipuri county, where all the forest and common pasture were subdivided among the farmers. As the storskifte progressed northwards the allocation of land was enlarged until it reached 10 000 hectares per mantal in northernmost Lappland (N. Enontekiö). In some Ostrobothnian parishes up to two fifths or even half the present-day settlement and arable land are due to pioneering activity on these surplus crown lands.

Post-war pioneering

After the war of 1941–44 some 400 000 people from the ceded areas had to be resettled. Land

167

for evacuated farmers was provided by special legislation. Up to the present some 26 000 km², of which about 40 per cent is crown (state) land, has been converted into about 30 000 'self-contained farms' (with 6–15 hectares of arable land), 15 000 smallholdings (2–6 ha. of arable), 22 000 dwarf holdings less than 2 ha. arable), 34 000 residence plots (with no arable) and about 700 fishermen's holdings (2–6 ha. of arable land). More than 6 000 km² were taken from existing farm units, and 2 250 km² from neglected farms and farms held by non-farmers. Holdings with above 30 ha. of arable land were obliged to give up lands for resettlement and other post-war colonization. As a consequence estates with above 100 ha. of arable land shrunk from 700 to 225. The great majority of the large holdings were situated in the Southwestern Core Region, so that the majority of the Karelian farmers were resettled here. A line roughly following 64°N was drawn, northwards of which resettlement of Karelian evacuees was only voluntary and, in fact, did not occur (Fig. 9.12). Thus the Karelian resettlement has not led to any large extension of the settled and cultivated area. The immediate result has been a denser rural settlement in areas which were already densely settled.

Arable land could not be provided in all cases. About 20 000 new 'cold farms' (1965) were created. The evacuees from Salla, Kuusamo and Petsamo in northern Finland have been almost entirely resettled on settlement areas of this kind.

The rural settlement pattern

In Finland there is a great variety of site types and settlement patterns. As a general rule the overwhelming majority of rural settlements is related to clay, silt and fine sand deposits, the best soils for reclamation in Finland. There is one big exception, the hill or *vaara* settlements of eastern Finland, which are most common in a broad belt along the eastern frontier up to c. 66°N. Here villages and even parishes commonly have names ending in -vaara. This type is also found further west up to and beyond the northwestern edge of the Lake Region. The farms lie wholly on the till-covered hills, and cairns of boulders from field clearance are frequently seen. The hill tops sometimes lie above the upper marine limit, where the fine-grained, fertile material of the drift has not been washed out. A more important factor is, however, freedom from radiation frosts of summer nights which effect surrounding lowlands. Hill settlement is by no means predominant in the area. The largest fields, here as elsewhere, are situated on low-lying, fine-grained sediments along the lake shores. Lake-shore settlement is by far the most common in the interior of Finland, and still shows a tendency to expand, whereas the hill settlement, situated far from the main traffic routes, shows clear signs of decline.

Farmsteads are very often located on rocky or till-covered hills which protrude through the sediment cover and provide a firm, dry site, leaving the fine-grained deposits entirely in arable. Many Finnish rural settlements are on eskers. The esker ridges have always been good lines of communications, and the esker soil was easy to cultivate with primitive tools. The settlements partly remained here when pioneering activity advanced upon the clay deposits, which constitute the distal and lateral parts of glacifluvial deltas. In the Lake Region esker villages are very common.

Villages and farms

It is commonly stressed that in southwestern Finland agglomerated settlement originally predominated, while the interior and eastern Finland had dispersed settlement. Isolated farms are frequent everywhere in thinly settled areas. Coexisting with villages they are common in the northern part of the country and in Suomenselkä. Big agglomerations of 20 farms or more have developed only where there were sufficiently large continuous areas of fine-grained sediments, i.e. on the clay plains of southwestern Finland, in Southern Ostrobothnia, and on the valley plains of the Kokemäki and Kymi rivers. The smaller agglomerations found elsewhere, and also in the same regions as the larger ones, were initially dispersed settlements and have arisen by repeated subdivision of farms during the 19th century. Many became quite dense clusters of habitations. An agglomeration in an Ostrobothnian coastal parish developed thus from a loose cluster of 5 farmsteads in 1700 to a large village with, in 1880, 56 farm sites and 23 additional crofter's houses. It completely occupied a morainic hill of 12 hectares and was nicknamed 'Chicago' by returning emigrants from the U.S.A.'s Middle West.

By amendments of 1848 and 1881 to the old *storskifte* and by the *nyskifte* of 1916, which made it possible to move farmsteads out from the village clusters, these dense rural agglomerations have been so widely dispersed that agglomerated agricultural settlement is now very seldom seen in Finland. It is worth mentioning that at the first redistribution of land performed under the law of 1881, and carried out in 1889–1905 in two parishes in southern Ostrobothnia, 260 out of 637 farms were removed from their old sites.

The enforced redistribution of land has complicated the pattern of agglomerated and dispersed rural settlement. New agglomerations serving as local centres have also grown up all over the country regardless of old settlement patterns. In the areas of post-war resettlement and pioneering activity the houses are often set in loose agglomerations. The social structure of the old village is thus deliberately retained. It may often be more important to share the walk to school or other community buildings with neighbours than to have all arable land in one block around the farmstead.

Rural depopulation

Up to the present, rural depopulation has occurred only in the southwestern half of the country. Here, and most markedly in the southwest, a retreat of settlement is more or less clearly discernible. The smaller and most isolated settlements, on islands in the outer skerry guard, on the upper reaches of the rivers, on isolated lake shores or hills in the interior, are apt to be abandoned, especially when the population falls below a total sufficient to maintain a school. Retreat of settlement is most serious in the Swedish-speaking areas. It is partly caused by further emigration from this area, this time to Sweden, especially from Åland and the southwestern archipelago and from Southern Ostrobothnia.

As to the trend of rural settlement, Finland can at present be divided into two areas. The southwest is a region of retreat, the northeast a region of advance. The borderline between these regions is obscure, but the contrast grows clearer when moving southwest and northeast

respectively. Of the 21 rural parishes in Lappland county, 13 show a population increase exceeding 20 per cent, and 6 even more than 30 per cent during the period 1950–60, whereas of the 15 Åland parishes 11 had a decrease of more than 20 per cent, and one more than 40 per cent during the same period.

URBAN SETTLEMENTS

Urbanization started late in Finland, much later than in Denmark, Sweden and Norway, but it has steadily accelerated during this century, and will soon bring the country to the same level as her western neighbours. In 1880 only 200 000 people, or 9.3 per cent of the Finnish population, lived in urban communities. In 1950 it was 42 per cent, and in 1960 c. 50 per cent. Greater Helsinki (Swedish Helsingfors)[1] increased in 1950–65 from 415 000 inhabitants to about 700 000, i.e. about a sixth of Finland's population.

Finnish towns are usually young compared with their Norden neighbours (Fig. 6.4, p. 79). Only five[2], all on the southwest coast, date from medieval times, two[3] are from the 16th, and fourteen from the 17th century. Unlike many Norden towns Finnish urban communities lack old centres with narrow, winding streets and old stone buildings. Provoo may be mentioned as an exception.

The network of service centres is not very dense. It is related to the relatively thin and new settlement of Finland, and to a recent development of modern communications. The first railway dates only from 1862, and the first trunk roads were not built until the end of the 1930's. The airline network, the densest in Norden (Iceland excepted), is of recent growth. Many widely spaced regional centres have grown rapidly because of these developments, and some of them, like Rovaniemi in the far north, which had 27200 inhabitants in 1967, have mushroomed during the post-war period. There is however a great contrast between the densely settled and 'old' Southwestern Core Region with a fairly dense network of urban communities and communications, and the rest of

[1] Incl. Espoo west of Helsinki, with 79 000 inhabitants (since 1962 a borough) and the rural commune of Helsinki with 58 000 inhabitants.
[2] Porvoo, Pori, Turku, (Viipuri), Rauma, Naantali.
[3] Ekenäs and Helsinki.

169

the country with its much thinner net of towns. The former region has 98 urban communities, i.e. about half of the national total. A great many Finnish urban communities are predominantly mining or manufacturing towns or communications centres, without, or with only a secondary importance as service centres for the immediate hinterland. Out of 158 urban communities in southern Finland 58 can be classed as predominantly manufacturing, and 9 as predominantly communications centres. Access to raw materials explains the river-mouth location of many large Finnish towns which largely depend on the timber and pulp-wood floated down the rivers from the interior. Coastal location is also important because Finland depends largely on foreign trade, and many of her other industries use imported raw materials.

Some Finnish cities

The growth, and decline, of towns is a fascinating phenomenon. Mention has been made of the development of Helsinki, whose growth follows Mark Jefferson's law of the primate city. Next come two towns which each have, with their suburbs, about 180000 inhabitants, viz. old Turku (Åbo) on the southwestern coast, and young Tampere (Tammerfors) just inside the border of the Lake Region.

Turku is Finland's old capital, her best winter harbour, especially during severe winters, and an important regional centre for Finland's foremost agricultural area. Industrial expansion, notably in shipbuilding and food processing, is rapid.

Tampere is the largest inland industrial town, and 61 per cent of its active population are employed in manufacturing. It was founded in 1779, but developed only in the second half of the 19th century, when its textile mills grew quickly. It had an ample supply of soft water,

and of water-power, and its mills benefited by exemption from taxation. It is not only Finland's Manchester, but also its leather and shoe centre, and makes much machinery.

The fourth, fifth and sixth towns, with about 60000–85000 inhabitants, are Lahti at the southern border of the Lake Region, Oulu at the outlet of the Oulu river and Kotka-Karhula at the mouth of the Kymi river. Lahti was founded in 1905, Kotka in 1879, Oulu as early as in 1605. All of them have more than half their active population engaged in manufacturing.

The role of Kotka is obvious from its site: it has a large, old-established (i.e. old for Finland) but modern wood manufacture, and it is also a vital export port for the products of the important pulp and paper industry of the Kymi valley. It is Finland's biggest export harbour. Its sister town Karhula on the west bank of the river specializes in iron- and glass-manufacturing based on imported raw materials.

The growth of Lahti is not so simply explained. Today it is the greatest furniture-making centre of the country, and it also has other wood-industries, e.g. plywood, and brewing, machinery and textiles. Its site on the shore of Vesijärvi in the Kymi river system means ready supplies of wood, but a large quantity of birch logs is also procured by rail and road from the eastern part of the Lake Region. For a large post-war influx of evacuated Karelians Lahti is their 'new Viipuri', a centre of wholesale and retail trade.

Oulu, on both sides of the mouth of Oulujoki, became, shortly after its foundation, the main harbour of northern Finland. It is also its cultural centre, and since 1959 has a university. Its industries (pulp and chemicals) have progressed rapidly, particularly since 1939, favoured by the water-power development of the Oulu river.

AGRICULTURE

FARMING ECONOMY

Ownership of land

Finnish farming no longer has an ownership and tenancy problem. Until 1918–21, when the crofters were allowed to hold land independ-

ently, this problem existed and was important, regionally and even nationally. As it influenced agricultural development, it is worth giving a short account of the growth of a tenant class and of the interplay between peasantry, crofters and landless agricultural workers.

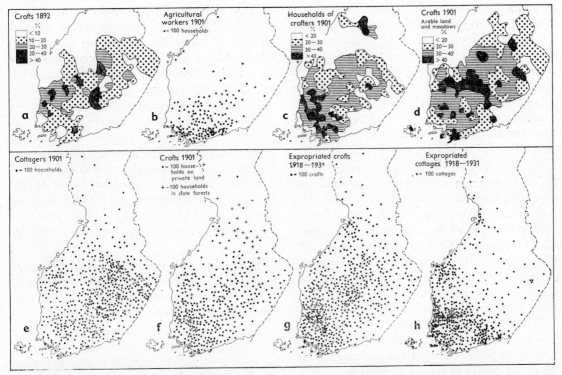

Fig. 9.9. Tenancy before and after 1918. a. Crofts *(torp)* per 100 freehold farms and estates. b. Agricultural workers annually employed (17 313 households). c. Households of crofters *(torpare)* and cottagers *(statare)*, percentages of all agricultural households. d. Arable land and meadows on crofts, percentages of total arable land and meadows. e. Cottagers (agricultural workers on rented land) (55 075). f. Crofts on private land (39 740) and in the state forests (2 247). g. Expropriated crofts (58 409). h. Expropriated cottages (50 978). Number of households added in brackets for maps b, c, f, g and h. — After Waren: Torpparikysymys Suomessa. (Suomalaisen Kirjallisuuden Seura.) Helsinki 1958 (a), H. Gebhard: Statistisk undersökning af socialekonomiska förhållanden i Finlands landskommuner år 1901. I. Jordbruksbefolkningen. Helsingfors 1913. III. Den odlade jordarealen. Helsingfors 1908 (b—f) and K. Haataja in Suomen maanmittauksen historia II. Helsinki 1933 (g—h).

Until the mid-18th century tenancy existed only on ancient demesnes and farms exempted from taxes *(frälsejord)*. In 1747, the total number of crofts in Finland was only about 3 000, of which three quarters were in the three southwestern counties.

In 1767 consent was given to the foundation of crofts on land belonging to the ordinary farmers, and given this freedom and the ample potentialities offered by the subdivision of forest and outfield, this new type of settlement expanded very rapidly. By 1805 there were more than 25 000 crofts in Finland, of which 60 per cent were in the southwestern counties. In 1860 there were 60.000 crofts and half of these were in the southwest. The proportion of tenants to independent farmers rose simultaneously from 9 per cent in 1747 to 44 per cent in 1805 and 60 per cent in 1860.

In the early stages land had frequently been rented to younger sons and/or daughters with freedom to reclaim land around the croft. For an initial period of 10–20 years, during which enough land was being reclaimed to feed the crofter's family, very little or no rent was paid. Even after these years the rent remained low, commonly not more than 12 or 24 days of work a year. If the croft was situated on a distant, separate block of land, rent was paid in cash. With time, however, as the supply of reclaimable land became more restricted, especially in the southwest, and as the subdivision of farms to the same end progressed, the situation of the crofters worsened.

By the late 19th century two regional types of crofts had developed: in the old agricultural areas of the Southwestern Core Region there was the system of estate-crofts, in the interior and in the north that of farm-crofts. In the former region, with crofts on estate-land, each estate had an average of 20 crofts. Their main function was to supply trained farmworkers for the estate, the duty averaging three days of work a week per croft, commonly with horse, giving a supply per estate of from 50 to 150 days of work a year. The crofts had as a rule a quite substantial arable area (the mean, according to a survey of 1896, was 5.8 ha.), but they had a small forest area, and thus limited possibilities of reclaiming new fields.

In the area where farm-crofts predominated, the main importance of the crofts lay in the reclamation work performed by the crofter. The duty in days of work was small, and a rent in cash usual. The crofts' arable area was small, on an average only 2.7 ha. This is understandable as a great many of the crofts were newly established on unreclaimed virgin land. A contemporary Finnish statement that "the foremost land clearer of our time is the crofter" held true only for the interior of the country. The fields cleared by the crofter reverted to the farm when leases fell in. By a law of 1800 the maximum length of lease was 50 years.

In both regions the economy of the crofts was based mainly on animal husbandry, the crofter usually enjoying the same privileges of free pasture in the forests as all cattle owners. On the average a croft possessed a horse and four cows. Most crofters owned a horse and derived their main cash income from transport work done by it, especially in the forests for the big timber companies then emerging in Finland.

The mid-19th century shows a maximum of crofts in Southern Ostrobothnia and Southern Karelia. In both these regions the subdivision of farms had progressed to a point at which new crofts were neither possible nor necessary. In the Southwestern Core Region crofting seems to have reached its maximum in 1860–90. But in the interior and the north, croft settlement continued to expand. In 1901 Finland had 67 000 crofts, not much fewer than Sweden, but whereas Swedish crofts had fallen in numbers by 20 000 from 1880 to 1900, they had increased in Finland by 7 000. This expansion occurred mainly in Oulu and Kuopio counties.

The economic situation of the crofter was not his main burden. Much worse was his legal position, aptly described in a recent novel by Väinö Linna. A third of the leases were only oral agreements. In the written ones the landowner retained the right of giving notice on very slight grounds. The crofter lived under an unceasing fear of losing the fruit of his reclamation labour. Added to it was the economic misery of the growing landless population in the late 19th and early 20th century.

There were many gradations between crofters and landless agricultural workers. The 1896 survey uses six different categories of rural non-farmers in Finland, and a survey of 1901 four. It is significant that of the 67 000 enumerated as crofters at the 1901 census only some 40 000 are classified as agricultural, having a leased arable area of at least 3 ha. and at least one horse and two cows (or less land and more livestock).

In an earlier census, carried out in Uusimaa county in 1876, about 4 000 crofters, 6 000 cottagers and 9 000 agricultural workers were enumerated, against about 6 000 landowners.

A class of agricultural workers developed first in the southwest where the need was greatest, and a system of annually renewed contract was introduced. On the estates it usually included a house free of charge and a wage, which was partly paid in victuals. The 1901 survey registers 17 000 annually employed agricultural workers in the whole of Finland, of which four fifths were in the three southwestern counties. In addition, the census recorded about 55 000 agricultural workers on rented land (cottagers) of which 40 per cent were in the southwest, and over 40 per cent in Kuopio, Vaasa and Oulu counties. Other agricultural workers who, like the above group, did transitory and casual farm labour, but unlike it rented no land for their own crops, and lived in rented houses or rooms at the farmstead, i.e. the migratory farm labourers, constituted in 1901 some 41 000 families and and 23 000 single persons. This group was very common in the two interior counties, which had 42 per cent of the total. Häme county and the Suomenselkä area in Vaasa county also had a large number of these 'lodgers' and 'vagrants', as they were called (cf. Fig. 9.9).

The scene was set for the civil war, unluckily a part of Finland's fight for independence in 1918. Immediately after the war, the emancipation of the crofters was decided upon in the Finnish Diet. Larger groups of tenants were included by legislation in 1921 and 1924, and their smallholdings were allocated with great speed. In 1930 only 30 000, and in 1941 only 14 000 tenants remained in the whole of the country; there had been 152 000 in 1912.

Size of holdings

The inevitable result of the continued subdivision of farms, of the emancipation of the tenants and of post-war settlement activity is an aggravation of the smallholder problem, which has long been a crucial point in Finnish farming.

The total number of holdings with more than 2 hectares of arable land has grown from 166 000 in 1910 to 289 000 in 1959 (Table 9.1). At the same time the average size of these farms has decreased from 10.9 to 8.9 ha.; in the group above 5 ha. the fall was even more marked, i.e. from 15.7 ha. to 11.6 ha.

Table 9.1. *Number and arable acreage of farms, 1910 and 1959.*

Size group	Number		Acreage	
	1910	1959	1910	1959
	%	%	%	%
2– 5 ha.	38	35	14	13
5–10 »	30	35	18	29
10–25 »	23	26	32	41
25 »	8.5	3.7	36	17
Total, per cent . .	100	100	100	100
» , thousand . .	166	289	1931 ha.	2531 ha.

In mechanized farming 25 hectares has been considered the lowest economical size for a Finnish farm. But in 1959 Finnish holdings exceeding that size totalled only about 11 200, i.e. merely 3.9 per cent. On the other hand, these farms possessed 17 per cent of Finland's arable acreage. Extensive land clearance has to a certain extent counteracted the consequences of subdivision.

Most significant in contemporary development in Finland is the quasi-elimination of the estates. In 1910 there were 900 farms of over 100 ha. and they held 11 per cent of the total arable area of Finland. In 1941 the number had decreased to 739 and their share of the arable acreage to 5 per cent; in 1959 their number, as a result of post-war resettlement, was reduced to 239 and their arable total to 1.6 per cent.

CLIMATIC FACTORS

Finland lies at the northern limit of grain farming and indeed on the northern margin of farming of any kind. Hay and other fodder crops, vegetables and potatoes are successfully grown up to the northernmost tip of the country, but in grain farming there is always a considerable risk of failure because of killing frosts or an unusually short summer. Frosts menace farming throughout the country. Severe frosts seriously damaging crops over the whole country occur on the average every fortieth year, i.e. in the lifetime of every generation of Finnish farmers, and a less severe one once every ten years. A regional crop failure due to frost is likely once in every four years.

Finnish farming is therefore markedly marginal. Use of early-maturing and/or frost-resistant varieties has partly reduced the risk of crop failures. Crop yields have also been stabilized by improved techniques such as deeper drainage, use of weed-free seed, rotation of crops, use of mineral fertilizers and liming. Whilst crop failures are now less severe, they may still destroy all grain crops over large areas, as, for example, over large parts of central and northern Finland in 1952 (Fig. 9.10). Though crops in northern half of Finland are naturally most liable to frost damage, there are also some southerly regions where frosts are common. The largest is the Suomenselkä region with adjacent parts of Southern Ostrobothnia; a tongue of cold air from the north often extends over this region (Fig. 9.4). Another minor frost region lies in the southeast. Local conditions are all-important, and radiation frosts during clear summer nights can affect valleys, plains and low-lying fields. Fields on peatlands are specially liable to frost damage, the more so if badly drained. All these factors make for crop failures in the badly drained Suomenselkä-Southern Ostrobothnia region.

Climatic factors, and especially the length of certain temperature periods, such as the growing season and the period of consecutive days with a mean temperature above 10°C (Fig. 9.4), determine the regional diversification of farming. They successively limit the extension of crops northwards, until north of 69° only grass and potatoes are left.

The length of the growing season (daily mean temperature over 5°C) varies from 180 days in the southwest to only 120 days in Lappland. The period with a daily mean temperature over 10°C ranges from 120 days on the southern coastland to only 55 days in the extreme north-east. The length of the farming year (cf. Fig. and disastrous, in the north the hay crop particularly may be waterlogged in some summers and more or less completely ruined, as for example in 1952.

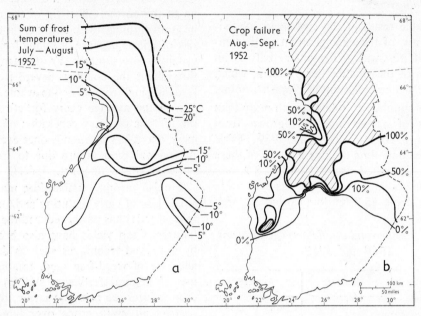

Fig. 9.10. *Crop failures and summer frost in 1952.* a. Isolines for the sum of daily minimum temperatures below 0°C during July–August. b. Isolines for crop failures; grain fields damaged by frost are shown as percentages of the total area sown with grain. The area of total crop failure is shaded. — After Katokomitean mietintö. (Report of the Crop Failure Committee 1953.)

12.10, p. 309) varies from 210 days in the south to 120 days in Lappland, and that of the outdoor grazing period from 160 days in the southwest to 100 days in Lappland. Whereas the maritime southwest has a longer growing season, the continental southeast has somewhat warmer, even if shorter summers. In practice this means that the southwest, and especially Åland, is best for winter wheat and the southeast for spring wheat.

Throughout Finland the rainfall is sufficient for all crops in normal summers, as the smaller precipitation of northern Finland is compensated for by reduced evaporation and a larger amount of moisture stored in the winter's snow cover. Crop failures through lack of moisture do occur, however. May and June are the critical months, especially along the western coasts. Excessive moisture may also cause damage, although the average annual precipitation nowhere exceeds 750 mm in Finland. In the south, too, much rain may make the harvest difficult

SOILS

Relief is nowhere a serious obstacle to cultivation in Finland. Level lands are found everywhere, and they usually have the better soils though they also have drainage problems.

Areas with soil suitable for tillage and fertile enough for crop production are limited. The ground moraine, which covers the greater part of Finland, is neither easily brought into cultivation nor is it as a rule fertile. More fertile tills do however exist: 1) above the upper marine limit, i.e. mainly in the eastern interior, 2) in places where the bedrock is rich in lime as in parts of the schist belts, and 3) in places where an accumulation of drift has taken place with subsequent grading of the material (lower slopes of morainic ridges, drumlins). In many regions the area of more fertile and more easily reclaimed soils is very restricted, and till-covered ground has had to be brought into use. The most valuable agricultural soils are the clayey and silty soils, whose reclamation, if on level plains, is usually recent, because older drainage techniques could not adequately deal with them. An investigation of 1920 proved that 48 per cent of the arable area was located on clay and silt, 31 per cent on till and sand, and 21 per cent on peat.

Regional contrasts in soils are considerable. Clayey soils are mainly found in the southwest; a 1957 survey shows that the percentage of clayey soils in the Southwestern Core Region varies from 59 to 62. Further north are smaller areas with predominantly clayey soils, as in the northeastern part of the Lake Region or in the centre of Southern Ostrobothnia. Coarse-grained mineral soils are most common in the Lake Region, especially in its southeastern part, and in parts of Suomenselkä, the coastland of Ostrobothnia and in the southwestern archipelago. Peat soils predominate in the whole of northern Finland, in the northern part of Suomenselkä, in the southeast and in the interior of Southern Ostrobothnia and in some small areas of the Southwestern Core Region.

POST-WAR LAND CLEARANCE

The acreage of arable land has steadily expanded since the first reliable evaluations of the extent of the cultivated fields. In 1813 the total arable area was estimated at 450 000 hectares, and the meadow area at 1 600 000 ha. In 1910, at the first agricultural census, the figures were 1 865 000 and 960 000 ha. Much of the quadrupled arable area was reclaimed meadow land. Land clearance, largely subsidized by the state, continued steadily from 1910 by reclamation of meadows as well as by clearing of virgin lands. By 1939 800 000 more hectares had been reclaimed, largely from meadow land whose area had decreased by 700 000 ha. Most of the reclaimed land is found in the Suomenselkä region, Central and Northern Ostrobothnia and in the northern and eastern parts of the Lake Region; only very insignificant areas were cleared in the Southwestern Core Region. This clearance thus followed the traditional pioneer fringe pattern.

After World War II Finland had to face a double task, that of resettling 420 000 people, mostly farmers, from the war-ceded areas, and of clearing the equivalent of the 260 000 hectares of arable land which had been lost. Actual-

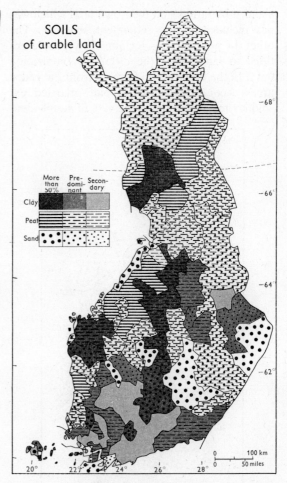

Fig. 9.11. *Soils of arable land* according to the 1941 agricultural census.

ly, 360 000 ha. were cleared from 1945 to 1966.

Post-war land clearance was preceded by inventories of reclaimable land in different parts of Finland, giving as a final result (1954) the considerable total of 1 613 000 ha., of which nearly four fifths were in northern Finland, a tenth in the east and north of the Lake Region, and a tenth in the remainder of Finland. In northern Finland nine tenths, and in southern Finland three fifths of the reclaimable area are peatlands.

Only two fifths of the reclaimable land provided by the 1945 Land Acquisition Act had been cleared by 1957. Contrary to common belief the Karelian evacuees are not the main land reclaimers, though their role in some parts of Finland is a major one. Of the total reclaimed during the post-war years, 56 per cent was re-

175

claimed by farmers on their own land which was not included in the settlement schemes. The other 44 per cent was reclaimed by people entitled to land under the different colonization laws. In the latter group farmers from the ceded areas account for about a half, married ex-soldiers for a third, and receivers of supplemen-

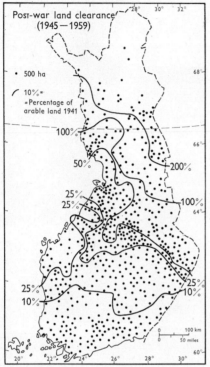

Fig. 9.12. Post-war pioneering. The dots indicate the area reclaimed, isolines show these areas as percentages of the total arable land.

tary land (i.e. as a rule very small farms) for more than a seventh.

A major reclamation, 125 000 ha. up to 1965, has been on 'cold farms', usually in special settlement areas. The name 'cold' means that the pioneer has had to start from the wilderness without, or with only an insignificant plot of cultivated land, most of which is meadow land. A premium varying according to size and situation has been paid to the pioneer when the planned holding has developed into a 'warm farm' with the necessary farm buildings, cattle and cleared fields. This state activity has been quite successful, and as the principal cold farm areas are in the north, where land has most easily been acquired, it has accentuated the northward shift of pioneering, so clearly discernible in the post-war period.

Post-war reclamation has been facilitated by increased use of machinery. A special state-backed company, Pellonraivaus Oy, was established to undertake large-scale land reclamation with the aid of bulldozers and other modern equipment. Special Finnish machines and vehicles have been developed for the different phases of reclamation. The intention from the beginning was to speed up reclamation, but this aim has not in general been achieved, because large continuous areas of reclaimable land do not exist in most places. Nor has mechanization always cut costs. The area cleared mechanically has not been very large, at the most a third of the cleared acreage. But much work formerly done by hand, such as the digging of drainage ditches and the removal of tree stumps, is now mechanized, and the labour force here can usually be halved.

As shown on Fig. 9.12, a major part of the land clearance is located in northern and northeastern Finland. The northward trend is indicated by the doubling of the arable acreage in the period 1941–58 in thirteen parishes in Lappland county and five in Oulu county.

The pioneering tradition is now very weak in southern Finland. Before 1939 the pioneer fringe formed a broad arc around the northern edge of the Lake Region, from Jyväskylä to Pielinen. Since the war it has moved north. Today, in a belt running from east of Pielinen and northnorthwestwards parallel to the eastern frontier, the great pioneering tradition of the Finnish people is still very much alive.

Much criticism has been directed against the post-war settlement and land-clearance activity because it appears to have added so many small farms to those already existing. This is true of the resettlement programme: the 6–15 hectares group was increased by 30 000 holdings and that of 2–6 ha. by 15 000, i.e. by about 30 per cent and 20 per cent respectively of their pre-war number. State-subsidized reclamation has, however, acted in the opposite direction. The recent agricultural census (1959) shows that in the twenty 'pioneer' communes of the northeast, where the total number of farms (holdings with over 2 hectares of arable) has almost doubled from 1950 to 1959, the greatest increase is in the groups 10–15 ha. (by 250 per cent) and 5–10 ha. (202 per cent). The group with 2–3 ha. has grown only slightly (11 per cent), or less than the group with over 15 ha. (14 per cent). Post-war land clearance has thus changed the structure of North-Finnish farming. In 1950 the 2–3 and 3–5 hectares groups still predominated throughout northern and northeastern Finland. Today the former predominates only in the two northernmost communes, and the latter group is interspersed, up to the Arctic circle, with areas where the 5–10 hectares group predominates.

MECHANIZATION, FERTILIZERS AND INCREASED YIELDS

Mechanization is of special significance since Finnish farming has for a long time been overmanned, and this will be much more strongly felt as mechanization progresses. The agricultural population constitutes, according to the 1960 census, 29 per cent of the total population, as against only 12 per cent in Sweden. The area of arable land per agricultural worker was 4.4 ha. against 9.5 in Sweden. As the number of tractors is now eleven times that of 1950, the surplus of farm workers is more and more acutely felt.

The increase of farm tractors has been as follows: 1930 2 000, 1940 6 000, 1950 14 000, 1959 75 000, 1965 160 000. In 1959 the national average was 35 hectares of arable land per tractor. But distribution is uneven. First comes Åland with, in 1959, 13 hectares of arable per tractor, second is the southwestern archipelago and coast region (21 ha.), whilst the agricultural society embracing the eight parishes of northernmost Lappland quotes 33 ha. per tractor as an average. The areas with the most advanced agriculture have the greatest number of tractors, but regions with a marked small-farm structure have a large number of tractors in relation to their arable acreage, simply because each farmer wants to have his own tractor. A large number of tractors in relation to the arable land area often means that full use is not made of them. In Finland tractors are, however, frequently used in forestry; and in thinly settled areas like those of northern Finland the tractor is often used in local transport.

Other labour-saving equipment, like hay mowers and threshing machines, has been an integral part of Finnish farming for a generation, seed drills and potato lifters have also become common. In 1950 combine-harvesters were a rare exception in Finland, but in 1959 4 500 were used on Finnish grain fields, 1964 15 000. They were most common in the Southwestern Core Region. In 1965 there were 50 000 milking machines. They were widely distributed throughout the country. Mechanized farming, though still lagging behind that of Sweden and Denmark, has taken a big step forward, and its consequences will be an increase in the rural exodus, especially from the small-farm districts.

Drainage is vital in Finland. It is necessary after the spring thaw and also during autumn rains, with diminished evaporation and later frozen subsoil, but it is badly neglected. The difficulty of maintaining good drainage is particularly great on the level lands of Ostrobothnia. The average gradient of the main drainage channels in the Vaasa area is 28 cm/100 m, and in the Kokkola area 33 cm/100 m. Peat, and in the south peat and clay, predominate. The large amount of water stored in the snow cover is an additional problem in the north.

Basic drainage by digging big channels to control spring floods and surplus autumn water usually has priority. It receives large state grants, is organized by the State Board of Agriculture, and supervised in the field by the Board's engineers. Some 1 000 000 hectares, well over a half of them arable, have already been drained in this way, and the work has lately been accelerated. As an average over 60 000 hectares have been annually drained during the last decade, in 1959 even 115 000 hectares, the greater part of it in the north and in southern Ostrobothnia.

Surface drainage through subsoil pipes is rather an exception, open-ditch draining being normal. This not only gives less effective surface drainage, but also occupies too much of the scanty arable land. It is a great obstacle to the effective use of farming machinery, and is expensive to maintain. As the total length of open ditches in Finland has been put at 1 400 000 km, and the average width of the ditches and their margins at 132 cm, the gain by substituting subsoil drainage would be 185 000 ha.

But pipe drainage has made little progress. Of the total arable acreage of 2.7 million hectares, 2.2 millions are still in open ditches. About 200 000 ha. have neither ditches nor

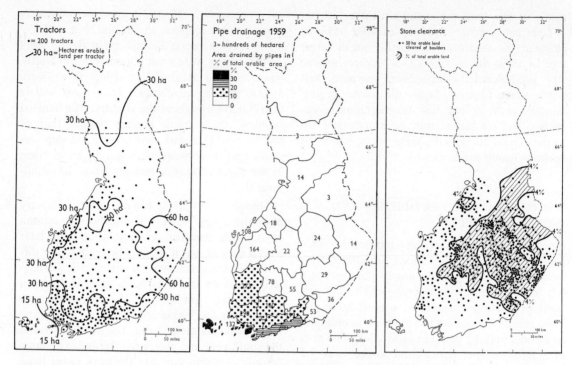

Fig. 9.13. Tractors in rural communes, 1959. Isolines indicate arable acreage in hectares per tractor. — *Fig. 9.14. Pipe drainage,* 1959. Figures indicate the area drained by subsoil pipes in each of 21 agricultural districts; the shading shows these areas as percentages of the total arable land. — *Fig. 9.15. Stone clearance,* 1953–1958. Area freed of stone and boulders with the aid of state premiums. Isolines show these areas as percentages of the total arable land.

pipes because they are located on dry soils; 400 000 ha. have subsoil drainage (1967). State subsidy has evidently been too small, compared with other forms of state aid. Small farms have received 30 per cent of the total costs. The larger holdings tend to carry out their own subsoil drainage schemes. At the present rate of 40 000 hectares a year it will take 50 years for all fields to have subsoil drainage.

The highest percentage of subsoil drainage is found in southwestern Finland (Fig. 9.14). Like so many other agricultural innovations it was adopted earliest in the Swedish-speaking areas, and firstly on the South Ostrobothnian coast, a small-farmer's region.

Post-war research has shown that 175 000 ha., i.e. 7.2 per cent of the total arable area, could be greatly improved if freed from stones and boulders left after initial clearance. The main area of these boulder-strewn fields is the southeastern and greater part of the Lake Region. In Mikkeli county such fields form about a third, and in Kuopio county a fifth of the total arable area. About a third of the cost

of stone and boulder clearance, now largely a mechanized operation, has been paid by subsidy since 1953. The total state-aided stone clearance in 1953–67 freed an area of about 110 000 ha., mainly on land which is naturally well drained, fertile and suited to mechanization. Most of it is in the Lake Region (Fig. 9.15).

After the war ampler supplies of mineral fertilizers were expected to increase yields considerably. It was thought necessary for the state either to supply the small-farmers with free fertilizers, or to pay transport to isolated farming regions, and to pay part of the cost of fertilizers to all farmers. The use of mineral fertilizers in kg/ha. per annum increased, as compared with 1936–40, thirteen-fold for nitrogen, eight-fold for phosphates, and seven-fold for potash, whilst the use of lime, which is greatly needed because of the acid soils, increased eight-fold (1965/66 averages). But yields increased only 10–25 per cent between 1936–40 and 1961–65, the explanation may be the different weather conditions of the two periods. Production has, however, increased due to a considerable enlargement of the sown area, and Finland is now almost fully self-sufficient in grain. In good years it may even be possible to export grain.

CROPS

Only in the southernmost part of Finland is the growing season long enough, and high summer warm enough, for demanding crops like sugar beet, winter wheat and oilseeds, or even in colder years, for peas, spring wheat and fodder beet. The need to be as self-sufficient as possible has, however, compelled the Finnish farmer for generations to cultivate some uncertain crops, and this has pressed the northern limit of cultivated plants further polewards than anywhere in the world.

Since natural meadows gave place to cultivated ones, grass has been the main crop in Finland, covering in 1959 over half the total arable area. The Finnish climate is more suited to the growth of the vegetative parts of plants than to the ripening of seeds, but there has repeatedly been much heated argument whether the main emphasis in Finnish farming should be on grain or fodder. Usually the grain area has expanded during periods of warm summers, until cold summers and crop failures have produced a diminished grain area and an increase in grass and other fodder crops. This happened after the devastating cold summers at the end of the 1860's, and again in the 1950's.

The dispute centering on grain or hay is primarily between big or medium farmers with a large income from grain, and small farmers, whose mainstay is their barn. It is also a dispute between the southerner who is grain-minded, and the northerner who is cattle-minded.

Arable land in a northern country like Finland is best used for the production of fodder, which can be harvested in bad summers. The most convincing proof that animal husbandry pays in Finland is the higher yield of milk per cow in relation to the yield of grain per hectare, if compared with Swedish yields.

Post-war developments have emphasized the conflict of ideas. Land acquisitions which were part of the resettlement programme so reduced the arable land of most big farms that their former dairying became a liability, the more so because post-war social reforms made it necessary to employ more workers in the barn, if dairying was to be maintained. These farms therefore turned to grain and/or special crops, sometimes so completely that farms without or almost without cattle came into being, a phenomenon hitherto unknown in Finland. The numerous small farms created during resettlement and other post-war settlement schemes naturally concentrate on grass and fodder crops.

Another important factor was the critical food situation and the big post-war import of foreign grain, unparalleled in the recent history of Finland. Gradually, however, more grain was grown in the country and imports were reduced. A subsequent tendency to restrict the grain area, partly caused by crop failures, reached its climax in 1957. In the years 1950–57 farmers in central and northern Finland replaced exacting wheat crops by hardier crops like barley and turned from grain in general to hay and fodder crops. Wheat was becoming the principal bread-grain before the war, and was dominant in 1950, but in 1959 barley covers almost twice the area occupied by winter and spring wheat. In Finland, as in other Norden states, barley is increasingly grown for fodder rather than for human consumption.

Cereals

As shown by Fig. 9.17, barley is the principal grain crop throughout northern Finland down to about 63°N. The barley cultivated in the south belongs to the two-rowed variety. It is used for malting and grown under annual contract with the malthouses. Rye is the main bread-grain in a belt across southern Finland between about 63° and 61°N. Spring wheat is the main bread-grain of the south and west coastlands. Up to 1950 it was more common than rye up to 63°N, but the boundary of the area where spring wheat predominates has now retreated to 61°N (Fig. 9.17 d and e). During 1950–59 the spring wheat area decreased by 30 per cent (50 000 ha.). Since then the area of spring wheat has increased.

Except in northernmost Finland (north of 63°N) and Åland, oats are the most common cereal (Fig. 9.16). The greatest surplus of grain is in the Southwestern Core Region which produces more than two thirds of the marketed grain, because of its better climate and larger arable farms. Farms of over 50 ha. have increased their wheat/rye area during 1950–58, whereas small farms below 10 ha. have reduced it by half. Grain surpluses were formerly characteristic of Southern Ostrobothnia and even of the northeastern Lake Region.

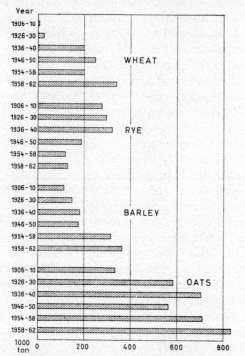

Fig. 9.16. *Production of wheat, rye, barley and oats* 1906–10—1958–62.

Grass

During the cool 1950's the area under rotation grass (for both hay and grazing) has increased, notably in central and northeast Finland (by 50 and over 200 per cent respectively). In the north 70–90 per cent of the arable land is sown for hay and in central Finland 50–70 per cent. Only in the southwest is the hay area less than half, and in the archipelago and an inland area northwest of Turku less than 30 per cent of the total arable land.

Roots and oilseeds

Sugar beet cultivation has greatly extended during the post-war period as a result of deliberate and subsidized efforts to attain a small degree of self-sufficiency. Three more raw sugar mills have been built in the south, in addition to the Salo mill southeast of Turku and the Turenki mill near Hämeenlinna, and sugar beet cultivation has expanded correspondingly. Sugar beet is a typical small-farmer's crop which needs

much attention. It seems to thrive quite well in the whole of southwestern Finland, and a sugar content of up to 18–20 per cent is not uncommon. It is grown successfully beyond 63°N in Southern Ostrobothnia (Fig. 9.17 f).

Another exacting crop which has been more widely cultivated in Finland only after the war is oil-seed rape (winter rape), whose seeds go to a newly built oil mill northwest of Turku. Two thirds of the rape-seed crops are concentrated in the southwest where the climate is mild enough for the plant to survive the winter. Rape seed is primarily a crop of the big farms.

The potato is important throughout Finland, but if an exception is made for some small areas with a suitable sandy soil, which provide the larger towns with this national food, such as Loppi parish inside the orbit of the capital, it is a crop whose acreage increases northwards and eastwards. Furthest north the climate makes grain crops unreliable, and both in the north and the east conservative eating habits are a factor. Twice as many potatoes are eaten in northern as in southern Finland, and the potato is one of the few crops whose yield increases northwards, as witnessed by the fact that Central Ostrobothnia has the highest yield per hectare in the whole country, and by the fact that Finnish potato yields, on an average, are bigger than Swedish. The large acreages of potatoes in the Lake Region are due to an extended use for fodder; as much as a half of the crop may be fed to stalled animals.

Fig. 9.17. *Crops 1959.* Solid circles, areas 1959; open circles, areas where oats, rye or wheat north of a line indicated on the maps were replaced by other crops in 1950–59. a. Barley. b. Oats. c. Potatoes. d. Rye. e. Wheat. Isolines indicate areas in barley, oats, rye and wheat as percentages of the total grain area, and areas in potatoes as percentages of the total arable land. Areas which grew more rye than wheat in 1950 are shaded on map d, areas with more rye than wheat in 1959 are shown on map e. The northern limit of rye (rye area 1 per cent of arable land) in 1950 is shown on map d, the 1959-limit on map e. f. Sugar beet, 1959. g. Grass on arable land for hay and silage, 1959. h. Pastures on arable land. New grass areas and pastures 1950–59 (north of the Polar Circle) have separate symbols. Isolines indicate hayfields as percentages of the arable land, and pastures as percentages of the area of rotation grass. i. New and disused holdings, 1950–59. Isolines indicate the former as fractions of all holdings in 1950. The fields of the disused holdings are now mostly used by other farmers and their houses are occupied by other, mainly non-farming people.

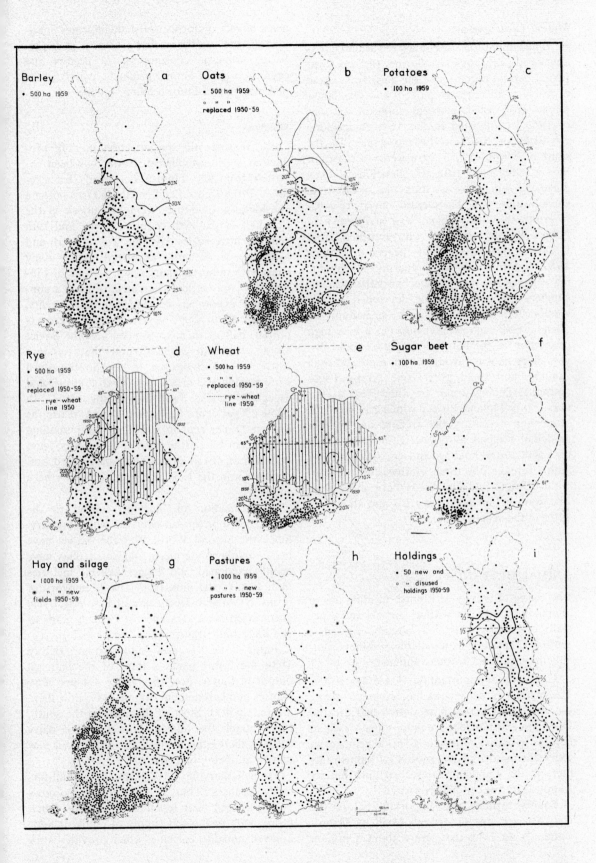

Barley
• 500 ha 1959

a

Oats
• 500 ha 1959
○ " " replaced 1950-59

b

Potatoes
• 100 ha 1959

c

Rye
• 500 ha 1959
○ " " replaced 1950-59
---- rye - wheat line 1950

d

Wheat
• 500 ha 1959
○ " " replaced 1950-59
···· rye - wheat line 1959

e

Sugar beet
• 100 ha 1959

f

Hay and silage
• 1000 ha 1959
⊙ " " new fields 1950-59

g

Pastures
• 1000 ha 1959
⊙ " " new pastures 1950-59

h

Holdings
• 50 new and
○ " disused holdings 1950-59

i

Market gardening

In some small-farm areas market gardening has developed very quickly during the post-war period. About a quarter of the glasshouses, and probably a still greater part of the glasshouse tomato crop listed in the agricultural statistics of 1959, are located in the Swedish-speaking coastland of Southern Ostrobothnia. In the south of Närpes parish there were, in the summer of 1959, more than 300 glasshouses. They make the whole district look like a suburban truck-farming belt. The tomato, never previously grown in Ostrobothnia, was first grown in Närpes by an emigrant who returned from U.S.A. at the beginning of the century. Since 1959 the tomato houses spread into neighbouring parishes. Market gardens specializing in cucumbers and onions have developed in the southwestern skerry guard, and especially in the Åland archipelago. This region has a very high proportion of the national output of these two vegetables as it is favoured by a mild and long summer, and small progressive farms. These market-gardening areas are, however, exceptional. It is Finland Proper which has been for more than a century the orchard and market garden of Finland. With one tenth of the country's agricultural holdings and one seventh of its arable acreage, the three southwestern agricultural districts (cf. Fig. 9.14) have more than one third of Finland's fruit trees and about two fifths of the vegetable area.

ANIMAL HUSBANDRY

The centre of gravity of Finnish farming lies in animal husbandry, in rearing animals and especially milk cows. This is, as already stressed, a natural adaptation to unreliable summers, notably in central and northern Finland.

Cattle are all-important (cf. Table 7.6, p. 85). The number of dairy cows has remained stable, but sheep and horses have diminished greatly. Only pigs and reindeer are more numerous than before the war. There were 171 000 reindeer in 1959, the majority being owned by Finnish farmers in the Lappland forest belt, and not by Lapps as in Sweden and Norway.

Poultry farming was important before the war, and remains so, though small by Danish standards. In 1966 there were about 5 million hens, largely on farms in the smallfarmer coastland districts northwest and southeast of Turku. Rising domestic consumption of poultry and eggs, as of other animal products, is part of the post-war rise in Finnish living standards.

Dairying

Cattle rearing and specialization in milk production is old-established. Butter has been exported from the Finnish coastlands for centuries. From Central and Northern Ostrobothnia considerable quantities went to Lübeck in the first half of the 19th century. In the mid-19th century large-scale dairying was started and local breeds of cattle improved. After many trials with imported dairy cows, a stock of Finnish Ayrshire cattle was created; of these a considerable export has developed in recent years. In 1965 about 2 000 Ayrshire cattle were exported, half of them to Sweden and the Soviet Union. It is interesting to note that Ayrshire cattle are mainly raised in the Southwestern Core Region and in Southern Ostrobothnia, and especially in the Swedish-speaking areas. In 1959 27 per cent of all cows were Ayrshire (as against 15 per cent in 1950), of the remaining 73 per cent four fifths were of native breed and one fifth of mixed stock. The native breed predominates in the Lake Region and in northern Finland.

Modernization of dairying started in the south, but soon spread over the whole country. Since the Second World War the dairies have been rapidly modernized, old small ones have been abandoned and bigger central factories built to take the milk from a wide network of farms. Nothing in recent times has so effectively encouraged snow-clearance of Finnish roads as the daily milk transport.

Farm butter is now unimportant. Before 1939 the farms made a third of the national output of butter; now they make 4.4 per cent. Dairies numbered about 600 in 1939; now there are barely 400. Most of them are in the south, even though the relative importance of dairy cattle is increasing towards the north, and new dairies are being built there.

Finnish dairying is very much a small-farmer's business. Thus 77 per cent of the cows belong to herds with less than 10 animals. Small farms, with their good supply of family labour, are well suited to dairying, which provides work throughout the year and a regular income. The numerous owners of small dairy-herds co-operate and employ an assistant who regularly records output and fat content. They also maintain a thoroughbred bull or are members of larger groups which deal with artificial insemination. Most dairies are members of a larger co-operative organization, Valio, whose head office and active research laboratories are in the capital. Valio is also an effective marketing organization, with storage facilities for huge quantities of butter, mainly intended for export. As a result of research at Valio, Finnish cheese is now widely exported. There is a corresponding organization for the Swedish-speaking farmers (Enigheten).

Whilst the yield per hectare of Finnish grain, despite deliberate and tenacious efforts, has only just regained the pre-war level, milk-production per cow and fat content have markedly surpassed the pre-war level. The average annual production per cow in the milk-testing associations was 4 063 kg in 1964–65 against 2 851 kg in 1937–38. The average fat content was in the same years 4.5 per cent against 4.1 per cent. Butter and cheese production has increased threefold, but the number of milk cows is, by and large, the same as before the war.

This result has been achieved without any considerable increase in imported fodder. Domestic fodder and, especially, improved pasture are now more important. Milk output is highest at the height of the outdoor grazing season, i.e. throughout southern Finland in June, but in northern Finland and in the Ostrobothnian coastland in July. Spring calving also increases yield at this period. The pastures produce 30 per cent of the fodder on an average, with a smaller percentage in the south because some stall-feeding continues even in summer and, of course, in the north because of the shortness of the outdoor grazing period. Beyond the Arctic Circle pastures produce only a seventh of the fodder. It is not uncommon for a tenth of the arable area to be reserved for pasture. In northernmost Finland large forests are still grazed in common; in the Lake Region fenced forest pastures are usual.

About a third of the total annual fodder consumption is hay (as a rule straw is insignificant). The part played by home-produced grain is important. Recently about a sixth of the wheat and rye harvest, a half of the barley, three quarters of the oats, and two fifths of the potato harvest has, on an average, been fed to livestock.

Finnish animal husbandry produces a surplus for export of pork and bacon, eggs, milk (i.e. powder milk), and especially of cheese and butter. This may seem strange in a country which has to feed its dairy cows during a long winter in large costly barns on fodder often harvested under difficulties, and in addition, usually has to import as much as 10 per cent of the fodder.

State subsidy is partly responsible for the large milk surplus. In the 1960 budget export premiums exceeded price-stabilizing payments for all kinds of domestic food, the prices on the world market for animal food products being, on an average, 70 per cent of those within Finland (1958).

In Finland, as elsewhere, rising living standards involve a larger consumption of animal food per capita. The consumption of dairy butter has increased to values unknown before the war. In 1958/59 it was about 60 million kg (plus 2.6 million kg of farm butter), i.e. more than 15 kg annually per inhabitant. Few countries have a higher consumption. In addition 21 million kg were exported (in 1965 19 millions). Cheese production and export exceeded pre-war totals by 1949, in 1965 export reached 20 million kg. In addition, 26 million kg of evaporated milk and cream were exported. In 1936–40 the annual output of butter was 45 million kg, of which 11.8 million kg were exported, and of cheese 9.7 million kg, of which 5 million kg were exported. The predominance of dairying in Finnish farming has never been so great as it now is.

Fur farming

Fur farming is much more important than it was in 1939. It is mainly mink rearing. Half the food used on mink farms is fish, mainly small Baltic herring, hence their coastal location. Newly-erected freezing plants store the spring surplus of fish for the mink farms. Their biggest concentration is in the coastal region near Vaasa, which produces about half the mink fur of Finland. This is almost wholly exported, notably to U.S.A.

Farming in the balance

In Finland's trade there is a big gap between payments for such things as imported fertilizers, oilseed, grain and other fodder, and income from exported farm produce. Imports of fertilizers and foodstuffs, excluding foodstuffs imported from subtropical and tropical regions, are about 12 per cent of the total imports, whereas farm produce usually is only 6 per cent of the total export. More than half of the revenue gained through export of milk products is lost in importing fodder to produce the same items. A considerable part of the imported fertilizers is applied to leys and fields sown to fodder. If the big annual sums paid as export premiums and for stabilizing the prices of animal foodstuffs are also considered, it is obvious that this export is not renumerative. But Finnish farming is in every respect marginal, and cannot therefore be renumerative.

Forestry as a subsidiary activity

Forestry and lumbering are vital to Finnish farming, and are at least as important as grain farming or dairying. Without the sale of timber

Table 9.2. *Number and area of forest plots, 1950.*

Size groups ha.	Number	%	Area 1 000 ha.	%
5– 20	104 245	41.7	1 220	11.4
20– 50	85 263	34.2	2 690	25.2
50– 100	38 882	15.6	2 700	25.2
100– 200	15 845	6.3	2 140	20.0
200–1 000	5 185	2.1	1 660	15.6
1 000–	146	0.1	270	2.5
Total	249 566	100.0	10 680	100.0

or the income from winter work in the forests, or both, most Finnish farms could not exist. The number and acreage of forest plots of over 5 ha. in 1950 are given in Table 9.2. The importance of forestry to farming is also evident from the fact that 61 per cent of Finland's forested area, 63 per cent of its total growing stock and 72 per cent of the total annual growth belong to the farmers.

The size of forest plots increases eastwards and northwards, and it can be said that on an average the arable area varies inversely with the forested area. One reason why the farmers of Lappland have so many tractors is the large areas of their forest plots. The subdivision of farms has considerably diminished the size of the forest plots. In 1929 plots with more than 200 hectares occupied almost a third and those under 50 hectares less than a fifth of the total area. Post-war distribution is shown in Table 9.2.

Income from the forest plays an important role in the management of the farm, even if it may only appear at intervals of 5 to 10 years. With it machines are bought and other outlays financed. It mitigates the constraint of crop failures. There is a marked trend towards contract-selling (contracts of delivery) instead of the old 'selling on root', i.e. as standing timber; the former now embraces more than 60 per cent of the total traded timber from private forests as against 30 per cent in 1939. The small farmer thus adds the income from felling and transport to the price for his timber. It is reckoned that lumbering, including transport, provides 36 per cent of the average farmer's income in Finland, comparatively more on small farms than on large, and, of course, more on central and northern than on southern farms.

For the smallest farmer with 2–5 ha. of arable land, forestry provides the main income. He earns money principally by work in the big winter camps of the forest companies. In large tracts of Suomenselkä, the Eastern Border Region og Forest-Lappland farming is subsidiary to forestry. The former still provides most of the daily food, but the latter produces the cash income.

FORESTS, FORESTRY AND FOREST INDUSTRIES

Her forests are Finland's foremost natural asset, and products of the forest and forest industry have been her main exports since the end of the 19th century. Both before and after World War II forest products have been from 80 to 85 per cent of the export total, though in recent years they have formed only 70–75 per cent of it. In 1965 2 per cent was exported as unsawn timber, 21 per cent as sawn timber, 7 per cent as plywood, furniture etc., and 70 per cent as

Table 9.3. *Forest area, 1951–53.*

| | Productive forests | | | | | | Poor types of forests | | | |
| | Finland | | North Finland | | South Finland | | Finland | | North Finland | South Finland |
	1 000 ha	%	1 000 ha	%	1 000 ha	%	1 000 ha	%	1 000 ha	1 000 ha
Pine	8 624	49.7	4 370	59.1	4 252	42.9	3 492	77.2	1 971	1 521
Spruce	6 125	35.3	2 226	30.1	3 894	39.3	338	7.5	274	64
Birch	2 273	13.1	732	9.9	1 543	15.5	675	14.9	546	129
Other deciduous trees..	208	1.2	15	0.2	199	2.0	5	0.1	3	2
Total[1]	17 352	100.0	7 394	100.0	9 918	100.0	4 532	100.0	2 800	1 716

[1]) Incl. clear-felled areas and other bare areas in the forests.

pulp and paper. The contribution to the Finnish economy is unmatched by any other activity in any Norden country. In absolute area Sweden has somewhat larger forests, but lowlying Finland has 4.9 ha. of forest per capita, whereas Sweden has 3.0 ha. and Norway 2.0 ha.

Types of forest

The state and development of Finland's forests are detailed in three large national surveys made in 1921–24, 1936–38 and 1951–53. A fourth, incomplete survey (1961–63) has not been used below.

As a rule the proportion of forest increases from south to north, with a corresponding decrease of arable. Treeless bogs also cause a reduction of the forested area within the belt of maximum bog development between 64° and 66°N (Fig. 9.6). Of the 19 Forestry Board Districts, five have a forest percentage above 80. Four of these are found in the Lake Region, and one east of Lake Oulu. The three forestry districts with a percentage below 65 are in the southwest, in the boggy interior of Southern Ostrobothnia and in mountainous northwestern Lappland. Cf. Fig. 9.23.

The forests are classed in the forest surveys as productive or poorly-growing forests (Table 9.3). The former constitute about four fifths and the latter about a fifth of the total forested area. The poorly-growing forests mainly border swamps and bogs and are common in northern Finland. In silvicultural terms this is the region lying north of a line drawn from about 64°N in the west to about 63°30′ in the east. Most of the productive forests (about 60 per cent) is in southern Finland.

The forests are also classified according to the predominant tree species and the character of the undergrowth. The latter is of special interest in forestry as it is often a more reliable indicator of the productivity of the forest land than the standing crop itself (Figs. 9.18 b–f).

The most productive type of forest has an undergrowth of herbs and grasses; it constitutes about an eighth of the productive forests. It is seldom found in northern Finland, but in some southwestern districts it forms a third and in the northern part of the Lake Region a fifth of the total.

The second type in fertility, characterized by blueberry *(Vaccinium myrtillus)* brush, dominates southern Finland where it forms a third of the productive forest as against a sixth in northern Finland. The third type, that with an undergrowth of cowberry *(Vaccinium vitis-idaea)*, constitutes about a quarter of the total productive forest area; in the north the crowberry *(Empetrum nigrum)* is also common in the undergrowth. This third type dominates interior Finland, the whole of Ostrobothnia (except its southern coastland) and Karelia, and the northwestern Lake Region. A rather less productive forest type, with an undergrowth of crowbery and blueberry, is frequent in the north, where it forms a fifth of the productive forests or, in the Lappland district, almost a third.

The most unproductive forest types with an undergrowth of heather *(Calluna)* and lichen (reindeer moss) form one ninth of the productive forests of the northern half of Finland, and in the Lappland district as much as a sixth, but they cover very restricted areas in southern Finland. Swamp forests constitute about 20 per cent of the total, spruce swamps of the *korpi* type (including drained swamps) being more common in the south, and pine bogs of the *räme* type in the north. Half the swamp area is classified as productive or potentially productive forest land.

The annual growth of timber in the most productive type with an undergrowth of grasses and herbs is 6 m³ per hectare, that of the cowberry type 4 m³, that of the heather type 2.5 m³ and that of the lichen type 1 m³, all categories with bark included. North of the polar circle the annual growth is usually less than 1 m³ per hectare, further south, as far as Lake Oulu, 1.5 m³ and in southern Finland 3.6–4 m³.

Pine-, spruce- and birch-dominated forests constitute 55, 30 and 14 per cent respectively of the total forested area. As a rule the pine favours the sandy, drier sites (eskers, marginal deltas) and the boggy areas (especially räme), whereas the spruce prefers damper and more fertile soils. Birch is common on burnt-over lands.

Pine forests constitute 50 per cent of the productive and 77 per cent of the poorly-growing forests (Table 9.3). There is a distinct contrast between northern and southern Finland, pine forests totalling not much more than two fifths of the productive forest land in the south, but three fifths in the north. The southwest and the southwestern archipelago have high percentages of pine forest as only poorer soils with stands of pine forests have remained untouched by the reclaimer. The poorly-growing forests of North Finland are dominated by mountain birch (*Betula tortuosa*).

Spruce forests cover 35 per cent of the productive and 7.5 per cent of the poorly-growing forest land. In southern Finland they cover 40 per cent of the productive forest area as against 30 per cent in the north. In some of the southern districts, in the northern part of the Lake Region and in the coastland of Southern Ostrobothnia, a half or more of the productive forests are of spruce.

Birch forests make up 13 per cent of the productive forest and 15 per cent of the poorly-growing forests. They are dominant in two regions, viz. the north, where for climatic reasons they replace conifers, and in the eastern Lake Region, where the spread of birch has been favoured by burn-beating.

Since the first forest survey in 1921–24

pine forests have slightly shrunk and spruce forests have extended considerably. In 1921–24 the latter constituted nearly 29 per cent of the productive forest area, but in 1951–53 over 35 per cent. In southern Finland the spruce forests have greatly extended (from 27 to 39 per cent) at the expense of the pine. At present the two conifers are of almost equal status in the forests of southern Finland. In northern Finland the position has been reversed, the pine forests now being more, and the spruce forests less common than in the early 1920's. The birch-dominated forest area has decreased. It now forms 13.5 per cent of the total forested area as against 17 in 1921–24. This is partly because the large birch forests of southeastern Karelia were lost in 1944.

Growing stock and annual growth

At the end of the war Finland lost about 13 per cent of its forested area. In spite of this, and the clearing of highly productive forest land for fields in post-war years, the 1951–53 survey shows only a small loss in stock and annual growth (Table 9.4). The main reason seems to be the great saving of timber during the war; the annual cut of industrial timber 1940–45 was 7.7 m³ against 15.4 m³ (solid metres) in 1922–36. In addition, silvicultural improvements including drainage, and the great reduction in forest pasturing have increased yields.

Broadly a third of the growing stock is located in northern, and about two thirds in southern Finland, because the northern forests have much thinner stands of timber. The growing stock of pine is somewhat smaller than its share of the forested area, whilst that of birch is larger. The more valuable *Betula verrucosa*, a raw material for the plywood industry, has a growing stock equal to that of *Betula pubescens* in southern Finland, but constitutes only a fifth of the total birch stock in the north.

The distribution of growing stock and annual

Fig. 9.18. Forest types at the 1951–53 forest survey, by forest board districts. a. Poorly-growing forest. b–f. Fertility types, arranged according to decreasing fertility, rough estimates of the average annual growth, incl. bark, per ha. being added in brackets: b. First type (6 m³/ha.), c. Second type (5 m³/ha.), d. Third type (4 m³/ha.), e. Fourth type (2,5 m³/ha.), f. Fifth type (1 m³/ha.), g. Predominating pine stands. h. Predominating spruce stands. i. Predominating birch stands.

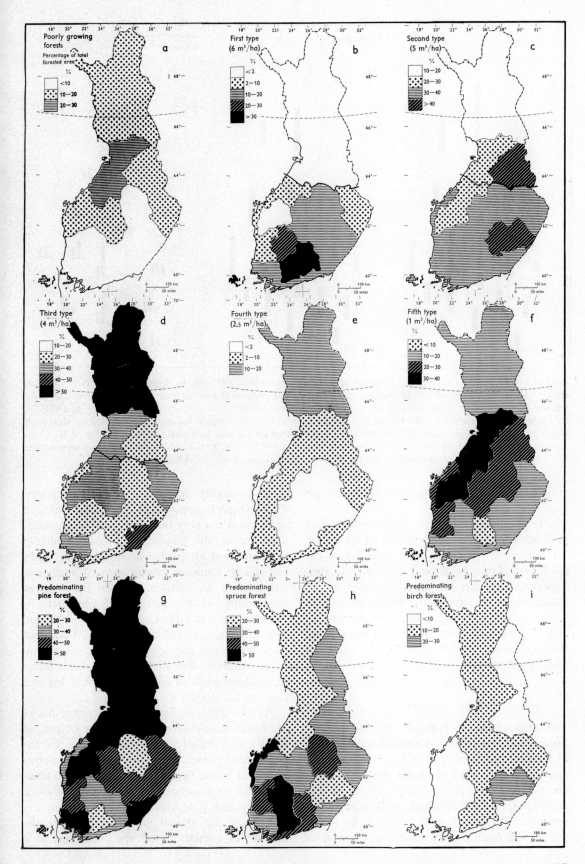

187

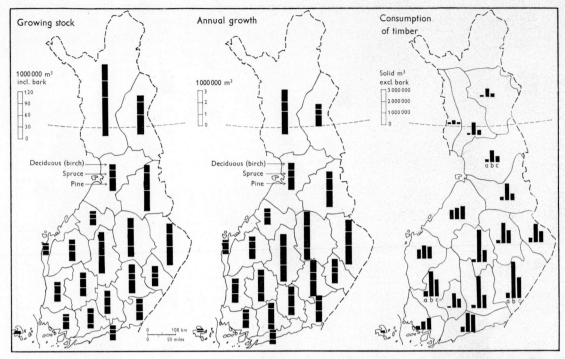

Fig. 9.19. Growing stock in million m³ at the forest survey of 1951–53, by forest board districts, of pine, spruce and deciduous wood. — If assessed according to the regions shown on Fig. 9.2, the share of the Lake Region amount to two fifths. — *Fig. 9.20. Annual growth in million m³* at the forest survey of 1951–53, by forest board districts, of pine, spruce and deciduous wood. — If assessed according to the regions shown on Fig. 9.2, the Lake Region has 44% of the annual growth of spruce and half that of birch. — *Fig. 9.21. Consumption of timber* by the main river system, averages 1955–57. a. Export of round wood, b. Consumption of timber by industry, c. Other consumption, mainly fuel. — After Pöntynen 1959.

growth at the 1951–53 survey is shown on Figs. 9.19 and 9.20.

Whereas thirty years ago the growth of pine in South Finland outweighed that of spruce by 7.1 million m³, the growth of spruce now exceeds that of pine by about 1.2 million m³. Biological factors may be partly responsible, but the change is also due to the encouragement of spruce in Finnish silviculture. The decrease in annual growth of birch in South Finland, and the increased pine growth in North Finland is also significant (Fig. 9.22).

Size groups and age classes

The exploitation of Finland's vast timber resources for export started much later than that of Sweden and Norway. The latter in particular had easier access to the main timber markets on the southern and western shores of the North Sea. Finland thus had, until recently, extensive virgin forests with large stocks of log size, which fetch the highest prices because of

their suitability for many special purposes. These virgin forests, which regenerate after fire or storm when very old, represent an unprofitable use of the ground, and have gradually been replaced by quicker-growing stands. They can still be found in remote parts of northeastern Finland. In southern Finland the younger age groups (41–80) predominate; in northern Finland the older ones, groups 121–160 and over 161 years, constituting 23 and 24 per cent respectively of the total growing stock, are more common. But timber grows much faster in southern Finland and age class and log size thus do not coincide.

As two thirds of Finland's total forest stocks are found in southern Finland, a major part of the log-size timber is also found there. Of the largest size group, trees with a diameter above 35 cm at breast height, northern Finland, however, has a somewhat larger number, and twice as many such pine logs as southern Finland.

Even if the annual growth determines the amount of annual cutting, the latter may as a

Table 9.4. *Growing stock and annual growth.*

| | Growing stock[1] in million m³ | | | | | Annual growth[2] in million m³ | | | | |
| | Finland | | | North Finland | South Finland | Finland | | | North Finland | South Finland |
	1921-24	1936-38	1951-53	1951-53	1951-53	1921-24	1936-38	1951-53	1951-53	1951-53
Pine	777	706	653	261	392	21.4	19.5	17.9	5.3	12.6
Spruce	481	503	533	155	378	13.2	15.2	16.9	3.1	13.8
Birch	290	295	273	89	184	10.2	9.8	9.4	2.3	7.1
Other deciduous ..	40	56	34	8	26	2.1	2.2	1.8	2.3	1.6
Total	1 588	1 560	1 493	513	980	46.9	46.7	46.0	13.0	35.1

[1]) Incl. bark. [2]) Excl. bark.

silvicultural measure exceed the former considerably for shorter periods. As a rule such a large regulated cut is recommended in the north, where old forests are common. Here spruce forests will be so cut and replaced by pine forests more suited to the climate.

Ownership

The state owns considerably more forest than in the other Norden states, in northern Finland as much as 60 per cent (Fig. 9.24). In southern Finland state-owned forests cover less than 7 per cent of the total forest area. Along the west coast nearly all forests are privately-owned as far north as 65°N. Extensive state forests cover 16 per cent of Central Ostrobothnia (mainly northern Suomenselkä) and 20 per cent of Northern Karelia (Eastern Border Region).

The highest percentage of company-owned forest is found in the Lake Region and espe-

cially in its northern and eastern parts (Fig. 9.25). Here it may rise to 20 per cent and in individual parishes to 40 per cent.

The above figures refer to areas. Distribution by growing stocks and annual increase is rather different (Table 9.5). The majority of the state forests, situated far up in the north, have a much slower growth than, as an aver-

Table 9.5. *Ownership of forests.*

	Area	Growing stock	Annual growth
	%	%	%
Private	60.3	63.2	72.2
State	30.8	25.2	16.3
Company	7.0	8.9	8.9
Others	1.9	2.4	2.6
Total	100.0	100.0	100.0
» thousand ha. ...	21 874	·	·
» million m³	·	1 493	46

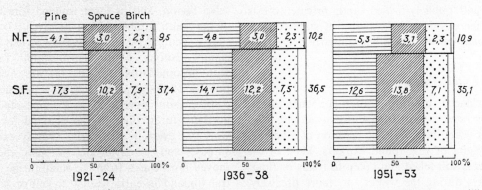

Fig. 9.22 Annual growth at the three forest surveys of 1921–24, 1936–38 and 1951–53 in million m³ (solid), divided between Northern and Southern Finland as defined on p. 185. The white columns are deciduous wood other than birch, i.e. mainly alder and aspen. The diagram emphasizes the difference between northern and southern Finland and the important changes in production which have resulted from the altered areal distribution discussed on p. 188. This has transformed Finland's former big surplus of pine wood into a slight surplus of spruce.

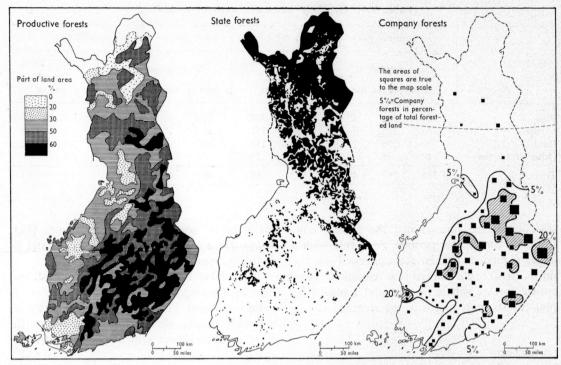

Fig. 9.23. *Productive forest area* expressed as a percentage of the land surface. The map is based on the taxation plots. — *Fig. 9.24. Distribution of state forests,* 1959. After Metsähallitus - Forststyrelsen 1859–1959 (1959). — *Fig. 9.25. Distribution of company forests,* 1953. Isolines indicate company forests as percentages of the total forest area.

age, those owned by companies and private landowners. Nevertheless, the state's influence on forestry in Finland is of the greatest importance. The autumn sales of timber from state forests set the price-level for timber during the coming season.

Since the first forest survey of 1921–24, mainly because settlement activities focused on state and publicly-owned land, private forests have increased at the expense of state forests. Company-owned forest has similarly decreased.

Felling and transport of timber

In Finland as in other Norden countries forestry has been a markedly seasonal activity. But recent years have seen the creation of a permanent cadre of year-round workers. Most of the timber is still felled and taken to roads or floatingways during the winter, or, more precisely, during that part of the winter in which the snow cover is thick enough to take log-laden sledges, and the ice of the forest swamps will bear them. Reliable snow and ice conditions do not normally occur in the southern half of Finland un-

til January when they produce weeks of great activity in the forests. It is fortunate that these weeks are slack ones on the small farms from which most of the seasonal forest workers come.

In southern Finland the timber feller often travels daily to work. In the north, in the forests of the Eastern Border Region and the Suomenselkä region, and in some isolated forest areas of the south, timber felling involves periods at state-, company- and privately-owned forest camps. About 3 500 transportable lodgings with accomodation for 40 000 are available, but in 1962/63 only 2 200, accommodating 6 800 persons were used. In the sparsely settled northern forest districts the demand for forest workers, even in the early 1950's, exceeded supply, and a cavalcade of men therefore moved northwards from the small farms of central Finland in early winter, to return home in spring. Some of the forest workers, perpetually moving around, were known by the name of *jätkä*. They were a characteristic feature of the Finnish forestry scene, legendary figures in the northern towns, above all in Rovaniemi. Here they produced an atmosphere reminiscent of Klondyke at the heyday of the gold-rush: money was quickly earned and quickly spent. The recent rapid mechanization of timber felling, the universal use of tractors and the extension of the working period to the whole year, has decreased both the numbers of forest workers and their seasonal migrations. A surplus of manpower in northern Finland has resulted in seasonal migrations southwards.

Timber transport is a more complicated business than felling. It implies haulage from the sites of felling either to roadsides for further transport to mills or ports, or to shores of floating-ways (rivers or lakes). Means of transport include sledges pulled by horses and tractors, trucks, trains; in rivers and lakes timber is either loose-floated (Pl. 9.5), or bundled and pulled by tugs in rafts (Pl. 9.4). Formerly the carrying of wood across lakes on lighters was rather common, but is now only used for firewood, especially birchwood.

Floating and rail transport are cheapest. Forests situated too far away from floating-ways or railways are outside the limit of profitable timber felling. The area of profitable felling is considerably larger for sawn timber than for the cheaper pulp wood. It expands with high and shrinks with low prices of timber. The main regions lying outside it are found in the north and along the eastern border of Finland, the natural water outlet of which is often towards the east. One of the main aims of the present industrialization programme is to open up the woods of these areas for industrial use by cutting roads for timber transport into them. 11 600 km of new forest roads have been planned for the period 1966–70, i.e. as much as during 1945–65.

Water is still the main means of cheap mass-transport of timber. In 1965 the average costs per m³-km were 0.02 Finnish marks by floating, 0.03 by rail and 0.10 by lorry; the average distance over which timber was carried was 57 km by road, 251 km by rail and 192 km by floating-ways.

In the same year mills received 44 per cent of their timber supply by floating, 44 per cent by road and 12 per cent by rail; the transport work performed, measured in m³-km, amounted to 53, 27 and 20 per cent respectively. Haulage by truck directly to the mill is increasing rapid-

ly. Of the 20.4 million solid cubic metres of timber carried by truck in 1965, 59 per cent was brought directly to the mills (against 34 per cent in 1952). The average length of truck transport has constantly increased.

Truck transport plays an important role at the upper reaches of the floating rivers, for short-distance transport of export timber to harbours in regions devoid of floatingways, and for transport of firewood. Tractor transport is employed for hauls of up to 20 km. For shorter distances, usually up to 3–4 km, horse transport is most economical, and it is unlikely that the horse will be completely displaced in timber transport in Finland. In the forest timber haulage is usually carried out by the small forest-owner himself on 'winter' roads which often consist merely of forest rides following boundaries of holdings.

Finland is estimated to have some 40 000 kilometres of natural floating-ways, which have gradually and continuously been improved by

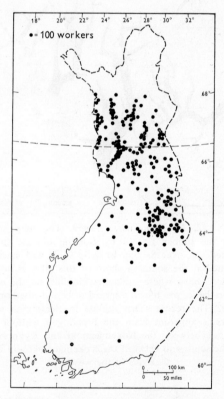

Fig. 9.26. *Home communes of workers in winter camps* for selected years during 1952–58. The maps include the workers of three timber companies (Veitsiluoto, Kajaani and Kemi), totalling 24 000. No information is available for the Oulu company. About 20 000 men were employed in state forest camps.

191

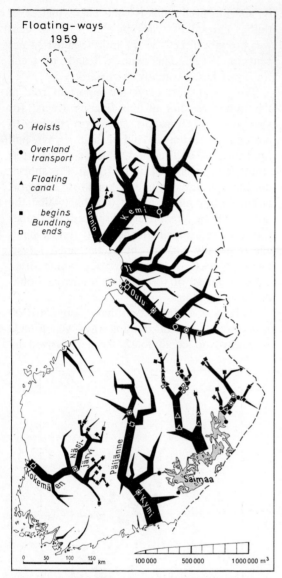

Floating-ways
1959

o Hoists

• Overland
   transport

▲ Floating
   canal

■ begins
   Bundling
□ ends

Tornio
Kemi
Ii
Oulu
Näsi-
järvi
Päijänne
Kokemäen
Kymi
Saimaa

0 50 100 150 km

100 000   500 000   1 000 000 m³

Fig. 9.27. Floating-ways, 1959. The map shows only the timber floated by floating unions; timber floated e.g. over Saimaa by pulp mills and sawmills situated at the southern shore of this lake, is not included. Sites where timber is bundled on the shore or on the ice are too widespread to be indicated on the map. The recent sharp decline in floating in small rivers is apparent from the broad gap without any floating between the Kokemäenjoki and Kymi rivers in the south and between the Kokemäenjoki and Oulu rivers in the west.

digging new cuts, by increasing their depths and by building canals through isthmuses. A major part of the earlier floating-ways have been abandoned, this is particularly true of the upper reaches of rivers. A recent survey of one

of the most important floating systems of Finland, that of Oulu river and its tributaries, shows that of a total length of 4 500 km of natural floating-ways, some 434 km have been abandoned and some 1 625 km are only occasionally used. Truck transport is replacing floating in small rivers with a short and capricious floating season. The length of the floating season varies from a few weeks in small rivers to several months in the main ones.

Timber now reaches its final destination in one floating season, whereas formerly, especially in the northern rivers, two summers were quite commonly needed to get the timber floated to port or mill. This involved big losses in stranded or sunken logs.

A special difficulty in Finland is that timber has to be towed across lakes, and, owing to the flatness of the country, also along considerable distances on the rivers. This problem has recently been aggravated by hydro-electric developments which, besides obstacles to floating at power sites (dams), have created artificial reservoirs with an inadequate flow. The insufficiency of natural water-flow has gradually become more serious as there is a clear trend from loose-floating and floating in circular booms to rafts of bundles hauled by tugs. Bundle-floating demands considerable investments. As the dimensions of log bundles are up to 8.5×3.5×2 m and of pulpwood bundles up to 3.6–4×2.6×2 m (the last figure indicating the depth below water level), channels have to be deepened and mechanical hoisting installed to lift the bundles over dams at power stations.

In the long run bundle-floating is cheaper than loose-floating and cheaper even than raft-floating. It has the advantage of being fast, of reducing floating losses to nil, of transferring the barking of pulp wood to the mills and of causing smaller losses of water-power in harnessed rivers. Bundle-floating is now universal on lakes and is increasing on rivers. The Oulu-joki river system has been equipped throughout for bundle-floating by the installation of hoists at power stations. Kymijoki and other rivers are being similarly improved; only Kemijoki is still wholly used for loose-floating. Bundle-floating is likely to become the only method, with a consequent reduction of floating-ways to about 5 000 km.

192

Utilization of timber

In a northern country like Finland, with long cold winters, much of the annual cut of timber (usually about a third) is used as fuel. As wood is widely used, especially in rural Finland, for both dwelling houses and farm buildings, more than two fifths of the annual cut is for domestic consumption. Until recently a tenth was exported as round wood, and slightly less than a half utilized as raw material in the wood-processing industry. During 1951–52 the total annual cut amounted to 40 million m³. In recent years it has increased to 50 million m³, greatly surpassing the annual regrowth. The export of round wood is insignificant.

Regionally there are some differences (Fig. 9.21). The largest amount of exported round wood came from the western and southern coastal districts. Industrial wood consumption has been both absolutely and relatively largest in the Lake districts. It is also high in northern Finland. In the Kemi district more than 75 per cent of the total cut is processed.

Industrial wood is made up of almost equal quantities of pine and spruce, with spruce slightly outweighing pine. Birch constitutes only a modest part although the use of birch for pulp tripled in 1960–63.

Wood-processing

Processing of wood has been an important activity in Finland for centuries and its products have long headed the export list. Tar distilled from pine was a major export item from Ostrobothnia in the 17th and 18th centuries, and planks and boards from water-driven sawmills were, from the mid-18th century, important exports of the southern and, especially, the south-eastern coast region. Wooden ships built mainly for Swedish purchasers have been a speciality of Ostrobothnia since the 17th century.

Wood-processing as a large-scale modern industry is however young, and of a more recent date than in Norway and Sweden. Steam-driven sawmills were founded at the river mouths in the 1860's. Though the first water-driven mechanical pulp mills were erected in the interior at the same time, a sulphate pulp mill as early as 1874 and a sulphite mill in 1885, the Finnish pulp industry is essentially a creation of the 20th century, and mainly of the period after 1920.

As in other Norden countries, the trend has been towards a higher degree of processing: pulp and paper production has increased at the expense of sawmill products, and chemical pulp at the expense of mechanical. Up to 1955 the sawmills nevertheless consumed more timber than all the pulp mills together. In 1964 consumption of industrial wood was as follows: sawmills 38 per cent, sulphite mills 21, sulphate mills 22, mechanical pulp mills 10, plywood mills 4, other mills 5 per cent.

Though Finland lost about a quarter of its pulp-mill capacity with the war-ceded areas, the total pulp production has increased considerably (Tables 9.6 and 9.7). The output of sulphate pulp has quadrupled in 1938–64, that of sulphite pulp has increased more in quality than in quantity, a higher proportion being bleached or processed into paper. The production of paper has nearly quadrupled during the same period.

The forest industries are big enterprises, embracing by vertical integration the whole gamut of forest activities from timber felling to all kinds of wood-processing, including paper making. The companies have their own forest lands, but have normally to buy most of their timber. Fourteen big companies, of which four are state-owned or state-controlled (in that the state owns more than 50 per cent of the stock), account for half the total sawmill output, and three quarters of the pulp and paper. The state-owned company, Finnlines, ships pulp and paper from the state mills. (It has recently shipped ores also.) The state-owned mills are partly in the southeast, where in 1918 the state purchased a bankrupt private company, and partly in the north (Kemi, Oulu), where the state owns large forests.

Finnish wood manufacturing is closely tied to waterways. This is due to the mass-transport of timber by water, to the great quantities of water needed, especially in pulp processing, and to the great amount of water-power consumed by wood-processing mills, especially mechanical pulp mills. Almost half the energy generated in Finland is used by pulp and paper mills.

Originally wood-processing was centred on falls. The names of some of the great pulp mills: Myllykoski, Äänekoski, Walkiakoski, Jämsän-

Table 9.6. *Production and exports of sawn goods, plywood, fibre board and pulp, 1913, 1938, 1960 and 1966.*

	Sawn goods		Plywood		Fibre board		Mechanical pulp		Sulphite pulp		Sulphate pulp	
	Prod.	Exp.	Prod.	Exp.	Prod.	Exp.	Prod.	Exp.	Prod.	Exp.	Prod.	Exp.
	1 000 std.		1 000 m³		1 000 tons		1 000 tons		1 000 tons		1 000 tons	
1913	1 031	861	244	207	—	—	155	50	80	21	65	21
1938	825	719	299	260	23	19	746	225	909	670	562	352
1960	1 360	1 143	414	358	244	152	988	176	1 285	919	1 181	500
1966	1 025	811	546	460	206	131	129[1]	130	1 433	909	2 305	1178

[1]) For sale only.

koski, etc. terminate in *koski,* the Finnish word for rapid. As so much Finnish wood and paper is exported, sites at seaports and especially at river mouths, where floating ways and sea routes meet, have proved attractive, cf. Fig. 9.27.

The most important is the Kymi river district (Kotka), which in 1966 made nearly half the national output of mechanical pulp, an eighth of the sulphite pulp, a sixth of the sulphate pulp and a quarter of the paper and board. It has maintained its lead from the outset, thanks to its large productive hinterland which includes the forests bordering on Lake Saimaa. The strong position in mechanical pulp (and newsprint, which is mainly made from mechanical pulp), is explained by the ample supply of soft water and by the early start, based on the water-power resources of the Kymi river, which are now inadequate. The state-owned Summa plant, east of Kotka, constructed in the mid-1950's, was until recently the biggest newsprint mill in Europe. Since 1961 it has been surpassed by a new paper mill west of Lake Päijänne with a capacity of 370 000 tons, cf. Fig. 9.29.

The Southern Saimaa Shore District accounted in 1965 for one fifth of the national output of paper and board. As the Vuoksi river, its natural outlet, leads to Lake Ladoga, its importance as a floating channel has always been negligible, and the artificial outlet, the Saimaa canal with its many sluices, was even before its cession to the U.S.S.R. in 1944 unimportant compared with the Kymi and Kokemäki rivers. The wood-processing plants in the Southern Saimaa Shore district are of pre-war date though some of them, like the Kaukopää Sulphate Pulp and Card Board Mill (Pl. 9.8) have

been enlarged since the war (output 1966/67 450 000 tons pulp and 450 000 tons kraftliner boards).

During recent years there has been a shift northwards so that the northern districts (Oulu, Kemi, Kemijärvi) at present account for about a fifth of the total output of chemical pulp.

The sawmill industry, which had reached its present production level in 1914, has undergone a great reorganization. Bigger units, some of them among the biggest and best equipped in Europe, like Kemi Oy's Karihaara which produced in 1966 60 000 standards (300 000 m³), have largely replaced older and smaller sawmills.

The first plywood mill was erected in 1913 in Jyväskylä. During the late 1920's and the 1930's a number of big plywood mills were built, especially in the eastern part of the Lake Region where extensive birch forests are common. The production of the existing 26 mills amounted in 1964 to 575 000 m³ or about six times that of 1930. Finland's newest plywood mill in Ristiina, in the southeastern part of the Lake Plateau, a region very rich in birch forests (see p. 186) is starting production in 1968.

The great expansion of wood-processing during 1955–65 has not markedly altered the distribution pattern of the Finnish pulp and paper mills. It is cheaper to enlarge existing plants, which have their harbours, communications and transport equipment in being, than to build new ones. It does not pay to build small plants to use existing reserves of timber in isolated forest regions, a production of 100 000 tons of pulp being considered the minimum economic size for a new plant. The average capacity of all pulp mills in 1959 was 81 000 tons; in 1965 it was 154 000 tons. New plants have, neverthe-

Table 9.7. *Production and exports of paper and board*
1913, 1938, 1960 and 1966.

	Newsprint		Kraft paper[1]		Other paper		Total paper		Board[2]	
	Prod.	Exp.	Prod.	Exp.	Prod.	Exp.	Prod.	Exp.	Prod.	Exp.
	1 000 tons		1 000 tons		1 000 tons		1 000 tons		1 000 tons	
1913	.	.	.	.	—	—	168	146	57	54
1938	401	358	42	17	120	88	562	464	124	82
1960	780	691	297	218	373	327	1 452	1 236	526	363
1966	1 295	1 193	371	283	649	603	2 315	2 078	1 064	955

[1]) Wrapping paper made from sulphate pulp. [2]) Paperboard and cardboard.

less, been built in recent years with large state subsidies to provide employment, sulphate pulp mills in the north, plywood, particle board and sulphate pulp mills in the east.

The expansion of processing will necessitate an additional supply of timber, consumption being now in excess of regrowth. The latter is supposed to increase from 45 million m³ to 80–100 million m³ in 70–80 years by planned measures of drainage, afforestation and fertilizing. Since 1945 1.5 million hectares of swamps have been drained. Nowadays 150 000 hectares are drained annually. If all possible areas yet undrained (7 million hectares) could be planted, this would mean an annual growth increase of 19 million m³ or a 41 per cent increase in the annual growth of all Finnish forests. A more rational arrangement of the cuts will give a better age composition of the forest and increase yields.

Technical progress in wood-processing permits the use of smaller sizes of timber (down to 5 cm diametre) and of birch wood. At present only 1.5 million of an annual increase of 9 million m³ of birch wood are used for pulp. In future part of the arable land may be planted with spruce. It may sound paradoxical, but Finland seems to need more forest and less arable land.

MINING AND MANUFACTURING

As an industrial country Finland is much younger than her Norden neighbours. Some big industrial plants were founded in the 19th century, largely to supply the Russian market, but there was little industrialization before 1918. In 1880 only 6.6 per cent of the total population, and even in 1930 only 16.8 per cent, got their living from manufacturing, including construction. In 1960 30.9 per cent were classified as industrial workers.

Before the war Finland had one big industry, wood manufacturing and wood-processing, producing mainly for export and employing in 1938 45 per cent of the total industrial population. In 1960 it occupied 23.1 per cent. Its development and present status are discussed on pp. 193–195. The other branches of Finnish manufacturing, which mainly produce for the home market, are dealt with below.

The reparations programme was a strong impetus to accelerated industrialization. Finland was obliged to pay six annual payments to the U.S.S.R. of goods valued at 300 million US dollars on the basis of 1938 values. The burden was lowered to 227.5 million dollars in 1948 and lifted at the end of an extended payment period in 1952 when three quarters of the original total had been paid.

More than four fifths of the reparations were to be manufactured articles, and over three fifths were to be delivered in the form of machinery and ships, and only one fifth as pulp and paper. This involved a change in industrial structure as well as an acceleration of industrialization. In employment figures in 1948 metal manufacturing and machinery surpassed the wood-processing industries, and in output value almost caught up with them. Their share of the exports,

195

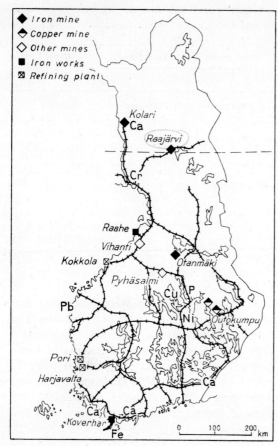

Fig. 9.28. Mines, ore bodies, quarries, iron-works and refining plants, 1967. Major mines are named, minor mines, quarries and large unworked ore deposits are shown by symbols. Cu = Copper, Pb = Lead, Ni = Nickel, Cr = Chromium, P = Apatite, Ca = Limestone.

insignificant before the war (1938 4.2 per cent), has grown considerably. After reparations payments ended in 1952 it slowly rose to 16.5 per cent of the export value in 1959. It has since varied between 15 and 20 per cent.

Finland lacks Norway's abundant water-power and Sweden's adequate reserves of both water-power and iron. She has an adequate supply of only one industrial raw-material, wood. She is poorly endowed for manufacturing as is Denmark, and like her, Finland has to rely on the inventiveness of the human mind and on human skill.

Mineral wealth

Finland it not entirely devoid of mineral raw-materials. Prospecting has been retarded by lack of capital and by sparcity of population in

the northeastern half of the country. The almost unbroken cover of glacial drift is a less serious obstacle today when geophysical methods are replacing older methods of prospecting. Although Finland has only a small, and, in respect of iron, quite inadequate mineral production, the outlook for the future is not altogether unpromising, many valuable ore bodies having been detected in recent years, especially in the north of the country. Finland now ranks first among the Norden countries in the production of copper, sulphur (from pyrites) and zinc (1965).

Iron ores have been exploited since the Swedish period, but owing to their small size and low iron content only sporadically and on a modest scale. In 1938 a magnetite-ilmenite deposit was found in Otanmäki south of Lake Oulu. Production, which started in 1953, was 476 000 tons of iron ore concentrate, 215 000 tons of ilmenite concentrate and 17 000 tons of vanadine-pentoxide in 1965. The iron ore concentrates are exported through Oulu.

Two smaller deposits with a high iron content, Kärväsvaara and Raajärvi, have been found east of Rovaniemi, close to the railway; the former closed in 1967 after ten years of production, the other started production in 1962. Further north, at Kolari on the Tornio river in Lappland, an older deposit of magnetite and haematite has recently been thoroughly investigated. A new state ironworks, built at the port of Raahe, south of Oulu, produced in 1966 650 tons pig-iron, of which 75 per cent came from Finnish ores—from Raajärvi, Kärväsvaara and Pyhäsalmi.

A private group reassessed the content of the submarine ore deposit at Jussarö off the south coast as 200 million tons of ore. Its exploitation ceased in 1967 and the new ironworks of Koverhar now uses imported iron ores.

In contrast to its modest production and meagre resources of iron, Finland has considerable deposits and yields of copper, and, as a result of successful prospecting in recent years, of zinc and lead also. The Outokumpu copper ore was found in 1910 and was first exploited in 1913. Successful mining did not really start there until the twenties, when Outokumpu was bought by the state. Output is at present about 550 000 tons annually, the mean content of copper being 3.5 per cent, of zinc 0.8 p. c.,

196

of cobalt 0.3 p. c., of sulphur 22 p. c. and of iron 25 p. c. Since 1935 the Outokumpu ore has been refined electrolytically at Imatra and since 1950 in newly constructed plants at Pori and Harjavalta (on the Kokemäki river), to which until recently all non-iron concentrates have been sent. Of the copper output, c. 30 000 tons in 1965, half is exported. The sulphur is used by Finnish pulp mills and the residue, the purple ore, with a high content of cobalt, has been treated since 1965 in a new refining plant in Kokkola.

Finland is the largest European producer of primary copper apart from Russia. New copper deposits, containing, on an average, 1.6 per cent copper and 0.7 per cent zinc, have been discovered northwest of Outokumpu. A pyrite deposit, found in 1958 at Pyhäsalmi in the interior of Central Ostrobothnia (0.8 per cent copper and 3.5 per cent zinc), is considered to be of about two thirds of the size of Outokumpu. Mining started in 1962, the annual output being 600 000 tons of raw ore. The sulphur is extracted at Kokkola, the copper will be refined at Pori and the zinc concentrate is exported. A new, large copper deposit has recently been found at Pielavesi, northwest of Kuopio.

In 1945 mining of a large deposit in Vihanti south of Oulu, containing 9 per cent zinc, and also copper and lead, was started. The output, 500 000 tons a year, is processed on the spot to give a 60 per cent zinc concentrate, containing 55 000 tons of pure zinc, and is at present exported. An ore body containing 5 per cent of lead has been intermittently mined since 1956 in Korsnäs at the coast south of Vaasa. The lead concentrate is exported.

As a replacement for the lost nickel mines in Petsamo a new nickel-copper ore deposit containing Ni 0.6 and Cu 0.3 p. c. has been found at Kotalahti in the eastern part of the Lake Region. The output, 470 000 tons, is refined at Harjavalta.

A considerable chromite ore deposit has been discovered at Kemi in northern Finland. It is not of high quality (because the iron content is difficult to separate), but is favourably situated. Exploitation started in 1960, a ferro-chrome plant is being built in Tornio, with normal gauge railway connection to Sweden.

Limestone is found in scattered deposits associated with the schist belts. The three biggest quarries (Fig. 9.28), with an annual production totalling 2.7 million tons, are situated in synclines or downthrusts of the Sveco-fennides. Most of it goes to the cement works. Smaller quantities go to raw-sugar mills or pulp mills or are applied on the acid soils as ground limestone. A new cement works to provide building material for power schemes has been built at Kolari in northern Finland.

Asbestos, quartz and felspar are also quarried, but production of the first two does not meet the national demand.

A deposit of apatite has recently been discovered at Siilinjärvi, north of Kuopio. The state-owned sulphur-acid company has started mining and will supply Finland's total needs for phosphate.

Power resources

Finland's hydro-electric potential is small. Southern Finland has only about 6 milliard kWh, owing to shallow lakes and low relief. Northern Finland, including the Oulujoki basin, possesses well over 12 milliard kWh. The southern resources were developed first and virtually all of the 3.2 milliard kWh available in 1939 was centered on the three southern river-basins. The war-losses included close on 1 milliard kWh, mainly on the Vuoksi river. But Imatra power station, still the biggest in the country, remained on the Finnish side of the new frontier.

Immediately after the war the state-owned Imatra Power Company was entrusted with the exploitation of the northern rivers. In 1964 2.75 milliard kWh has been harnessed in the Oulu river basin, and 1.94 milliard kWh in the Kemi river.

The centre of gravity in developed power has shifted northwards. As the demand is greatest in the south, a power grid uniting the northern sources of supply with the southern centres of consumption had to be built. In addition to a 100 kV line built along the coast from the mouth of the Kemi and Oulu rivers in the 1940's, two 200 kV lines were constructed from the power stations of Oulujoki to the old high voltage line from Imatra in southern Finland. The newest (400 kV) line from the power stations at Kemijoki was completed in 1960 and

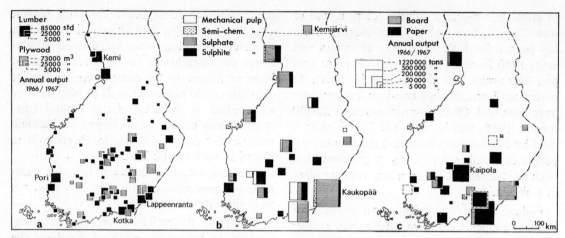

Fig. 9.29. Wood- and wood-processing industries. Squares indicate annual output 1966/67 in each industrial agglomeration. Same scale for maps b and c. Broken lines for paper-mills (map c) built later (after 1966/67). Board includes paperboard and cardboard. — After Helmer Smeds and Paul Fogelberg: Nyky-Suomi kuvin ja kartoin, Helsinki 1967, revised by Paul Fogelberg.

Finland's traditional export industries (a–c) have fewer workers than the rapidly rising metal industries. The latter are mainly found in the largest towns, Helsinki, Turku and Tampere. The sawmills (a) are rather widespread, with the largest plants in the export harbours of Kemi, Oulu, Pori and Kotka. The chemical pulp mills have a similar distribution with the largest plants in the ports and on the southeastern shore of Lake Saimaa. Many of the medium-sized sulphite pulp mills are located in the Lake Region on railway lines leading to the southwestern winter export harbours. Mechanical pulp and newsprint mills mostly have water-power sites (Kymi river, Tampere). The oldest plywood mill is found in Jyväskylä in a region with an ample supply of birch wood (cf. Fig. 9.18 i).

follows a more westerly course down to southern Finland (Fig. 7.4, p. 85).

The harnessing of the remaining power of the Kemi river involves the construction of many extensive storage dams, the two biggest having a capacity of 2 milliard m³ each. It is planned to complete the scheme in 1975 and 45 per cent of the total annual discharge will be stored. It is estimated that the Kemi river contains about 5.2 milliard kWh or almost half of the total power of northern Finland.

The extensive bogs are estimated to hold 120 milliard m³ of peat, but only 6 milliard, the calorific equivalent of about 300 million tons of coal, are exploitable. Waste wood from felling and from the different stages of wood-processing is estimated at 6 million m³ a year. A tenth of Finland's energy supply consisted in 1958 of such industrial waste, and three tenths of fuel wood, sold or used on the farms (in 1938 it was c. 45 per cent). Imported fuel represented nearly two fifths, and hydro-electric power the remainder. Cf. Table 7.9, p. 92.

Industry

Metal manufacturing and machinery now has the largest number of workers. Some 980 000

tons of pig iron are produced, and 370 000 tons of steel (1966). The ironworks on the south coast mainly use scrap. Some of these date back to the Swedish period when they were fed by imported Swedish iron ore, but others, like the Vuoksenniska plant at Turku and the Karhula electro-metallurgical plant at Kotka, are more recent.

During the post-war years there has been specialization in shipbuilding and electrotechnical equipment, including cables. Another speciality is machinery and equipment for pulp and paper mills. As in paper and pulp manufacture big companies are dominant. One of these, known as the Wärtsilä group after an 19-century ironworks in Karelia (now ceded) which refined bog-iron for the Russian market, employs about a sixth of all the workers in metal manufacturing and machinery. Many wood-processing companies own large metal manufacturing and machine plants. State-owned factories are also important in this branch, partly because the Finnish railways are state-owned, and partly because war reparations were handled directly by the state, largely at the former arms factories in Jyväskylä. Over four fifths of the establishments, and nearly 85 per cent of the workers in

198

this branch of manufacturing live in towns and market towns. Exports from the metal manufacturing and machinery branch are second to those from wood-processing.

Stone, clay, glass and peat are manufactured in a large and widely distributed number of establishments. Tile and pipe works are numerous, but are largely concentrated on the clay deposits south of Salpausselkä, with a preference for sites by the railway lines Helsinki–Hämeenlinna and Lahti–Riihimäki. The few glass and ceramics plants are either survivals from the Swedish period, located mostly in forested regions of the southwest, or modern establishments in towns, like the glass works of Riihimäki and Kotka, or the big pottery and ceramics plant of Arabia in Helsinki. This is owned by the Wärtsilä group, and has a large and diversified export of a quarter of its total output. The main raw-materials for the Arabia works are imported from England, East Germany and Czechoslovakia, but all felspar and most of the quartz comes from Finnish quarries.

About a half of the total output of the young, rapidly expanding chemical industry is produced at the new (1958) oil refinery in Naantali (NW of Turku). Other new works are the state-owned nitrogenous fertilizer plant in Oulu, another fertilizer plant in Uusikapunki (northwest of Turku); those at Harjavalta and Kokkola which make sulphuric acid from sulphide ores, and

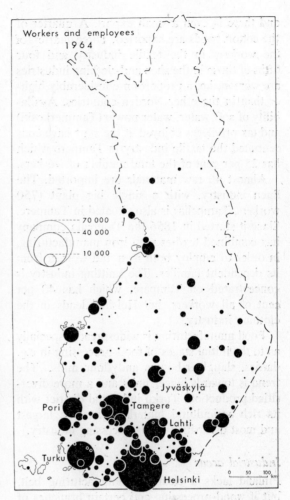

Fig. 9.30. *Manufacturing.* Circles indicate number of workers and employees in manufacturing 1964 in each commune. — After Helmer Smeds and Paul Fogelberg: Nyky-Suomi kuvin ja kartoin, Helsinki 1967.

factories making explosives, chlorine, plastics and insecticides.

The leather, rubber and shoe industry is largely concentrated in and around Tampere. These mills employ more than 40 per cent of all Finnish workers in this branch. The raw-material is mainly imported, and Tampere's lead seems to be due to an early start, and to links with its still older textile and clothing industry.

Finland's textile industry was already considerable during the Russian period, and was exporting a large part of its output. Horizontal and vertical integration are typical, as are big plants. About a half of the workers are employed in 10 plants with more than 1 000 workers. Finland produces four fifths of her textiles,

Table 9.8. *Workers in main branches of manufacturing.*

	1934	1946	1964
	%	%	%
Metal manufacturing and .... Machinery (incl. Mining)	16.8	33.0	30.8
Stone, clay, glass manufac.	6.3	6.4	4.1
Chemicals	1.6	2.4	3.4
Leather, rubber and shoes..... Textiles and clothing	21.3	18.3	15.9
Food, drink and tobacco	6.7	6.2	11.9[1]
Printing	3.1	3.5	5.6
Paper and pulp	10.8	8.7	10.3
Wood manufacturing	31.7	19.3	11.6[2]
Electricity, gas, waterworks....	1.7	1.9	4.0
Other.....................	—	0.3	2.3
Total, in per cent...........	100	100	100
» in thousands	162	237	416

[1]) Incl. dairies and slaughter-houses.
[2]) Incl. furniture and fixtures.

and there is even a small export. A quarter of the cotton goods are exported. Three quarters of the workers in the textile industry and four fifths of those in the shoe and clothing industries are women, i.e. a proportion considerably higher than in the other Norden countries. Availability of soft water, water power (Tammerkoski) and tax privileges enjoyed at the start have concentrated the textile industry in Tampere which has 25 per cent of the total number of workers.

Almost all raw materials are imported. The linen industry, with a single big plant (750 workers, Tampella) is also situated in Tampere. Since it started in 1856 the Tampella company has combined textiles with iron manufacturing, in order to employ both men and women from its dependent families. The knitting industry is concentrated on Tampere, which has 40 per cent of all workers, but Helsinki leads in the clothing industry.

Food manufacturing is widespread, especially as to the initial stages of food-processing in e.g. dairies, slaughter-houses and flour mills. The trend is towards bigger units and a more diversified production. Turku industrial district with its rich agricultural hinterland has the largest and most diversified food-processing industry.

Industrial areas

Finland lacks a clear-cut manufacturing belt, but if wood-processing and certain branches of food-processing are excluded, the Southwestern Core Region stands out as the most industrialized part of the country, with about 70 per cent of the total industrial production, mainly concentrated in the big towns. Helsinki, Tampere and Turku together have 31 per cent of the total number of industrial workers, the capital alone having 16 per cent (cf. Fig. 9.30). Together with the Kymi river and Kokemäki river industrial districts (with the industrial towns of Kotka–Karhula and Pori respectively) they represented 34 per cent of the gross value of the industrial production of whole Finland in 1963 (cf. Fig. 9.29).

Northern Finland lacks industry apart from wood-processing in Kemi and more recently in Kemijärvi, and somewhat more diversified manufacturing in Oulu. The rural districts of this extensive northern region have much underemployment or unemployment, and to remedy this, new manufacturing plants in Lappland and Oulu counties were exempted from taxes after 1957 for a period of 5 years.

As a result of the high birth rate immediately after the war the annual increase of the group over 15 years of age in the 1960's will be 35 000, and even at the end of the decade 25 000, whereas in 1951–58 it averaged about 17 000. In absolute figures this computed supply of new workers is largest in the south, but relatively it is biggest in the eastern and northern districts, where, e.g. in Lappland and in northern Karelia, it will be twice as big in 1961 –70 as in 1951–60. In northern Savo it will be more than three times as big. A considerable emigration to Sweden has resulted from this surplus of young labour.

COMMUNICATIONS AND TRADE

Land transport

In land transport Finland lags behind her Norden neighbours, with the obvious exception of Norway. Her extensive lowlands are fragmented by many intricate lakes and extensive bogs, and after the long severe winter there is much damage to road surfaces. The first railway in Finland, a 108 km stretch northwards from the capital, was constructed as late as 1862, the first macadamised road, running 52 km eastwards from Helsinki, was not built until 1931.

The railway network in 1967 comprises 5 540 km (of which only 440 km are double-tracked). This is rather less than in 1939, because 1 000 km were ceded to the U.S.S.R. Several new lines have been added to the inadequate rail network since the war. Electrification started in 1965 and the first electrified section (38 km), from Helsinki to Kirkkonummi will be opened in 1969.

Although both layout and equipment are inadequate, rail traffic continues to be important in transportation of heavy freight. There has been a 50 per cent increase in freight traffic since the war. Of the 18.5 million tons carried in 1964 about a fifth was construction material, an eighth agricultural raw materials and food, a quarter was logs and sawn timber, a fifth was processed wood, mainly pulp and paper, and a sixth was other goods, led by ores, metal goods and raw materials for the chemical industry. Finnish railroads are especially important to the wood-processing mills, supplying them and taking their finished products down to the export harbours.

As external trade to the east has greatly extended there is heavy traffic on the old eastern trunk line, technically easily managed as Finnish railroads are broad-gauged (1524 mm) like those of Russia.

Recently roads have outrivalled railways for transportation over short distances. Within 30 km of the ports most goods are carried by road, and up to 100–200 km, roads are competitive with railways. In 1957 roughly 100 million tons of goods were transported by truck, i.e. six times the total carried by rail. Sixty per cent of Helsinki's import are distributed by road. Truck transport increased from about 3 milliard ton/km in 1957 to 4.9 milliard in 1964.

There has been a heavy increase in the number of motor vehicles, particularly during the last decade. In 1966 Finland had 635 000 motor vehicles, of which 530 000 were passenger vehicles and 95 000 trucks.

The highways are, however, quite inadequate for fast and safe motor transport. In recent years there has been much progress in widening and straightening of roads and 14 000 km of the 37 000 km of state highways have been built or improved during the postwar period. But only 4 300 km are hard-surfaced, and the 88 ferries, necessitated by the interior lake-systems, slow down motor traffic.

The maintenance of roads for winter traffic has recently progressed greatly. The whole length of state high roads, up to the northern frontiers, is nowadays kept open for traffic throughout the winter as are most of the 32 000 km of communal and village roads. During the spring thaw (late April – early May) traffic is restricted or wholly prohibited on some roads, in 1964 on 6 000 km of roads.

Inland water transport

Lake traffic has played an important part in the economic life of Finland. The first steamboat was used on Lake Saimaa in 1833, and a number of important canals were subsequently dug. The longest one, the 56 km Saimaa canal cut in 1845–56, created an outlet to the sea for Finland's greatest lake-system. Motor transport has, however, replaced passenger traffic on inland waterways except for tourist purposes. The waterways, including canals, continue to be important for the transport of bulk cargoes. The use of Finnish canals is now a third of the 1939 figure in terms of tonnage. Thus in 1959 some million tons of goods (almost wholly timber) were carried by canal. Saimaa canal, cut by the new frontier, before the war carried about half the canal traffic. Between 1963 and 1968 this canal has been improved to take seagoing ships of up to 1 000 tons.

Winter traffic

Until fairly recently winter was the best season for transport. Ice-bridges over rivers, lakes and bogs and the use of sledges facilitated transport everywhere. These short 'winter roads' were typical of Finland up to the twenties, but when the horse was displaced in land transport by autobuses, tractors and trucks, the old system of winter roads was almost completely abandoned within a few years. The system partly survives in isolated districts and for lumbering throughout the country.

Sea ice is the most serious transport obstacle in Finland. It develops almost every winter and reaches its maximum in March. Only during exceptionally mild winters do the southwestern ports of Finland remain free of ice. During 1880–1948 there were seven such winters. As an average for 1934–54 the harbours have been ice-covered from a period of well over one month in Turku to about five months in Kemi. Ice-breakers make it possible for ships to use five to seven ports in the southwest and south in normal winters, and to use at least two (Turku and Hangö/Hanko) during severe winters. Finland has at present five ice-breakers built since the war, and some older ones. As a channel through the ice is easier to keep open through the archipelago than in the open sea, where pack ice soon forms and closes channels, the winter shipping lanes lie close to the coast inside the skerries. An ice-free shipping lane is being prepared to complete the system eastwards from Hamina. Cf. Fig. 9.31.

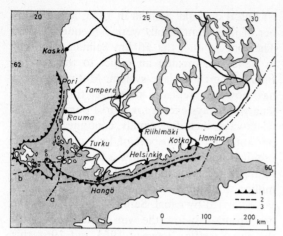

Fig. 9.31. *Shipping lanes and ice border*. 1. Edge
of solid ice in mid-winter (average position 20 January, 1880–1948). 2. Winter lanes kept open in the ice,
(a) those used at the beginning of the winter and (b)
those in use after (a) are closed by pack ice. 3. Railways used for winter transport to export harbours.
The ice reaches its maximum development in March.

Ice normally closes the northern ports in December and January and the eastern ones in
February–March (Fig. 4.4, p. 59). The northern and eastern wood-processing mills are then
forced to export through southern and western
ports and in severe winters can use only two,
Turku and Hangö. This overloads the ports,
their loading equipment and storehouses, and
the railroads and junctions. The export goods
carried by these railroads swell to 3–4 times the
normal amount. A difficult situation often develops, especially at Riihimäki, north of Helsinki. Here wood products from the Kymi river
and Southern Saimaa districts meet those from
the northern mills, and here also the inland
traffic from Helsinki has to pass through. Special rail tariffs are available to exporters who
send goods in advance to the southwestern harbours.

Airborne traffic

The first Finnish air-line was opened in 1924
between Helsinki and Stockholm. Since the war
development has been rapid. The state took over
most of the air transport existing in 1946. A
private company, Karair, which had expanded
since 1950, was affiliated to Finnair in 1963.
At present about 40 domestic routes are in use,
with a total length of about 8 200 km, and daily
flights. The majority of the 15 civil airfields, including that at Helsinki, and the military air-

fields, are situated on esker plateaux or marginal deltas.

In addition to domestic routes, services are
regularly maintained with Finland's Norden
neighbours and with all West European countries, except Portugal, Ireland and Iceland, and
with Yugoslavia and U.S.S.R.

External trade

Her large surplus of forest products has long
been the mainstay of Finland's export trade and
is likely to remain so. With changes in foreign
demand exported forest products have successively, included furs, tar, sawn goods, pulp and
paper, and gradually exports have become increasingly diversified. Table 9.9 shows that timber and lumber are constantly yielding to pulp
and paper, and that while pulp exports reached
their highest relative values before the war,
those of paper show a rapid post-war increase.

An increasing export of cheese and of mink
furs, has counterbalanced the decreasing export
of butter.

Table 9.9. *Finnish exports by value 1913,
1938, 1960 and 1965.*

	1913	1938	1960	1965
Timber and lumber	55.2	40.1	32.1	20.0
Pulp	4.5	25.9	17.1	18.2
Paper and paper products	10.9	12.7	20.7	18.6
Cardboard and cartons..	2.6	2.5	5.5	9.3
Butter and cheese	9.3	5.6	3.1	2.2
Others	18.5	13.2	21.5	31.7[1]
	100.0	100.0	100.0	100.0

[1] Including pig-iron 8.5%, ships 5.3%, machinery and
electro-technical equipment 4.4%, ores 1.4%, copper 1%.

Manufactured products other than processed
wood, e.g. textiles, glass and pottery, appeared
on the list of Finnish exports just before the
war. Post-war additions are furniture, clothing,
shoes, ore concentrates and metals (zinc, lead,
copper, iron) and above all, metal manufactures
and machinery. Up to 1952 the latter was largely war-reparations to the U.S.S.R., but since
then there has been an increasing export of ships
and machinery to many countries. Most of the
exports of ice-breakers, trawlers, river boats,
lighters, tug-boats, cargo-boats and tankers, still

go to the U.S.S.R. Exports of equipment for paper and pulp mills are worldwide.

Imports are largely raw materials. In 1966 42 per cent of the imports, by value, were raw material for industry and 11 per cent was fuel. Next come fertilizers and fodder. Consumer goods are increasingly imported, but for the time being are surpassed by capital goods needed for industrial development.

For many years Britain has been the foremost consumer of Finnish exports, while Germany, less markedly, has been Finland's foremost supplier. Before World War I Russia was the leading buyer and the second customer for Finnish goods. At present the U.S.S.R. is almost as important as was Czarist Russia in Finland's external trade, taking in 1966 a seventh of Finland's exports, viz. second only to Britain. West Germany is Finland's first supplier, followed by Britain, the U.S.S.R. and Sweden. The large deforested countries of Western Europe are the natural and old-established buyers of Finnish wood, pulp and paper. The two European trade blocks of EFTA and EEC absorbed 64 per cent of Finland's exports in 1966, and supplied 69 per cent of the imports, the COMECON countries 19 and 20 per cent respectively. Cf. Table 7.15, p. 97.

CHAPTER 10

ICELAND

by Sigurdur Thorarinsson[1]

THE FACT that Iceland belongs to the 'Scandinavian World' is founded on historical, linguistic and cultural bases but not on geographical or geological ones. But the geographical situation of the country justifies its inclusion among

[1]) The sections on human geography have been written in conjuction with Valdimar Kristinsson, cand. oecon.

the Norden countries. Iceland is still listed among arctic countries in some geographical periodicals. But as a matter of fact only one of the Norden countries, Denmark proper, reaches less far north than Iceland and, since Greenland has become a part of Denmark, Iceland is the only one of the Norden countries that is

Fig. 10.1. The main bedrock formations of Iceland. The Basalt Formation is a remnant of the Brito-Arctic flood-basalt region that extends from East Greenland to the British Isles. The Palagonite Formation fills the zone between the two main areas of Tertiary Basalt. Its most characteristic rock is a brownish tuff breccia formed by Pleistocene subglacial eruptions.—After G. Kjartansson. (Úr sögu bergs og landslags. Náttúrufræðingurinn, Vol. 26, 1956.

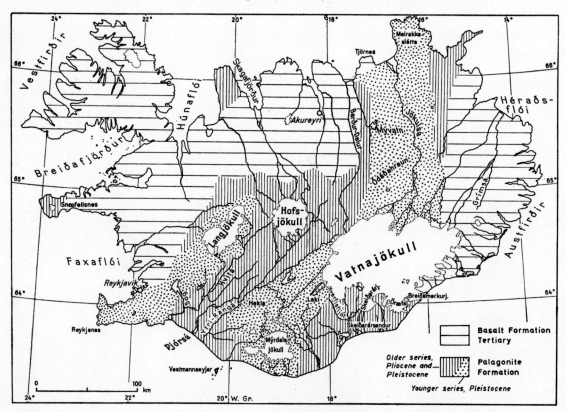

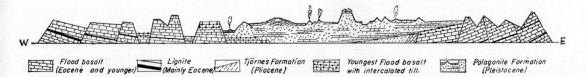

| Flood basalt (Eocene and younger) | Lignite (Mainly Eocene) | Tjörnes Formation (Pliocene) | Youngest Flood basalt with intercalated till. | Palagonite Formation (Pleistocene) |

Fig. 10.2. Schematized W-E section of the bedrock in north Iceland. The Tertiary basalts are broken up by tectonic movements and dip mainly towards the interior of the country. The lignite beds are of Eocene or Miocene age. Intercalated between the lava beds in the boundary zone between the two main bedrock formations are tillites that are mainly of early Pleistocene age. Postglacial vulcanism is restricted to the areas covered by the Palagonite Formation (cf. Fig. 10.4).—After G. G. Bárðarson (Ágrip af jarðfræði, 1927, modified by S. Thorarinsson.

situated practically entirely south of the Arctic Circle. Its northernmost point, Rifstangi, lies at 66°33′N. It should not be forgotten, however, that all the other Norden countries, even Greenland, extend much farther south than Iceland, the southernmost mainland point of which lies at 63°23′N. The shortest distance from Iceland to Greenland is only 287 km and to Scotland 798 km, but to Norway it is about 990 km. The area of Iceland is 103 000 km² and its population (1967) is 200 000.

PHYSICAL GEOGRAPHY

GEOLOGY

Geologically Iceland is the youngest of the Norden countries and its geological history supplements splendidly that of the Scandinavian countries as it begins about the same time that the building up of those countries comes to an end, and its building up is still going on. Whereas the age of the oldest rocks in Fennoscandia has to be counted in thousand million years, the oldest rocks in Iceland are hardly more than about 60 million years old, and probably only half that age, big areas in the country were built up within the last million years and about one tenth of its area is covered by lavas less than 10 000 years old. And whereas fold-forming movements have played a dominant role in forming the Fennoscandian bedrock, the movements in Iceland have been predominantly fault-forming and oscillatory.

The Basalt Formation covers about half of the country (the Vestfirðir area, the western part of North Iceland, and the Austfirðir area (Fig. 10.1 and 10.2). It is in the centre of the Brito-Arctic flood- or plateau-basalt region which extends from East Greenland via Iceland and the Faeroes to the British Isles. Many palaeobotanists and palaeozoologists are still of the opinion that these basalt areas were once connected, forming a landbridge between the Old and the New World, but most geophysicists now think this unlikely.

The Icelandic plateau-basalts are partly tholeiites, partly olivine basalts. Acid and intermediate rocks (rhyolites, dacites, andesites) amount to 5 to 10 per cent of the Basalt Formation and indicate the possibility of a sialic substratum, although it is nowhere exposed. Plant-bearing sedimentary intercalations, mainly lignites, are common in the lower part of the Basalt Formation, especially in the northwest. It is now considered most likely that the lignites are of Miocene age. Macroscopic remains in the lignites have produced about 50 species, among them beech, maple, vine, liriodendron and others indicating a temperate to hot temperature climate.

If volcanic activity had ceased in Iceland as it did in other parts of the Brito-Arctic area in the late Tertiary, Iceland would now probably be a group of elevated basalt islands, an enlarged copy of the Faeroes. But in Iceland vulcanism continued during the Pliocene and Pleistocene, connecting the separate basalt blocks as one mainland.

The mainly Pleistocene Palagonite Formation covers a broad median zone running from Melrakkaslétta in the northeast to the Reykjanes Peninsula in the southwest. It also covers the

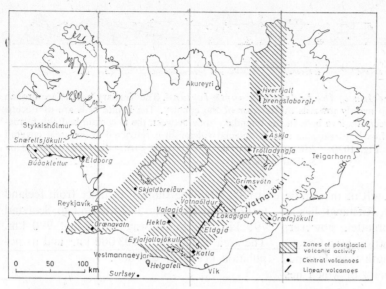

Legend in figure:
Zones of postglacial volcanic activity
Central volcanoes
Linear volcanoes

Fig. 10.3. Iceland's best known postglacial volcanoes.

western part of the Snæfellsnes Peninsula and the peninsula between Húnaflói and Skagafjörður (see Fig. 10.1). The median zone is a part of the Mid Atlantic Rift Zone. Many geologists and geophysicists favour the view, not yet proved, that this zone is the result of tensional movements which have torn apart the original Tertiary basalts; subsequently the gap has been filled with younger volcanic products.

The Palagonite Formation is a complex one, a mixture of on the one hand subglacial and subaerial eruptives, on the other of glacial, fluvial and aeolian deposits. The most characteristic rock is a brownish tuff breccia (Icelandic *móberg*) rich in hydrated basalt glass known as palagonite. This breccia is produced for the most part by subglacial eruptions and it has built up two types of mountains, ridges and table-mountains. The ridges, the prototype of which is Jarlhettur, are steep-sided, normally serrated, and they run in straight lines NE-SW in South Iceland, but N–S in North Iceland. The table-mountains (prototype Herðubreið, north of Vatnajökull) are isolated, steep-sided mountains, circular or sub-rectangular in form. The top is flat or gently convex and consists of one or more sheets of basalt. Usually there is a crater on the top. The underlying socle is built up of pillow lavas and of pillow lava and tuff breccias. These mountains have formerly been explained either as horsts or as erosion remnants, but they are now regarded as constructive

features built up under the Pleistocene ice sheets. The table-mountains are the result of central eruptions. Their socles are steep-sided because of the icewalls resting against them while they were consolidating, and the lava flows on their tops were extruded when these mountains had grown high enough to protrude through the ice cover. The table-mountains would then correspond to the interglacial and postglacial shield-volcanoes and the ridges to the crater rows.

In the boundary zone between the two main formation tillite beds are found between basalt layers that date back to the earliest Pleistocene (age 2 to 3 million years).

Recent studies have revealed that in the Basalt Formation, series of normally magnetized layers, with the direction of magnetization close to the present location of the geomagnetic field, alternate with layers where the magnetism has the opposite direction. The reversals of the geomagnetic field can often be detected with an ordinary field compass. In the East Iceland basalts about 60 reversals have been established. The last reversal occurred about 0.7 million years ago, and a large part of the Palagonite Formation is normally magnetized.

Gradually the vulcanism became more and more limited in extent. In Postglacial Time volcanic activity has been limited to the median zone covered by the Palagonite Formation and to the Öræfajökull area and a small zone running from Snæfellsjökull 100 km eastwards (Fig. 10.3). More than 150 volcanoes have been active during the last 12 000 years or so and the median zone is still more productive than any other area of comparable size in the world. Since the settlement of Iceland about 1 100 years ago nearly 30 volcanoes have been active, and during the few last centuries an eruption has occurred on an average every fifth year. With activity on the same scale Iceland's volcanoes could build up a lava mass of the

Table 10.1. *Icelandic types of basalt volcanoes.*

	Eruption products	Number of eruptions	FORM OF VENT	
			CIRCULAR (central eruption)	LINEAR (linear eruption)
Decreasing temperature and Increasing explosivity	(Besides gases)			
	Lava (Effusive activity)	1	Lava ring Type: Eldborg	Lava crater row Type: Þrengslaborgir
		1 or >1	Shield volcano Type: Skjaldbreiður	
	Lava and tephra (Mixed activity)	1	Mixed crater Type: Búðaklettur	Mixed crater row Type: Lakagígar
		>1	Stratified cone Type: Snæfellsjökull	Stratified ridge Type: Hekla
	Tephra (Explosive activity)	1	Tephra cone Type: Rauðaskál	Tephra crater row Type: Vatnaöldur
		1	Tephra ring Type: Hverfjall	Explosion fissure Type: Valagjá
		1	Maar Type: Grænavatn	

present volume of Iceland above sea level (50 000 km³) in less than 1.5 million years.

Icelandic vulcanism is predominantly effusive, producing more lava than tephra[1]. About one third of the lava produced on the earth since 1500 A.D. is 'made in Iceland'. With regard to their surface structure the Icelanders distinguish between two types of lava flows: *helluhraun,* with a rather smooth billowy and ropy surface, easy to traverse, and *apalhraun,* with a fragmented irregular and scoriaceous surface, often a result of more viscous flow. Corresponding lava types on Hawaii are *pahoehoe* and *a-a.* In the helluhraun lava flows caves are common. Groups of so-called pseudocraters, formed when glowing lava has overflowed ground rich in water, are a typical feature of some lavaflows in Iceland. Skútustaðagígar at lake Mývatn form a typical example. The post-glacial lava flows cover about 30 per cent of the neo-volcanic zones and about 10 per cent of the entire country.

[1] Tephra is a collective term for volcanic ash and other pyroclastic ejecta, such as pumice, bombs, lapilli etc.

VOLCANOES

Icelandic volcanoes represent nearly every type of volcano found on the face of our globe. The shape and size of a volcano depend essentially on three things: the form of the eruption vent, the character of the eruption products and the number of eruptions. The eruption vent may be either linear (fissure) or approximately circular. The eruption products, besides vapour and gases, are either lava or tephra or both.

In Table 10.1 these three factors are used as a base for classifications of the main types of basaltic volcanoes in Iceland. The volcanoes listed on the Table are shown on Fig. 10.3. With regard to the form of the vent they form two main groups, central volcanoes and linear volcanoes.

The result of a single purely effusive central eruption is a lava ring, the type of volcano which in Iceland is called *eldborg,* i.e. fortress of fire or lava. Sheets of lava, overflowing the crater rims, build up a very regular crater wall and this flowing lava spreads to all sides. The prototype is Eldborg in the Mýrar district, of western Iceland, which erupted in the Settlement Time. An eldborg may be regarded as an embryonic shield volcano of the Icelandic-Hawaiian type as the shield volcanoes are built up around a circular vent by purely effusive eruptions, producing lavaflows mainly of the helluhraun (pahoe-hoe) type. There are about 30 postglacial shield volcanoes in Iceland and they have been the main producers of postglacial lava in the country besides the crater rows. At least some of the Icelandic shield volcanoes may have been built up by a single eruption. A typical shield volcano is Skjaldbreiður (the broad shield) near Þingvellir. The angle of slope is 7.5°. No Icelandic lava shield except the one of Surtsey has been built up since the Settlement Time.

Volcanic edifices resulting from a single but mixed central eruption are rare in Iceland, as usually there is a row of such craters. Búðaklettur, south of Snæfellsjökull, is an example of a single, mixed cone.

Repeated mixed central eruptions result in a cone volcano (strato volcano) of the Fuji or Vesuvio type, the commonest type of volcano outside Iceland. In Iceland these volcanoes are not common, but to them belong the biggest volcanic structures in the country, such as Iceland's highest mountain, Öræfajökull (2 119 m), second in volume only to Etna in Europe. In 1362 A.D. it had a tremendous eruption, completely destroying extensive settlements. Eyjafjallajökull erupted in 1821. The volcano Dyngjufjöll in North Iceland has a vast caldera, Askja, formed partly after a big explosive eruption in 1875. The extinct Snæfellsjökull is a beautiful regular cone visible from Reykjavík in clear weather. The highest strato volcanoes are all ice-capped.

The purely explosive central eruptions form many types of explosion craters. If the explosivity is moderate the result is a scoria cone such as Rauðaskál near Hekla. Higher explosivity leads to the formation of tephra rings, the prototype of which is Hverfjall east of lake Mývatn, built up about 2 500 years ago. Typical for the tephra rings are their great diameter compared with their height. Then there are explosive central eruptions leading to a mainly negative landform, a 'maar', a deep crater which nearly lacks a ring and is more or less filled with water. Maars are especially numerous between Hekla and Vatnajökull. Grænavatn, 30 km south of Reykjavík is a typical 'maar'.

The linear volcanoes of Iceland also show a great variety of form, from purely effusive to purely explosive ones. By far the most common type of volcano in Iceland is the crater row. Usually its craters are of different types, the result of a mixed linear eruption. The most famous of such crater rows is the 25 km long Lakagígar, with about 100 craters. It erupted from June 8th until February 1784 and poured out the greatest mass of lava produced by any of the world's eruptions in Historical Time. It covers 565 km². During the whole summer of 1783 a bluish haze covered both Europe and Western Asia. It was caused by the Laki eruption. In Iceland this haze stunted the grass crop and the disastrous famine that was the result of the eruption is still referred to as the Haze Famine.

A predominantly effusive linear eruption results in a lava crater row and an explosive one is a tephra crater row such as Vatnaöldur northeast of Hekla. The impressive Eldgjá fissure is partly the result of subsidence and slumping.

As to Hekla (Pl. 10.1), Iceland's most famous volcano, it is morphologically neither a crater row nor a cone volcano, but rather a mixture of both. It is a vaulted ridge, built up by many mixed eruptions around a linear vent. Both Hekla and the biggest strato volcanoes have had a cyclic activity, each cycle starting after a long period of quiescence, with a violent and highly explosive acid (rhyodacitic or rhyolitic) eruption producing acid tephra. The last cycle of Hekla started in 1104 A.D. Since then Hekla has erupted 14 times.

The explosive extreme of the linear eruption leads to the explosion fissure, that is a row of explosion craters cutting into each other so that they form a continuous chasm with garland contours. Valagjá north of Hekla is a typical example. All linear volcanoes in southwest Iceland run SW–NE, in north Iceland they run N–S.

Table 10.1 does not cover structures composed of acid lava, such as cumulo domes and tholoids. Such volcanoes are on the whole rare in Iceland, but some pyramid-shaped mountains such as Hlíðarfjall, north of Mývatn, and Baula, in the southwest, are of these types. East of Hekla are postglacial rhyolite (obsidian) lava flows, some of which have been squeezed out

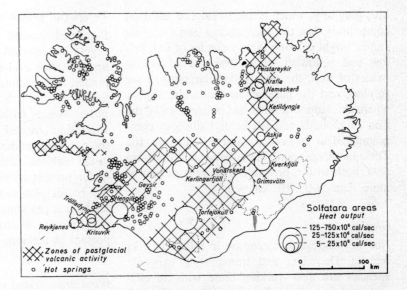

Fig. 10.4. Solfatara areas and hot springs in Iceland. Cf. Fig. 10.1 (geology). The high-temperature or solfatara areas are all situated within the areas of young volcanic activity, whereas hot water springs are found all over the country, although there are very few in the East-Iceland plateau-basalt area. Compiled from maps by J. Jónsson (Náttúra Íslands 1961), G. Bodvarsson and S. Thorarinsson.

like toothpaste from a tube, without any crater formation in the normal sense.

Submarine volcanic eruptions occur quite often in continuation of the neo-volcanic zones off the Icelandic coast. In November 1963 the biggest of these eruptions in historical times started southwest of Vestmannaeyjar, and built up an island (Surtsey) with an area of 2.8 km² and at present 155 m high.

NATURAL HEAT

Even for a volcanic country Iceland is exceptionally rich in natural heat. The temperature gradient in the bedrock is on an average two or three times the normal. Two types of thermal areas can be distinguished, low temperature or hot spring areas and high temperature or solfatara areas.

The low temperature areas are characterized by hot water springs, by subsurface temperatures not exceeding 100°C and by a relatively low degree of thermal metamorphism. Hot water springs (Fig. 10.4) are found all over the country. Their water is usually alkaline, clear and precipitates silica. It is groundwater that has percolated deep enough through the rocks to be heated so that it reaches the surface with temperatures up to boiling point. The circulation basis may be the base of the flood basalts, at 2–3 km depth, where one may expect temperatures between 100°C and 150°C. In general the thermal areas are controlled by permeable contacts between lava beds, permeable dikes

and faults. Some of the boiling springs are intermittently spouting springs or geysers, the most famous being the Great Geysir in South Iceland. Its eruptions seem to be caused by overheating of the water at a depth of 10 m in the feeder tube. Hot water springs are found at more than 300 localities, and the number of springs is about 800. By far the biggest one is Deildartunguhver in Borgarfjörður, which has a flow of 150 litres per second of boiling water.

The high temperature (solfatara) areas are limited to the neo-volcanic zones (Fig. 10.4). Their steam is also mainly derived from percolating groundwater, but they differ from the low temperature areas in subsurface temperatures which are usually above 200°C at the circulation base. It is thought that under these areas intrusives, which still have very high temperatures, supply the heat. The circulating water seems to have a direct contact with these hot intrusives, and the thermal gradient in these fields may be up to about 1°C per metre. This results in a violent convection and upward movement of water at high temperatures. At great depths the water may remain in the fluid state, but on reaching a higher level a partial evaporation starts, with the result that a mixture of water and steam issues from springs at the surface. The water is usually acid and precipitates sulphur.

In all there are 14 solfatara fields in Iceland. The incredible wealth of colour in these areas is their most striking feature. In the solfataras themselves there is seething thick mud with a

209

14

blue-grey tinge which is due to sulphur and iron compounds, but the surrounding earth has assumed bright colours; mainly shades of red, yellow and yellowish white. The red is due to oxides of iron, the pure yellow largely to pure sulphur, and the pale yellow and white appear where the sulphuric acid has washed away the iron compounds and left behind siliceous compounds. The biggest solfatara fields are the Torfajökull area and the subglacial Grímsvötn area, both with a probable total heat output of more than 500×10^6 cal/sec.

Glaciers

Not only endogenic forces are in full activity in Iceland. Denuding and transporting exogenic agencies are also working there with an efficiency almost unparalleled anywhere. Glaciers cover 11 800 km² or 11.5 per cent of the total area of the country, and nearly all types of glaciers, from small cirque glaciers to extensive plateau ice-caps, drained by numerous valley glaciers, are represented there.

Vatnajökull (8 400 km²) is the biggest glacier outside the Polar Regions and Greenland, and has a maximum thickness of 1 000 m. The margin of its biggest southern outlet, Breiðamerkurjökull, reaches more than 100 m below sea level. Other big ice-caps are Langjökull (1 020 km²), Hofsjökull (995 km²) and Mýrdalsjökull (700 km²). With the possible exception of the highest parts of Vatnajökull all glaciers in Iceland are temperate, which means that throughout these glaciers surface temperatures correspond to the melting-point of the ice, except in winter time when a top layer is frozen to a depth of some metres. The glaciation limit in Iceland is highest, about 1 500 m, in the interior north of Vatnajökull, and lowest, about 750 m, in the northern part of the Vestfirðir area. The south sides of Vatnajökull and Mýrdalsjökull have a very intensive glacial energy as the ablation and accumulation per unit area are very high, and as the Icelandic rocks are on the whole easily eroded, glacial erosion and mechanic fluvial erosion are particularly effective in the country, whereas chemical erosion is on the whole rather insignificant. The extensive sandur (outwash) plains (Pl. 10.4) in front of the biggest glaciers give with their braided streams a living picture of conditions once prevailing at the margins of the Pleistocene inland ice.

Periglacial phenomena

Patterned ground occurs in Iceland in both vegetation-covered and bare areas. At heights up to 400 or 500 m the dominant surface formation of vegetation-covered ground are the hummocks which in Icelandic are termed þúfur (sing. þúfa). The dominant type of vegetation-covered soil on the inland plateau is the palse (Icelandic flá). Tundra polygons occur in the highland, although they are rarely formed under present climatic conditions. Polygons on the basalt plateaux are anchored, but in the lowland areas small floating and well assorted polygons are most common. Solifluction is important in Iceland.

Wind erosion and abrasion

Wind erosion plays a considerable role in Iceland, especially in the more continental interior of the country, and it effects not only the soil cover but also the rock, especially the tuff breccias. A very important role is played by frost weathering, due to frequent shifts of temperature around 0°C—in the highland mainly in summer, in the lowland in winter—combined with a wet climate and facilitated by the cleavage of the Icelandic basalts. Consequently many mountain slopes and old cliffs are more or less smothered in accumulated screes. Big rockslides are a common feature, especially in valleys in the basalt areas whose sides have been oversteepened by glacier erosion.

Opinions differ as to the role played by marine abrasion in Iceland. In the author's opinion tectonically directed abrasion has played a role in the formation of the shelf and of the broad strandflat that fringes great areas of the west and south coasts of Iceland. Presumably glacial erosion also played a role, as the strandflat must at least mainly be of Pleistocene age. A striking fact is that the supra-marine strandflat is found mainly south of the Wyville-Thomson ridge and the ridge that connects Iceland with Greenland.

Thus Iceland is really a magnificent laboratory for the studies of various geomorphological processes, and not without reason it has been claimed that "no other country illustrates so completely within its borders the geological dictum that the present is the key to the past".

THE ICELANDIC LANDSCAPE

Although the Pleistocene glaciations have stamped their marks on Iceland as on the rest of the Norden countries, the Icelandic landscape differs greatly in many respects from that of Scandinavia. It bears all the signs of a young country still in the making. It is in most places roughly hewn and jagged and without that softness of outline that characterizes a more mature landscape. Even its colours give in many places the impression of immaturity, being bright and strong, in places almost brutal. The roughly hewn powerful forms and the sharp contours of the landscape are particularly noticeable as the country is so devoid of forests and in wide areas nearly without any vegetation at all. The landscape is on the whole more dramatic than idyllic. But there is also a great difference between the landscape of the old plateau-basalt areas and that of the young volcanic areas.

The old basalt plateau units, built up by thin flowing lavas, have been broken up by tectonic forces into a mosaic of tilted blocks (Fig. 10.2), the majority of which dip towards the interior of the country so that the greatest heights occur near the coasts. Whether this dipping is due to subsidence towards the interior or to an isostatic uplift of the marginal zones is an open question. The main tectonic period was followed by a large-scale erosion, maybe leading to peneplanation, but the interplay between erosion, uplift and piling up of lava during the latter half of the Tertiary has not yet been worked out in detail.

The landscape in the basalt areas may be designated a plateau- and fjord-landscape (Pl. 10.3). The numerous fjords are mainly the result of glacial deepening and widening of valleys that were originally eroded by rivers more or less guided by fractures. In the formation of some fjords, such as Skagafjörður and the northern part of Eyjafjörður, faulting may have played a dominant role. The succession of lava sheets, whose uppermost and lowermost parts are more vesicular and broken up, and therefore more easily eroded than the middle part, gives the fjord- and valley-sides their characteristic 'trap' appearance. The average thickness of the lava flows is about 10 metres. The lava sheets are cut through by numerous dykes that guide many of the rivulets cascading down the valley sides.

Usually the fjord sides are steep and there is very little lowland along them, but inland from their heads stretch long valleys with flat floors formed by the sedimentation of the rivers and usually with marked gravel terraces along the valley sides, the result of the postglacial uplift. In the Vestfirðir area the original plateau character is relatively well preserved in spite of the many cirques that are incised into the fjord sides. The area between Eyjafjörður and Skagafjörður is more 'alpine'. In the Austfirðir area, which is probably the oldest part of the country, the basalt formation reaches its greatest total stratigraphic thickness (about 10 000 m above the layers now exposed at sea level). Here acid vulcanism has played a considerable role and numerous acid intrusions, sills, stocks and laccoliths, have shattered the basalt rock and facilitated the work of the denuding agencies, producing a very rough and broken surface.

The palagonite tuff areas present a landscape of quite another type. Here also fault-forming has played a role although the constructive features dominate. A characteristic feature in this area is the uniform direction of the dominating fracture zones. In the southwest they run NE—SW and in the north they run nearly N—S. This holds true not only for the valleys, as reflected in the course of the main rivers, but also for the *móberg* ridges, crater rows and the numerous open fissures (*gjá*, pl. *gjár*). In these two main physiographic units can be discerned: 1) the shelf—the coastal plains, between about −200 and about +100 m, and 2) the inland plateau, mainly between about +300 and about +700 m. The coastal plains are mainly strandflat, partly covered by sandurs.

Above the inland plateau rise the massifs under the big glaciers and a few rhyolitic massifs, many tuff ridges and table mountains, and the numerous extinct and active sub-aerially built volcanoes. This landscape is on the whole very open. Characteristic of the scenery are extensive plains bordered by steep-sided mountains, and out of the plains rise single isolated mountains visible at great distances from all sides.

The coasts

The coasts of Iceland are mainly of two types, rock coasts and sandy coasts. Rock coasts are dominant within the basalt areas. They are ir-

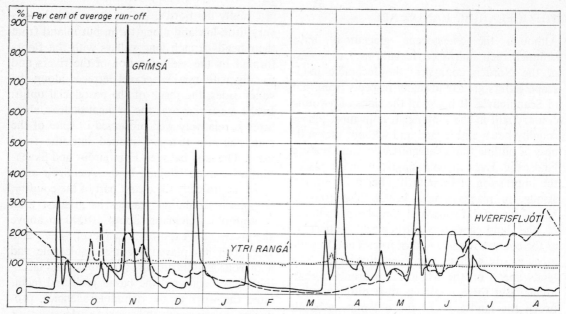

Fig. 10.5. Run-off graph of three rivers: A glacier river (Hverfisfljót), direct run-off river (Grímsá) and spring-fed river (Ytri Rangá) during the hydrographic year 1956/57 (cf. Fig. 10.1).—Hverfisfljót has summer floods and late-winter low water. Grímsá is situated within the Tertiary Basalt Formation, where the rocks are rather impervious. It has many sudden and short floods; those in Sept.—Nov. are due to heavy rainfalls, the rest to snow melting. Ytri Rangá drains an area mainly covered by postglacial porous lava-flows and has a very even flow throughout the year.—Based on measurements by S. Rist.

regular in outline, cliffed and incised with numerous fjords and inlets. In many of the fjords curved shingle spits project from the shores. Some of these spits are formed by delta deposits, others are due to marine action and alongshore transport. Inside these spits are good natural harbours and most of the villages and towns in the fjord areas are built on such spits (Pl. 10.3). Parts of the coasts of Breiðafjörður and Faxaflói are typical *skjærgård* coasts of the Norwegian type, the skjærgård being a part of the strandflat.

The sandy coasts are smooth in outline and have extensive off-shore bars backed by lagoons. The southeast and south coast from the southern part of the Austfirðir area to just west of the mouth of Ölfusá is almost entirely of this type. It has no natural harbours, and long stretches of it are a graveyard of wrecked ships. Most of the material that builds up the bars comes from the debris-laden glacier rivers, and the same type of coast is found in those parts of the basalt area where glacier rivers discharge at the head of broad inlets such as Héraðsflói and eastern Húnaflói. Along the south coast of Snæfellsnes runs an offshore bar consisting mainly of shellsand.

Rivers and lakes

Because of the high rainfall the rivers in Iceland are numerous and relatively large. The largest one, Þjórsá, is 237 km long and has an average run-off of 400 m³/sec. The Icelandic rivers are of three main types. The first is the glacier river *(jökulá)* to which most of the biggest rivers belong. The prototype is Skeiðará (Pl. 10.4). Usually the glacier rivers split into a great number of braided streams which are constantly changing, and the river system as a whole oscillates over the sandur areas that are formed in front of the glaciers and in some cases even at a long distance from the glacier margin (Héraðssandur, Kelduhverfi). The maximum run-off of these rivers is in July and early August. Glacier bursts *(jökulhlaup)*, due either to vulcanism or to the sudden emptying of ice-dammed lakes, occur in many of these rivers, the best known being those from the volcanic Grímsvötn area in Vatnajökull. They used to flood Skeiðarársandur on an average every tenth year and reach a maximum run-off of about 50 000 m³/sec., or as much as eight times the average run-off of the Danube at its mouth. Still bigger are the floods caused by the eruptions of the volcano Katla in Mýrdalsjökull. They flood Mýrdalsandur twice every century. On Fig. 10.5 Hverfis-fljót has been chosen as an example of a glacier river.

The non-glacier-fed rivers are of two types. These are very different, from geological, hydrological and biological standpoints. The direct run-off rivers (dragá) drain the old basalt areas which are not ice-covered. These rivers are made up of a number of small brooks in areas where the bedrock is relatively watertight and the soil cover thin. They have a very varying flow as they react quickly to snow melting and rainfall, and their floods have great erosional power (Grímsá).

The spring-fed rivers (lindá) mainly drain areas covered by permeable postglacial lava-flows and have a very constant discharge (Ytri Rangá). The temperature of their water is practically the same all the year round, very near the average annual temperature. The water is very clear and its erosional power small. They are very suitable for harnessing, and the two rivers so far most extensively harnessed, Sog and Laxá, are of this type.

Typical of the young tectonic landscape are the numerous waterfalls. The largest one is Dettifoss (44 m) in Jökulsá á Fjöllum (Pl. 10.2).

The lakes of Iceland are also numerous and of widely diverse origins. Some of them are mainly tectonic (Þingvallavatn), some are due to deepening of valleys by glacier erosion (Skorradalsvatn), others are dammed up by lava-flows (Mývatn), glaciers (Grænalón), rock slides and glacial deposists. Caldera lakes occur (Öskjuvatn) and maar lakes are numerous. The rapid retreat of glaciers during the last few decades has resulted in the formation of many 'Zungenbecken' more or less occupied by lakes. The Zungenbecken in front of Breiðamerkur-jökull now reaches about 110 m below sea level and its lake contains brackish water.

CLIMATE

The climate of Iceland is influenced by the geographical situation of the country and by its situation in the boundary zone between two very different air masses, the one of 'polar' and the other of 'tropical' origin. It is also influenced by the confluence of two different ocean currents. Because of the submarine ridge between Iceland and Scotland a branch of the North Atlantic drift—a continuation of the Gulf Stream—is deflected westwards and flows clockwise along the south and west coasts of Iceland. As a consequence these coasts are ice-free throughout the year. Some of the Atlantic water reaches the north coast, but because of its higher salinity it is there submerged under arctic water brought to the north coast partly by a branch of the East-Greenland Polar Current, and partly by the currents circulating between Iceland and Jan Mayen. The amount of Atlantic water that flows eastwards north of Iceland varies from year to year and has a profound influence on the biology of the North Iceland waters, especially in late spring and early summer.

A third factor affecting the climate of Iceland is the arctic drift ice. The drift ice border varies greatly during the year and from year to year. In some years the northern coasts of Iceland are completely ice-free, in other years the ice moves into these coasts, especially in the late winter and early spring, and in extreme years fills every fjord in the north and northeast until late August.

The seasonal fluctuations of temperature and climate depends, however, mostly on the atmospheric depressions crossing the North Atlantic. The passage of a depression south of Iceland brings relatively cold and dry weather, whereas one passing northeastwards between Greenland and Iceland brings mild but rainy weather.

On the whole the climate of Iceland may be characterized as cold temperate oceanic, with a high positive temperature anomaly in the winter half of the year.

The temperature and precipitation averages at six coastal meteorological stations are shown on Table 10.2 (the stations are indicated on Fig. 10.3).

Table 10.2. *Average temperature and precipitation, 1931–1960*

Place[1]	Temperature C°			Precipitation mm		
	Year	Jan.	July	Year	Jan.	July
Reykjavík	5.0	−0.4	11.2	805	90	48
Stykkishólmur	4.2	−0.8	10.4	756	83	36
Akureyri	3.9	−1.5	10.9	474	45	35
Teigarhorn	4.4	0.1	9.8	1235	133	79
Vík í Mýrdal	5.7	1.2	11.3	2258	182	169
Vestmannaeyjar	5.4	1.4	10.3	1391	138	84

[1] Cf. Fig. 10.3.

The annual rainfall at Vík is the highest measured along the coast, but on the southern slopes of Mýrdalsjökull it is at least twice as high. In the northwest the number of days with snowfall is at least 100, in the southeast it is about 40.

On the whole the weather in Iceland is very changeable ("if you don't like the Icelandic climate just wait a minute"), and the monthly averages fluctuate greatly. Storms are frequent especially in winter. Fogs are rather rare except for the east- and northeast-shore districts. Thunderstorms are rare and occur mainly in winter.

During the last few decades Iceland has been much affected by climatic amelioration. The northern fjords were never blocked by ice between 1920 and 1965, and the average annual temperature of Stykkishólmur was 1.4°C higher in 1919–48 than in 1859–88. The glaciers are still on the whole receding and thinning. This climatic amelioration has affected both vegetation and animal life on land, especially the bird life, and has caused important biological changes in Icelandic waters.

SOILS AND VEGETATION

Soils

Roughly speaking the soils of Iceland may be grouped as mineral soils and organic soils. Intermediate types are also found. The mineral soils may be termed loessial. They are to a greater or lesser extent formed by deposit of wind transported material. This material is supplied by the powerful physical forces of weathering and volcanic eruptions (tephra falls), and causes a rapid thickening of the soil profile. Because of the cool climate the chemical and biological forces of soil formation are slowed down, and hence the chemical and physical properties of the soils reflect strongly those of the basaltic rocks and tephra. Thus the soils are well supplied with biologically important metallic constituents and are generally rather weakly acid (mineral soils pH 6–7, organic soils pH 5–6). Due to loess deposits the widespread Icelandic bog soils are rich in mineral matter (frequently 40–60 per cent), and the organic matter of the surface layer is raw and turfy. The mineral soils contain rather a low clay fraction, their structure is therefore weak, and they are susceptible to wind erosion.

The most extensive potentially good agricultural soils in Iceland are of the organic type. These soils require expensive drainage systems, yet when properly cultivated they are more productive of grass than the mineral soils.

Although the Icelandic soils possess many desirable properties as agricultural soils the fertilizing requirements are rather high, because of the slow biological activity in the rigorous northern climate.

Vegetation

When comparing the natural vegetation of Iceland with that of the rest of Norden three differences emerge. One is the nakedness of the country, namely the great areas that are desert or semi-desert, another is the lack of woods and the third is the small number of species of higher plants.

The nakedness and the lack of woods are partly due to natural conditions. Throughout Postglacial Time big areas in the interior have been bare of vegetation and the upper limit for a continuous carpet of vegetation has been lowered considerably since sub-Boreal Time. The tree line is now at 300–400 m, and where there is a plant cover on the highlands it consists mainly of bogs with palses. These bogs are a facies of the subarctic tundra. In the lowland there has always been big areas nearly bare of vegetation, such as the sandurs and newly outpoured lava-flows.

It is evident that the present nakedness and lack of forests is to a considerable extent due to the influence of man. There has always been a struggle between the soil-building and soil-eroding processes, and both have worked speedily. As long as the country was uninhabited there was a fair equilibrium between these processes, but that equilibrium was seriously disturbed by the advent of man and his animals. Previously there was no herbivorous mammal in the country. Through grazing (mainly sheep grazing) and woodcutting, the chief protectors of the easily eroded mineral soils, the birch woods and scrub, were gradually destroyed. There is probably no great exaggeration in the statement of Ari the Wise that the country was "wooded between the coast and the mountains" in the Settlement Time (870–930) when the

214

settlers came in. Of this extensive wood- and scrubland only about 1 000 km² remain. In the young volcanic areas especially, soil erosion has been on such a catastrophic scale as to lay waste vast areas. It is roughly estimated that even below the 400 m level about half of the land area, or at least 20 000 km², is now more or less bare. The greater part of that area had a vegetation cover in the Settlement Time. Recent tephrochronological and palynological studies have revealed that soil erosion by wind and water began to increase very soon after the beginning of settlement in Iceland, or about 900 A.D. and has been going on continuously since then and on an increasing scale. Deterioration of climate since the 13th century and volcanic activity may have, and in all probability have played some role in this destruction of soil and vegetation cover, but not at all a decisive one. During the last few decades successful efforts have been made to stop soil erosion and bring bare areas under cultivation.

The phanerogams and vascular cryptogams of Iceland total 550–600 species. A corresponding figure for the British Isles is about 2 300. The small number of species in Iceland is partly conditioned by the climate but is partly due to the Pleistocene glaciations and the limited possibilities of immigration because of the isolation of the country. The majority of the species that have not been accidentally introduced by man are regarded by Icelandic botanists as glacial survivors. Many plants, among them trees that could grow in Iceland, have not been able to find their way to the country in Postglacial Time. Consequently the Icelandic flora is not a reliable reflection of the recent Icelandic climate.

In recent years successful experiments— somewhat helped by the climatic amelioration— have been made in re-afforestation with trees from areas with climates comparable to Iceland, for instance, parts of Alaska (Sitka spruce). These experiments have proved that under present climatic conditions coniferous woods can grow in Iceland, at least in climatically favoured districts.

The isolation of the country is also the main reason why, when man arrived, only one land mammal, the arctic fox, existed in Iceland. Mice and rats have since then been accidentally introduced, and reindeer were imported from northern Norway in the second half of the 18th century and still exist in a wild state in the highland north and east of Vatnajökull. In the 1930's mink escaped from captivity and has reverted to the wild state; it is increasing rapidly and is seriously threatening bird life.

Iceland's bird life is rich. 72 species nest there, 240 species are known to have occurred there, and the country is a very important breeding ground for many waterfowl such as ducks and geese. Most of the birds of Iceland find it a land of peace and are therefore tamer than in most other places. They constitute the main idyllic element in this largely barren country.

AGRICULTURE

Physical background

Two consequences of the Icelandic climate make the country fundamentally different from the Scandinavian countries from the farmer's standpoint. One, the lack of woods, has been mentioned above, another is that agriculture could never be based on cereals. The immigrants in the Settlement Time soon learnt that barley was the only type of grain that could be grown. Gradually it appeared that it could not be depended on except in the south and southwest, but even in these areas grain growing was never very important, and climatic deterioration terminated it before the end of the 16th century. It was not until the 1920's that barley growing started again on an experimental scale. Because of the recent climatic amelioration these experiments proved rather successful, but this grain growing has not yet passed the experimental stage.

The material welfare of Icelandic farmers has from the first depended mainly on the raising of sheep and cattle, together with salt- and fresh-water fishing, and up to the 20th century the breeding of livestock was based mainly on grazing and haymaking from natural pastures, and not from cultivated (i.e. drained and manured) meadows.

There was thus from the beginning a basic difference between Icelandic farming and that of the countries from which the immigrants came, i.e. Scandinavia and the British Isles. This difference exerted a profound influence on Icelandic civilization. The farmer's attachment to his farmstead depends first and foremost on the cultivation of the soil. With cultivation goes stability and immobility, but Icelandic farming has always had a touch of nomadism. The Icelandic farmer has never been so closely attached to his farmstead as his Scandinavian counterpart. Movement between districts and different parts of the country has been much commoner in Iceland. This mobility has no doubt played a role in maintaining the uniformity of the economy and spiritual culture of the Icelandic farmers all over the country. No separate cultural areas and no real dialects ever rose in Iceland. It may well be that the love of epic poetry and sagas so typical of the Icelanders, may to some extent be traced to the nomadic element in the farming economy.

Changes in farming

The present century has seen great progress in Icelandic agriculture, the main changes being rapidly increasing cultivation of grass-land, development of dairy farming and increased mechanization.

Agriculture is now mainly based on the drained and manured land. The volcanic (basaltic) loessial soil is generally fertile and the extensive marshlands are also suitable for cultivation when drained, because of the high mineral content of the peat soils. Grass on manured land is usually harvested twice each summer and is either stored dry in barns or green in silos. The average crop of hay per hectare of cultivated land is 4 500 kg. Extensive natural pastures can be used for the grazing of livestock, not only in summer, but also, for sheep and horses, during long periods of the winter season. Meadows for cattle are confined to the inhabited areas, but large numbers of sheep and ponies roam the uninhabited interior of the country without any control from June until the middle of September.

Reclamation of new land, of which there was very little for centuries, has been developing gradually since the turn of the century, and most rapidly during the last one and a half decades. The cultivated area is five times that of 1900. Nevertheless, only about 100 000 hectares are so far under cultivation. This is only a twentieth of the potential cultivable land of similar quality. At first the main stress was laid on the fencing of the home fields and then on

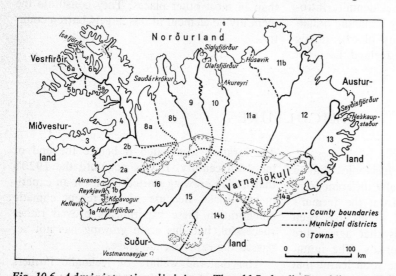

Counties

1a. Gullbringusýsla
1b. Kjósarsýsla
2a. Borgarfjarðarsýsla
2b. Mýrasýsla
3. Snæfellsnessýsla
4. Dalasýsla
5a. Austur-Barðastrandarsýsla
5b. Vestur-Barðastrandarsýsla
6a. Vestur-Ísafjarðarsýsla
6b. Norður-Ísafjarðarsýsla
7. Strandasýsla
8a. Vestur-Húnavatnssýsla
8b. Austur-Húnavatnssýsla
9. Skagafjarðarsýsla
10. Eyjafjarðarsýsla
11a. Suður-Þingeyjarsýsla
11b. Norður-Þingeyjarsýsla
12. Norður-Múlasýsla
13. Suður-Múlasýsla
14a. Austur-Skaftafellssýsla
14b. Vesur-Skaftafellssýsla
15. Rangárvallasýsla
16. Árnessýsla

Fig. 10.6. Administrative divisions. The old Icelandic Republic was divided into four administrative units *(fjórðungur):* western, northern, eastern and southern ones (see p. 7). Now Iceland is for administrative purposes divided into 16 counties *(sýsla),* each governed by a sheriff *(sýslumaður)* and each forming one or two municipal districts which are also called sýslur. These are again subdivided into civil parishes *(hreppur),* 213 in all. There are also 14 towns *(kaupstaður)* with town councils, independent of the counties and forming separate administrative units.

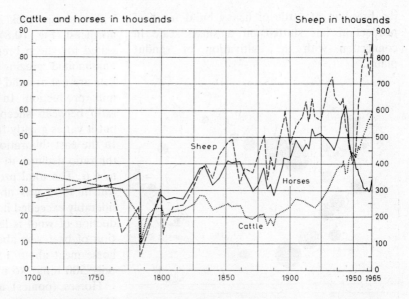

Fig. 10.7. Number of live-stock, 1703—1965. In spite of the recent doubling of the number of cattle, sheep are now relatively far more numerous than 200 years ago. The sharp drop in all graphs in 1783/84 is due to the Laki eruption (see p. 208), that of the sheep graph in the 1940's is due to virus diseases brought to the country by foreign breeding animals.

their levelling, as they are usually so hummocky, due to frost action, that levelling is a prerequisite for the use of hay rakes and mowing machines. Since the Second World War the main projects have been the draining of marshland and the cultivation of desert sandur areas. Soil erosion has been halted in many places, mainly by the building of stone-walls and the sowing of lyme grass. Afforestation has not passed the experimental stage; it is, however, planned on a considerable scale.

Livestock and animal products

The livestock of Iceland consist primarily of cattle, sheep, horses and poultry. Pigs and geese are of negligible importance. Until the 1930's goats were fairly numerous in some districts in the northeast as well as in many villages, but now only a few score are left. It is estimated that for centuries sheep were 8–10 times more numerous than cattle (Fig. 10.7), but since the middle of the 19th century sheep have increased more rapidly in numbers. Between 1940 and 1950 sheep greatly decreased owing to severe virus diseases that were brought into the country a few years earlier by foreign breeding animals. These diseases have now more or less been overcome and the number of livestock in 1965 was as follows:

Sheep	800 000
Cattle	56 000
Horses	30 000

Icelandic farmers now derive more than nine-tenths of their income from livestock. About 45 per cent of the farmers' gross income is from fluid milk, 37 per cent is from sheep products, and garden and greenhouse products account for 6 per cent.

The lowlands of the Suðurland area are the main cattle area in Iceland (Fig. 10.8). A third of the country's cattle is found there. These lowlands are situated within easy reach of by far the biggest market, Reykjavík and its neighbouring towns. The milk is mainly processed at Selfoss, where one of the largest dairies in Norden is located.

The second largest cattle area is Eyjafjörður, the climatically most favoured northern district. Milk products are in considerable demand in the local towns, and at Akureyri there is a large dairy. In Borgarfjörður there is also considerable cattle farming, the milk being shipped to Reykjavík.

By scientific breeding and by the use of better feeding stuffs the average yield of milk per cow has increased from 1 600 litres at the turn of the century to 2 950 litres in 1965. In the same year the dairies received 100 000 tons of milk, of which 45 per cent was sold to consumers as milk and cream and the rest went into the production of butter, cheese and *skyr,* a special icelandic dish made of coagulated milk.

Dairy farming is dominant.. Some veal is marketed, however, and in the last few years

217

the breeding of cattle of heavy build for beef production has started on a small scale in connection with the cultivation of sandur plains.

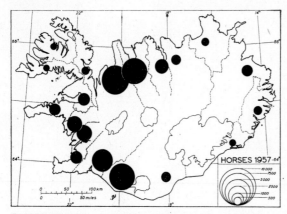

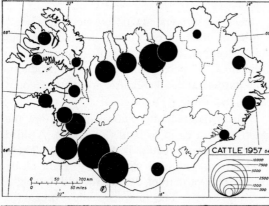

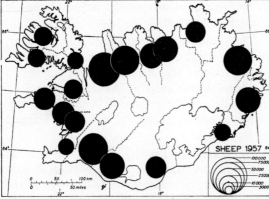

Fig. 10.8. Distribution of horses, cattle and sheep, 1957. The scale for sheep is 10 times that for cattle and horses. The main concentration of cattle is on the southwestern plains, where Reykjavík is the main consumer of dairy products. Cattle are also relatively numerous in some of the northern valleys, especially Eyjafjörður. Sheep are relatively more numerous in the northwest and northeast. Horses have for centuries been most numerous in the western part of Norðurland.

The sheep stock is largest in the north and northeast (Fig. 10.8) where the country is well suited for sheep breeding because of extensive uninhabited grazing areas and because markets are not at hand to encourage any extensive milk production. In the whole of Iceland the ratio between sheep and cattle is 15.5 to 1, but it varies greatly from one district to another. In the east this ratio is 30.1 to 1, in the north the ratio declines to 16.3 to 1 and in the south to 6.6. The total production of lamb and mutton in 1965 was about 12 100 tons, and considerably exceeded home consumption. The production of wool is less important. The production of beef was about 1 850 tons in 1965, of horse meat about 1 500 tons, but that of pork only 500 tons. No meat is imported.

Horses (ponies) are most numerous in the Húnavatn and Skagafjörður counties in the north, whose upland regions are well suited to the grazing of horses (Fig. 10.8). There are also still fairly large numbers of horses in the south. The relatively large number of horses still kept in Iceland is due to tradition rather than necessity. Right down to the 20th century horses were the only available means of transport on land; they carried both people and goods throughout the country and assisted with many kinds of work on the farms. The Icelandic pony possesses exceptional endurance in spite of its small size. But nowadays the horse's role on the countryside is very small. Machinery has to a large extent replaced it in agriculture, and for riding it is now first and foremost used for pleasure, although it is still useful when sheep and horses are collected from the interior in the autumn.

Greenhouses and market gardening

There is some market gardening in Iceland, especially for growing potatoes and turnips. The annual production of potatoes varies a good deal, but usually it falls short of the home demand. People in villages and towns grow considerable quantities of potatoes. (About 15 per cent of the total crop is grown in Reykjavík.) The biggest acreage under potato is in the sandur areas in the southeast and the south, where machinery is used for harvesting purposes. Some types of cabbage are grown too, but most other vegetables are grown in greenhouses.

218

In 1924 the first greenhouse using natural hot water was erected. Since then many have been built in various parts of the country, especially in the hot spring areas. The largest number of greenhouses is in the south. The village of Hveragerði, for instance, with 770 inhabitants, largely subsists on the greenhouse industry, as natural hot water is plentiful in the vicinity. Of fruits and vegetables grown in the greenhouses tomatoes come first, and then cucumbers. Melons, grapes, and even bananas are grown on a small scale as are a large number of decorative plants.

Recent developments

In 1965 13 per cent of the Icelandic population was engaged in farming as compared with 31 per cent in 1940. The decrease in the population of the rural areas has not usually involved desertion of farms, but the average number of people per farm has substantially decreased. Many farms went out of use during the Second World War, and the total is now 5 200. Deserted isolated farms have been replaced by new farms in more prosperous districts.

The last 15 years or so have seen a rapid increase in mechanization. At the end of 1960, for example, there were about 7 800 tractors in use in the countryside, i.e. more than one tractor per farm, a higher proportion than perhaps in any other country. In addition many farmers have jeeps which they use for transport and traction. Milking machinery is common.

Haymaking is the most important part of Icelandic farming, and a wet hay harvest often played havoc with the crop when it was dried in the open air. In recent years many farmers have become less dependent on weather conditions, as many of them now use hay blowers which dry the hay inside the barns. A large number of silos has also been erected.

Contributory sources of livelihood

Seal hunting is carried out to a small extent at various places on the coasts. Two species of seals breed there, the common seal and the grey seal. The yearly catch (mainly common seal) amounts to some 300 adult seals and about 3 000 young ones taken for their skins. Trout are abundant in many rivers and lakes, the richest one being Mývatn and Þingvallavatn. The average annual catch for the period 1960–65 was about 350 tons. Over 50 rivers are frequented by salmon, and angling is a very popular sport. The average annual catch in 1960–65 was about 25 000 salmon (about 100 tons).

As already mentioned Iceland is very rich in birds, but only a few of them are of any economic importance. The eiderduck is protected the whole year round because of its down. The yield in 1898–1939 averaged 3 582 kg per year, but has recently decreased and was 1 648 kg in 1963. The only bird extensively shot is ptarmigan, but because of its great cyclic variation in number (a cycle of 10–12 years) the number shot varies greatly. It may reach as high as 400 000. Fowling and gathering of eggs on birdcliffs is still of some, although rapidly diminishing, local importance. The number of birds caught in 1936 was about 144 000, of which 112 000 were puffins.

FISHERIES

The fishing grounds

Iceland is situated near the Polar Front in the middle of a great mixing area where cold and warm currents meet. Most biological and ecological phenomena are related to this fact. The country is surrounded by a shelf. This shelf is indented by submarine valleys which usually lie in the direction of the present fjord or river systems. It seems appropriate to define the boundary of the shelf as the deepest isobath that can be drawn round Iceland without deviating markedly from the present contours of the country. This isobath lies at 400 metres approximately.

The fish population comprises about 150 species of which 66 are known to propagate in Icelandic waters. Icelandic sea-fisheries are mainly based on three different biological phenomena. 1) The congregation of spawners on the spawning grounds. The seasonal fisheries in

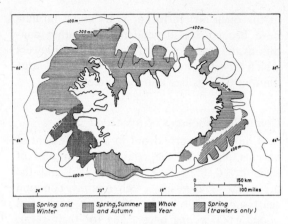

Fig. 10.9. *The main codfishing banks of Iceland.* The 400 m isobath roughly indicates the border of the continental shelf, that of 200 m the extension of the major banks, the larger part of which lie outside the new Icelandic fisheries limit of 12 nautical miles (22.4 km).

Spring and Winter   Spring, Summer and Autumn   Whole Year   Spring (trawlers only)

February–May belong to this category. The chief species fished are the bank spawners of the boreal group, viz. cod, haddock, saithe, whiting etc. 2) The congregation of plankton-feeders. Herring and saithe belong to this category. 3) The congregation of feeding fishes outside the spawning season in certain areas where they purse crustaceans, capelins (small fish like smelt), sandeels and various bottom animals. Localized fishing of cod, haddock, plaice, catfish and halibut is due to this phenomenon. Only 20 species are commercially important, and in 1965 cod and herring made up 84 per cent of the total catch. Although caught in smaller quantities, redfish, haddock, saithe, catfish and various species of flatfish such as plaice and halibut are collectively important.

Exceedingly rich nursery grounds for young fish are found in Icelandic territorial waters. Scientific investigations have revealed that, owing to greatly increased fishing during recent years, protection of young fish on these grounds against trawling and seine netting is of the utmost importance as signs of overfishing have been observed. This applies especially to such species as haddock and plaice, and in a lesser degree to cod. To provide a better protection, the Icelandic government in 1952 simultaneously established 'base lines' (straight lines between points along the coast) and extended the fisheries limit for foreign vessels from 3 to 4 miles and in 1958 to 12 miles.

History

Ever since they entered the country the Icelanders have carried on some fishing, and from about 1340 fishing products have formed the most important export. But for centuries Icelandic fishing was rather ineffective because the seas are stormy and there is no barrier of skerries to protect the coastal waters. As long as open rowing-boats were the only fishing vessels the catch was small. It is not until about 1890 that decked vessels began to be used extensively for codfishing. This initiated the rapid expansion of the fishing industry which was further advanced by the advent of steam trawlers in the first decade of the present century and has continued to grow up to the present time. In 1954 –1958 the total catch of cod (round fresh weight) averaged about 300 000 tons, which is 6 times that of 50 years ago.

The expansion of the herring industry was not less rapid. Until 1870 it was not of great importance, and during the following decades the herring fishing was mainly carried out by Norwegians. By the turn of the century herring was being caught in drift nets and in purse seines, and subsequently fishing was no longer confined to the fjords. From then on the herring industry increased rapidly.

There have been great fluctuations in the herring catches during the last few decades, the catch reaching a maximum in 1944 of 222 000 tons (cf. Fig. 10.10). This was followed by a period of very poor catches (the minimum was reached in 1952 and 1954 with 32 000 tons), but in 1956 the yield started to rise again, partly owing to the use of acoustic sounding, both horizontal (asdic) and vertical (echo-sounding), by which herring concentrations are located. In 1966 the catch reached a new maximum with 769 000 tons, but in 1967 it was considerably lower.

Fishing areas and seasons

The Icelandic catch is mainly taken on the rich fishing grounds around Iceland. There are, however, considerable annual variations in fishing areas, and the large ocean-going trawlers often go to distant waters such as those of Greenland, Labrador and Newfoundland.

Cod is caught off any part of the country (Fig. 10.9), but codfishing is most intense off the south and southwest coast during the winter season, which extends from January to the end of April.

During this period the cod comes in enormous shoals into coastal waters for spawning. While Reykjavík is the most important centre for the large steam trawlers, Vestmannaeyjar is the base for the smaller diesel-powered fishing boats. Akranes and Hafnarfjörður are also important fishing ports and so are even Grindavík and Keflavík on the Reykjanes Peninsula (Fig. 10.11).

During the first half of the winter season the motor vessels use long lines but change to gill nets during the second half of the season.

Considerable annual variations, partly due to the very changeable weather conditions, occur in the catch (Fig. 10.10).

The herring fishery mainly takes place on the north and northeast coast where the season extends from the middle of June to the middle of September. A great disadvantage for the fishing towns and villages in the north is the instability of the herring areas. In some years the bulk of the herring catch is caught off the middle or western part of the north coast, in other years it is mainly caught off the northeast

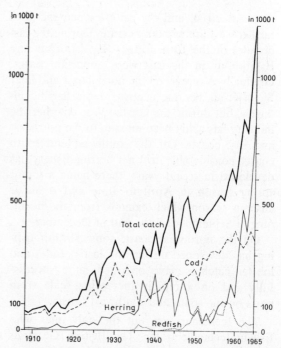

Fig.10.10.Total fisheries catch,1908–65. Round fresh weight. Newer larger fishing vessels and new gear (trawl and purse seine, more recently ring net and power block) have produced a tenfold increase in fifty years, but variations in weather and hydrographic conditions are reflected in violent changes in the catch, particularly of herring.

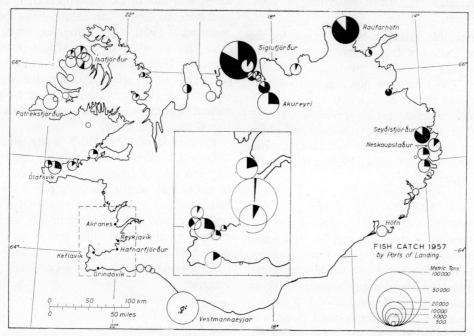

Fig. 10.11. Total fisheries catch, 1957, distributed by ports of landing. The black sectors represent herring. The trawler fleet mostly operates from Reykjavík and adjacent ports. The herring fisheries are mainly concentrated on the north and east coasts in summer, in autumn on the southwest coast, and the traditional codfishing in late winter on Vestmannaeyjar, Akranes, and the ports on Reykjanes.

221

and east coast, and the salteries and factories farther west are without herring. During the last decades of the 19th century Seyðisfjörður and Eskifjörður in the east were important bases. Gradually Akureyri on the north coast and later Siglufjörður became centres of the herring industry, but during the last ten years the herring industry has again been moving to the northeast and east coasts. Off the southwest and south coasts, considerable drift net herring fishery has developed in recent years, there being a minor spring season in April to June and a major autumn season which extends from the beginning of September till the end of December.

On the northwest coast, some shrimp fishing has developed during the last decade, and lobster catchers have operated quite successfully and on a rapidly increasing scale from ports on the south and southwest coasts.

The Icelanders are not the only ones who fish in Icelandic water. The British, Germans and Russians carry out large-scale fishing, and Belgians, Faeroese, Norwegians and a few other nations also fish considerable quantities on the rich Icelandic fishing grounds. The Icelandic proportion of the total catch (44 per cent in 1936) has gradually increased. Since 1955 Icelandic fishermen have caught about 55 per cent.

Considerable variation in preference for the different species of fish is observed among the different nations fishing on Icelandic fishing grounds. The Icelanders place most weight on the cod and herring fisheries, but the haddock and redfish fisheries are also of great importance. The British prefer haddock, halibut and plaice while the Germans go in for redfish and saithe fishing and the Norwegians keep mainly to the herring fishery.

Fish processing

The processing of the fish catch has undergone great changes during the last three decades. In the years between the two world wars salted cod was Iceland's most important export. From the beginning of the Second World War until 1949 fresh fish on ice transported directly to Britain by trawlers was the most important export. In the year 1946 large-scale export of filleted quick-frozen fish began. The quantity processed by this method has since increased

rapidly while the export of fresh fish on ice has correspondingly decreased.

Many quick-freezing plants have been built in all parts of the country, the largest being situated at the main fishing ports on the southwest coast. Fishmeal plants are operated in connection with the quick-freezing ones, so that the raw material is completely utilized. Cod liver oil plants receive all useable liver and waste products are frozen and exported to feed mink.

In 1949 and 1965 the fish catch was processed as follows (landed weight):

	1949 1 000 tons	1965 1 000 tons
Fresh on ice	142	40
Quick-frozen, excl. herring ..	78	188
Dried	0	54
Salted, mainly cod	42	88
Salted herring	17	61
Quick-frozen herring	8	33
Meal & oil, herring	46	718
Various	3	16
Total	336	1198

The production of stockfish, which for centuries was one of the most important exports, had been negligible for a long time, but was restarted in 1950, when a large export began to Italy and to some of the African territories, especially Nigeria. The production of salted cod *(klipfish)*, which stopped during the war, was restarted in 1946 and, though there have been annual variations, production has since continued on a large scale.

Production of canned fish is negligible.

During the first decades of this century herring was mainly exported as salted (cured) herring. Oil and meal processing plants were few and were foreign-owned. About 1930 the Icelanders started to build large oil and meal processing plants. Since then many such plants have been built, especially at the north coast herring ports, but also at the east coast and at Faxaflói.

The fishing fleet

Although fishery products have for centuries been Iceland's most important export it is not until the late nineteenth century that one can speak of a seamen class. Fishing was closely linked with farming, and those engaged in it were chiefly farmers whose lands extended to the shore, and who owned one or more rowing-boats.

As early as the fourteenth century fishing stations began to spring up in the neighbourhood of rich fishing grounds. From these stations there was seasonal fishing, especially in late winter, by agricultural workers, who often came from distant farms.

The above-mentioned types of fishing gradually disappeared when decked vessels began to increase, and since the First World War the farmer's role in the fisheries has been negligible. Most of the fishing is now carried out by professional seamen even though a lot of other people, for instance a considerable number of students, take part in the herring fishery during the summer.

In spite of the importance of the fishing industry only 6.5 per cent of the inhabitants had their livelihood directly from fishing in 1967. The corresponding percentage was 16 in 1940 and 22 in 1930. Apart from those who are directly concerned with fishing many work at the processing and curing of the fish ashore. These number more than half the total of fishermen. Repair shops, and manufacturers of fishing gear, clothing etc. contribute to the fisheries.

Icelandic fishermen are very efficient. In 1963 for instance each of them caught on the average 100 metric tons, in 1966 200 tons. In spite of the very small population Icelanders now rank as fifth among the European fishing nations.

At the end of the Second World War the fishing fleet had lost most of its efficiency because no replacement had taken place for several years and ships had been lost in war activities.

During the immediate post-war period the whole fishing fleet was replaced and the older ships were either exported or broken up.

In October 1965 the Icelandic fishing fleet consisted of 38 large trawlers with a total tonnage of 26 700, 172 other fishing vessels larger than 100 gross tons, with a total tonnage of 30 877, and 620 decked fishing boats smaller than 100 gross tons with a total tonnage of 20 328.

Some of the trawlers are privately owned, but more often they are owned by municipalities and villages or jointly owned by two or more villages, at which the trawler lands its catches in turn. Most of the smaller fishing vessels are privately owned. The larger vessels often bring their catches to the owners' own freezing plant.

Whaling

The marine mammal fauna round Iceland is rather poor. There are only two breeding species of seals (see above). Seventeen species of whale have been observed in Icelandic waters. Five are of economic importance, i.e. the fin whale, the sei whale, the blue whale, the sperm whale, and the humpback. The only resident species is the porpoise.

From the 1880's until 1915 the Norwegians carried out considerable whaling in Iceland. As a result of this the whale became so scarce that it was given complete protection from 1915 to 1935. An Icelandic firm restarted the whaling industry in 1948. Four whaling boats are now operating and the processing takes place ashore at a whaling station in Hvalfjörður, 35 km north of Reykjavík.

The average annual catch was 430 whales in 1961–65. The catch consists almost exclusively of whalebone whales, mainly fin whale and blue whale.

POWER AND INDUSTRY

SOURCES AND UTILIZATION OF ENERGY

Iceland has three main sources of energy: water-power, thermal power and peat. It has no coal except for some lignite which mostly occurs in thin and hardly exploitable beds in the Tertiary Basalt Formation. It has no oil, hardly any

forests and so far as is known no raw material for nuclear energy. It is roughly estimated that the peat bogs contain about 1 000 million tons of peat calculated as air-dried fuel. Peat was formerly of considerable importance for domestic heating, together with birch wood and dried sheep manure. But owing to its high mineral content it is difficult to exploit and at the moment it is of no economic value.

Hydro-electric power

The main source of energy in Iceland is hydro-electric power. Iceland has an average height of 500 m. The average run-off is calcu-

The first use of water-power in Iceland dates back to 1752 when it was harnessed to drive a small fulling-mill just east of Reykjavík. From the 1770's farmers began to erect small water mills for the grinding of imported grain for domestic use, and they became rather common in the 19th century. Electricity was first generated by water-power in 1904. The first hydro-electric plant of any size was inaugurated in 1921.

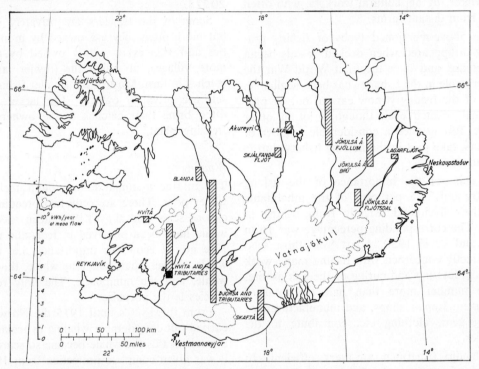

Fig. 10.12. Developed (black) and potential (shaded) hydro-electric power in milliard (10^9) kWh per year at mean discharge. During 1957—1964 the developed hydro-electric power increased from 77 000 to 133 000 kW.

lated at approximately 55 litres per second and square km, corresponding to a mean annual precipitation of about 2 500 mm, if the evaporation is taken as 100–200 mm per year.

The potential water-power in Iceland is estimated at c. 30 000 GWh, whereof only 1 330 are in use, but 15 000–20 000 GWh are estimated to be capable of economic development. This means as much as 120 000 kWh/year per capita and 200 000 kWh per km². Of this power, c. 30 per cent is in the longest river Þjórsá, and its tributaries. Next in order are Hvítá (with tributaries, including the Sog) with 13 per cent, Jökulsá á Brú, including Jökulsá á Fljótsdal (13) and Jökulsá á Fjöllum, the second largest river of Iceland (12).

It was a 1500 hp plant in the river Elliðaá near Reykjavík. The developed power is mainly concentrated on the two biggest springfed rivers in the country, Sog, a tributary of the Hvítá, and Laxá. The total developed capacity of the Sog is 88 800 kW, the developed capacity of the Laxá 12 600 kW. The building of a 105 000 kW power plant in Þjórsá started in 1966 and will be finished in 1968. Cf. Table 7.9, p. 92.

In the 1950's great efforts have been made in the electrification of the rural districts. This is very expensive because of the long distances between the farms. So far this electrification has been limited to those areas where power lines need not run farther than 1 km per household. By the end of 1965 nearly 100 per cent of

224

the inhabitants of towns and villages and 76 per cent of the inhabitants of the rural areas had electricity, altogether 188 000 or 97 per cent of the population.

Natural heat

As previously stated, Iceland is very rich in natural heat. The total integrated flow of its 800 hot-water springs is about 1 500 litres per second and its mean temperature around 75°C. The total heat dissipated by these springs is about 10^8 cal/sec. The total heat dissipated by the natural-steam fields (the subglacial Grímsvötn field excluded) has been estimated at around 10^9 cal/sec., or about 10 times the total heat dissipated by the hot-water springs. The steam-fields have a steady upflow of high-temperature water, and a large volume of rock heated to high temperature by this water. One way of utilizing the heat energy of these fields is by using their steady power, that is by drilling boreholes into the hot ground, cutting fractures through which the upflowing water ascends and thus diverting some or all of the water into the wells. The steam-water mixture produced in this way cannot exceed the steady flow of water from below. But there is a second means of producing steam, i.e. by tapping the heat which has accumulated in the rock. This is done by drilling wells into those zones which are permeable enough. If water is pumped out of such a horizon, the static pressure in the rock will decrease and a boiling of the pore water is induced. But as the water is in very close connection with a great mass of rock, the boiling will for the most part be supported by the heat content of the rock. The possibility of using the heat accumulated in the rock greatly increases the potentialities of the natural-steam fields. For example, the Krýsuvík area could produce 10 megawatt continuously for a period of 75 years using the accumulated heat, and 10 kW of steady power, using the steady upflow of high-temperature water.

From the first occupation of Iceland natural heat has been of some domestic use. The hot springs were used for washing and bathing. The 13th century bathing pool of the great historian Snorri Sturluson at Reykholt is still preserved. In the 18th century some salt was produced by evaporating sea water, using the heat of boiling springs. Up to our own days bread has been baked in some places by burying the dough in the hot ground. In the late 1920's some boarding schools and a sanatorium were built near hots springs and heated by natural hot water. By now the utilization of the natural heat for domestic and greenhouse heating has become very important. Most important is the Reykjavík Hot Water Supply (Hitaveita Reykjavíkur) which was started on a small scale in 1930 and new serves 75 000 of the inhabitants. The Hitaveita pipes the hot water over a distance of 16 km from about 300–620 m deep boreholes in the thermal area of Reykir and Reykjahlíð. The temperature of the water at the wells is 87°C and it reaches the city 3°C colder. Considerable amounts of water are now added to the system from some 600–2 200 m boreholes within the city itself. Four other communities, Hveragerði and Selfoss in the south, Sauðárkrókur and Ólafsfjörður in the north, with a total of about 5 000 inhabitants, are heated in a similar way. Nearly all greenhouses in the country are heated by means of hot water or steam and so are about 80 public swimming pools spread all over the country, which has made swimming a very common sport in Iceland.

The next stage in the utilization of natural heat in Iceland will be to use it for the generation of electricity or for the production of salt and heavy water. It should be kept in mind, however, that the sources of exploitable thermal power are more limited than those of hydro-electric power, but under some circumstances the use of the thermal power may prove more economic.

OTHER NATURAL RESOURCES

Except for the above mentioned sources of energy and the richness of the surrounding sea and fertile soils, the utilization of which is limited by climatic conditions, Iceland possesses few natural resources. The igneous bedrock is on the whole very poor in exploitable minerals. An extensive layer of limonite is found intercalated between lava beds in Önundarfjörður in northwest Iceland, but the layer is too thin to be workable. The working of bog iron was of domestic importance from the early days of settlement until the early 19th century. The Helgustaðir mine at Reyðarfjörður in east Iceland was

225

for many decades the world's most important source of the transparent, colourless Iceland spar used in optical instruments where polarization of light is required. It is no longer worked. Workable sulphur deposits are found in some of the solfatara fields, especially at Námafjall, Þeistareykir and Krýsuvík (Fig. 10.4). The working of sulphur began in the 13th century and was of considerable importance especially in the first half of the 16th century, when up to 400 tons per year were exported. Working ceased completely towards the end of the 19th century when large-scale production of sulphur began on the American Gulf Coast. The Icelandic deposits are too limited for any large-scale production.

Very large amounts of perlite, a hydrated rhyolitic volcanic glass, are found in Loðmundarfjörður in eastern Iceland, and at the western edge of Langjökull. It might become an important export article as there is a steadily increasing demand for it in the building industry especially in U.S.A. It is easily expanded by heat and is then very insulating and is used as an aggregate in plaster and light-weight cement. Natural rhyolitic pumice and basaltic scoriae are abundant in Iceland and are used on an increasing scale in the building industry because of their insulating qualities. On the bottom of Lake Mývatn are the biggest deposits of diatomite found in Europe, and large-scale working will begin in 1968.

INDUSTRY

Apart from cottage handicrafts there was very little industry in Iceland down to the end of the 19th century. Thus only 2.6 per cent of the nation earned their living in crafts and industry in 1890. When decked fishing craft increased in number and trawlers were introduced, various towns began to grow rapidly. Unprecedented prosperity resulted in increasing demand, creating conditions that required various types of industrial services. As in many other countries, tariff protection has influenced industrial development in Iceland. Similarly various import restrictions imposed since 1930 have largely contributed to the creation of several manufacturing industries.

Industrial development has been very rapid in the last few decades. In 1920 11 per cent of the population earned their living by manufacturing, in 1940 this figure was 22 and in 1965 36 per cent. Of the latter figure nearly one third were in the building industry. Manufacturing is now the leading occupation in Iceland.

The most important industry producing for export in Iceland is fish processing. In almost every fishing town there is a freezing plant, and in some towns there are several, equipped with up-to-date machinery such as highly efficient filleting machines. Herring factories, producing chiefly herring meal and herring oil, numbered 30 in 1965 with a total capacity of 14 200 tons of raw material per 24 hours. Full utilization of these factories is much handicapped by the changeable positions of the herring shoals.

In addition to fish processing there are various types of servicing industries that are of great importance for the fishing industry. Some fairly large engineering works and shipyards maintain the fishing fleet. They also build small boats and some vessels of moderate size. The engineering works also make various types of machinery and equipment for the fishing industry. One large company and many smaller ones turn out fishing gear. The production of sailors' kit is a fairly large industry. One large factory and some smaller ones produce packing for fish products.

Besides fish products, som meat and wool, requiring some processing, are exported. Other exports are of negligible importance.

Other industries in Iceland turn out products almost exclusively for the home market. The small size of the market is a great obstacle to the expansion of many firms that use imported raw materials. The printing industry is bigger than might be expected as Iceland produces many more books per-capita than any other country.

Distribution of industry

The fishing industry is distributed practically throughout the coastlands. In only 6 counties is there little or no processing of fish, but in most of the others about a half, or more than a half, of the industrial labour force was engaged in fish processing in 1950. This holds also for most of the towns, the main exceptions being Reykjavík and Akureyri where only 8 and 6 per cent respectively were engaged in this industry. Corresponding figures for Vestmannaeyjar and Siglufjörður were 69 and 77 per cent.

In spite of Reykjavík's low percentage some of the largest fish-processing factories in the country are located there, but industry in general is more diversified there than anywhere else. In 1965, the city of Reykjavík had almost half of the country's industrial establishments, and a total value of industrial production that nearly equalled that of all other towns and districts put together. The town of Akureyri ranked a poor second with about 10 per cent of the country's industrial production.

Akureyri is the only other town in Iceland whose industries may be said to be diversified to any degree. The main industries there are food-processing and the manufacture of clothing and textiles. In most other towns the fishing industry predominates. Other industries include the Cement Works at Akranes, the manufacture of electrical equipment at Hafnarfjörður, and milk-processing and other industries based on the produce of neighbouring agricultural areas at Selfoss, Sauðárkrókur, Borgarnes and Húsavík.

Substantial extension and advances have been made in fish-processing in recent years. However, large quantities of only partly processed fish are still exported, and there seems to be scope for much future development in this sphere. Canning of fish products is still negligible.

Iceland has great resources of energy which so far have been utilized only to a very small extent, and there are great power potentialities for various types of industry which consume much power and need relatively little labour. In 1965 the share of industry in the total consumption of electricity had gone up to 45 per cent from 20 in 1953. This sudden rise may to a great extent be traced to a fertilizer plant, producing ammonium nitrate, which began operating at the end of 1953. This factory is in the vicinity of Reykjavík and was the first large-scale plant in Iceland with the exception of the biggest herring oil and meal factories. In 1965 20 000 tons of ammonium nitrate were produced. Almost all the output was absorbed by the home market. An aluminium plant (capacity 30 000 tons) is at present being built at Straumur outside Hafnarfjörður and will use energy from the power plant at Þjórsá.

Because of the complete lack of timber and of suitable building stone and clay for brick-making, Iceland is Europe's greatest per capita consumer of cement (about 0.5 ton per capita per year). The cement works at Akranes started operation in 1958 and produces over 100 000 tons of cement a year as well as 25 000 of lime. Iceland has no limestone, but the cement works gets the lime it needs by pumping up sea shells from a layer 1–5 m thick on the seabed in Faxaflói at a depth of about 30 m.

TRADE AND COMMUNICATIONS

FOREIGN TRADE

The Icelanders have always depended greatly on foreign trade. Admittedly the quantities of exported goods were not very large for several centuries. Owing to lack of diversification in domestic production there were always certain imports of food products, tools and timber, which were necessary to maintain a minimum standard of living. When new fishing techniques were introduced, largely increasing the yield, a basis was created for a greatly expanded foreign trade. There has never been much variety of export products; for the most part they have been fish products of various kinds, but they have also included considerable quantities of agricultural produce. In recent years increased processing has added variety to the export industries.

The case of imports is quite different. As the total of imports increased so did their variety, and today Iceland imports a great variety of goods, many of which cannot be manufactured within the country because of its limited natural resources and small population.

Foreign trade has greatly increased in volume during recent years, and this has resulted in a rapidly growing transportation of freight to and from the country. The following table shows the total volume of goods transported between Iceland and overseas countries:

	Imports 1 000 tons	Exports 1 000 tons
1935	334	117
1945	329	200
1955	644	199
1965	826	508

Imports are now two and half and exports four times what they were in 1935. Throughout this period approximately half of all the imports has been fuel of one form or another. Previously this consisted mainly of coal, but this has now been almost entirely replaced by fuel oil.

The number of countries with which Iceland trades is now larger than it has ever been. This constitutes a great change from the turn of the last century, when two thirds of all imports came from Denmark, while one third of the exports went to that country. In the years between the two World Wars there was a lively trade with Spain, Italy and Greece, and the principal export item was klipfish. This trade has been relatively much smaller in recent years. After the processing of quick-frozen fish began on a large scale, trade has been established with many countries which previously did not buy from Iceland.

Exports and imports in recent years

In 1965 exports from Iceland totalled 5 563 million Icelandic krónur and the main categories were:

Quick-frozen fish	1245 million kr.	
Salted fish	545	» »
Herring meal and oil	1576	» »
Salted herring	491	» »
Stockfish	376	» »
Fish on ice	189	» »
Fish meal	133	» »
Sheepskins and hides	105	» »

In 1965 90 per cent of the total exports were products of fishing and whaling. The biggest buyers of quick-frozen fish were the United States (nearly the half of the total), Britain and the Soviet Union. Salted fish is mainly bought by Roman-Catholic countries, such as Portugal, Italy and Brazil. Salted herring is widely sold,

the largest buyers being Sweden and the Soviet Union. The production of stockfish began on a large scale after markets opened in Africa, and by far the largest quantities are exported to Nigeria.

In 1965 imports totalled 5 902 million krónur, and the main categories were:

Machinery (electric included) ..	941	million kr.
Fuels and lubricants	534	» »
Transport equipment	970	» »
Textile yarn, fabrics, textile articles	491	» »
Base metals	213	» »
Manufactures of metal	220	» »
Cereals and cereal products ..	212	» »

In recent years petrol and fuel oil has been imported from the Soviet Union, automobiles and machinery mainly from West-Germany, Britain and the United States. Textiles and yarn are purchased from a large number of countries.

In spite of a rather narrow range of exported commodities Iceland has established trade relations with a surprisingly large number of countries. Actually the diversity in imports is too great in some respects since the great variety of servicing which is required may not always be available in such a small country. For the most important partners in 1965, see Table 7.14, p. 97.

The negative trade balance of most post-war years has been partly counterbalanced by the direct and indirect dollar earnings from the American Defence Base at Keflavík. In 1965 these receipts were about 4 per cent of total receipts from exports of goods and services.

DOMESTIC TRADE

Until the end of the 19th century Icelandic commerce was, for the most part, in the hands of foreigners. Around the turn of the century this began changing and all trade has long been in Icelandic hands. In 1964 13.7 per cent of the population made its living by commerce.

At first the co-operative movement was largely responsible for bringing trade and commerce into Icelandic hands. The first co-operative society was founded in 1882, and they soon grew in number. The Federation of Icelandic Co-operative Societies, founded in 1902, owns and operates most of the domestic slaughter-houses and dairies and many of the freezing plants. The Federation is the largest single importer (15 per cent of the total import in 1962), and a large exporter as well (20 per cent of the total), and its allied companies are active in the fields of insurance, oil distribution, various manufacturing industries and other trades.

Reykjavík, Akureyri, Hafnarfjörður and Vestmannaeyjar are the most important trade centres, and 90 per cent of all wholesale firms in Iceland are located in Reykjavík, which shows clearly its vital position in trade and commerce.

COMMUNICATIONS

Sea transport

Since Iceland is a remote island and since the range of national industries is limited, sea communication with the outside world is of vital importance to the Icelandic people. Coastal shipping is also very important because most of the towns and villages are situated on the coast. For centuries sailings to and from Iceland were scarce and irregular, but in the second half of the 19th century they increased in number and regularity. Until the First World War practically all shipping to and from the country was in hands of foreigners, especially Danes and Norwegians, but in 1914 the Icelandic Steamship Company was founded.

At the end of 1965 the Icelandic merchant fleet consisted of a total of 51 vessels having a gross tonnage of about 73 500. Seven were passenger-cargo ships, 33 dry-cargo ships and 11 oil tankers. About 65 per cent of Iceland's imports and exports were carried by Icelandic ships. Bulky merchandise, such as coal, salt and timber, is shipped to the country mostly in foreign bottoms.

The Icelandic coastal services have generally shown a financial loss. Hence they have been, and still are, run by various companies which receive state subsidies. The improvement of roads, the rapid motorization of land transport and the introduction of the aeroplane have meant that competition has increased sharply on the most heavily travelled routes, for instance Reykjavík–Akureyri.

Icelandic shipping companies are now running regular services between Iceland on the one hand, and New York and the principal West- and North-European ports, on the other. Icelandic ships also sail, though not regularly, to the Mediterranean and Africa and South America.

In the first decade of this century, there were few ports in Iceland which could boast of even as much as a wooden wharf at which ships could be loaded and unloaded. The first major harbour construction projects were begun at Reykjavík in 1913. Since that time harbours have been constructed in most parts of the country.

The first lighthouse in Iceland was built on the tip of Reykjanes in 1878. In 1953 it was possible for the first time to go around the island and have a lighthouse always in sight. Today a total of 110 lighthouses dot the coasts of Iceland.

Land transport

Until late in the 19th century, the age-old pack-horse routes were the only 'roads' in Iceland and practically no wheeled vehicles were in use. Indeed, it was not until the year 1880 that construction was begun on the country's first wagon road. This was the road that led from Reykjavík eastward over the mountains to the Southern Lowlands.

About 1900 planned construction of roads began in various parts of the country. The greatest barriers to easy communications in the past were the big rivers, which had to be bridged. The first suspension bridge was built in 1890. By now, most rivers have been spanned by bridges, some of them in many places.

Virtually all inhabited areas of the country are now served by motorable roads, as a great effort has been made in recent years to form a continuous road network. It is now possible to drive around the entire island, except for a 33 km gap across the Skeiðarársandur in southern Iceland. This gap will be difficult to fill because of its constantly oscillating streams and its exposure to glacier bursts from Grímsvötn.

Under the Road Act of 1947 the road system was divided into four categories: state roads, mountain roads (i.e. roads across the highlands), county roads and parish roads. The state roads are the main roads that connect separate districts. The cost of building and maintaining

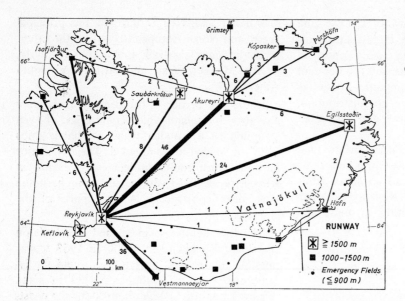

Fig. 10.13. Scheduled flights per week by Icelandair. Planes in transatlantic service use Keflavík Airport, all domestic routes use Reykjavík.

them is paid exclusively by the state. State highways are now over 9 000 km in length.

Relatively more money has been spent on roads in Iceland than in most other countries. In recent years, between nine and fifteen per cent of the national budget has been devoted to road and bridge building. Nevertheless the Icelandic roads are poor (they are practically all surfaced with gravel or volcanic slags) and most of them are narrow. In winter most lowland roads are kept open with the aid of snowploughs and bulldozers.

There have never been any railways in Iceland. The country has stepped from the packhorse stage straight to the motor vehicle or even to the plane. In 1965 there were about 35 000 motor vehicles in Iceland. Of these 28 400 were passenger vehicles and the rest were trucks and buses. Iceland has more motor vehicles per capita than most other European countries.

All public transport on land is effected by road services (buses, trucks and combined truck-bus vehicles). These are owned and operated by private companies, but as they are responsible for distributing mail, they are scheduled and co-ordinated by the Post and Telegraph Administration of the Government.

Tele-communications

In 1906 a telegraphic cable was laid from the Shetland Islands, through the Faeroes, to Seyðisfjörður on the east coast of Iceland. From there a combined telephone and telegraph line ran overland to Akureyri and then west and south to Reykjavík. By 1929 all inhabited districts of the country had been linked to the national system. Today the telephone is used more extensively in Iceland than in most other countries; there is one telephone for every 5 persons. Around 95 per cent of farms in Iceland have telephones, a remarkably high ratio in such a sparsely populated country.

Short-wave radio-telephone connections between Reykjavík, København and London were established in 1935. In 1938 the first regular radio-telegraph connections were established between Reykjavík and New York, in 1946 these were expanded to include radio-telephone communication. In 1962 a new submarine cable was laid between Scotland and Iceland (Scotice) and another one between Iceland and Canada in 1963 (Icecan).

Air transport

In 1919, Iceland had her first aircraft and nine years later the first aircraft company was established but maintained air services for only a few years. In 1938 air services were resumed, leading to the foundation of *Icelandair,* which now carries on all domestic air transport. In recent years regular summer air services operate to 18 places in Iceland, most of them directly from Reykjavík. There are from 1 to 46 flights per week on each route (Fig. 10.13).

Aircraft are used more often in Iceland than in most countries, chiefly because of the relatively large area of the country and the unsatisfactory road system. Numerous bare sand and gravel areas have facilitated the construction of inexpensive airfields suitable for the domestic air service, and it has been possible to maintain the air service at such a low cost (without any government subsidy) that it has been within the means of everyone to use it. In 1965 100 000 passengers travelled by air between various places in Iceland. This is equivalent to more than every second inhabitant travelling that year by air within the country. The freight and mail carried was 1 500 tons.

Air cargoes vary; for example, agricultural produce is flown from isolated districts to market. The air mail service is extensive, and emergency flights for sick people are a constant feature.

In 1947, the first long-range commercial aircraft flew in, and since that year both Icelandair and Icelandic Airlines (Loftleiðir) have run air services between Iceland and other countries.

Icelandair maintains services to Norway, Denmark, Great Britain and Germany. Icelandic Airlines flies exclusively between New York and northwestern Europe via Keflavík. With the lowest fares of any commercial carrier in the North Atlantic service it has been able to compete very effectively with larger airlines. In 1965 overseas passengers on the Icelandic Airlines numbered 190 000, and 886,9 million passenger-kilometres (corresponding figures for 1951 were 10 981 and 18.7 millions).

Five airfields in Iceland are of sufficient size to accommodate transoceanic aircraft. They are Keflavík and Reykjavík in the southwest, Akureyri and Sauðárkrókur in the north, and Egilsstaðir in the east (Fig. 10.13). The first three of these have tarred runways and are by far the biggest ones.

Icelandair planes fly frequently to Greenland and most of the commercial flights from Europe to that country in recent years have been in their hands.

POPULATION

Iceland's struggle for existence is vividly depicted in the marked fluctuations in population which have occurred since the island was first settled. Settlement began about 870 A.D. with people coming mainly from Norway, but also from the British Isles and mainly from their Celtic fringe. Immigration is regarded as having come to an end by 930; it is estimated that at that time there were about 30 000 people in Iceland. The population is believed to have increased to around 75 000 by about the year 1100, and to have been approximately the same two centuries later.

It is of interest to make some comparison with Norway, the country from which the majority of the settlers came. It has been estimated that in about 1100 the population of Norway was somewhere around 250 000. This means that the population of Iceland was then nearly a third of that of Norway, and densities were similar in both countries. This partly explains Iceland's position among the Norden countries at that time. Seven hundred years later the ratio was quite different. In 1800 Norway had a population of 883 000, having more than

trebled since about 1100, but the population of Iceland had been reduced to 47 240 (in 1801), or to little more than a half of what it was in 1100. Population density was about one sixth of that of Norway, which was then by no means a densely peopled country by European standards.

When the first census was taken in Iceland in 1703, the population numbered only 50 358, as against 47 240 in 1801. The greatest drop in population was caused by the smallpox epidemic of 1717, and by the Laki eruption of 1783, which led to the death of 50 per cent of the cattle, 76 per cent of the horses and 79 per cent of the sheep (Fig. 10.7). In the resulting famine, more than nine thousand or about one fifth of the population died.

Since about 1800 there has been a steady annual increase of population apart from a few years in the 1880's when there was a drop, mainly due to emigration to Canada. The birth rate in Iceland has long been high and in good years in the 18th century the birth surplus was about 10 per mille. During the period 1876–85 the birth rate was 31, the death rate 25 and the surplus 6 per mille. Corresponding figures for 1960–64 were 26.2, 6.9 and 19.3 per mille. The birth rate is thus still very high, but the extremely rapid drop in the death rate has been a much more important factor in the rapid population increase in the 20th century. For the last two decades the death rate has been lower than in almost all other countries, and in the past few years the infant death rate has been lower in Iceland than anywhere.

In 1901 the population of Iceland was 78 140, but in 1967 it reached 200 000.

Immigration and emigration in recent years have had very little effect on population growth. Thus 300 individuals immigrated into Iceland during the period 1946–65 in excess of the number who emigrated.

Distribution of population

Almost the whole interior of Iceland is an anoecumen and so are considerable peripheral sandur and mountain areas. Approximately 20 per cent of the total area is inhabited. Except for the South Iceland lowland and the Borgarfjörður area in the southwest, the settlements are limited to a narrow coastal belt and to the valleys in the north and northeast. The rural settlement pattern in Iceland has from the very beginning been predominantly one of single farms, usually widely dispersed. Only in a few districts, especially south of Vatnajökull, where the habitable land has been curtailed by glacier rivers and glacier bursts, are the farms grouped. The majority of the farms are still on the same sites as those selected for them in the 9th and 10th centuries and keep unaltered the names given to them in the Commonwealth Time.

Each single farm is surrounded by a patch of cultivated grassland (tún). The uncultivated lowland areas are divided between the farms, whereas the uninhabited areas between the settlements and in the interior are for the most part common land divided between the districts that use them for summer grazing. The areal extent of the settled land bordering the interior anoecumen has varied considerably over the centuries. During the Settlement Time and the first centuries of the Commonwealth Time (until about 1 100 A.D.) the settlements expanded rapidly. In many valleys in the north the settlements stretched further up the valleys than they do now and some small areas on the

inland plateau which are now deserted were then inhabited. So also were some lowland areas later destroyed by lava-flows, glacier bursts and wind erosion.

The increasing population and the rapid expansion of sheep rearing in the 19th century led to the extension of some settlements towards the interior, especially in the northeast. Most of these new farms have been abandoned again. Most settled areas in Iceland are now situated wholly below the 200 m level. Two rural districts in the northeast (Mývatnssveit and Fjallasveit) lie wholly above the 250 m level and four farms lie above the 400 m level.

The main reason why the farms climb so high in this area is that because Vatnajökull acts as an effective barrier to the rain-bringing southerly winds. The climate of the inland plateau of the northeast is more continental than elsewhere in the country, with low precipitation (400–500 mm), and a thin and dry snow cover which allows the sheep and horses to graze for most of the winter. It is the relation between the length of the period during which the animals must be fed indoors, and the possibilities of securing enough hay for that period that determine the limits of the habitable rural areas in Iceland.

Until the middle of the 19th century the population of Iceland was almost entirely rural. The biggest agglomeration, Reykjavík, had 301 inhabitants in the year 1801 and 1 200 in 1850. But the removal of the trade monopoly in 1854 led to a more rapid growth of the trading villages, and initiated an urban development that later became closely linked with the increasingly important fishing industry. The increase of population and the growth of urban settlement since 1850 is shown on Fig. 10.15. Until the 1930's all towns and agglomerations were situated by the sea. In recent years some inland agglomerations have grown up, especially in the Suðurland area. The biggest ones are Selfoss (2 070 inhabitants in 1965)—like most of the others a typical service and communication-centre—and Hveragerði (770 inhabitants), the centre of greenhouse cultivation. But the main bulk of the rural population still lives in dispersed single farms.

The movement of the population towards towns and villages, and from climatically ill-favoured areas towards those better favoured,

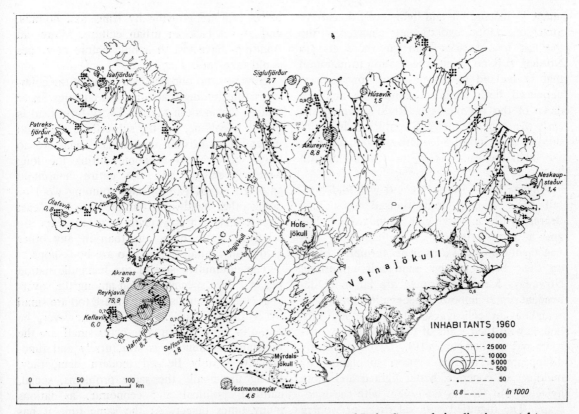

Fig. 10.14. Distribution of population, 1960. A major part of Iceland's population live in coastal towns. The immediate surroundings of Reykjavík are barren and almost uninhabited. The main rural concentrations are the agricultural populations of the southwestern plains and some of the northern valleys.

increased during the two World Wars. Some remote valleys and out-of-way peninsulas, mainly in the northwest, have now been almost or completely deserted. In two of the census areas, the Vestfirðir area and the Breiðafjörður area (Fig. 10.6), there has been an absolute drop in the population since 1910.

The population of the towns was 64 960 in 1940, i.e. 53 per cent of the total population. In 1965 it was 130 920 or 68 per cent. In 1940 Reykjavík had 38 196 inhabitants or 32 per cent of total, in 1965 77 980 or 40 per cent. It is thus the biggest capital in the world in proportion to the country's population. Akureyri, the second town, had 9 630 in 1965, and the smallest town, Seyðisfjörður, 845.

Because of its great contrasts Iceland is frequently spoken of as the Land of Ice and Fire. Another name often given to it is the Land of the Sagas. Foreign visitors will soon discover that the first description is well justified, but they are not now likely to see much that re-

minds them of the second. Iceland is no longer an isolated rock in the wide ocean, of interest only to natural scientists and to students of the old Norse language and the Saga literature. Its isolation has been broken. It is a half-way house on a frequented air route between two hemispheres, and a point of strategic impor-

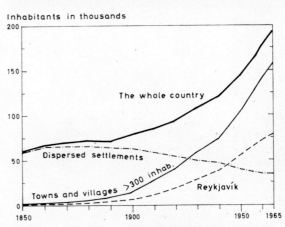

Fig. 10.15. Urban and rural population, 1850–1965.

233

tance. In Iceland life and living conditions have undergone more revolutionary changes during the last few decades than anywhere else in Norden. It is no great exaggeration to maintain that in Iceland the same generation has experienced both medieval conditions and the dawn of the Atomic Age. Right down to the early years of the present century living conditions and industrial methods remained in the main the same as in the Commonwealth Time.

Anyone now visiting Iceland will find himself in a country industrialized to a high degree, with a very high standard of life, and a modern outlook. The household management of the farms was formerly based on their being in the main self-supporting. Nowadays Icelandic farmers are far more dependent upon imported necessities than their Scandinavian colleagues. The old-style farmhouses with their walls of turf and stones, turf-roofs and wooden gables (Pl. 10.6) have mostly disappeared. They have been supplanted by buildings of concrete, better lighted and more hygienic, but far less congruent with the landscape. The dignified national dress of women is going the same way, its place being taken by a strikingly modern and international style. The capital, and the towns in general, do not conceal the fact that they are newly sprung into

being and are growing by leaps and bounds, and as yet lack an urban culture. Many old traditions have lost their hold before new ones could take root.

However, no one need stay long in the country before finding that some old customs linger behind the modern façade. Every farmstead is on the telephone, but the subscribers are listed under their Christian names. The sagas are no longer read aloud at home during the long winter evenings with the entire household gathered round carding and spinning wool or doing other handwork, but they are broadcast almost daily. In Reykjavík luxurious cars are relatively more numerous than in any other European capital, but so also are bookshops.

The diminutive size of the Icelandic nation places it in a special position among the sovereign Norden nations, though these too are small by world standards. It should, however, be borne in mind that in spite of its small size the Icelandic community is structurally and functionally a fully fledged modern democracy, facing principally the same problems, social, cultural, political and economic, as nations many times bigger. At the same time it has stamped upon it the marks of its peculiar history and its geographical environment, which are so different from those in which most other civilized nations have their being.

CHAPTER 11

NORWAY

by Tore Sund [1]

PERSONALITY OF NORWAY

NORWAY is unique, even strange in many ways both as regards the physical and the man-made environment. It runs from 58°N to the northern tip of Europe at 71°, covers more degrees east—west and is longer and narrower than any other European country. Even more remarkable than the odd shape of Norway is the length of its coastline. No other coast in Europe is so tattered and broken by fjords or so sheltered by thousands of islands, islets and skerries. Whereas the main outline of the coast is about 2 650 kilometres long, the full length of the mainland coast is estimated to be about 20 000 km or half way around the globe. Inland water surfaces are also common features of the landscape, because lakes are found everywhere in glaciated Norway. A whole series of fresh water 'fjords'—so they are named—in southeast Norway, continues northwards in Sweden east of the Scandinavian watershed.

Norway is one of the most montainous countries in Europe. In relation to the total area the fairly smooth lowland areas are very small. Most of the surface has either only a thin layer of moraine or is nearly or completely bare. As in Finland and Sweden the post-glacially raised marine deposits offer the biggest and best areas of cultivable soil, but the Norwegian ones are very small compared with those of the other two countries.

The climate of Norway is relatively very mild, thanks to the currents of tropical air and the warm waters of the Gulf Stream. In the outermost of the Lofoten Islands the temperature is 24°C above the average for that latitude, i.e. the highest plus anomaly in the world. On the other hand the mountains cause a rapid deterioration of climate owing to the effect of altitude. Close behind the favoured coast and lowlands are also found the mountains with the highest precipitation and the most extensive glaciers of the European mainland. Most of them are of a type known as 'Norwegian', i.e. ice caps covering high mountain plateaux.

Temperature anomalies are therefore only a small compensation for a physical background which is hostile to settlement. Apart from the tiny countries of Europe no other country has such a small agricultural area, its proportion of the total area of Norway is only 3 per cent.

In sharp contrast to the land, the sea around Norway has everywhere a high natural productivity in food and abounds in fish of many different kinds. Unlike many other European catches the bulk of the Norwegian one is taken just off the home coast. The landings in Norway are nevertheless the biggest in Western Europe. Measured by quantity Norway ranks sixth among the world's fishing nations.

The fishing grounds in Greenland and Icelandic waters are familiar to many Norwegian fishermen. Sealing and whaling from Norway are carried out in even more distant waters. The sealing grounds are off Greenland and Newfoundland, and the scene of pelagic whaling on the other side of the globe, in Antarctic waters.

The most world-wide and large scale of all Norwegian industries however is shipping. Nor-

[1] Professor Tore Sund died in 1965 and Per-Christian Endsjø, Department of Geography, Norges Handelshøyskole, Bergen, has kindly revised the text and maps. Professor Gerhard Meidell Gerhardsen and Professor Arnljot Strømme Svendsen, both Norges Handelshøyskole, Bergen, have kindly revised the sections on fisheries and shipping respectively.

235

way has the third or fourth largest merchant marine in the world. If smaller than the American or British fleet, it is quite enormous in relation to the small population of Norway and the country's own needs in sea transport. Most of the Norwegian merchant marine is naturally chartered for transport between other countries. Norway has a negative trade balance with a very big gap between its exports and imports. The shipping business is therefore of fundamental importance in paying for the import of all the goods that are familiar items of other peoples' diet and for consumer goods which cannot profitably be produced in Norway.

Nowadays Norwegians certainly do not lack many of the articles of western good living. They need, and get, a substantial diet and plenty of warm clothes. In the case of food the consumption of milk products and fish is remarkable—and indicative of natural advantages for that kind of food-production. As Malthus noticed last century, natural and social conditions make Norway a healthy country. A Norwegian's expectation of life is among the very highest in the world.

Norway was by necessity an early participant in international trade, and in the old days traded fur and fish for grain. The modern Norwegian contribution to an industrialized manufacturing world is again associated with water, namely fresh water from parts of the country that until recently have had no value to man. Modern techniques have released the sources of energy latent in the rough and wet surfaces of Norway. The hydro-electricity compensates for a complete lack of coal and oil in Norway proper. These resources of power have come into use fairly recently, and their exploitation requires, like shipping and whaling, much capital. The reserves of hydro-electricity are still ample, and compared with those of other countries still very cheap. Already hydro-electricity forms a larger part of the total energy consumption in Norway than in any other country, and the production of hydro-electricity per head of population is by far the highest in the world. The domestic consumption of electricity, however, is only a small part of the total. Consumption by manufacturing industries is dominated by the electro-metallurgical and electro-chemical industries. The importance of these industrial branches, and of those having fish as their raw material, is greater in Norway than in any other Norden country.

Norway's exploitation of its forest resources and export of forest products goes much further back in history than the use of hydro-electricity. The wood-processing industries are still among the most important ones in the Norwegian economy; their contribution is, however, relatively smaller than that of the same industries in Finand and Sweden. The connection of forestry and wood-processing with water as a source of power, as a raw material and as a means of transport, is typical both of Norway and of Norden as a whole.

Compared with the great industrial nations of Europe—and Sweden and Denmark as well—engineering industries play a relatively humble role in Norwegian manufacturing. So does mining. Norway is, again in relation to its small population, a big exporter of metals and a big importer of machinery and transport equipment, especially ships. Besides shipping and whaling tourism is worth noticing as a part of the 'invisible exports'.

SETTLEMENT

The natural environment, mountainous, barren and cold over the greater part of the country and relatively pleasant along the coast, accounts for the character of Norwegian settlement. The population is mainly distributed along the coast; three quarters live less than 15 kilometres (10 miles) from the sea. The inland pattern of distribution is also linear, people can live only in the valleys that dissect the mountains. The conventional method of measuring population densities by the number of persons per square unit of an administrative land area does not therefore give an illustrative picture of actual habitational densities when applied to Norway. With the use

Fig. 11.1. Inhabited Norway, 1950. Based on a 1:400 000 population map of Norway (Statistisk Sentralbyrå: Bosettingskart over Norge. Oslo 1955), which shows population with symbols graded down to dots representing 25 dispersed people. The present map has been constructed by adding circles with a radius corresponding to 2.5 km (1.5 miles) to the symbols on the outskirts of the inhabited areas. The areas of land or sea thus encircled are shown in solid black. This has been done for the sea areas because of their importance as means of communication and as fishing grounds. Same scale as Fig. 11.3.

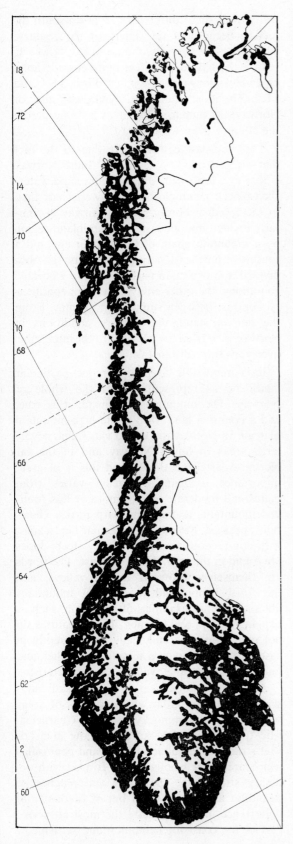

of this method intensely used surfaces of the sea are omitted, whereas vast areas of unused mountains can be included. Colour Map 9 therefore exclude the uninhabited areas, and Fig. 11.1 shows 'inhabited Norway' when no distinction is made between land and sea surfaces.

Any map that shows where people actually live in Norway explains why sea transport and provisions for sailing along the coast have played, and still play, a role that probably has no parallel outside Norway. The map also gives some illustration of the difficulties and costs involved in the construction of a modern system of railways and roads. Well into the period of air and road transport, the Norwegian railway net has not been completed to reach, for instance, the northwestern part of South Norway or North Norway north of Bodø.

Urban agglomerations have about half the population of Norway, which is not in any way a remarkable proportion. But what is even more typical of Norway than the other Norden countries, except Iceland, is the sea-side situation of the towns because of the dependence on sea transport in and beyond Norway. Water power sites in the lower part of the forested valleys have located wood-processing plants close to the sea, where the forest products are also readily available for export. Thanks to the possibilities for transmitting electric power, many of the originally commercial towns of Norway have developed into manufacturing towns as well. Completely new sites for manufacturing towns had to be chosen only for the mining centre and—more important—for some of the power-requiring plants. For them a location close to an ice-free fjord and a hydro-electric plant has been more advantageous than a site in an already existing town.

Relative richness in forest has caused Norwegians to build their houses in wood. This applies not only to the forested part of the country, but also to the barren coast and to most urban buildings, even those built in recent times. Norwegian houses are generally well built for the purpose of keeping one warm and dry, and weather and darkness compel Norwegians to spend much of their time indoors. But this makes life in the open air attractive, and for this the opportunities are ample so far as space is concerned.

Whether rural or urban, most Norwegian habitations are situated close to wide areas of uncultivated land and water surfaces. Otherwise considered poor, these areas form valuable amenities, and many Norwegians can afford to go fishing or hunting, and have developed a liking for boating and bathing and for tours on foot or skis in the mountains and forests. Among the winter sports, skiing can be considered the national one. Its wide-spread popularity is indicative both of an advantageous natural environment and of a high standard of living. So are all the cottages which in recent times have come to form quite frequent and extensive features of the landscape on the coasts and in the mountains.

REGIONAL CONTRASTS

It should be stressed that Norway is a country with sharp regional differences: few areas of the same size, 324 000 km², have such or more marked contrasts. Many of the characteristics mentioned here are, in fact, not representative of the whole of Norway, but refer only to parts of the country. Within Norway natural features, living conditions and occupations vary greatly from one part of the country to another. Many examples can be given.

Physical features

The general impression of daylight in Norway is one of very long days in summer, correspondingly short ones in winter, and very rapid changes in the duration of daylight from season to season. This is an expression of the northerly position of the country as a whole. Its length north-south, however, and the great width expressed in longitude, makes daylight conditions in the south very different from those in the 'land of the midnight sun' (Fig. 11.2).

In addition to the daylight, climate and weather make Summer-Norway entirely different from Winter-Norway. Not only does the landscape, because of the snow, take on a different appearance, but the outdoor activities, whether work or pleasure, must change very markedly throughout the year. Again one has to bear in mind that the contrasts between winter and summer are not the same throughout, but vary a great deal around the country. One

will expect great differences in north-south direction because of the length of the country. The prevailing currents of air and sea, however, reduce the latitudinal effect quite considerably, especially along the coast, cf. Figs. 11.3 and 11.4. The most significant climate contrasts of Norway are therefore found by moving across the country from west to east.

The west-east contrasts are due to the fact that the general cross-section of South Norway is that of a lop-sided roof, with the main watershed placed much closer to the west coast than to the Swedish border. North Norway is similarly divided into a coastal and an inland region by a mountain chain of Caledonian age and a southwest-northeast strike. Norway is thus divided into two main parts, one having oceanic conditions, the other enjoying a more continental contrast between summer and winter. From the human standpoint weather conditions in Norway vary from the pleasant to the intolerable over very short distances.

It is impossible to pick out one particular landscape as representative of the whole of Norway. The mountains dominate, it is true, and a common land form is the high-mountain plateau. In Norway it is called *vidde,* and covers large areas in South Norway and in the far North. Apart from these—and this is of great importance to man—the relief varies from plains and moderate hills to more or less rounded mountains and needle-sharp peaks. Generally speaking, the more spectacular landscapes, with conspicuous heights and very steep slopes are found in the west along the coast. The fjords are themselves drowned trough valleys, and the fjord region and the coastal mountains abound in other examples of glaciation, such as hanging valleys and cirques. These features do not come out so dramatically or frequently in eastern Norway, where a moderate relief and long, roughly parallel, valleys are characteristic.

An important element in the coastal landscapes is the strandflat which consists of areas of more or less hummocky lowlands. Characteristic too are the submarine, shallow areas of 'wet strandflat' adjoining islands and peninsulas which are either wholly flat or fringed with ordinary strandflat. The strips and patches of strandflat are mostly small but of fundamental importance in that they are the most attractive part of the coast for habitation and settlement.

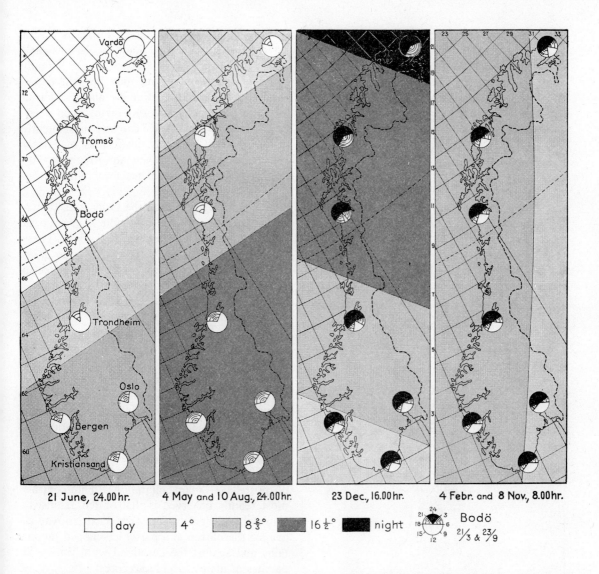

21 June, 24.00 hr.   4 May and 10 Aug., 24.00 hr.   23 Dec., 16.00 hr.   4 Febr. and 8 Nov., 8.00 hr.

day   4° $8\tfrac{2}{3}$° $16\tfrac{1}{2}$°   night   Bodö $\tfrac{21}{3}$ & $\tfrac{23}{9}$

Fig. 11.2. Daylight conditions. The shadings of the four maps refer to particular dates and to the Norwegian (i.e. Middle European of 15°E) times noted below each of the maps. Norwegians distinguish between three different categories of twilight, here shown in grey shadings. From the lightest to the darkest they are so defined that (1) the upper edge of the sun is between the horizon and 4° below it, (2) between 4° and $8\tfrac{2}{3}$° and (3) between $8\tfrac{2}{3}$° and $16\tfrac{1}{2}$° below the horizon. The first two maps show the light situation at midnight at mid- and early (and late) summer. The third map illustrates the midwinter situation in the afternoon when many Norwegians leave their work. The last map shows the situation at the beginning of the day's work in early (and late) winter. — The sectored circles are placed on selected towns and show the light situation during a 24 hours' day at the dates noted below the maps. The white sector shows daylight according to the definition given above, the grey sector symbolizes twilight (because of the scale the darkest and the two lightest categories together can only be vaguely indicated), and the black sector illustrates the night. The sectors are drawn according to the local time, and the borderlines between day and twilight therefore show the direction to the sun from that particular place at sunrise and sunset. The key has a circle for Bodø, where local and Norwegian time coincide, at 21 March and 23 September. — The shadings of the first map show that from about 66°N there is midnight sun proper, and the shadings of the second map that even in early and late summer there is nowhere dark night in Norway. The sectored circles of the third map illustrates that Nord-Norge north of Bodø has no daylight proper in midwinter, only twilight. The circles of the fourth map show the similarity in all parts of the country in respect of duration of dark night and the great differences in respect of duration of some sort of twilight.

239

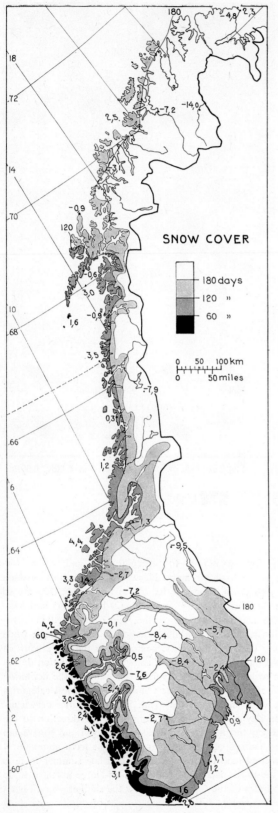

180 days
120 "
60 "

0   50   100 km
0   50 miles

For climatic reasons alone, lowlands are of course assets in Norway. Southeast Norway and the region around Trondheimsfjord are the only parts of the country that may be said to resemble the lowlands of Finland and Sweden in size and postglacial history. Having been deeply pressed down by the ice cap and subsequently uplifted, these lowlands have areas of former sea beds at varying levels up to about 200 metres above the present sea level. The former submarine gravels, sands and clays have formed plains and ridges around the Oslo- and Trondheimsfjords which are cultivable to an extent that is unparallelled elsewhere in Norway. These same lowlands also have relatively large areas of Cambro-Silurian rocks which, in contrast to other rocks, have been soft enough to produce valuable soils by postglacial weathering. A cover of ground moraine which in quantity and quality is particularly favourable to agriculture is another asset of these two basins. A kind of negative illustration of the importance of the lowlands of Norway is found in the fact that the rural districts in the mountains of South Norway have 24 per cent of the area and only a little more than 3 per cent of the population.

As shown in Chapter 5, Norway has several zones of vegetation, which are the result of both the intricate pattern of climatic conditions and of postglacial plant migrations. The contrast most readily observed is that of the extensive, primarily coniferous, forests of East Norway as against the barren and partly ice-capped mountains and against the coastland with heath and patches of mainly deciduous forest.

Five main regions

On the basis of these major contrasts in Norway's physical background, the country can conveniently be divided into five main parts. This division is familiar to all Norwegians, and

Fig. 11.3. Winter illustrated by the duration of snow cover, averages for 1901–30. The figures indicate the mean, unreduced temperatures in °C for January in the same period at selected places. The mean surface temperatures of the sea for January (1935–39) are shown for selected points by sloping figures. — The map shows the great differences in snow cover east–west and the effect of height above sea level. In the southwest corner of the country there are less than 30 days with snow cover. The lowest sea temperatures are off the southeast coast; here ice forms on the sea in severe winters.

the regions in question all have names that are in common use, and they will be used here: *Østlandet* (East Norway), *Sørlandet* (southernmost Norway), *Vestlandet* (West Norway), *Trøndelag* (the Trondheim region) and *Nord-Norge* (North Norway). Østlandet, Sørlandet, Vestlandet and Trøndelag are parts of *Sør-Norge* (South Norway), cf. map on p. 7, which also gives the names of Norway's 20 counties.

In addition to the characteristics already noted a few others for each of the regions may be mentioned.

Østlandet consists of a few large catchment areas which drain into or are close to the Oslo-fjord. In contrast Vestlandet is an extremely dissected region, with many short valleys leading down to the great fjords.

Sørlandet lies between east and west. It has valleys and forests more like those of Østlandet, and the mountains are generally of a moderate height. The continuous region of spruce forest ends in Sørlandet. Strictly the name Sørlandet is confined to a narrow strip of coastal land, which like Vestlandet has fjords and is sheltered by a line of islands and islets. But the fjords and islands are smaller in Sørlandet. These features, the high summer temperature and the relatively low winter temperature of the sea, the pleasant summer weather and the occasional violent winter snowfalls make Sørlandet a region of its own.

Trøndelag comprises an inland region around Trondheimsfjord and a coastal, outer district. The moderate heights and the spruce forests of the inner part naturally classify it as a northern extension of Østlandet, although it is actually separated from it by mountains running southwest–northeast. The outer part of Trøndelag can be considered a transitional zone between Vestlandet and Nord-Norge.

Fig. 11.4. Summer illustrated by the number of days with a mean temperature of at least 10°C, averages for 1901–30. The figures give the mean unreduced land temperatures at 14.00 in July for selected places and the mean surface temperatures of the sea (1935–39) for selected points in July (sloping figures). — The map shows the favourable climatic conditions of the southern littoral in regard to duration of summer as well as in regard to land and sea temperatures. Compared with the winter conditions of Fig. 11.3, the more marked differences of temperature north–south stand out, and both maps demonstrate the oceanic conditions of the coast and the continental climate of eastern Norway and the inner fjord districts of Vestlandet.

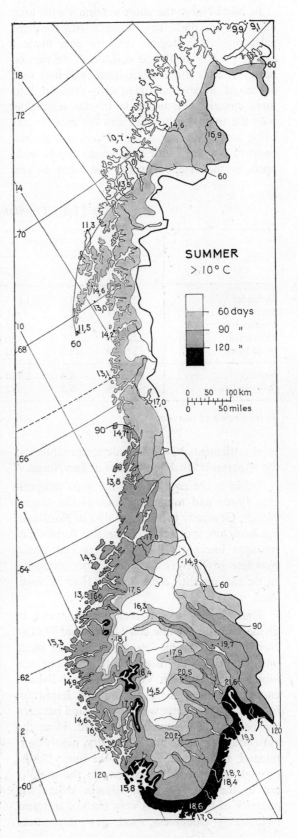

SUMMER
> 10° C

60 days
90 "
120 "

0   50   100 km
0   50 miles

241

In Nord-Norge the short summers with long days and the dark, cold winters with frequent gales produce a region with its own distinct character. The length and vastness of the region, however, calls for a subdivision, which is well expressed in the administrative division into three counties. Finnmark in the far north has both the most gentle relief and the most brutal living conditions. It has the longest unsheltered coast in Norway, with long broad fjords wide open to the Arctic Ocean, and even at sea

between summer and winter temperatures and lack of a lasting snow cover.

Lastly, Østlandet has an extension inland that calls for a more conventional subdivision of its long valleys into three parts from the sea up into the high mountains. In the outer division of plains and low hills many of the broad and shallow river courses are not recognized or named as valleys. The valleys proper start with the central division which is also the forested part. As can be seen from Colour Maps 2–3 Østlan-

Table 11.1. *Population by regions, 1960.*

Region	Urban[1]				Rural		Total
	200 — 2 000	%	> 2 000	%	Total	%	
Østlandet	128 703	7.4	1 033 448	59.1	585 621	33.5	1 747 772
Sørlandet	18 987	10.2	81 210	43.7	85 740	46.1	185 937
Vestlandet	74 506	8.3	382 617	42.9	435 395	48.8	892 518
Trøndelag	22 077	6.7	130 831	39.9	175 375	53.4	328 283
Nord-Norge	57 949	13.3	122 306	28.0	256 469	58.7	436 724
Norway	302 222	8.4	1 750 412	48.7	1 538 600	42.9	3 591 234
Oslofjord district	*88 649*	*6.8*	*932 157*	*71.9*	*276 283*	*21.3*	*1 297 089*

[1]) Irrespective of town status.

level settlements have the same temperatures as the uppermost inhabited valleys of Sør-Norge.

Troms is the county with the most magnificent fjords and mountains and of the largest islands. Generally they are smaller in Nordland, but here, too, spectacular mountains form a picturesque background to the strandflat areas. Nowhere in Norway are these more extensive or the shallow shelf areas broader than in Nordland.

Sometimes it is convenient or necessary to divide even the narrow coast- and fjord-land of Nordland and Troms into two parts, an outer one comprising the islands and an inner one around the fjords. In Vestlandet a subdivision east-west is even more natural and important because of the greater width of the land between the ocean and the main water-shed. Here the variations in climate are from a dry, nearly continental, type at the heads of the inner fjords, through an extremely wet zone in the middle, out to the outer zone of islands, where the oceanity of the climate is very marked in terms of humidity, cloudiness, wind, small differences

det's extensive forests grow on rather infertile moraine derived from rocks such as gneisses and sandstones, and extend several hundred metres upslope from the valley bottoms. In the mountains coniferous forests give place to mountain birch scrub; this continues to the tree line and changes to alpine vegetation at a height of about 1 000 m.

Occupations and habitations

It goes without saying that all the contrasts and differences in nature are reflected in human living conditions in Norway. When we add to this all the different urban occupations which have become important and widespread in Norway, we can register a range of human activities which is rare in such a small population. Not only agriculture but also other diversities of economic activity can be conveniently illustrated by referring to the regions mentioned.

Fig. 11.5 shows occupational structure in Norway and in its main regions. Having in mind the regional subdivisions, one notices that it illustrates the regional diversity of occupations

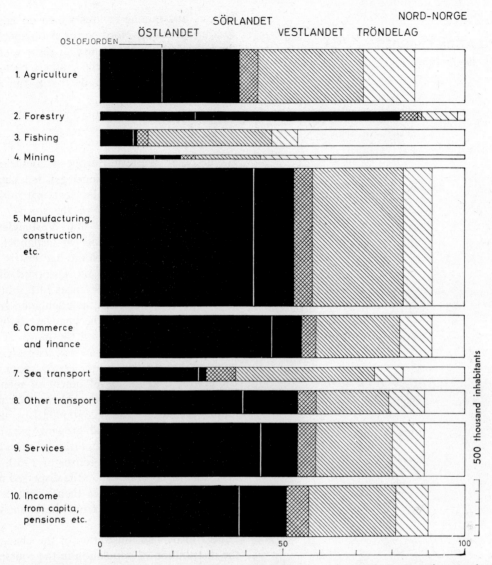

OSLOFJORDEN

ÖSTLANDET   SÖRLANDET   VESTLANDET   TRÖNDELAG   NORD-NORGE

1. Agriculture

2. Forestry

3. Fishing

4. Mining

5. Manufacturing, construction, etc.

6. Commerce and finance

7. Sea transport

8. Other transport

9. Services

10. Income from capita, pensions etc.

500 thousand inhabitants

0   50   100

Fig. 11.5. Resident population by industries and regions, 1960. Vertically the diagram shows the population in 10 main industries, and horizontally the regional share of each industry. Of Norway's total population 49% were living in Østlandet, 5% in Sørlandet, 25% in Vestlandet, 9% in Trøndelag and 12% in Nord-Norge.

in Norway in simplified form. Table 11.1 also includes the peripherically situated 'core region' of Norway, the Oslofjord district, consisting of four counties around Oslofjord, Oslo, Akershus, Østfold and Vestfold, plus the lower part of the counties of Buskerud and Telemark. Here, in this 'subregion' of Østlandet, which covers only five per cent of Norway's land area, is no less than one third of its population, and it is by far the most urbanized part of the country.

According to Fig. 11.5, the greater part of the Norwegian population make a living in 'urban' industries, and Table 11.1 shows that

a little more than half the population of Norway live in towns or small town-like agglomerations. The proportion between dense, urban and dispersed settlements varies from region to region, following more or less the proportions between urban and rural occupations already noted in Fig. 11.5. Going around the coast from the Oslofjord district, the dispersed population increases its share of the total population. Nord-Norge is the least urbanized part of Norway, but in Nord-Norge small town-like agglomerations have relatively more inhabitants than in other regions, because of the many fishing-

243

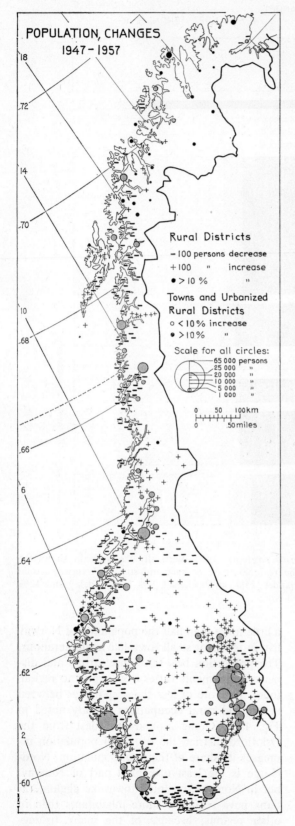

POPULATION, CHANGES
1947 – 1957

Rural Districts

  – 100 persons decrease

  + 100   "   increase

  ● > 10 %   "

**Towns and Urbanized
Rural Districts**

  ○ < 10 % increase

  ● > 10 %   "

Scale for all circles:

  65 000 persons
  25 000   "
  20 000   "
  10 000   "
  5 000   "
  1 000   "

0   50 100 km

0   50 miles

villages and mining centres which do not possess urban status. Nord-Norge is obviously behind the rest of the country in respect of economic development, but the southern part of the region has been rapidly industrialized in recent years.

Population trends

As in other Western European countries the fertility of Norwegian marriages fell substantially from the end of last century until the 1930's, and particularly in the towns. Thus families in Nord-Norge and Vestlandet are generally bigger than those in Østlandet. The average family in Nord-Norge had nearly three children in 1960 and in the Oslofjord district less than two. These differences in fertility are not, however, reflected in the population growth of the regions, because the changing industrial structure has put people on the move. A hundred years ago Norway had half its present population, but it was nevertheless overpopulated. Emigration and the development of manufacturing industries in Norway relieved the population pressure. The geographical result of changing occupations and growing population has been an increasing proportion of town dwellers. It was not until the census of 1950, however, that an absolute fall in the dispersed population was registered. Since then a considerable movement to the towns from the country has occurred.

Fig. 11.6 is an illustration of the changes in the distribution of population in the course of a

---

Fig. 11.6. Population changes, 1947–57. The map shows differences of population in administrative districts *(kommune)* between the census of 1 Dec. 1946 and the registration of 1 Jan. 1957. Rural districts are here defined as those having more than half the total population (according to the 1950 census) in agriculture, forestry, and fishing. Towns and their surrounding suburban districts are indicated by one circle only. In some cases several towns are put together in one circle, e.g. Fredrikstad–Sarpsborg and Skien–Porsgrunn–Brevik; these in fact form continuous urban areas. — Depopulation of rural districts, and an urban increase of more than 10 per cent, is the rule. Exceptional increases of more than 10 per cent in some rural districts occur in south and north Vestlandet and in north Nord-Norge. The latter increase is partly due to war damage: in 1944 the German occupying forces burnt all buildings in Finnmark and North-Troms (east of Lyngenfjord); the people had to be evacuated and some could not return until after 1946.

decade after World War II, and it shows that some parts of the country are losing their population, whereas in others it is rapidly increasing. Comparing this map with Colour Maps 9–10, it is evident that the densely populated and urbanized districts around the Oslofjord and the bigger towns are still growing faster than, and probably at the cost of, the less densely populated and more rural districts. The Oslofjord district had 35 per cent of Norway's population in 1950, and 45 per cent of its increase during the period 1947–1957. This may be due to original advantages in resources and location and to the snowball effect, which makes a favoured successful area more and more attractive for all kinds of production. There are, however, other areas, which may be rural districts, that have had substantial increases. The geographical pattern of backwardness, stagnation and progress—and historical changes as a whole—should be kept in mind during the studies of Norwegian industries which follow. They can, of course, give only a rather generalized picture in terms of space, and more so in terms of time.

AGRICULTURE

Agriculture is no longer the 'mother industry' of Norway. The total employed in manufacture did not exceed that in agriculture until the 1930's. About 13 per cent of the Norwegian population still make a living in agriculture. The role of agriculture in the national economy is however much more humble than is indicated by this figure. In recent years the share of agriculture in the national income of Norway has been only 4–5 per cent. (Table 7.3 p. 83.) Norwegian agriculture is subsidized quite considerably, partly in order to try to keep wages for workers in agriculture up to the standard of other industries. Another motive for subsidizing agriculture is to make the country as independent as possible in case of war.

Norway has never been adequately fed by the produce of its own farms. The old deficiency in grain is still there, and many of the fruits and vegetables consumed today are imported. All sugar has to be imported. The potato yields well in Norway and serves as food and fodder. Some fodder too, such as maize and cakes of oil seed, has to be imported. But Norway is self-sufficient in milk and meat products. Fish constitutes an important part of the protein-food.

Although now inferior to the urban industries, agriculture has been the dominant factor in forming the pattern of settlement and economic activities. Even the majority of the fishermen live and settle where they can make agricultural use of the land. The agricultural districts form markets for the towns and supply them with food and manpower, thus influencing the pattern of urban settlements. Nearly the whole human geography of Norway is therefore directly or indirectly dependent on the same natural factors as the agricultural environment.

Physical background

The small areas of soil useful for agriculture originate from three main sources, marine deposits, weathered soil from Cambro-Silurian sedimentary rocks, and morainic material. The marine sediments are by far the most valuable ones in all parts of the country, and in recent times they have the additional advantage of being the most level land, well suited for farm machinery. The Cambro-Silurian and morainic soils are widely distributed, but the use of them is greatly reduced by climatic conditions. In the mountains of Sør-Norge for instance, they can be used only for pasture in the short summer.

In absolute values temperature conditions are tyrannical in Norway, only a small part of the country has for instance an average summer temperature higher than 10°C, which is commonly considered a limit for the growing of grain. Nowhere do the summer temperatures permit, for instance, profitable cultivation of sugar beet. Grain growing in Nord-Norge and on the outer parts of the west coast is rather exceptional. In the coastal parts of the country a long growing season, at Bergen about 200 days with temperatures above 6°C, compensates for a cool summer. The amount of heat, measured in day-degrees, is as high as near the Oslofjord, which has a growing season of 140 days only.

245

Excessive rainfall is Norway's salient problem in respect of precipitation, and the rain is so unevenly distributed from season to season that even the wet coastal parts of the country may quite often lack rain in early summer, while the drier, eastern parts of the country may often have poor crops because of excessive rain at harvest time.

of Sørlandet, Vestlandet (except Jæren), and the coastal districts of Trøndelag and group 5 Nord-Norge.

Group 1, of good agricultural land, is quantitatively very important in Norway's agricultural production. It has 38 per cent of the country's total farmland, and as much as 61 per cent of Norway's areas under grain, potatoes and roots.

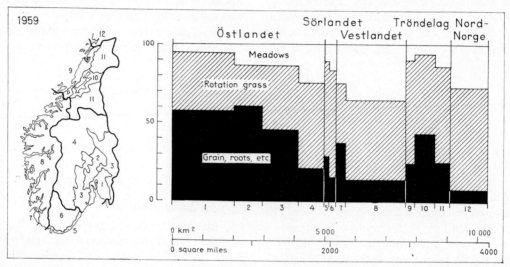

Fig. 11.7. Land use in agricultural regions, 1959. The diagram shows the use of agricultural land (total 10 400 km²) in the main and secondary regions shown on the adjoining map. Region 12 is Nord-Norge. The black and shaded areas constitute the arable land (cf. Colour Map 8). The agricultural land includes meadows, recorded at the decennial agricultural censuses. — Regions 1, 2, 7 and 10 are classed as the 'best agricultural regions'.

AGRICULTURAL REGIONS

The differences in climate are the dominant criteria for the division of Norway into agricultural regions, although soil and other natural factors must also be considered. The agricultural censuses use 20 regions, derived by subdividing the 5 main regions already mentioned. These 20 regions may conveniently be put together into 5 groups irrespective of the borders of the 5 main regions. Group 1 is called the group of the 'best agricultural regions', namely the plains around Oslofjord, some inland basins of mainly Cambro-Silurian sedimentary rocks in Østlandet (cf. Colour Map 2), the region around Trondheimsfjord and the small region of Jæren, south of the city of Stavanger in Vestlandet (regions 1, 2, 7 and 10 on Fig. 11.7). Group 2 consists of the intermediate or forest districts in Østlandet, Sørlandet and Trøndelag and in the same regions group 3 is the mountain districts. Group 4 includes the coastal districts

In group 1 nearly one third of the farm land is under arable crops. Permanent grassland and rotation grass for grazing also have a relatively bigger share of the farmland in group 1 than in the other ones, which are dominated by areas under rotation grass for cutting and by meadows.

Types of farming

Norway is a country of very small farms. There are nearly twice as many farm holdings under 2 ha. (5 acres) as there are above. Of those above 2 ha. (138 012 in 1959) only one farm in seven has an agricultural area of more than 10 ha. But in group 1 the proportion is nearly one in two, and this group has all the country's few bigger farms of more than 400 ha.

In addition to the physical factors the economic climate has to be taken into consideration as a factor determining the type of farming. Norway's best agricultural districts are around

246

the Oslofjord towns and around Trondheim and Stavanger, and provide examples of the zonal arrangement of types of farming around bigger towns.

The subsidizing of grain production accounts for its recent marked increase. The order according to quantity is barley, oats and wheat. Traditionally Norwegians eat rye-bread, but wheat-bread has now become more common. Rye is, in fact, very rarely grown in Norway at present. Barley and oats, best suited to the climate, are most extensively grown (Table 7.5, p. 85). Formerly eaten as hardbread and porridge, they are now mainly used as fodder.

In amount of grain production, group 1 deviates notably from the characteristic Norwegian farming. Østlandet has some new, and few, grain farms which are very highly mechanized and have relatively large areas of level land. As a rule Norwegian farmers get much more of their income from the cow-shed and domestic animals than from arable crops.

The principal system of rotation on good agricultural land in Norway covers a period of 6 years, of which 3 years are in grass, 1 (or 2) in potatoes and 2 (1) in grain or roots. The system is again indicative of the importance of milk production.

The type of farming in Østlandet's best agricultural districts is nearly the same as that of the good agricultural land in Central Sweden and southern Finland. It is very different from the greater part of Norway where farming is carried on under marginal conditions. The two other regions in group 1 are also worth mentioning. Inner Trøndelag, despite its northerly position, has fairly good possibilities for grain growing. The southern part of Trøndelag generally has a surplus of hay for sale to other parts of the country, but its wetter climate is less suited to ripening grain.

The other remarkable region, Jæren, with very mild winters and a long growing season with moderate heat, is less suited to the growing of grain than inner Trøndelag. The climate, the flat landscape, and the type of farming make Jæren a bit of Denmark, hinged on to the mountains of Norway. Jæren's soils are mostly not emerged sea beds (the postglacial upheaval is negligible here), but are derived from a thick layer of moraine. Nowhere in Norway is the land so intensively cultivated as in Jæren. The

farmers there use more manure and fertilizers and get higher yields, they use more concentrated fodder and get a higher milk production per cow, and they produce relatively more pork and eggs than anywhere else in the country. Stavanger and other nearby markets are too small for the Jæren region, which was linked by rail during World War II with its principal market, the city of Oslo. The population of Jæren is increasing (see Fig. 11.6) in sharp contrast to other agricultural regions of Norway, and especially to neighbouring Sørlandet, where sparcity of soil and a hummocky terrain make farms very small and inconvenient to run.

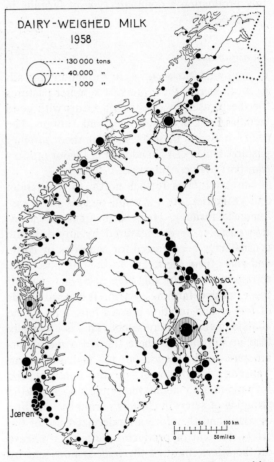

Fig. 11.8. *Dairies* in Sør-Norge, 1958. The quantities of milk supplied by the collecting centres of Oslo, Bergen and Trondheim are indicated by the outer, shaded rings. Their supply areas are delimited by broken lines. Smaller shaded circles show affiliated dairies inside and outside the supply areas which normally produce butter and cheese, but which augment the milk supply of these three cities in periods of shortage. Most of the other dairies are combined dairies, selling milk as well as producing butter and cheese. Dairyweighed milk increased in 1958–65 by 22%.

The islands just north of Stavanger have good soils on Cambro-Silurian schists. Like Jæren the region has specialized in early potatoes and vegetables and tomatoes and cucumbers under glass. In fact these two regions are the only ones in Vestlandet that grow vegetables on a noteworthy scale.

Most of the farming in Vestlandet is located in its outer, coastal region. In spite of a relatively small postglacial uplift, the emerged sea beds are here much more extensive than in the inner, steep fjord regions. The wet climate, the restricted areas of agricultural land and the big demand from Bergen and other towns make milk production a dominant type of farming in Vestlandet.

Transhumance

In southwest Norway, i.e. in the mountains adjacent to Jæren, there are vast summer pastures for sheep, used by coastal hill farms with good facilities for grazing in spring and autumn. The tracks between these farms and their summer pastures have been abandoned in favour of lorry transport over considerable distances.

The mountains further north, in Vestlandet and Østlandet, are the main regions for transhumance farming. Here large areas of mountain pasture, never measured by any accurate census, have been grazed for centuries by cattle and goats from the seters. In the old days these were a more important, even necessary, part of the extensive farming system. Increased yields of fodder and rotation grasses have lead to the abandonment of many seters. This is especially true in Vestlandet, where the steep mountains are serious obstructions to rational and cheap transport. In Østlandet, on the contrary, the high mountain plateau, the gentle slopes and the grouping of seters in clusters permit the building of roads and therefore a modernized use of the seters. Instead of producing butter and cheese on the seters, most of the milk is now sent by lorry to the dairies in the permanently inhabited valleys. Seters may survive with this adaptation. In 1959, 13 400 Norwegian farms used seters, but this was only half the total for 1939.

Since 1939 the number of sheep has increased. Half of Norway's sheep are found in the four western counties where the grazing season is longer than in eastern and northern Norway.

The number of goats has decreased. The steep mountain slopes of Vestlandet are admirably suited to goats, but the fruit growing and forestry of the area is incompatible with goat rearing. One third of Norway's goats are now found in North Norway. In eastern Norway supplies of goat's milk for making the traditional Norwegian brown cheese are becoming scarce.

The limit between Østlandet's permanent upland farms and seter settlements is very vague. Mountain settlements are very sensitive to local climates, hence the sunny sides of the valleys are settled and the shaded slope is either forested or partly used for grazing from seters in the spring and autumn.

Northerly extremes

Vestlandet's fjord districts are interesting examples of what are probably the world's most northerly fruit-growing districts. The more continental climate, including the oven effect of the mountain walls, make the growing of apples, pears, plums and soft fruit a profitable use of the steep slopes. Proper ripening is a problem in particularly wet summers, and the location of fruit farming is often dependent on sites with a favourable local climate or a warm soil. It is for instance necessary to avoid the cold air caused by inversion or exposure on a windy site. A future concentration of fruit growing on the better sites may be expected.

In coastal Nord-Norge too there is a surprising example of the northward extension of the main type of Norwegian agriculture. A good and limy soil, long warm summer days, warm air from Russia, and light nights causing a small daily amplitude, are the reasons for the remarkable results in the production of hay, potatoes and vegetables. On the whole, however, the climate is a very limiting factor to cultivation, and fishing tends to take a bigger occupational share the further north—or out on the islands— one goes.

In Nord-Norge especially a great problem is that the long winters and the small farms make agriculture a part-time employer. For centuries fishing in Lofoten has been a 'winter harvest' and the main source of cash income at a slack period of the farming year in Nord-Norge, though recent fishery developments do not readily combine with part-time farming. The industrialization of Nord-Norge aims at reducing winter unemployment. This part of the world provides outstanding examples of how difficult and sometimes impossible it is to classify people by occupation. In Nord-Norge outer districts, fjord districts and mountain conditions are situated close together, and the farmers very often combine farming with fishing or vice versa, and census data thus give an inaccurate picture of an ever-changing situation.

FORESTS AND FORESTRY

Combination of occupation is also very common in the forest districts, in an environment entirely different from that of the fishing districts. This is obvious from the fact that 4 of Norway's 7 million hectares of forest land belong to about 100 000 farms, which also own forest in common and have the right to take fuel and lumber for building purposes in the state forests (17 per cent of the Norwegian forests are state-owned). The owners of these farms therefore work the forests and draw an income from the forest in varying proportion to that from agriculture. Of about 15 000 wage-earning forest workers, some have forestry work as their sole, others as their main or subsidiary occupation.

As shown on Colour Map 8 and Fig. 11.5, forest and forestry is mostly found in Østlandet, Trøndelag and Sørlandet. Here the forests cover nearly all unfarmed land below the climatically determined timber line. In Østlandet 40 per cent of the total area is under forest.

Forest areas

Forest areas are obviously only one of the factors to be considered in evaluation of forest resources; the cubic content of the timber stand and the annual growth in cubic metres must be considered. So 'productive' forest does not include the forests near the timber line, which are very slow growing and protect the forests below, and some inaccessible forest is also omitted. Table 7.8, p. 89 gives the figure 5.76 million hectares for the forest area actually used in Norway. It has a net annual growth (annual increase in cubic content excluding bark) of 13.5 million m³ or an average yield of 2.2 m³ per hectare.

As shown on Colour Map 8, Østlandet is above the average, and Vestlandet and Nord-Norge far below it for reasons that are partly due to the soil, partly to the climate in its widest sense, partly to the productivity of the tree species growing there, and partly to forestry practice.

The soils occupied by forests in Norway are mostly of a quality which make them unsuitable for farm use. The highest forest yields possible are therefore much higher than the normal ones, derived from the usual poor forest soils. The morainic forest soils of Østlandet are derived from infertile rocks such as Precambrian gneisses and granites and from coarse sandstones belonging to the Eocambrian. Very thin soil layers and much bare rock are also responsible for the low yields. Norwegian forests, all factors considered—soil, climate, water supply and others—are divided into five forest categories, ranked from very good to very bad. In Hedmark county the average annual growth in category 1 is 7.2 m³ per hectare, in category 5 less than 0.6. In Norway's forest districts only 5–10 per cent of the forest areas are in the two best categories. Categories 3 and 4 predominate.

The variation in height of the timber line above sea level is an indication of the climatic forest conditions that is easily observed. The higher timber line in Østlandet, as compared with Vestlandet, is an effect of a higher summer temperature. Wind and humidity combined are a detrimental influence in Vestlandet. In its outer districts summer temperatures should allow for a forest line of several hundred metres, but the actual one is down to 200 m and lower. In the middle zone of Vestlandet the height limit for productive forest is 4–600 m, as against 6–800 m in Østlandet.

The pine is a native tree of Vestlandet, but it thrives better in the warmer and drier climate of Østlandet and Trøndelag, where a little more than 20 per cent of the coniferous forests consist of pine. On the other hand Vestlandet's heavy precipitation is an advantage for the growing of spruce and other tree species that are not native to Vestlandet. Given the same quality of soil and the same summer temperature, the spruce has a higher annual growth, and can be felled earlier in Vestlandet than in Østlandet. The coniferous trees of Norway are ready for felling when they are from 65 to 130 years old, i.e. when the average annual growth starts to decrease.

FORESTRY

In forestry practice the forests of Norway are divided into five cutting classes, number I being the quite young trees, number II and III young forest with little value as a source of timber, IV is mature forest and V is forest ready for felling and old forest. At present 40 per cent of the Norwegian forest areas belong to class V, which is far too much from a rational point of view. For actual and optimal production of timber, see Fig. 7.3, p. 83.

The reason for the badly-balanced composition of Norwegian forests is partly speculative forestry by thousands of forest owners, and partly fluctuating demand and prices for the products of Norway's wood-processing industries, with large fellings when the prices have been high, and small fellings in slump periods, restricted to nearby forests with low transport costs. Large forest areas have thus passed maturity and have small annual growth, but serve as a kind of bank to the owners.

Norwegian timber production is capable of considerable improvement. A better age composition of the forests can be obtained by fellings in class V and sowing or planting to get rid of the great deficit of young trees, that may cause a fall in timber production in the future. The present rate of plantings after felling amounts to 60 million plants on about 20 000 hectares. Drainage could also improve production in the existing forests.

Afforestation

Increases in the forest area are also occurring, especially in Vestlandet where a public committee proposes to plant before 1990 360 000 hectares, including Vest-Agder county. 35 million trees have to be planted each year according to this programme. It involves both afforestation and reforestation in the sense that native, mainly deciduous, forests have to be replaced by spruce and other higher yielding forests. Great care is taken to use seed from districts with conditions similar to those of the new forests of Vestlandet, and from trees that have proved to have a high yield. For instance spruce seeds from the Harz (Germany) are frequently used in the nurseries in Vestlandet. Of special interest are the tree species from the humid Pacific coast of America, such as Sitka spruce, Douglas fir and Hemlock. They all seem to thrive in Vestlandet, and Sitka spruce has become quite a common tree. The middle, wet zone of Vestlandet is especially promising for the future production of timber. A special problem in Vestlandet is the uncontrolled grazing of sheep and goats, which destroy the seedlings.

The afforestation plan for Vestlandet is well under way, and in the future the afforested areas are expected to have an annual growth of c. 2 million m^3. It is intended that the small farms in the afforestation districts will get their subsidiary or even their main income from the new forests. Vestlandet's first wood-processing plant based on the local forests has recently started production.

Nord-Norge provides the other marginal areas for afforestation. In spite of the fact that the most valuable existing forests are south of the Arctic circle, which is also the limit for the native spruce forest, the largest new forests of spruce are expected to be planted north of the Arctic Circle, in Nordland and Troms counties, and on ground now occupied by birch forest. The soil is better than in Vestlandet, and, in spite of the higher latitude, the annual growth seems to be almost as high as it is there. Finnmark has a noteworthy but slow-growing pine forest along the Russian border; it forms the northwestern limit of the Russo-Siberian taiga.

Altogether a future net annual growth of 25 million m^3 is estimated possible in the Norwegian forests. The major part of the increase will come from existing forests. This estimate assumes of course that the climate will not worsen. The registered increase of forest growth in recent years is partly due to the climatic amelioration.

The annual total fellings of coniferous and deciduous wood in Norway amount to nearly 10 million m^3, or 8 if one excludes the rural consumption of wood. Of this quantity about three quarters is produced in Østlandet and a little more than one tenth in Trøndelag; Sørlandet produces 6–7 per cent.

Timber transport

The last-named regions are well suited to forestry in having a number of rivers that are suitable for the floating of timber. They penetrate the forest land to an extent that even in the old days left relatively small areas of forests as inaccessible. During the last decade, however, the volume of floated timber has been halved and in 1966 it totalled 15 million logs (1.6 million m³). The Glomma alone carried 10 million logs. The floating of timber starts in the spring and lasts throughout the summer. It includes tugging on some of the larger lakes, e.g. Øyeren and Randsfjorden, respectively east and north of Oslo.

The busiest time in forestry is, however, the winter, because a snowcover is indispensable for the transport of logs from the felling places down to the floating rivers or to the new roads for lorry transport. In the old days all timber transport by land was done by horse. In recent years thousands of kilometres of roads have been constructed for timber transport by lorry or tractor, thus making it cheaper and faster and less dependent on the winter snowcover. The winter climate also facilitates motorized transport in that the frozen surfaces of bogs and lakes provide excellent courses for 'winter roads' which are used only for timber transport. Their 'construction' is very cheap. Expensive horse transport with a man and a sledge, which has small capacity compared with a lorry, can therefore be restricted to short distances of a few hundred metres.

The winter peak in the rhythm of forestry activities is still there. The felling of the trees takes place in the autumn and winter, and transport in the forest goes on as long as the snow cover lasts, usually into April. Both felling, now usually by a motor saw, and transport is often hindered by snow conditions, and very cold weather makes it difficult to get the bark off the logs.

FISHERIES

Fishing is probably the oldest of all Norwegian industries, and the fish trade has linked the nation to others from the earliest days of trading. At present, the catch contributes less than two per cent of the national income; but its value is doubled by fish-processing and marketing, and in 1967 fish products made up a seventh of Norway's total exports. Norway remains an outstanding example of a nation that catches far more fish than can be consumed in the country. At least two thirds, perhaps more, of the catch is sold abroad.

The seas off Norway are rich in phyto- and zoo-plankton and thus provide food for myriads of pelagic and demersal fishes. Fishermen take their harvest from life that has not usually been sown or cared for by man, and that consists of moving creatures. No wonder therefore that the output of the different fisheries has varied from sheer affluence to catastrophically small quantities. Small yearly variations can be explained by weather conditions, but the long-term variations, both in total catch and in movement along the coast, are still the main problem of Norwegian fishery research. Research is part of the fishing industry in Norway, and remarkable results have been achieved.

The Lofoten cod fisheries, which have highly varying annual yields, are an example of a very stable fishery as far as the location and the fishing season are concerned; records of this fishery occur throughout Norwegian history. On the other hand, the herring shoals have come and gone for longer or shorter periods and on different parts of the coast, which therefore have seen prosperity, dark depression and ruin.

Along the Norwegian coast there are about 70 species of fish and other sea animals that are caught or collected for consumption and sale. Of these, however, only a few are significant in regard to quantity or value. Herring, with about a half, and sometimes much more of the total, is still the most important species. Cod, with c. 12 per cent (1964), has been overfished, and is no longer as important as it used to be. Fig. 11.9 illustrates the distribution of three main groups, one for herring and sprat, a second for cod and related species, and a third for all other species. The diagram on Fig. 11.9 shows variations of the catches in the past decade. The greatest variations are obviously in the herring fisheries. The quantity landed by Norwegian fishermen has been tripled since before World War II, from about one million tons to about three million tons (live weight) in 1967, mainly due to an increase in the catches of herring, and, during the two last years, of mackerel.

HERRING FISHERIES

The winter herring fishery

The Norwegian herring fisheries in Norwegian waters and off Iceland exploit the same herring stock, which, apart from the 0–2 year herrings, lives in the Barents Sea and in the Norwegian Sea, but visits the Norwegian coast, either to spawn on the shallow bottom, or in search of food. The herring fisheries are dominated by the spawning herring, which under the common name of winter herring causes an extremely hectic season.

The important winter herring fishery on the southern and central coast of Vestlandet has decayed. In the fifties the fishing grounds off northern Vestlandet became more important than they were before World War II, and in the early sixties the emphasis shifted to Nord-Norge. In recent years the season has started as late as the middle of February. Waiting for weeks is however no longer necessary. Since 1950/51 one or several research vessels have discovered and located the shoals of herring in the Norwegian Sea by means of sonar and echo sounder. From the end of November the shoals are virtually 'herded', and observations and even forecasts are radioed about the location, movements and speed of the shoals.

This recent research has shown that the adult herring is migrating between three different types of water. Summer is the time of 'pasturing' in the border region between Gulf Stream waters and the Arctic water off the coast of Greenland. But in the dark period of minimum plankton production, the herring lives in the cold Arctic water. The fish takes on the same tempe-

rature as the surrounding sea, thus consuming a minimum of the calories collected as flesh and fat in the pasturing period. After migrating through the Gulf Stream water again, spawning takes place in the relatively cold coastal water of low salinity on the banks off the Norwegian coast. The spawning and ripening of the roe on the bottom requires a temperature of about 6°C. On the coast of Vestlandet, where most of the spring herring used to be caught, cold water from the Baltic Sea has been a hindrance to spawning in some years.

Hydrographic factors thus influence the spawning and maturing of herring. The spawning herring can be from 3 to 24 years old, and regular investigations show that a few age groups, or even one age group—herring born in one particular year—may dominate the whole mature herring population for a series of years. For instance, the age group born in 1950 constituted the bulk of the herring population after 1955, and did so until the herrings born in 1959 became winter herring.

The size of the winter herring shoals may have been favourable in the post-war period, although the shoals have rarely been visible at the surface. The spectacular rise in catches was certainly, and primarily, due to improved fishing techniques and a rapid expansion of the fishing fleet, as well as to the increased size of the vessels and the increased capacity of the herring meal and oil factories. The most remarkable improvements are the extensive use of echo sounder detectors and radio telephone. Echo sounders are now installed, not only in the 'mother' vessels, but also in the small motor boats used by the bosses. Radio telephone is used, not only for distant calls, but also between two vessels operating the same catch, for instance between the purse seiner and its auxiliary vessel.

All kinds of gear take advantage of the herring's habit of moving in shoals. During the last few decades considerable improvements have been introduced. The purse seine and the drift net are still predominant. More recently manmade fibres have replaced cotton and hemp, and equipment such as ring net and power block have been introduced.

The purse seine is a long net, which in its modern version is called a ring net. It is set out from the boatdeck of the vessel in a ring around,

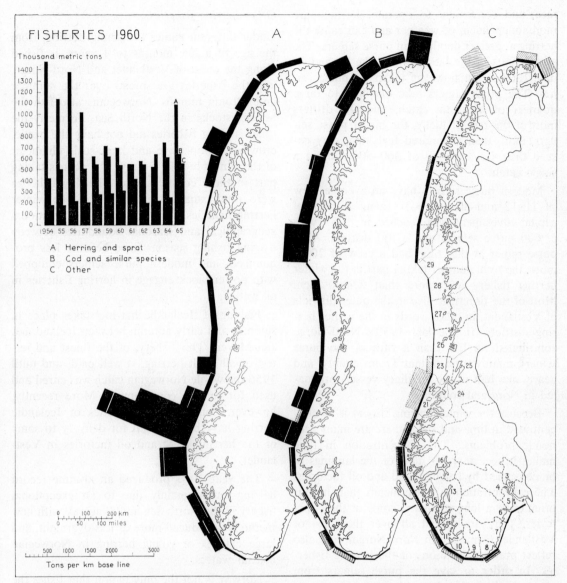

FISHERIES 1960.

A   B   C

Thousand metric tons

A Herring and sprat
B Cod and similar species
C Other

0   100   200 km
0   50   100 miles

500   1000   1500   2000   3000
Tons per km base line

Fig. 11.9. Fishing of main fish groups. The maps A, B, C show average quantities (live weight) for 1960 per fishery district or group of fishery districts (outer districts together with adjacent inner ones). The districts are numbered on map C. Except for herring, which is partly landed in districts other than those in which it is caught, the maps illustrate the landings in different districts and the 'intensity' of fishing, expressed as quantity per km of the column base-line (scale on lower left). The base-line is the then fishery limit, running 4 nautical miles from the outer skerries, and here slightly modified and simplified. A white line across the black columns marks off the catch taken in 'distant waters', e.g. Shetland, Iceland, West Greenland, Newfoundland. The shaded columns of districts 21 and 22 (C) show quantities of kelp (seaweed) gathered for use in manufacturing. — The diagram on the upper left shows variations in catches during the last decade. The ruled columns on map B and C denote catches of pout and sand eel (8, 10–11) and of capelin (34, 37–38, 40–41), used for the production of meal and oil, or kelp (14, 17, 19–23), collected for industrial production. — Important fishery districts: 11 = Ryfylke, 12 = Sunnhordland, 16–17 = Sogn, 18 = Sunnfjord and Nordfjord, 19 = Sunnmøre, 20 = Romsdal, 21 = Nordmøre, 31 = Lofoten, 32 = Vesterålen, 33–35 = Troms (county), 36–41 = Finnmark (county).

or in, a herring shoal, located by sonar and echo sounder. By means of a rope the net is then drawn together—'pursed'—at the bottom, and placed alongside the vessel, which is loaded by means of a scoop net or—more recently—by suction pumps. An auxiliary boat— the 'skiff'—tugs the seiner towards the wind and thus helps to keep the seine open at the surface, and convenient to operate. Drifters are more independent of weather and can catch the herring at greater depths than purse seiners. The greater part of the landings and the big individual catches are however taken by purse seines. The purse seiners take one half to three quarters of the total catch, and the drifters most of the rest. If lucky, the bigger purse seiners, more than a hundred feet long, may exceed their full capacity of 300–500 tons in a single catch.

Modern purse seiners have an average crew of 11–12 and drifters 9–10 men. A peak of capital investment was reached in 1957 with c. 600 purse seiners and 1300 drifters. As a purse seiner at that time had a crew of 20 or more, the total number taking part in the winter herring fishery was more than 27000 men. Most of the fishermen live in the outer districts of Vestlandet, in other words in the winter herring districts. In the late 1950's Nord-Norge contributed no less than a fifth of the purse seiners, mainly from distant Troms county, and nearly one half of the auxiliary vessels originated in Nordland county.

Because the winter herring fishery is so concentrated in time and space there are many economic problems. The concentration in time makes it necessary for most of the landings to be consumed by herring meal and oil factories. The concentration in space means that there is often quite a long voyage to some of these factories. They are spread all over the coast of Vestlandet (some are in Nord-Norge), and also reflect previous locations of the herring fisheries. In order to save the purse seiners from wasting fishing time by sailing between distant harbours and the fishing grounds, a special transport has been organized from nearby harbours, where the purse seiners conveniently call and tranship their catch.

The winter herring fisheries require concerted efforts sustained by many organizations. Apart from the technical arrangements, the economic ones are also worth mentioning here. In principle the fishermen's own organization (Norges Fiskarlag) pays the fishermen the same price for every weight unit of large or spring herring landed, irrespective of different prices paid by the different consumers of herring. The fishermen's organization also owns some of the biggest herring meal and oil factories.

Other herring fisheries

Under different names the young herring, from the age of a few months to 4 years, is fished along the coast of Vestlandet and Nord-Norge, and the fisheries are spread over the summer and autumn months. Norwegians also fish the herring stocks in the North Sea. Formerly the other herring fisheries did not have the hectic, crowded, competitive and large-scale character of the winter herring fishery. The vessels taking part in these coastal summer herring fisheries were often smaller than those of the winter herring fisheries. In recent years the traditional geographical and seasonal boundaries between herring fishing seasons have become less pronounced, and modern purse seiners equipped with power-block engage in herring fisheries in all waters.

Fishing of 'Icelandic herring' takes place in summer and early autumn between Iceland and Jan Mayen. This fishery, of the finest and fattest of all adult herring, is well paid, and until 1956 the whole Norwegian catch was cured and used for human consumption. More recently, however, considerable quantities of Icelandic herring have been caught for delivery to some of the herring meal and oil factories in Vestlandet.

The year 1967 produced an all-time record herring catch, mainly due to an exceptional fishery in the North Sea and Skagerak with new methods introduced more or less overnight, and large catches of young herring in Norwegian coastal waters.

Norway is not the only nation that fishes the herring in the Norwegian Sea, the Russians, for instance, have a big pelagic fleet operating there. Nobody has been able to show, however, that the herring population of the Norwegian Sea has been overtaxed, and no Norwegian fish researcher has argued that the rather meagre winter herring yields in 1957–63 were due to overfishing. After all, man's influence seems to be small compared with the laws of nature that determine the size and rule the life and death of the plankton-feeding herring shoals.

Such is unfortunately not the case with the other big fisheries of Norway, which exploit the demersal-feeding fish species.

COD FISHERIES

The cod population that is fished by Norwegians migrates like the herring to Norway in order to spawn, or in search of food. The Barents Sea is the domain of the cod which seasonally migrates to Nord-Norge.

The Arctic cod is born in Nord-Norge waters, notably in Lofoten, and in the course of its first year is brought into the Barents Sea by currents heading northwards. The young cod, around 6 years of age, migrates to the coast of Finnmark in search of food in April –June. The earliest age of maturity is 6 years, and mature cod leave the Barents Sea annually and make their way in the depths of winter along the coast of Finnmark and Troms to the spawning waters, which are principally in Vestfjorden between the spectacular Lofoten islands and the mainland. The bulk of the spawning cod are however 9–10 years old, so that a particular age group is best represented in Lofoten 10 years after its birth. An age group also attains its maximum weight after several years, in spite of a drastically reduced number of individuals.

The female cod spawns approximately four million eggs during one spawning, and may spawn several years in succession up to its last year. Bearing in mind that the number of spawning cod in Lofoten can be kept up by only two eggs of the four millions reaching the stage of mature cod, one realizes again that nature is the big regulator of the size of the cod population. The death rate is highest among the eggs and the very young cod, an overwhelming majority never reaches the stage suited to man's fishing. Registration of the age distribution of the Lofoten cod over a series of years has shown that even minimum years in regard to yield have given birth to rich yields 10 years after. Intensive fishing of young cod has however reduced the abundance of cod in Norwegian waters.

Before other nations started to trawl in the Barents Sea or along the coast of Norway, Norwegians alone worked the population of Arctic cod, and then only the migrating cod in Norwegian waters, which is at least 4 years old. Trawling by other nations increased the exploitation very markedly, and it has been tripled in 20 years. The increase is far greater in terms of catches of individual cod than in terms of total weight. Norway's share of the total yield, still mainly from home waters, has become a minor one. In Lofoten especially there have been very small catches in recent years, down to less than a quarter of the average in the thirties. Comparisons of the catch per vessel in Finnmark during the spring fisheries and of Lofoten cod, with similar gear, have led to the suggestion that the present Lofoten cod population is less abundant as compared with the population of young Finnmark cod than it was before the last War, and that this reduction is due to the increased total exploitation of the Arctic cod.

The Lofoten cod fishery

In Lofoten the shifting hydrographic situation may have a marked effect on the annual yields: the cod stays in water that keeps at 4–5°C, which is often in the transition zone between the warm water of the Gulf Stream and the cold coastal water. Dominance by greater masses of cold water may therefore keep the shoals of cod at a depth that makes fishing difficult. This applies especially to the purse seine. This gear was introduced in Lofoten after World War II, and in 1951–54 as many as a half of the fishermen were using purse seines, and a half of the total catch came from them; they were, however, not allowed to fish for more than a part of the total season. Since then the total catch has been small, and fearing unemployment among fishermen with traditional gear, the purse seine has legally been forbidden since 1959. Thus again, the fishing grounds have been left to the nets, the long lines and hand lines. For them, and for a long period, the crowded Lofoten sea has been divided into areas where only one kind of gear is allowed to operate. The great masses of gear and the mixture of lines and nets would otherwise have resulted in a hopeless mess on the restricted fishing ground.

The traditional gears have been greatly improved by the introduction of man-made fibres. The nets have become much more efficient and drying is no longer a problem. The cheapest gear of all, the hand line, has been equipped with an improved tin bait, and the nylon line is easily pulled up and down by means of a wheel. The difference between the Lofoten cod fishery and the winter herring fishery is, however, striking.

The numerous small boats, of less than 30 feet in length, are characteristic of Lofoten. Here the hand liner carries 1–2 men, the long liner 3–4 and the netter usually 6–7. The large number of small boats and all the fish-processing activities demand quite a lot of accommodation in the Lofoten fishing villages, though most men live on their boats. During the fishery some villages have up to ten times the off-season population. Strandflat brims and islets in front of precipitous alpine mountains provide the necessary harbours and areas for building and fish-processing.

The relatively small capital invested in the Lofoten fishing fleet indicates that fishing is only a part-time occupation for many of the fishermen. A 'normal' number of fishermen used to be 25 000, in recent years it has been down to 8 000, whose catch was about 20 000–30 000 tons (live weight). Participation in the Lofoten fishery is much more local than in the winter herring fishery.

Other cod fisheries

Finnmark has its own cod fisheries, of mature cod, but mainly of the more important young cod. In some years the Finnmark cod fisheries exceed the Lofoten fishery in quantity. The vessels are long liners and gill netters, and those coming from Troms and Nordland have worked in Lofoten as well. The reason for the invasion of young cod is often shoals of the small capelin, which is also fished and used as a raw material for fish meal.

The banks off Finnmark, Troms and Møre of Romsdal are fishing grounds for the so-called bank cod and the ling. This long line fishery takes place in the summer months. Norway has fairly recently used a number of so-called 'small trawlers' of less than 300 G.R.T., which fish in the Barents Sea and have the advantage of short voyages to Finnmark harbours. Some 150 such trawlers have annually landed a considerable catch, c. 40 000 tons of cod and related species. Norway has only a few large trawlers.

Since 1924 there has also been successful fishing of cod on the west coast of Greenland. The vessels there are usually participants in the winter herring fisheries as well, and those fishing in Greenland waters therefore live in wintery conditions nearly all year. Taken together, the cod fisheries in distant waters, including the catch of Norwegian trawlers, may contribute even more than the Lofoten or Finnmark fisheries to the total yield of cod.

Finally, Norway has important fisheries of the so-called fjord cod, which is the common one on Norwegian tables, and which lives more or less stationary, thus forming a stock distinct from the migratory Arctic cod.

Of the other fisheries some of the more important ones take rather stationary species related to cod, and again northernmost Norway has the significant fishing grounds. The total catches of saithe (coalfish) and haddock compare favourably with one of the seasonal cod fisheries. Fishing goes on in the summer and autumn, and common gears are long line and gill net. The biggest catches of the saithe shoals are taken with purse seines, and trawls are also used.

OTHER FISHERIES

Sørlandet and the adjoining coast of Vestlandet used to be the principal areas for the trawling of prawns, but now Nord-Norge is equally important. Trawling of deep-water prawns started as a result of scientific investigations which discovered and delimited the bottom environment required for the prawns, thus revealing hitherto hidden vast resources of this valuable sea product.

Other notable fisheries are the fisheries of salmon and halibut, which are mainly caught in Nord-Norge and Vestlandet, and the lobster fishery in southern Norway.

The seasonal fisheries of the southern, pleasant part of the Norwegian coast also take place in the most pleasant part of the year, in summer and early autumn. Sprat is fished in the fjords of Vestlandet and in the Oslofjord. Sprat or brisling is the common and best raw material for Norwegian canned 'sardines', but small herring has often to be used as a substitute because the yield of the short-lived sprat is subject to violent fluctuations from year to year. The sprat comes in shoals to the coast in search for food. The mackerel migrates to Norwegian waters for the same reason. The blue mackerel dominates the catches of Sørlandet and is the most popular fat fish for domestic consumption from Stad to the Oslofjord. The equivalent fish in Nord-

Norge is the redfish. (Herring is herring in Norway, not a fat 'fish'.) During 1964–67 the use of power-block vessels and ring nets has increased mackerel catches in the North Sea sixteenfold, surpassing now by far those of cod.

Food supplies in Norwegian waters also attract the giant of Norwegian fisheries, the Mediterranean tuna that is caught in late summer in Vestlandet and in the southern part of Nord-Norge in specially constructed purse seines. This very dramatic fishery has grown considerably in recent years, and so also has the fishery of dogfish, which like the tuna is sold fresh, and almost never on the domestic market. Dogfish is a speciality of fishery district 18 (Måløy fishing village), cf. Fig. 11.9. The district has no particular 'natural' reason for this speciality, for the fishing goes on not only off the Norwegian coast in winter, but also in the distant waters near Shetland during the summer.

The marked rise during 1957–63 in the output of Other Fisheries, was mainly due to increased fishing of capelin by purse seine in Finnmark and to new fisheries of Norway pout and sandeel by trawl in the North Sea and off Vestlandet. All three are small and cheap fish species used exclusively for the production of fish meal (and a little oil). On Fig. 11.9 capelin and sandeel belong to group C, Norway pout to group B.

VALUE OF THE CATCHES

The fisheries discussed above were taken more or less according to their values, which in the end have a greater interest than the catch volumes. The variation in price per weight unit of landed catch is very marked, from 15 Norw. kroner per kg of salmon and trout to about 0.33 for winter herring (1966). Of the three groups of species shown on Fig. 11.9, the herring group is the cheapest. The cod group has about the same average price as the third group, which however contains both the cheapest species (capelin) and the most expensive (salmon).

The differences in price are partly due to taste and traditional evaluations and partly to the relations between supply and demand. In respect of value Norway is in an unfortunate position in that the herring is very low priced in spite of its very high nutritive value. The seasonal supplies of herring and cod are so colossal that it has not been possible to sell the catch in a fresh condition. Before the recent development of summer and autumn mackerel and herring fisheries in the North Sea, two thirds of each year's catch was landed in the three months of January–March. The fish is therefore preserved in various ways, and many of the preserved products have a lower price per weight unit of raw materials than does the fresh fish. The long distances between Norway and its foreign markets present another handicap, and long distances are similarly part of the reasons for the differences in price within Norway itself. Any fish fetches the highest prices in the southeastern part of the country, which provides the bigger part of the domestic market.

Fig. 11.10 illustrates the distribution of catches by value along the coast, a picture which, according to the difference in price between the three main groups of species and their different location, is much more even than the distribution of quantities (cf. Fig. 11.9). Even on the value-map, however, there is a remarkable concentration in Vestlandet, especially in its northern part. Another feature, characteristic of Møre og Romsdal county, is the importance of fishing in distant waters, which is more conspicuous in terms of value.

VESSELS AND FISHERMEN

In regard to the composition and distribution of fishing vessels Fig. 11.10 shows that the districts with the largest landings also have the biggest proportion of the biggest vessels. Norway's fleet of 36 000 fishing vessels (1960) is characterized by many small and open boats (24 000 have no deck). Those shorter than 30 feet are preponderant in every district, and this is particularly the case in Nordland. Troms has as many of the bigger vessels as has the much more numerous fleet of Nordland, and the composition of the fleet belonging to Troms is more like that of the counties of Vestlandet. Møre og Romsdal county is again outstanding in having a big proportion of the largest vessels.

Since World War I the whole fishing fleet has been motorized; but an increasing number of boats are open, whereas the number of decked boats has been fairly constant, 12 500, since before the last war and up to the beginning of the 1960's, though recently numbers

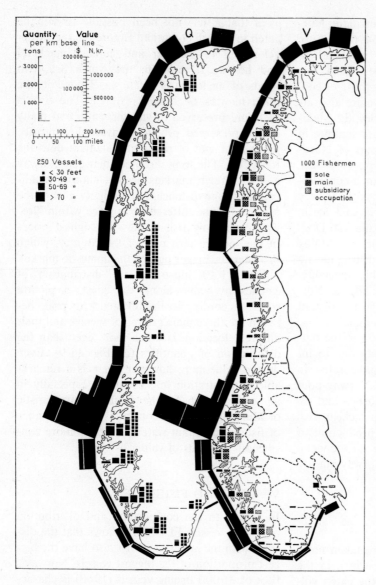

Fig. 11.10. Fisheries. Quantities, values, vessels and fishermen. Quantities (map Q) and values (V), average 1960, illustrated as in Fig. 11.9, with the scale for 'intensity' reduced to facilitate comparison of quantity and value. The national average of the total catch was c. 400 Norw. kr. per ton. In order to show regional differentiation the different prices of different species have been used on the map. The columns for Nord-Norge are thus longer on map V than on map Q. This is also the case with Sørlandet and Østlandet, which have fairly big landings of expensive species such as prawns, mackerel and sprat. The dominant districts of Vestlandet have comparatively low values because of their large proportion of low priced products, e.g. herring and dogfish (district 18) and kelp (21, 22). Capelin accounts for the low value of district 41. — The numbers of fishermen in three different categories in 1956 are given per fishery district (for these see map C on Fig. 11.9), except for districts 1–5 which have been grouped together. — Fishing as the main and subsidiary occupation is characteristic of Nord-Norge, except in the far north. Numbers of fishing vessels in four different sizes are given per county, except for Sørlandet and Østlandet. The occupation groupings of fishermen correspond well with the types of vessels. The larger the number of fishermen with fishing as their sole occupation, the greater the total of big fishing vessels. Fishery district 19 (Sunnmøre) is the outstanding example of a well equipped fishing area.

have decreased. In 1967 Norway had about 9 000 decked vessels of wood, and 560 of steel. Steam-driven vessels are now unusual. Vessels are still predominantly built of wood, but the biggest and newest purse seiners, long liners and trawlers are mostly steel-built. The average age of the decked boats is 27 years, but 30 per cent of them have been rebuilt or refitted.

During the 1950's the number of fishermen declined rapidly. Of a total of about 60 000 fishermen (1960) only one third had fishing as their sole occupation, but recently this number has increased. In 1966 as much as 45 per cent of the fishermen had fishing as their sole occupation. Those with fishing as their main occu-

pation now form the smallest group, and their number is only a quarter of what it was in the immediate post-war years. About one third of the fishermen have fishing as a secondary occupation.

Those who had fishing as their sole occupation spent 33 weeks engaged at sea on the average. More than half of them were engaged in fishing for more than 40 weeks (1960). These figures, together with other evidence, confirm that fishing has become a more specialized and demanding trade.

Even in Finnmark fishing is not the biggest employer among the industries of the whole county. Nevertheless, the outer rural districts

258

are predominantly fishery districts. This is also the rule along the entire coast from southern Vestlandet to eastern Finnmark, and not unexpectedly the part-time fishermen generally live further inland, on the inner islands and in the fjords.

SEALING AND WHALING

Sealing

This is a very old Norwegian industry, run through the centuries on a different scale and in different waters. The post-war output has been high compared with previous periods, and hunting is more widely spread than ever. The crew of some 60 sealing vessels that leave Norway every early spring varies from 15 to 35 men. The breeding grounds of pelagic seals are found in the pack-ice waters of two main areas west of, and one area east of the Gulf Stream: Newfoundland and Vestisen (east of Greenland), and Østisen (Barents Sea). Norwegian sealing thus extends from about 50°N and 60° W to 76°N and 50°E.

Off Newfoundland and in the Barents Sea the harp (Greenland) seals, and in Vestisen the hood seals are the main objects of hunting. The newly born seals, the 'blueback' of the hood seals and the 'whitecoat' of the harp seals, are especially sought. Their beautiful coats provide costly furs. The seals are killed on the ice by the sealers, who have to run or jump from one ice-floe to another and finally drag the heavy skins with the blubber still on to the ship. Sealing is therefore a very strenuous job, and the navigation of the vessels in the pack ice requires great skill and is very risky. Between 1936 and 1964 no less than 45 vessels foundered (nearly three per cent on an average of the yearly participation), and many sealers have lost their lives.

In the post-war years the total output has varied between 98 000 (1965) and 370 000 animals (1951), worth from 9 to 37 million Norwegian kroner, or around five per cent of the value of Norwegian fisheries. Though a small industry, the sealers may have good earnings, and locally sealing is economically important.

In the present century sealing has become a speciality of some Sunnmøre and Tromsø districts, where sealing vessels can readily combine sealing with ordinary fishing outside the sealing season. In February the bigger vessels (up to a length of 180 feet) make the 10 days long and hard crossing of the North Atlantic to Newfoundland, which to Norwegians is the newest and most profitable ground.

Sealing goes on mainly on the 'Front' east of Newfoundland, and the search for the breeding patches is guided by planes. Seal hunting is permitted from about March 10th to the end of April, and, if lucky, the vessels get fully loaded and return to Norway by the middle of May.

Most of the average-sized vessels with a crew of 15–20 men take the one voyage allowed to Vestisen where hunting for harp and hood seals goes on from March 20th to May 5th, the dates being set by international agreement for the protection of the seal population. A few of the sealing ships used to make a summer expedition to the Denmark Strait between Iceland and Greenland in order to hunt for adult hoods, but since 1960 this hunting ground has been temporarily closed to conserve stocks. The smallest vessels, mostly from Troms and Finnmark, go in winter to Østisen in the Barents Sea to hunt harp seals until May 10th. Later in the summer some of them go to the most northerly and easterly grounds to hunt for other types of seal and for polar bears, the latter as part of an expanding tourist activity.

In order to protect the seal herds hunting in the various areas is regulated by agreements between Norway–U.S.S.R. and Norway–Canada.

Whaling

Curiously enough the relatively important and famous Norwegian whaling industry has an even more local character than sealing. In the post-war years all the Norwegian Antarctic whaling expeditions except one have been fitted out and operated from the little county of Vestfold on Oslofjord. In addition, a substantial part of the fitting out of all the British expeditions and that belonging to Argentina has mainly been carried out in this densely populated and pleasant district where two thirds of the Norwegian whaling men have their homes. In particular the towns of Sandefjord, Tønsberg and Larvik and their hinterlands have profited from whaling. As pioneers in modern whaling in the Antarctic and other parts of the world, and as crews on the whaling expeditions of other countries, the men from Vestfold have led the world's whaling in the present century.

The technique, and accumulation of experience and capital needed for this expertise, started in the latter half of the 19th century, when people from Vestfold were occupied in sealing. Sealing was, however, soon abandoned as unprofitable, but it contributed to the financing of the subsequent whaling industry which in turn so reduced the whale population of northern waters that protective restrictions on whaling had to be introduced by law. Whaling from the coast of Norway is now only a small-scale undertaking, but every post-war autumn, until the late 1950's, about 7 000 Norwegian whaling men, 9 big and costly floating factories and about a hundred whale-catchers have left Norway to do their hard work on the other side of the globe. During the 1960's there has been a rapid decline in whaling, and only two floating factories and 900 men took part in the 1965–1966 season. The Antarctic season for whalebone whales starts in the latter half of December, but usually most expeditions catch sperm whales about a month before that. The ships return to Norway in April and May, bringing with them their production of whale and sperm oil besides by-products such as whale meal, meat extract, vitamin oil etc. Some of the factory ships send part of their oil by tankers which during the season bring fuel oil to the expeditions.

The modern whaling industry can be traced back to Svend Foyn, a shipowner and sealhunter from Tønsberg. Around 1870 he experimented with the finally successful invention of a shell harpoon which is shot out from the bowhead of a steam-driven whale-catcher and which explodes within the whale. This harpoon is still fundamental in the whaling technique, and it has made the able whale-gunners some of the best paid men in Norway. Foyn's successors sought the whales also in southern waters, and whaling off the coasts of Africa had a boom period in the beginning of the present century, when the exploitation of the world's richest whaling fields in the Antarctic also began. These first undertakings were carried out either from land stations or from factory ships at anchor in the bays of Antarctic islands, and the catch was restricted by British sovereignty of South Georgia and other islands and by the immobility of the expe-

ditions. (In 1966/67 no land station was left.) The greatest expansion in the history of whaling was due to the introduction of pelagic whaling, especially from 1925, when the first factory ship was equipped with a slipway in the stern so that the previous outboard flensing of the whales could be replaced by flensing and partitioning on deck.

Antarctic whaling reached its maximum in 1930/31 when Norway as the dominating whaling nation participated with 27 factory ships, 3 land stations and 147 whale-catchers. In that season a total of 40 200 whales were caught in the Antarctic, and yielded 600 000 tons of oil. Both whalers and scientists agreed that whaling had to be restricted in order to prevent a total depletion of the stocks, and the first international regulations for the preservation of the whale stocks came into being soon afterwards. In post-war years Antarctic whaling has been regulated by a convention agreed upon by all the nations participating in the Antarctic. From 1945/46 to 1958/59 the permitted catch for the pelagic expeditions averaged 15 600 blue whale units (1 blue whale unit = 1 blue whale or 2 fin whales or 2½ humpback whales or 6 sei whales), and Norway has taken between one third and one half of the quota. The permitted catch for 1966/67 was only 3 500 units. Norway's share was 800 units.

The largest of all mammals, the blue whale, no longer dominates the catch as it did in the inter-war period, and in recent years blue whales have constituted only a small percentage of the catch. The major part of the catch now consists of fin whales. From year to year considerable numbers of sperm whales have also been taken, but these whales are not included in the quota agreed upon. Sperm oil cannot be digested by man and has therefore mainly industrial uses.

The whales spend the winter in low latitudes and migrate in spring and summer to high latitudes, right into the edge of the continental ice. The sea around it is very rich in crustacea and squids (sperm whale food). The gregarious habits of the whale make them easy victims of the speedy and powerful whale-catchers of today. They are also slow breeders, the large whalebone species producing one calf every two years at the most, and there are several indications that even the maximum catches stipulated in the post-war seasons have been too high. In these seasons an ever-increasing number of factory ships and whale-catchers have competed for the largest possible share of the quota, and this has resulted in shorter seasons in the Antarctic.

MINING AND QUARRYING

Most rocks in Norway belong to the Precambrian and Cambro-Silurian formations, which include igneous and metamorphic rocks from the Caledonian orogeny. Devonian sedimentary rocks and Permian plutonic rocks outcrop only in small areas, and Carboniferous rocks and rocks of Mesozoic or Tertiary age do not occur at all. Not surprisingly therefore, the country lacks coal (except on Svalbard) and oil or gas, possibly under the North Sea; and the ores found are either metamorphic or magmatic.

Iron ores and pyrites are the most important ores of Norway. The iron ores are widely spread, they are found in Precambrian as well as in Cambro-Silurian rocks and are highly metamorphosed. The pyrites are mined only in Cambro-Silurian rocks. Associated with the pyrites are copper, zinc and lead minerals, most of them are actually produced in mines which have pyrites as their principal product. In the Precambrian formations there are also deposits of ilmenite and molybdenum, of which Norway is a big producer.

Most Norwegian mines produce for export, and they all have ores that have to be concentrated. These two circumstances and the fact that the mines are generally small make it an advantage, even a necessity, for the Norwegian mines to be situated rather close to the sea. Some of the mines virtually have a coastal site, others are remote in relation to other settlements and are located up to 1 000 m above sea level, and the hauls to the nearest ice-free fjord may be more than a hundred kilometres. With a few exceptions the concentrates are produced close to the mine. Both mining and concentration benefit from cheap electricity.

Mining areas

Nord-Norge is the principal mining region of Norway. It has mines in the Precambrian rocks of Finnmark, and its Caledonian area has iron ores as well as pyrites. Aktieselskabet Sydvaranger is the biggest mine of Norway, situated in the remotest corner of the country, near the Russian border, cf. Fig. 11.11. Mining was restarted in 1952 after war damage in 1944. The ore is a magnetite of 33–36 per cent iron content, and the iron appears in black bands between zones of quartz in a gneissic rock. The open-cast mining operations are highly mechanized and go on through the dark and very cold winter; usually transport is not hindered by snow. Large lorries transport the ore to a crusher which grinds huge blocks to stones. The ore is then transported by railway down to Kirkenes for separation. The concentrate for sale is a 65 per cent ferrous slime with a low content of phosphorus, of which about 1.5 million tons (1963) are produced annually. The fine-grained slime needs to be sintered or pelleted before being put into the furnace.

Ferrous slime from Kirkenes now also has a home market and is used, together with slime from Trøndelag and slime derived from local hematite-magnetite iron ores (30–35 per cent iron) in the new iron works at Mo i Rana in Nordland. Because of difficulties in economically concentrating the ore, large-scale mining did not start until 1964. So far Nordland county has mainly mined pyrites or ores of non-ferrous metals.

A coarse-grained ore of pyrite and impregnations of copper ore makes Sulitjelma a big producer of copper concentrates and the only smelter of pure copper in Norway. Being remotely situated in the mountains near the Swedish border, and until its railway was built, having poor winter connections with the export harbour, the smelting of copper close to the mine is also desirable at Sulitjelma. The mine is a big producer of pyrites too, in quantity it far exceeds that of the copper concentrates.

Trøndelag is the principal producer of pyrites in Norway. Its biggest mine is situated at Løkken near the river Orkla, after which the mining company is named. The mine has for

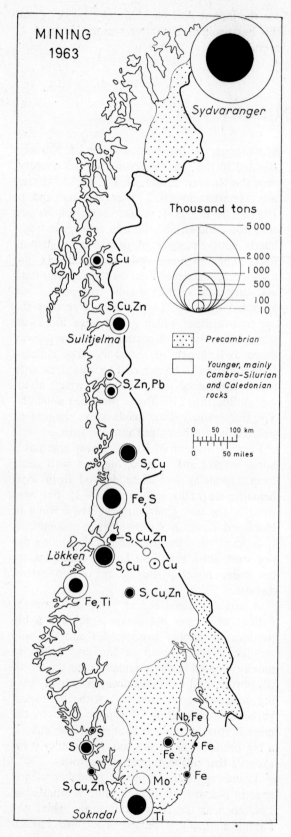

MINING
1963

Sydvaranger

Thousand tons

— 5 000
— 2 000
— 1 000
— 500
— 100
— 10

S,Cu

S,Cu,Zn

Sulitjelma

S,Zn,Pb

:::: Precambrian

☐ Younger, mainly
Cambro-Silurian
and Caledonian
rocks

0   50   100 km
⊢⊢⊢⊢⊢⊢⊢⊣

0   50 miles

S,Cu

Fe,S

—S,Cu,Zn

Lökken

S,Cu   ⊙Cu

● S,Cu,Zn

Fe,Ti

Nb,Fe

S

Fe

Fe

S

Fe

S,Cu,Zn   Mo

Fe

Sokndal   Ti

decades produced a half of Norway's total production of pyrites.

A new pyrites mine in Trøndelag has come into operation since World War II. Trøndelag also has the second largest iron mine in the country.

Vestlandet's contribution is iron ore mining in its northern part, pyrites in its central area, and ilmenite in the southern part. The ilmenite concentrate consists of titanium oxide and iron, of which the titanium oxide is used in paints and varnish. The ore reserves are large and close to the coast in southern Rogaland.

Sørlandet has a peculiarity in its molybdenum mine, which is the only one of its kind in West Europe. The mine is situated 50 kilometres from the export harbour, and the annual production is nearly 400 tons of 94 per cent MoS_2 derived from about 200 000 tons of ore.

Østlandet formerly had many mines, but most are now disused.

Quarrying

Although a small supplier of metals, Østlandet is the country's principal producer of limestone. Two quarries and one mine each have a production of about 800 000 tons of limestone, making them second only to A/S Sydvaranger measured by weight of material transported out of the mine or quarry. The limestone occurs in the Cambro-Silurian formation in, and just west of the Oslofjord, and is used in the manufacture of nitrogen fertilizers and cement.

In the county of Østfold granite quarrying, especially for export, was formerly important. In Vestfold bluish and reddish syenites are quarried for building and ornamental purposes. Inland Østlandet also has some quarrying of slates.

Fig. 11.11. Mining, 1963. The outer circles show ore totals produced by the mines, and the black circles quantities of ore concentrates for sale or further processing. Initials indicate the principal elements that are the objects of mining. The centres of the circles are located at the mines and concentration plants. Sydvaranger's concentration plant is situated at the harbour of Kirkenes, 8 km from the iron mine. Two small pyrites mines in Trøndelag share a concentration plant in Trondheim. — Pyrites, lead and zinc are mined in Caledonian Norway, and iron ore occurs in Precambrian (Sydvaranger) as well as in Caledonian rocks. A pyrites mine at Ballangen in Ofoten (exhausted) and the niobium (Nb) mine in lower Telemark have been closed since 1963. This niobium deposit is the largest in Europe.

Vestlandet and Nord-Norge are also represented in limestone (and marble) and slate quarrying. Specially noteworthy is Vestlandet's and Sørlandet's production of quartz, which like the limestone is used in the country's own industries. For instance, the production of ferro-silicon in Norway (cf. Fig. 11.16) is facilitated by quartz deposits near the works.

The superficial Quaternary deposits of Norway have given rise to sand quarries and brick works. Østlandet is in the most favourable position in this respect. In the Oslofjord district sand and gravel are mostly taken from the big marginal deposits, at spots that are close to the sea and from which there is cheap transport to the final consumer. Vestlandet uses some scattered marine terraces for sand and gravel supply, and the region is for the most part devoid of brick clay. Only in the southern part, and near Stavanger, is there clay in quantity and quality suitable for brickmaking. Some pottery is made in Rogaland, but most of it based on china clay from Great Britain. Østlandet and Trøndelag are more fortunate in having many good clay deposits. Again sea transport has favoured sites close to river or sea, and Østfold is the principal region for brick-works in the country. There are also many brick-works in or near Oslo.

ENERGY RESOURCES AND SUPPLY

RESOURCES

In an industrialized economy Norway's water-power must be considered as its most valuable asset. Not only is the share of hydro-electricity greater in relation to other forms of energy than in other countries, but it keeps the total consumption of energy per capita on the same level as that of the highly industrialized nations of Europe. Imported fuels are used in Norway where, for technical reasons, they cannot be replaced by electricity or where the efficiency of coal and oil is higher. The present energy balance is shown in Table 7.9, p. 92.

It should be noted that these figures do not include the bunkers of oil bought by Norwegian ships in foreign harbours, which in 1957 amounted to about 6 million tons (in 1967 c. 9 mill. tons). Engines in the Norwegian fleet have a total kW capacity nearly equal to that of all Norwegian water-power plants (1967).

With the present trend of energy consumption, totals will vary considerably. In Norway, as in most other countries, the use of oil has increased and the coal consumption has declined. The production of hydro-electricity has had an increasingly rapid rise: It was about 10 000 million kWh in 1939, 20 000 in 1954, 30 000 in 1960 and 53 000 in 1967.

If all the water-power resources of Norway were fully utilized the annual reliable production could be 120 000 million kWh. Projects with a cost per kWh above a certain limit have been omitted from this total. Wild life conservation could reduce the above figure of 120 000 mill. kWh. Improved development schemes, particularly tunnels transferring water over long distances will, on the other hand, increase the output. A combined tunnel length of 50 km has already been used.

It is estimated that about a half of the total resources can supply electricity at a price that competes favourably with any other kind of energy. About 40 per cent of the total (irrespective of development costs) and two thirds of the very cheap resources of Norway are already in production. A 1951-estimate in US cents per unit (1 kWh) illustrated the unrivalled cheapness of Norwegian electricity: Norway 0.4, Great Britain 1.4, Switzerland 1.6, France 1.9, West Germany 2.1 and Denmark 2.7. Since then lower fuel prices and increased efficiency of coal- and oil-fired power stations have seriously challenged Norway's lead in this field.

The extensive and varied use of electricity in Norway is partly explained by the greater cost of imported energy, while natural conditions explain the extremely cheap and abundant resources of water-power. Five natural advantages are significant in this respect. They are: (1) high precipitation, combined with (2) elevated land surface, glaciated relief with steep and high slopes; (3) numerous and good possibilities for water storage at high levels; the fact that at these levels (4) little economic damage is caused by the construction of reservoirs; and (5) rocks suitable for boring and use of unlined tunnels.

The two first advantages explain the abundance of water-power in Norway. Quantity as well as price is involved in good water storage facilities, which is perhaps the biggest asset of all. This is the more striking as the precipitation in the form of snow is a considerable part of the yearly total in most catchment areas and the demand for power is also at its maximum in winter. The period of deficit with bigger demand than discharge of water lasts for no less than 200–270 days. Numerous small and larger lakes compensate for all this and give ample possibilities for sufficient storage. The glacial overdeepening of the lake basin often permits the digging of a tunnel somewhere into the lake bottom, thus making a storage of water between the natural and the new lower outlet. In addition, storage by the construction of a dam at the outlet of a lake is facilitated either by steep valley sides at the dam site or because the surface of the lake is so large that even a low dam can give a large quantity of water to be tapped when needed. The possibilities for storing water at high levels, for instance on the high mountain plateau, is an additional asset, equally important as to the amount of water stored. In the autumn the water stored in the reservoirs represents a potential of nearly a half of the annual production.

Storage in the mountains means that the reservoirs are often situated so that comparatively small areas of useful land are destroyed by the dammed water. Fresh water fishing and other amenities in frequently visited and much appreciated mountain districts are now being threatened by construction works and reservoirs. The oscillations of the lake surface result in ugly areas of barren beaches and may make the crossing of the frozen lake on skis impossible.

Hydro-electric plants

In the beginning of the electric era water-power was used by a large number of small plants situated adjacent to the inhabited areas. With the small amounts of capital available and the losses involved in the transmission of electricity this was an advantage. But today it pays better to construct big plants. They generally have a lower cost per unit than the small ones, and the present technique permits profitable transmission over very long distances. Thus the larger and more remote plants now have an increasing proportion of the total electricity supply of the country.

The bigger plants usually need long tunnels, either to lead the water from the reservoir to the top of the head leading down to the plant or to connect different reservoirs or catchment areas. Underground heads and plants have also become common. The cost of tunneling has therefore become increasingly important, and tunnels in Norway are cheap because both the hard rock and a daring technical tradition allow most of the tunnels to be raw. Lining with concrete may often more than double the price of a tunnel.

There are about 2 000 power-producing plants in Norway. Of these about 1 500 are tiny, i.e. of 100 kW capacity or less; and they produce only an insignificant part of the total. The few bigger plants, on the other hand, c. 40 of a capacity of 50 000 kW or more, have more than 60 per cent of the total installed turbine capacity. In 1920 power plants of that size had only 30 per cent of the total capacity. Of plants bigger than 150 000 kW Norway has 16. The capacity of all Norwegian plants (1967) was c. 11; the annual increase c. 0.6 million kW (1957–67). The quotient between capacity and their production is close to 5 000 hours. This means that the plants do not run at full capacity through all the 8 750 hours of the year. Usually a power plant has a capacity well above the mean regulated flow of water.

The kW capacity of a water-power plant is a product of its head and its quantity of water, measured in metres and in cubic metres per second respectively. The relation between these two factors may vary considerably, and Norway has plants both with a low head and a large quantity of water, plants where the two factors count about equally and plants with a high head and a small flow of water.

The first category can also be called the lowland type, which in Norway is confined to the southeast corner of the country and to some rivers in Trøndelag. The great rivers that enter the Oslofjord have a number of waterfalls in their lower basins, whereas their middle and upper courses are more even. In late- and postglacial times the lower parts of the pre-glacial

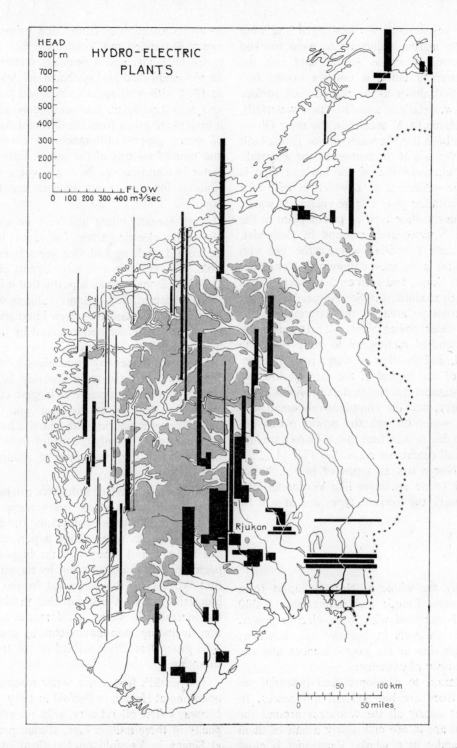

HEAD
800 m
700
600
500
400
300
200
100

HYDRO-ELECTRIC
PLANTS

FLOW
0 100 200 300 400 m³/sec

Rjukan

0   50   100 km
0   50 miles

Fig. 11.12. Types of hydro-electric plants in Sør-Norge; plants active or under construction in 1960. Plants with less than 20 000 kW of installed capacity are omitted. The horizontal width of the columns indicates regulated flow in m³/sec. in a median year, and their vertical length shows the head of water. The locations of the plants are at the lower end of the columns, except for two plants at Rjukan. Plants which use natural falls have the river course running through the columns. — The Rjukan area with six plants has the biggest concentration of power in the country, 581 000 kW. For the Rjukan area, see also Colour Map 7 and its inset. Norway's installed capacity increased in 1960–66 from 4.7 to 10.1 million kW. The location pattern remains **unchanged**.

river courses were partly submerged and were filled with marine sediments or were blocked by recessional moraines. As the land rose, the rivers generally cut new courses in the former sea bed, down to the rugged rock surface and with waterfalls as a result. These waterfalls, with heads up to 27 metres in the river Glomma, have been used in water-power plants built on the river bed at the bottom of the waterfall. Another characteristic of the lowland type is their large catchment area, which in spite of a low precipitation gives a large volume of water.

The intermediate type of power plant is the rarest in Norway and is found in Østlandet, Sørlandet and Trøndelag, whereas the type with a high head is the most common in Vestlandet and Nord-Norge, and even on the eastern flanks of the high mountains in Sør-Norge. Vestlandet is the prototype area for the extremes of this type of water power plants. Their heads are several hundred metres, up to more than one thousand, and the flow of water is only a tiny fraction of that typical of the extreme lowland type. Vestlandet has the highest precipitation in the country, and the comparatively small volumes of water through the power plants are therefore due to a surface that is broken up into many small catchment areas. See Fig. 11.12.

Nord-Norge has all types of plants. Nordland and Troms are more like Vestlandet, and in Finnmark the lowland types are or will be found.

SUPPLY

Practically the whole of Norway, apart from some remote islands and habitations, (4 000 people) is supplied with hydro-electric power. Transmission costs in Norway are, however, often high due to the long distances and the small number of consumers.

In relation to developed and potential resources there are big regional differences. In Østlandet nearly all the resources around the Oslofjord are in use and nearly a half of them for Østlandet as a whole. Vestlandet is close to the national average, one quarter. In the future, therefore, Vestlandet and Nord-Norge can be expected to increase their share very considerably. Future expansion will also lead to an increased inter-connection primarily between Østlandet and Vestlandet, but also between Østlandet and Trøndelag. Østlandet has an old-established grid system which was linked in 1964 with Vestlandet (which had five grids) and with Trøndelag. East-west links will make it possible to profit from the different conditions of water supply (differences in precipitation and time of melting of the snow). Excess flood water in south-eastern Norway, where the possibilities for storage are limited, can be used now.

Until recently there has been no export of Norwegian electric current, but export to Sweden from Trøndelag and vice versa is now possible. The objection to a large export of hydroelectricity from Norway is partly that it is cheaper to transport, for instance, aluminium than electric current, and thus even international interests are therefore better served by using the hydro-electricity in Norway.

Owing to losses by transmission, the consumption of electricity in Norway is 90 per cent of the production. The biggest consumer group is the electro-chemical and electro-metallurgical industries with nearly a half of the consumption. The only reason for their location in Norway is the availability of cheap hydro-electricity.

Other manufacturing industries can be put together in a group which takes about 10 per cent, and a third group comprising the pulp and paper industries takes about 8 per cent. This last and smallest group was the biggest at the beginning of the century, but by the end of the first World War it was passed by the electro-industries and by the group that in later years has increased its share, i.e. domestic consumption including non-manufacturing consumers. This group has about a third of the total consumption.

The world's first heavy water reactor started operating at Halden in Østfold in 1959. In 1960 Norway's first oil refinery, with an annual capacity of three million tons, started production at Slagen in Vestfold on Oslofjord. A second (2 mill. tons) refinery west of Stavanger started operation in 1967. In the Norwegian section of the North Sea prospecting for oil and natural gas is going on, mostly by foreign companies.

MANUFACTURING INDUSTRIES

Apart from the sawing of timber by direct use of water-power, which dates back to the sixteenth century, manufacturing proper with the use of more or less elaborate machinery is only a little more than a hundred years old in Norway. As in many other countries, the first Norwegian manufacturing industry was the textiles industry, which had moderate capital requirements and latent possibilities in the home market. The process of industrialization has continued to accelerate, and since World War II manufacturing has been the most important employer and source of income among the main groups of industries.

It is interesting to note, however, that in relation to primary industries (agriculture, forestry, fishing and mining) or to tertiary industries (commerce, finance, services and communications), secondary industries (handicraft, manufaturing and construction) have never become dominant in Norway. In fact, the tertiary group has been the biggest at least since 1875. The tertiary industries are dominant in several advanced industrial nations, but these have passed through a stage when manufacturing was the leading group.

Norway's manufacturing industry has a relatively simple structure, and lacks the many-sided production of great industrial nations. Norway is especially weak in key industries such as steel making and engineering branches making machines, tools, cars and other capital goods. The small size of the individual works is another handicap, 70 per cent of Norway's manufacturing firms employed less than 10 persons in 1963. There are several interconnected reasons for these weaknesses.

Before the introduction of electricity lack of coal was of course a handicap, but there are others that are still present and more serious. Lack of capital is badly felt, because Norway's resources in water-power and forest products require comparatively large capital for their exploitation. Weakness in technical and educational resources has its obvious background in the very small population, which in itself, and more so because of its wide distribution, forms a market too small for the big manufacturing units required to make many of the manufacturing branches competitive.

The requirements of capital are particularly large in the branches based on a heavy consumption of electric current. Behind each worker in an aluminium works, there is an investment capital of as much as about one million Norw. kroner, whereas his yearly salary will be about 20 000 Norw. kroner. It is quite natural therefore that foreign capital has played and probably will continue to play a vital role in the development of typical Norwegian manufacturing.

Until recently the export branches were based on what may be called Norway's natural resources, i.e. rock, fish, forest and water-power. It is characteristic also that most of the exported goods are not consumers' articles, but fabricates made for further processing abroad, namely pulp, paper, electro-chemical products, rayon, fish, liver oils, herring oil, ferro-alloys, aluminium and other metals. Several criteria are needed to reveal characteristic features. In 1956 the export branches occupied about 20 per cent of the total number employed in manufacturing. The corresponding figures for total gross value of production and of value added was 31 and 25 per cent respectively. The share of the export industries in value invested in buildings, machinery and so on was 40 per cent, and the consumption of electricity was even more remarkable, being nearly two thirds.

Industries which previously worked almost exclusively for the home market, have recently increased their export quota, e.g. the engineering, furniture and clothing industries. The spectrum of manufactured exports has been broadened. Limited supplies of raw material have restricted increases in quantities exported by traditional export industries based on wood and fish, but export values have been increased by processing. The exports of the electro-chemical and electro-metallurgical industries increased both in quantities and value.

DISTRIBUTION AND STRUCTURE

The main distribution of manufacturing and the quantitative relation between the different

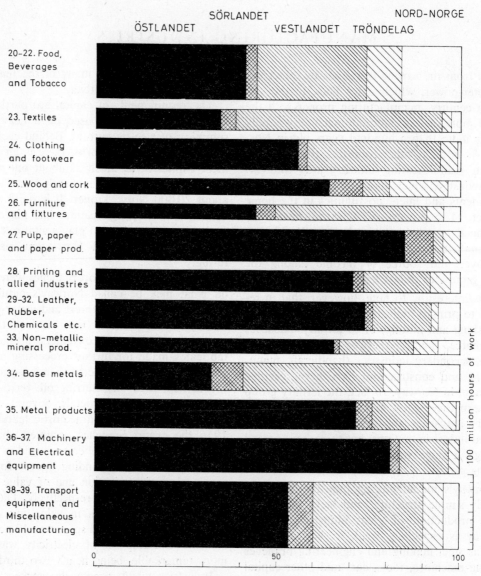

Fig. 11.13. *Manufacturing by regions,* 1963. Vertically the diagram shows million hours of work in 13 groups of manufacturing according to the ISI classification, and horizontally the regional share of each group (Østlandet 58%, Sørlandet 5%, Vestlandet 25%, Trøndelag 6% and Nord-Norge 6%).

groups of manufacturing is indicated in Fig. 11.13, which is broken up into the five main regions of Norway. Østlandet's leading position is evident. With scarcely half the population of the country, Østlandet has about 60 per cent of Norway's manufacturing, measured in hours of work, Vestlandet's and Sørlandet's proportion corresponds well to their share of the total population of the country, whereas the two other regions have the remainder, Nord-Norge being markedly the least developed part of the country in this respect.

Considering then the industrial structure of the whole country, one finds that means of transportation (mostly shipbuilding) is by far the biggest group in terms of hours of work, but is surpassed by food and drink and wood-processing in respect of value added to raw materials by manufacturing (cf. Fig. 7.4, p. 85). Taken together the machinery and electrical machinery groups, which are mainly producing capital goods for the home market, are also of considerable importance.

These two last groups serve well to illustrate

the uneven distribution of the different groups and Østlandet's more marked dominance in those requiring an industrial environment of a high standard. Only in wood-procesing is there a clear background of regional advantage in 'natural' resources.

Østlandet's obvious asset in relation to the rest of the country is that of having the most concentrated and the biggest part of Norway's population. No other part of the country offers such favourable conditions in regard to manpower and market, the last of which is a major factor for the location of many home market industries.

These advantages are partly a result of an early start in industrialization and the cumulative effect of existing industries attracting new ones and associated service industries.—Oslo forms the hub of Norway's core region and is characteristically dominant in such branches as the manufacturing of chocolate, tobacco, clothing, printing and allied industries and all sorts of metal industries making either capital or consumer's goods. In this Oslo resembles most of the big cities of the world.

Oslo made its early start in the textile industry and developed rapidly, keeping pace with the growing network of railway lines, which represented new routes overland to latent markets in Østlandet and other parts of the country. None of the long valleys of Østlandet lead down to the head of Oslofjord, and Oslo therefore did not get its opportunities before the age of the railways.

However, Vestlandet, which is favoured in the production of primary metals (water-power) and fish-processing, is also remarkably strong in branches such as textiles and clothing and in furniture making. Vestlandet's share in shipbuilding is also a substantial one.

Textiles started simultaneously in Østlandet and Vestlandet, and besides having the water-power needed, Vestlandet also had ample resources of cheap manpower from the many very small farms. For the further development of textile manufacture one must emphasize that the cost of transport for textiles does not loom large in the total cost, and hence the textile mills can afford to have their markets far away. Raw materials from local sheep may be added as a less apparent stimulus to Vestlandet's textiles industry which has become particular-

ly strong in woollens and (more recently) worsteds.

Not surprisingly textiles and clothing are rather heavily concentrated in the Bergen district. Their most important market is Østlandet.

Østlandet is also the biggest market for furniture making, a significant part of which is rather remotely situated in the northern part of Vestlandet, where it has created small industrial towns in the grand fjord region of Sunnmøre. Again poverty in regard to possibilities for work in agriculture partly explains the location. Transport costs are small compared with the cost of raw materials from Østlandet or abroad, and with the cost of manpower and machinery. A design that appeals to the consumers seems to be a decisive factor in the selling of such lasting articles as furniture. In explaining the location of furniture making in Sunnmøre and elsewhere in Vestlandet, relatively cheap labour and electricity must also be noted, and credit must be paid to human skill and initiative.

Shipbuilding in Norway is another example of local stimulus as well as of human skill and will. In view of what the country lacks for the fabricating of steel plates and engineering goods, there is no evident reason either for the present size of shipbuilding in Norway, or for its pattern of distribution. See also Fig. 11.14.

The building of ships of course appeals to and is needed by a great shipping nation like Norway. It is, however, striking that the 1905 record of 50 000 G.R.T. launched was not broken until 1949. Launchings amounted to 537 000 G.R.T. in 1966. and therefore showed a remarkable post-war expansion. This growth has involved a steadily increasing size of berths and large investments in machinery and construction works in the shipyards. For instance Stavanger has launched several ships of more than 100 000 dwt. On the island of Stord, between the two shipbuilding centres of Bergen and Stavanger, a new shipyard and dock have been equipped for the building of 100 000 ton ships.

Shipbuilding in Norway, outstanding as an employer, is a risky and difficult branch of industry. Apart from being vulnerable when international trade shrinks, the Norwegian shipowners' choice of shipyard is very much dependent on the financial stimulus—or restrictions—given by the government's financial poli-

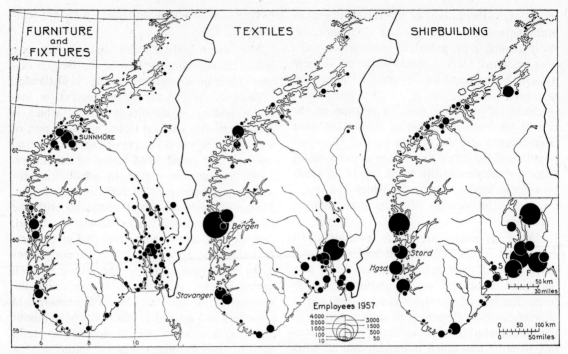

Fig. 11.14. Three branches of home market industries, 1957. Textiles includes hosiery, and ship-building repair work and motor factories. The circles show employees for administrative districts *(kommune)* except where the scale of the map makes it necessary to merge several districts in one circle, as in the Bergen and Oslo areas. — Furniture and 'fixtures' (doors, window frames etc.) are made at small plants in primarily rural districts, furniture mainly in Vestlandet (Sunnmøre) and fixtures in Østlandet. Textile factories are larger and the industry is half rural and half urban in location. In the Bergen district most of the textile, like the furniture, plants are outside Bergen proper. Shipbuilding represents a further stage in the transition to big units and to concentration in towns, e.g. the Oslofjord district where H = Horten. T = Tønsberg. S = Sandefjord. F = Fredrikstad. The textile industry of the Stavanger area is concentrated on Sandnes, south of Stavanger.

cy in regard to the shipbuilding industry. About 85 per cent of all ships built in Norway are ordered by Norwegian shipping firms. Some of the major ones are owners of shipyards. But the tonnage launched in Norway is less than a quarter of what is yearly launched in the world's shipyards for the expansion and renewal of the Norwegian fleet (1957–66).

The bulk of Norwegian shipbuilding is located on those parts of the coast where shipping is an important industry. The concentration in the Oslofjord district is also partly explained by the need for repair work in this most heavily trafficked part of the coast. The whaling fleet gets its repairs and maintenance work done in home town shipyards in Vestfold. On the other hand Fredrikstad in Østfold concentrates on new ships, like most of the shipyards along the coast of Sørlandet and Vestlandet.

Trøndelag has no large-scale shipbuilding. Nevertheless, as an employer this industry is surpassed only by the food industry there. The

Namsos area has important sawmills, but the pulp and paper manufacture has been weakly represented considering Trøndelag's forest resources. A big newsprint factory started to operate in 1966.

Nord-Norge's best-represented groups of industry are fish-processing, shipbuilding and primary iron and metals industry. The important role played by the last group is due to the iron and steel works built by the state in Mo i Rana and operating since 1955, and to the recent aluminium plant in Mosjøen nearby. Southern Nord-Norge has thus been caught up in the expansion of Norway's export industries. These demonstrate the peculiarities of Norwegian manufacturing compared with other countries and are therefore more fully dealt with below.

SITUATION AND SITE OF THE EXPORT INDUSTRIES

Probably most of the manufacturing industries are governed in their location by many factors, none of which seems to be the decisive one. Some are even irrational, reflecting that the location within a wide area has little influence on the total costs of production, as measured from the extraction of raw materials to marketing. In contrast the location of the Norwegian export industries gives good examples of dependence on close access to raw materials and to power.

Fish-processing

offers the simplest case, because nearness to the fishing grounds is in many branches an obvious necessity in order to prevent the deterioration of a highly perishable raw material.

The oldest method of fish preserving by simply hanging it, unsalted, on wooden racks for open-air drying, is still very much in use in Norway. Racks for stockfish are characteristic features of the cod-fishing villages in Lofoten, Troms and Finnmark. Bergen, is, however, the old and still the biggest export harbour of this product, and has warehouses in the harbour area for the stapling and sorting of the fish into various qualities. The stockfish keeps well in warm climates and has a good market in Italy and in West Africa.

The other main method of preserving cod species, the making of klipfish *(klippfisk)*, has two stages. The first is salting, which is done on board the boats in distant waters or where the fish is landed, and the next is the drying of the fish on bare rocks (klippe=cliff or rock). Rocks ground smooth by ice and waves, or stony beaches, are common all along the coast, but the climate in Lofoten or Finnmark is considered too raw and cold for good drying. The areas around Kristiansund N and Ålesund, in Møre og Romsdal, are climatically well suited for drying, being windy and not too wet or too cold or warm. Klipfish is now, however, mainly artificially dried, e.g. in Ålesund, Kristiansund and Bodø.

At the end of last century the city of Stavanger started and took the lead in the canning of 'sardines', using sprat *(brisling)* or small herring as raw material. Canning factories have since sprung up further north in Vestlandet, for instance in the Bergen area, and on the eastern side of the Oslofjord, all conveniently situated near the fishing grounds for sprat.

Salting in barrels is the old and still common method of preserving herring in all herring districts. A more recent, and now by far the biggest undertaking in fish-processing, is the making of herring meal and oil. About 8 tons of herring produce 2 tons of meal used as valuable concentrated fodder, and 1 ton of oil. The huge quantities of winter herring have been the most attractive raw material for these factories. They have spread all along the coast of Vestlandet and are also found in Nord-Norge. In general they have an extremely short season, in spite of the success in lengthening the period of storage of fresh herring by a preserving liquid. The economic difficulties caused by the short season were aggravated in the late fifties because of a drastic reduction in the quantity of herring landed. Recently the oil and meal factories have been busy processing herring and mackerel from the expanding North Sea fisheries.

The fish-freezing industry is quite new and particularly developed in Nord-Norge where a comparatively even supply of cod and related species is possible throughout the year. For instance the big new freezing plant in Hammerfest has provided much work for the town and for the fisheries off Finnmark.

Above all, fish-processing plants need good harbour facilities and ample space in the harbour for buildings and storage of raw materials and finished products. Water and power supplies must also be considered, the herring oil factories are rather heavy consumers of electricity. None of these requirements are, however, difficult to satisfy on the coast, so that other factors may have decided the final choice of site.

Wood-processing

The use of wood for paper making in Norway started about 1860, and from the turn of the century a rapid development in pulp and paper manufacturing took place. It soon surpassed in export value the sawn wood, which today is mainly produced for the home market and consequenty has moved further inland from its previous export location on the coast. Pulp and paper now account for more than one milliard Norw. kroner in export value and to this must be added the considerable value of synthetic fibres and chemical compounds originating from wood.

The costly transport of logs and the weight reduction, after processing, suffice to explain forested Østlandet's leading role in the paper and pulp industry. Road and rail transport has become an alternative to floating and rafting, but most of the existing wood-processing river sites were determined in the days when floating was the only means of long distance transport. The further down a river one could get, the greater the forest area to draw on as a source of supply of logs. Riverside location is equally desirable because of the needs for huge quantities of water. To put it simply, but not forgetting the complicated equipment, the making of pulp and paper consists of putting water into wood and taking it out again. Up to one thousand tons of water is required for one ton of mechanical wood pulp.

Water supply can be satisfied along all the bigger rivers, and the location of site was then determined by the availability of power. The initial period of wood-processing to pulp and paper dates back to the not too distant past when electricity and electricity transmission were unknown or still in their infancy. Waterpower was therefore used directly through turbines.

An old technical situation and old possibilities for transport of raw materials, fuel and finished products have therefore largely determined the location of wood-processing. The majority of the plants have been located at the falls in Østlandet's and Sørlandet's rivers. West and northwest of the Oslofjord there is both inland and coastal location at numerous small waterfalls. In particular those in rivers that lead down to the towns of Drammen and Skien, and which have large forested catchment areas, have a large number of wood-processing plants. In Østfold a few big falls close to the mouth of the rivers suffice to supply a large part of the total wood-processing industry with sufficient power, leaving nearby falls further inland to other consumers of electricity.

The making of chemical pulp and high quality paper was introduced later than mechanical pulp and manufacture of newsprint and has thus had a freer choice of site in relation to power. Some of the newest mills are thus found at the mouth of Dramselva (elv=river) and on the southern tip of the peninsula between the Dramsfjord and the Oslofjord, to which timber from the river Glomma can be rafted across the fjord. See Fig. 11.15.

Vertical integration, with one firm engaged on all stages of wood-processing, and even on one site, is also common. Borregaard, situated at Sarpsfoss (foss=fall), some 20 navigable km from the mouth of the river Glomma, is one of them and is the biggest of all Norwegian wood-processing firms. Before the plant was started, most timber was transported further down to Fredrikstad, the first big centre for steam-driven sawmills in Norden. Borregaard is also outstanding in having a varied production of a long series of products, all of them originating from timber, such as rayon fibres, alcohols and many other chemicals that require high technical and scientific skill and knowledge. Borregaard's development into a complicated chemical plant occurred mainly after World War II.

Most of the Norwegian wood-processing plants run well below their capacity. During 1965–67 one third of the pulpwood has been imported, but, nevertheless, about half the pulp is exported without further processing.

Power-demanding industries

The electro-chemical and electro-metallurgical industries are the most recent addition to Norwegian manufacturing and already the biggest contributor to the value of exports. From a humble beginning at the turn of the century these industries surpassed the wood-processing industries as the heaviest consumer of electricity just after 1910, rose rapidly during World War I and have more than tripled their 1945 consumption in the post-war years.

The electric current is partly used in electrolytic processes and partly for smelting. The first process demands most power and is applied in the production of nitrogen and of metals like aluminium, nickel, zinc and copper. Iron ore and scrap are smelted, and alloys like ferro-silicon, ferro-manganese and ferro-chromium are amalgams made by mixing different ores and rocks. The continuous self-baking Söderberg electrode is a Norwegian invention which is used by all electro-industries in Norway and is well known and world-wide. Norwegian production of carbon paste for Söderberg's electrode (anode) in Norway partly supplies the

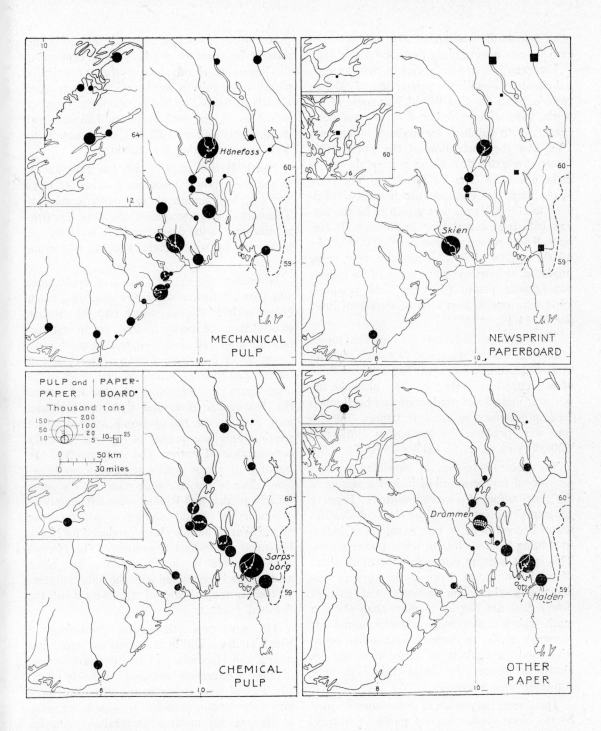

Fig. 11.15. Wood-processing, 1958. Mechanical pulp (air-dry tonnage shown) is used for the manufacture of newsprint and paperboard, and chemical pulp is the main raw material for other paper. Some mills produce two or more of the mapped products and therefore appear on each of the respective maps. Where two or more mills have had to be shown by one circle, the location of the plants is indicated by white dots. (In the case of the Drammen district on the map showing 'other paper', white dots indicate only the number of plants.) The inset maps show the Trondheimsfjord and Bergen districts. During 1959–65 production increased, particularly in the Halden, Hønefoss and Skien areas. A newsprint mill (future capacity 200 000 tons) in Trøndelag started production in 1966. A few minor plants shown above have been closed.

273

other Scandinavian smelters. The production of carbon paste runs to many thousand tons a year.

The era of electro-industries in Norway started about 1900 with the production of calcium carbide. Since the first World War some of the works have disappeared and some have been converted to produce ferro-alloys. The year 1905 saw the foundation of the world's first factory for extracting nitrogen from the air to make nitrate of lime for fertilizing. The firm, whose name for common use has been shortened to Norsk Hydro, has grown to be the biggest industrial undertaking in Norway. It employs 9 500 persons, consumes 6–7 000 of the 49 000 million kWh of electricity now being produced in Norway, owns some of its biggest water-power plants (Rjukan), and produces more than one million tons of nitrate of lime. See Pl. 11.11.

The aluminium industry also expanded rapidly between the two wars, and Norway's production of aluminium has never had a larger share of world production than in 1939, although the post-war increase of production has been much more pronounced in absolute figures. 360 000 tons were produced by Norway in 1967, and 600 000 tons are projected for 1970–71.

The electro-industries in Nordland mark a provisional northern and historical terminus of the distribution of electro-industries. From a geographer's point of view the electro-industries are of interest in being rare examples of industries being located close to water-power plants. This is not because power has the lion's share of production costs. Even in the very power-demanding aluminium industry, the cost of power does not run up to more than about a tenth. This low percentage however, represents Norway's ability to compete with other countries, and particularly in branches using an electrolytic process, for which there is no substitute for electricity.

The clue to the pattern of distribution formed by the electro-industries lies partly in history, partly in the transmission technique and economy and partly in the physical geography, which has determined the choice of situation as well as of site.

The distribution of the power-demanding industries as illustrated by Fig. 11.16 has its background in the simple fact that when they started they had to have a site close to the power plant, which should not at the same time be far from the sea because of export. At the beginning of this century the conveniently placed water falls in southeastern Norway were already developed or had been bought for other industries and domestic purposes. The westward trend, firstly within Østlandet, and secondly to Vestlandet, was therefore initiated.

Norsk Hydro started with the exploitation of the water-power resources just east of Norway's high mountain plateau in the county of Telemark. The geographical spread of this firm is indicative of the development in transmission technique, by which there was less restriction on sites.

Notodden was the first place of production, and soon after there was a new start on a much bigger scale at Rjukan, which had the obvious disadvantage of being located far inland, requiring both rail and lake transport of large quantities of lime from a coastal quarry and of the finished product, nitrate of lime, down to the coast again. In 1928 Norsk Hydro abandoned the Norwegian Birkeland–Eyde method and went over to the Haber–Bosch method which requires only one quarter of the first method's consumption of power. The shift involved the building of a new works at Herøya on Frierfjord close to the limestone mine. At the same time Notodden and Rjukan were left mainly as producers of liquid ammonia, which, since World War II, has also been produced for Norsk Hydro at Glomfjord (Nordland). The Herøya works converts the liquid ammonia into nitric acid, which is combined with the lime that constitutes a major part of the weight of the finished product.

The most power-demanding production of Norsk Hydro is still in the plants for liquid ammonia and Herøya's part in the whole nitrate of lime production requires relatively small amounts of power; but many other and more power-demanding products are now being made at Herøya, for instance magnesium, with sea water as raw material, and the whole development at Herøya would not have been possible without long-range transmission of current.

Since the end of 1963 Norsk Hydro has been building a new plant at Herøya for liquid ammonia based on oil gasification, which will be bigger than all the ammonia plants at Rjukan, Notodden and Glomfjord put together.

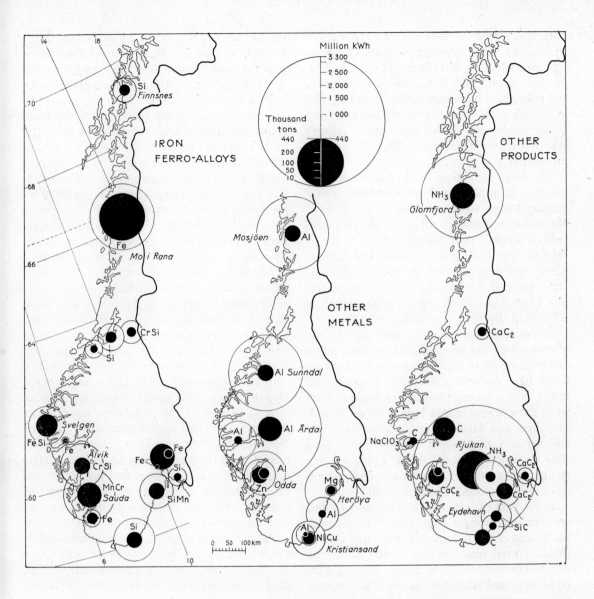

IRON
FERRO-ALLOYS

Million kWh

OTHER
PRODUCTS

Thousand
tons

OTHER
METALS

Fig. 11.16. Power-demanding industries, 1964. Black circles show production at individual works, and outer circles their consumption of hydro-electricity. The map on the left shows works using electricity for the smelting of iron (Fe), ferro-silicon (Si), ferro-chromium (Cr) and ferro-manganese (Mn). The metals (named by initials) shown on the second map are produced by electrolytical processing. The third map shows the electro-chemical production of calcium-carbide (CaC_2), silicon-carbide (SiC), sodium-chlorate ($NaClO_3$), carbon paste (C) and ammonia (NH_3). All data have kindly been supplied by the firms. — The large power consumption at Rjukan is used for the production of ammonia, which is transformed into nitrogen fertilizers at Herøya, the power consumed there is mainly used for the production of magnesium and calcium-carbide by the same firm (Norsk Hydro). The calcium-carbide shown at Herøya and Odda is partly used as a raw material for further production. About 85 per cent of the power consumption at Mo i Rana is used in the blast furnaces of the local steel works. No figures are available for a new carbon paste mill at Orkanger in Trøndelag or for the old calcium-carbide and ferro-silicon works at Notodden (between Herøya and Rjukan), their total electricity consumption amounts probably to 500 000 kWh. In 1965–67 new works at Husnes (Al) on the Folgefonn peninsula and at Valfjord in Sørfolda (Si), northwest of Sulitjelma, have started operation. — Magnesium is the heaviest consumer of power shown, using 22 000 kWh per ton in electrolytic processing, and carbon paste uses least, i.e. 1 000 kWh per ton.

Herøya's good flat industrial site is about one sq. km, one of the largest in Norway. The works was erected in an already well-established industrial district which thereby was extended and enlarged by factory and residential buildings. Such is also the case for the works in Sørlandet, where the nickel and copper refinery near Kristiansand has a notably high value of production.

Two large aluminium works now under construction or in planning have been located near existing towns. Both are joint undertakings of Norwegian and foreign concerns, one on the island of Karmøy near Haugesund, the other on the Lista peninsula near Farsund. The Karmøy plant started production in 1967. The new state-operated steel works at Mo i Rana was also located in a small town, the population of which had, by 1965, increased to 20 000.

In Vestlandet on the other hand the erection of new works has necessitated the construction and building up of completely new little towns, which have replaced a few and rather isolated farms, thus repeating the story of Rjukan. Such were, for example, Odda before World War I, Høyanger and Sauda shortly afterwards, Årdal and Sunndal after World War II. For a long time Glomfjord near the Arctic Circle was the northernmost site, but recently two ferro-silicon works have been built further north.

In the light of improved transmission technique one may wonder why the new plants were not placed in the outer more populated coastal districts, even near existing towns, where the new works could draw on already existing public services and amenities such as water supply, quays, sewage, roads, schools, shops and so on. Because of their remote situation in relation to the old towns the new ones have proved costly to equip and service. In the course of a generation their total population has run up to 4–5 times that of the number employed at the works.

The answer is that the available power resources are mostly far inland from the outer coast, and that a long transmission line after all is costly to construct and involves a loss of current. More important still is the fact that the heads of the inner fjords can also offer extensive areas of flat emerged sea beds, so fitted for the works requirements that equally favourable sites would be difficult to find near the already built-up areas. Finally the sea transport on the long but ice-free fjords means nearly nothing in added cost either in the import of raw materials or in the export of finished goods.

There are exceptions to this rule of sites being located at fjord heads, in the Hardangerfjord and at Glomfjord, where the site is on a flatter part of an otherwise steep fjord side. But even here the towns had to be built up completely and are expensively serviced because of the long distances to the nearest commercial centre.

A large part of the population which in its occupation is very representative of modern Norway, therefore lives in a geographical setting of steep fjord and valley sides. The precipitation is often a heavy one, and the houses are in the shade for an uncomfortably long part of the year and day. The factory pollutes the air, and the population also has to cope with the social handicaps of small, isolated communities. On the other hand there may be amenities rare in other towns, such as easy access to high mountains and even ski-lifts and swimming baths.

FOREIGN TRADE AND SHIPPING

The balance of payments

Many of the small countries belonging to the Western World have a large foreign trade in relation to their population. This is a reflection of their high living standard, because neither the natural resources nor the population of small countries suffice to supply them with all the goods of civilisation. Norway provides a typical example with about 0.15 per cent of the world's population and about 1 per cent of world trade. More remarkable still is the wide gap between its imports and exports. The trade balance is extremely negative, and balance of payments is arrived at by earnings of shipping, the share of which is unique amongst the world's nations.

To take 1967:

	Million Norw.kr.
Imports of commodities	16 250
Imports of ships	3 735
Total imports	19 985
Exports of commodities	11 430
Exports of ships	1 000
Freights, net income	5 550
Other services	790
Total exports and freights	18 770

After Økonomisk utsyn, 1967.

1967 was a year with a deficit in the balance of payments of 1 825 mill. Norw. kroner, whereas in 1965 there was a deficit of 730 million Norw. kroner. Norway has experienced equally drastic fluctuations in other recent years, and always mainly because of the rise and fall in freights and imports of ships. Thus Norway has a painful—at least exciting—problem of keeping a steady economic course whilst rolling in the waves of the world's trade.

Norway's vulnerable dependency on the outside world is part of its long history, and the volume of trade has of course increased enormously from the early days when mainly fish and fur were exported and grain and cloth came in return. Big incomes from shipping are a comparatively new phenomenon. The wars of the nineteenth century were a stimulus and the merchant fleet has continued to expand since then, but with serious setbacks caused by the two World Wars.

Exports and imports

The composition of exports by commodities has changed very much in the course of time. Around 1910 two thirds were derived from fish and lumber. Pulp and paper took the lead in the 1920's and in the post-war years wood-processing has been surpassed by more or less fabricated mineral products. The general trend is towards an increasing export of manufactured goods and an increasing import of raw materials and capital goods. At the beginning of the present century consumer goods were still the major part of the imports. For the time being manufactured goods amount to two thirds of the total value of imports. Of these ships and iron and steel are the most costly items. Fuels,

mainly mineral oils, have become a substantial part of the imports, with a value of about the same as for food. Of the value of exports nearly two thirds is for manufactured goods; food and inedible crude materials rank next to them.

The geographical pattern of imports by customs ports in Norway is rather a simple one. Oslo is by far the biggest port and has nearly half of the total value of imports or, together with the other Oslofjord ports, about 60 per cent. The rest is distributed mainly between Bergen and other big ports. The exports on the other hand are more evenly spread between many customs ports, which handle raw materials and manufactures typical of their hinterlands. To illustrate this the commodities can conveniently be arranged in four groups: one consisting of commodities based on raw materials from the sea, the second of raw materials from the forest, the third has commodities manufactured by heavy consumers of hydro-electric

Table 11.2. *Foreign trade by principal countries, excl. ships, in million Norw.kr. 1967.*

	Imports 15 893[1]	Exports 10 881[1]
Europe,[2]	*12 142*	*8 747*
EFTA	*6 812*	*5 341*
Austria	163	61
Denmark	1 010	766
Finland	246	233
Portugal	67	68
Sweden	2 636	1 838
Switzerland	330	118
United Kingdom	2 361	2 258
EEC	*4 570*	*2 723*
Belgium—Luxembourg ..	411	209
France	548	325
Italy	484	346
Netherlands	754	338
West Germany	2 374	1 507
United States	1 257	984
Canada	579	81
Brazil	186	127
Sovjet Union	253	133
Japan	149	161

[1]) Incl. countries not specified. [2]) Incl. the Soviet Union.

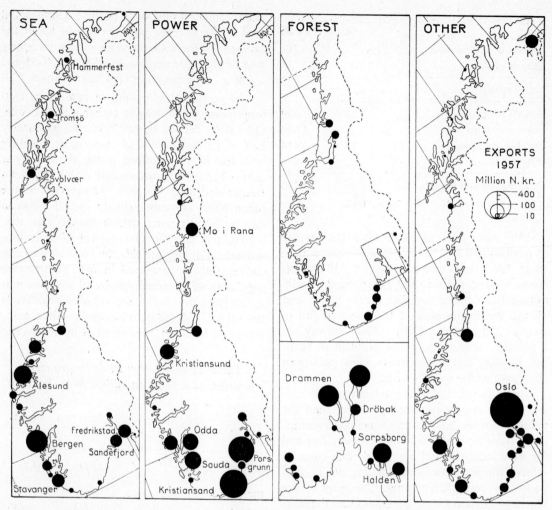

Fig. 11.17. Four groups of export commodities, 1957, by customs ports. The map on the left shows the exports of marine products (fish, shell-fish, seal, whale, and commodities processed from them). The map of power shows the products of the electro-industries, and that entitled Forest those of the wood-processing industries. All other exports, including mining products, are shown on the right-hand map. — The exports of marine products do not reflect the location of all fishing ports. Kristiansund, Ålesund and Bergen export the products of fish caught in Nord-Norge. Some power products are not registered as exporting from their actual place of production. For instance, aluminium from Sunndal and Årdal, and pulp from factories on the peninsula between Dramsfjord and Oslofjord are registered at Kristiansund, Bergen and Drøbak customs ports respectively. Drammen is an export harbour for forest products made further inland, and Oslo is a big export harbour for forest products and other goods from many parts of the country.

power, and the fourth comprises all other commodities. Of these four groups the third had roughly one third of the total exports in 1957. Commodities of the sea and of the forest each had about one fifth. Fig. 11.17 maps the distribution of each of these four groups by Norwegian customs ports in 1957, whereas Fig. 11.18 compares total exports and gross freight earnings. Fig. 11.18 also indicates the total exports in 1964.

The present situation is rather different.

During 1958–67 the share of the first two groups has been reduced to about one seventh for each. The power-demanding industries still claim one third of the total exports, as in 1957, whereas group four, which includes mainly home-market industries, has increased its share to about 42 per cent.

Norway has trade connections with practically all parts of the world, but the closest connections are with its European neighbours, as can be seen from Table 11.2.

The United Kingdom imports more than any other country from Norway and is her main customer for fish, pulp and paper and for base metals.

Inter-Norden trade has increased considerably. Norway is Sweden's main customer for ships. Denmark takes most of the Norwegian exports of nitrogenous fertilizers. Among the non-European countries the United States is of course the most important to Norway, Canada is her main supplier of nickel and copper concentrates and of alumina, and Japan of ships. Brazil has a good customer in coffee-drinking Norway and purchases cod (klipfish) and paper in return.

SHIPPING

This is much more world-embracing than Norway's export and import trade. At present about 19 million G.R.T. (1968) belong to Norway, and most of it is in non-European waters, with only one tenth of the active tonnage calling at Norwegian ports, but characteristically nearly one fifth of all ships. It does not pay to carry the small loads to and from Norway in the big-

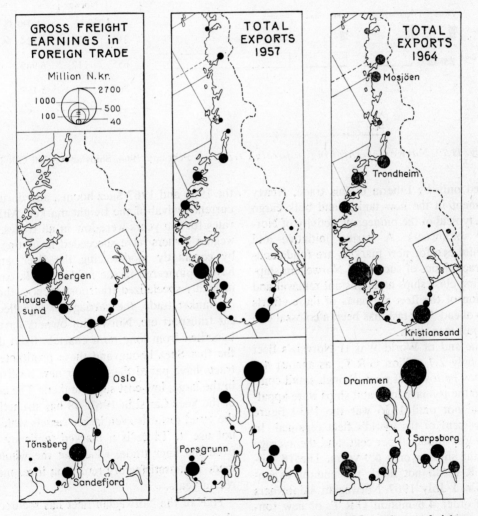

Fig. 11.18. Shipping, 1957, and exports, 1957 and 1964. Commodities and gross freight earnings in foreign trade compared and located at customs and registration ports respectively. The relatively small exports from Nord-Norge and exports and freight earnings of less than 10 million Norw. kr. are omitted. — Total exports of commodities were c. 5 500 mill. Norw. kr., and total gross freight earnings in foreign trade c. 6 200 mill. Norw. kr. Until 1967 (the second Suez crisis), 1957 had an all-time record in currency incomes from shipping. Total exports 1964 c. 9 200 mill. Norw. kr. (in 1957-values 7 100 mill.)

279

ger ships. Fig. 11.19 gives further information about the trading areas of the ships and their engagement in liner trade, tramp-shipping and tanker trade.

About a third of the ships are tankers which have 54 per cent of the total tonnage. A substantial part of the Norwegian fleet works on charter between the Middle East and Caribbean oil ports and the oil refineries of Europe and North America. In 1968 Norway had 16 per cent of the world's tanker tonnage and is

Although investments in ships are costly, in 1967 c. 1.5 million Norw. kroner per 1 000 G.R.T., the price is only 60 per cent of the 1957-level, the year after the Suez crisis. Financing becomes more difficult as average size of vessels increases (although cost decreases with increasing size). The new ships actually equal the sum of annual investment by all Norwegian manufacturing industries.

A topical question is how the Norwegian fleet has performed during the decade between

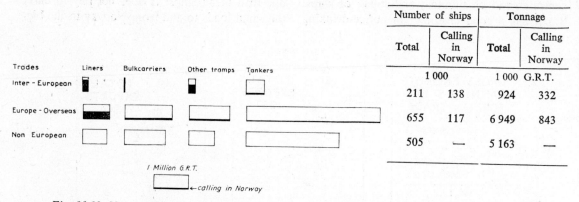

	Number of ships		Tonnage	
	Total	Calling in Norway	Total	Calling in Norway
	1 000		1 000 G.R.T.	
Inter-European	211	138	924	332
Europe-Overseas	655	117	6 949	843
Non European	505	—	5 163	—

Fig. 11.19. Norwegian shipping in foreign trade, 2. February 1964. Ships above 500 G.R.T.

exceeded only by Liberia in this trade. Heavy engagement in the new tanker and bulk cargo trade is typical of the pioneering activity of Norwegian shipowners. A daring initiative and a watchful eye for new markets are fundamental characteristics of successful Norwegian shipping. First class ships and constant renewal and expansion of the fleet are parts of these efforts to keep ahead. The task has been a colossal one in the post-war years.

By the end of World War II Norway's fleet was of only 2.7 million G.R.T., as against 4.7 in 1939. The losses of men (though small compared to the tonnage lost) and ships were appalling, and not until 1956 was the 1939 figure of 7 per cent of the world's fleet regained. In 1967 it was about 10 per cent, and the average age of the ships is only 6.9 years. The 18 million G.R.T. do not mark the end of expansion. On 1 July 1967 Norwegian shipowners had on order 4.6 million G.R.T. of new tonnage, c. 42 per cent from Japanese yards (1.9 million G.R.T.) and about 20 per cent from Swedish yards, while Norwegian shipbuilders accounted for 17 per cent of new tonnage on order.

the 1956 and 1967 Suez booms, and during the current revival of the freight market. Although rates for ten years were low in all trades, Norwegian owners have succeeded in cutting costs by constantly modernizing the fleet, and by having pioneered in the fields of bulk cargoes, in highly specialized transport such as the parcel tanker trade, the carriage of liquefied gas, car transport etc. Norwegian owners have also benefited from long term charters fixed during the first Suez boom, and these profitable contracts have paved the way for new investments in the large, low-cost super tankers. The closing of the Suez Canal in 1967–68 has strengthened the trend towards even larger vessels which will not use it. There is a marked tendency away from the liner trade, which on the whole has made an unsatisfactory return on investment in recent years.

Half of the Norwegian fleet has secured employment through long term charters (1 July 1965) and there is a trend towards an increasing number of freight contracts. Many Norwegian shipowners succeeded in 1967 in obtaining favourable long term contracts.

Seamen and shipping ports

In relation to the large sums of capital involved, the Norwegian fleet seems to be a fairly humble employer of labour. By the end of 1966 Norwegian ships employed 63 000 persons, 56 000 of whom sailed in foreign trade. Nearly 15 000 were foreigners; Spaniards provided the largest contingent. On the other hand foreign ships employed about the same number of Norwegian sailors. However, Norwegian shipping could not live up to its proud motto of 'speed and service' without the professional skill of either its shipowners or the seamen on bridge, deck and engine room. Recruiting and education of able men, who are willing to live a sometimes tough and strenuous life far away from home and family, is actually a major task for the shipping business. Sailors have good wages nowadays, but the dry land offers many a good alternative in this respect.

It has often been said that Norwegians are born sailors, and that Norway is such a great sailing nation because of its long coast. This is a deterministic over-simplification. Other nations have long and, so it seems, many-harboured coastlines without having taken to the sea to the same degree as Norway. Shipping, like other industries, is more a question of mentality and will to professional knowledge than 'natural assets'.

The history of Norwegian shipping exemplifies the suggestion that human factors are all-important. Fig. 11.18 shows approximately the present distribution of Norwegian tonnage. Oslo has an overwhelming leadership, although it is the Norwegian port situated farthest away from

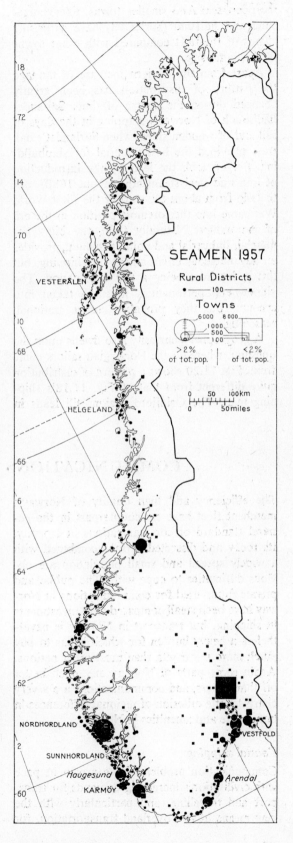

Fig. 11.20. Seamen engaged in foreign trade, 1957, by home communes. The map shows the distribution of 70 000 seamen who paid 'seamen tax' in 1957. Only those employed on Norwegian ships in foreign trade are included. The number includes those temporarily at home for some reasons, e.g. illness, education, unemployment etc. These 70 000 seamen constitute about 2 per cent of Norway's population. Rural districts are represented by circular and square dots and towns (including suburban communes) by circles and squares. Squares are used where the number of seamen constitute less than 2 per cent of the total population. Names indicate towns and districts where seamen (at least 500) constitute more than 5 per cent of the total population. Such towns and districts together have about 10 000 seamen in foreign trade. — This map should be compared with the freight earnings map, Fig. 11.18.

the open sea. And smaller towns, like Hauge-sund and Farsund (Sørlandet) have surprising shares of the fleet compared with other towns of the same size.

Apart from the modern increase of tonnage the pattern of distribution has been greatly changed during the course of time. Sørlandet had much of Norway's shipping in the days of sail and of wooden ships, when Sørlandet's oak trees provided the best material for shipbuild-ing. Bergen took the lead by the introduction of iron and steel steamships (about 1880), un-til Oslo from about the start of the First World War came into the foremost position in the era of motorships. Naturally Oslo, the big com-mercial, industrial and political capital, provides an advantageous environment for shipping, but this is far from being a full explanation. The shipowners' personalities must be taken into account, but they probably escape 'rational' reasoning.

A geographer's curiosity also dwells upon the question, where do the Norwegian sailors come from. Fig. 11.20 shows a pattern of distribution quite different from that of Fig. 11.18's ship-ping map. The Oslofjord region still leads in

absolute figures of seamen, but the lead is not very pronounced. Especially when seen in re-lation to other occupations, there is a striking proportion of seamen in the Bergen and Hauge-sund areas and in Sørlandet. True, sailing is 'in the air' in these districts, and nearness to shipping towns seems to be a very strong stimu-lus. But a further quick analysis provides evi-dence that the rural districts, with comparatively large numbers of seamen, are also those with small scope for farm work, little manufacturing and until recently little electricity. Half the num-ber of seamen have their homes in rural districts. Typical of the 1950-situation was a gradual diminution of numbers of seamen northwards, away from the shipowner's towns but into coast-lands where everyone is familiar with the sea. Since then Nord-Norge has proved to be a fer-tile area for recruiting seamen. Propaganda and erection and expansion of sailors' schools, for instance in Tromsø, have increased Nord-Nor-ge's number of seamen from 3 000 to 9 000 be-tween 1948 and 1964. But these results only stress an important point: times must be bad on the land or home waters before Norwegians take to a life on the world's oceans.

COMMUNICATIONS AND RECREATION

The efficiency and high quality of Norway's merchant fleet have no counterpart in the ge-neral standard of communications in Norway. Its rocky and dissected surface combined with a widely spread and small population are ob-vious difficulties to cope with. The public and private funds used for communications in Nor-way have been small compared with investments in shipping, but transport in Norway is never-theless a heavy burden for which it has to pay much more per capita than most other nations. Again some parts of Norway are much better off than others, and communications are a very characteristic criterion of regional differences in human life and amenities in Norway.

Coastal shipping

Communication problems have grown in pace with civilisation's increasing demands for trans-port and travelling, and particularly with the new means of fast overland transportation, for

which Norway is far from being well suited. In the old days when seaborne traffic had no rival as the best means of transport, and de-mands were small, Norway was of course lucky with its sheltered coast and littoral settlements. The country as a whole takes its name from this magnificent seaway to the North, which for sailing people was its most appreciated feature. And boats and boathouses have been and are necessities of life on the coast.

Seaborne traffic is still fundamental for Nor-way, not only for its international connections, but also within Norway. Over long distances sea transport is indisputably the cheapest for most commodities, and the old Royal Sea Road along the coast is used by thousands of small and bigger vessels, in regular lines as well as in tramp shipping, with calls at the smallest and remotest ports. Measured in ton-kilometres the seaborne transport is much larger than the transport by rail.

One is, however, widely in error, if one thinks that this northern seaway is a gratuitous blessing or that all harbour facilities are mainly gifts from nature. To assure and secure modern sea traffic, the fairways had to be equipped with thousands of seamarks, such as cairns and poles on land and poles and buoys in the sea, to mark out dangerous skerries, submarine ones as well as those appearing above the surface. Apart from fog and mist, darkness is of course a serious nuisance in all the narrows and curves on the twisting routes. The official list of small lighthouses and lightbuoys contains nearly 3 000, of which about 150 are manned.

When the express route between Sør-Norge and Nord-Norge started in 1893 to sail by day and night in winter as well as summer, this was rightly considered a courageous achievement, which freed Nord-Norge from days and weeks of isolation in the dark and stormy winter. The 2 000 km long express route with daily sailings between Bergen and Kirkenes, via Trondheim, is still the backbone of Nord-Norge's communications. The express fleet has been constantly renewed and modernized, but in spite of faster ships the improvements in travelling time have been almost insignificant. This is partly due to an increase in the number of calls, and in Nord-Norge the express route serves rather local connections.

Railways

Nowadays the express sea route has to compete with air traffic, which, after World War II, was introduced roughly simultaneously with north-south traffic by rail (Trondheim–Bodø) and road (Trondheim–Kirkenes). The railway through Nordland probably marks the end of railway construction in Norway, which has been continued into a period when air and road traffic might have been better alternatives.

From the beginning (in 1854), and with very few exceptions, the Norwegian railways have been run by the state. The cost of construction has seemed so high and profits so uncertain that there have been few objections to state ownership. At present, and this is not a new phenomenon, the railways are run at heavy losses, and to reduce them it is suggested that branch lines be closed with concentration on the main lines and longer routes where the railway is still competitive. Extensive improvements in railway equipment are also needed, for instance in electrification. Only half of the total 4 300 km of railroads is electrified.

The indirect benefits from Norwegian railways surely in general compensate for their costs. Østlandet's leading role in Norway's economy is to a great extent due to its railways, most of them completed before 1900. The railways from Oslo to Trondheim, Bergen and Stavanger will continue to play a vital role. In the case of the Bergen railway there is actually no overland alternative. The Oslo–Bergen line crosses the high mountains, its highest point being at 1 300 m, and is the only land connection between the two biggest cities for eight months of the year, when the road across the high mountains south of the railway is blocked by snow. The railway is very rarely blocked in winter, but only because costly snow clearance is constantly carried on. In addition to its 186 tunnels with a total length of 58 km there are along the high mountain section 27 km of wooden tunnels and, in addition, numerous snow sheds. The total length of the Bergen railway is 471 km; the western part of it, with most of the tunnels, was completed in 1883 (Bergen–Voss). The high mountain section came into use in 1909. At that time the successful construction and all-year running of the high mountain stretch seemed a technical fairy tale. Much later the Bergen railway, west of the main watershed, had two branch lines. The Flåm line (completed 1940) down a valley to the Sognefjord is the most dramatic piece of railway in the country. The 15 km long valley has a typical cirque head below Myrdal station on the Bergen railway at 864 m, and the railway was constructed by zigzags and tunnels through this steep wall. The maximum gradient is 55 m in 1 000 m, and the railway therefore had to be built as an electric line. The whole of the Bergen–Oslo line is now electrified.

Sørlandet's railway between Oslo and Stavanger provides other examples of nature's obstacles even at low altitudes. This line crosses a whole series of valleys and intervening mountains. Here are the longest tunnels in the country, and the railway was not completed until 1944. The violent snowfalls that sometimes attack Sørlandet have proved troublesome and expensive to clear.

Roads and local traffic

Norway's backwardness in relation to new systems of transport is perhaps even more pronounced in the case of roads. The 66 000 km of public roads (1966) are very far from adequate, and their standard is lower than desirable. Thousands of kilometres of public roads need to be built to connect farms and even small towns with the existing net of roads, or to be improved for car traffic. New roads are needed especially on the coast of Vestlandet and Nord-Norge, which have not enjoyed much of the benefit of the railway age, and which now try impatiently to get their share of road traffic. A substantial part of the coastal population, for instance one third of Hordaland's, live on islands, and even if bridges can be built to connect many of them, ferries will be inevitable between islands as well as across fjords. At present the whole country has about 100 ferry routes with a total length of more than 1 500 km, 80 per cent of which are in Vestlandet.

The high and wide mountains which separate Vestlandet and Østlandet are another handicap, all crossings except one being blocked by snow for six months or more. In spite of its altitude (1 004 m) but thanks to low precipitation (cf. Colour Map 6) the Lærdal road is kept open. In 1967 Vestlandet acquired a second all-year road connection with Østlandet by means of five tunnels totalling 14 km on the Odda–Oslo route. Low precipitation and altitude (670 m) permits winter traffic via Røros between Østlandet and Trøndelag, but further north all mountain roads are closed by snow in winter.

In the long run it pays to change from boat to road in short distance traffic. Compared with buses or cars, ships are costly because of their size and slower speed. Transport by bus is faster, and gives more frequent services than by boat, which is perhaps even more important.

For the time being this revolutionary change from sea to road is well under way, but with rather deplorable results for the economy of the still necessary boat traffic, which has been deprived of income by the new roads. In the name of what can be called geographical democracy, and in order to help the marginal settlements, the state therefore subsidizes the boat traffic in Vestlandet and in Nord-Norge. This help is particularly needed in Nord-Norge, where the population is more thinly spread than in Vestlandet and where some exposed stretches of sea necessitate comparatively big vessels.

Fig. 11.20 gives an idea of what sea traffic, even if it is only ferries, and other natural hindrances mean in respect of travelling time. The four hour's isochron for Oslo embraces 'half populated Norway', whereas that for Tromsø or Bergen takes only a part of their natural hinterlands.

Local boat traffic has been improved by the introduction of 'seabuses', speedy small boats in which passengers sit as in buses. Stavanger, which will always need boats to the islands and in and to the fjords that radiate from Boknfjord, took the lead in this development which, however, cannot compensate for roads or rail. However, speedy 'hydrofoil-boats', which were first introduced between Stavanger and Bergen, may again change the situation in favour of public transport by boats.

Since 1890 the total length of roads has been doubled in Norway, and 10 000 km have been constructed since the last war. They have greatly improved living conditions in the countryside, and the new structure of connections has had administrative consequences. On the west and north coast the borders between the administrative districts reflect the old sea communications. Now the roads have made former centres remote and made connections along fjords and sounds, rather than across them as before. The recent redivision of Norway into administrative districts, took into consideration this new traffic situtation.

Another consequence of the shift from sea to land communications is that some outer islands have become depopulated. Their relative remoteness and lack of public services were felt to be intolerable.

As in all other countries the roads and buses, and the door-to-door lorry and car traffic compete successfully with the railway. The bus traffic has for long exceeded the train traffic as measured in passenger-kilometres. In long distance traffic the railway is still in the lead, especially in winter when the roads are difficult or even blocked, for instance between Østlandet and Vestlandet, and in Nord-Norge.

Airborne traffic

has immensely improved, by shortening travel time, Norway's long distance connections abroad and within the country. In spite of all revolutionary improvements Norway has been slow in taking to the air. The reason is the same as with overland transport, airports represent big investments in relation to the number of passengers who pay for them. Post-war construction of airports is largely being done by foreign aid.

Apart from Stavanger really flat and large areas do not exist close to the bigger towns. Oslo's airport, with the drawback of frequent fog in winter, is constructed in an area with folded ridges, and at Bergen's airport (completed in 1955), the runways were formed by cutting down hills and by dumping the rock into the depressions between them. After all, Bergen is lucky in having a piece of lowland, on which the new airport is constructed, close to the many mountains that crowd in on the built-up urban area. Ålesund, which has fought in vain for a railway, is in the same lucky position of having adjacent bits of strandflat, relatively well suited for airport construction. Its airport, on an island, came into use in 1958 after a short period of construction. Nord-Norge has a regular all-year air route to Bodø, Tromsø and Kirkenes. During the summer season several hydroplane routes operate along the coast of Nordland and in the Lofoten area.

RECREATION

The time has come when people are freed from mere drudgery just to keep alive and have acquired leisure and an appreciation of the beauties of nature, even those hostile to their livelihood. Our generation of Norwegians, wealthy compared with that preceding it and using much of its income and long holidays for travel, realizes the joys of living in a thinly populated country. If the earnings in money are still modest, Norwegians have got so much almost free, which people from many other nations have to be rich to enjoy.

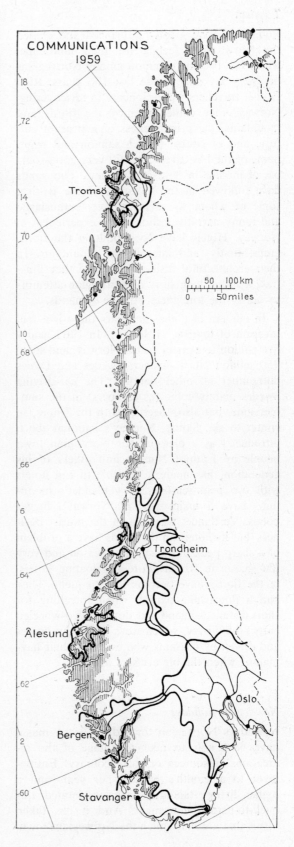

Fig. 11.21. Communications, 1959. Shaded areas have only boat or ferry connections with their nearest town, which is marked with a dot on the map. Four-hour isochrons for the fastest connections by public transport (other than airways) circumscribe six cities named on the map. Main railway lines are shown.

Tourism

Foreigners have greatly influenced and guided the Norwegians' feeling for their landscape, which has become common among Norwegians one may say only in the last 100 years. Rich British travellers were pioneers in 'discovering' Norway, they came to enjoy the fjords and mountains, the primitiveness of a peasant culture, and of course to fish salmon and trout. Some of the best rivers are still very good sources of income in British 'currency'. Thousands have followed in the footsteps of the British, some of whom wrote instructive, enthusiastic and funny narratives about their experiences in Norway. Hotels have been built in the fjordlands, firstly, and later in the mountains. In their architectural fashion and style they illustrate a rather long story of Norwegian attempts to satisfy the foreigners' strange demands.

In our era of planes and cars there is a real invasion of tourists to Norway. In 1965 nearly five million foreigners visited Norway, and spent 750 million Norw. kroner. Swedes and Danes outnumber all other nations. The car-driving Swedes mainly come (as campers) in the summer time, but also, together with the Danes, in winter to ski. Skiing, Norway's national sport, introduced as a pleasure for Norwegian town people by Fridtjof Nansen and others of his generation, has made it possible to run hotels with two peak-seasons. So Østlandet's mountains have a major part of Norway's bigger hotels. Vestlandet was first in the tourist business, but its hotels on the fjords have a problem of a sharp peak in the summer season and very few guests in winter. Foreign 'floating hotels' in the fjords have become less frequent. They had a flourishing period, when travelling for short distances inland was done in two-wheeled carts (stolkjærre), which were pulled by horses and driven by peasants who even left their haymaking when the big cruisers arrived.

Norwegian holidays

Nowadays Norwegian town dwellers en masse have been able to take advantage of the recreational resources of their country. Entitlement to a month's holiday per year, and a higher living standard, have accelerated this back-to-nature movement. And it has taken forms that are very much the Norwegians' own.

A Norwegian 'turist' is a person who takes tours in the mountains. A national association and many local ones have built and arranged an intricate network of hytter (literally huts, actually very decent hotels), mainly in the mountains of southern Norway. These tourist 'huts' are partly new buildings or partly converted and expanded seters which were formerly used for transhumance. They have made it possible to walk by short daily distances over nearly the whole mountain world of Sør-Norge, with just a rucksack for clothing and a little food.

From Christmas to April Norwegians as well as foreigners invade the mountains. But there is one important exception; very few foreigners ski at Easter time in the Norwegian mountains, for the simple reason that there is no room for them. Norwegians fill the hotels and thousands live in their own huts or in rented seters. At Easter time the sun again gives a little warmth and to a pale winter face an attractive tan, and skiing possibilities are still very good at high levels. By many Norwegians the Easter holiday is therefore considered the best of all.

The Easter terrain has been opened up by and is still very much confined to the areas near railways, and whole ski-hut villages have sprung up at high mountain stations. Typical Norwegian standards of life and living are no better represented than by this Easter holiday, which puts a very heavy burden on the railways and results in numerous ski-tracks over shining mountains and plateaux.

However much winter is appreciated for its skiing and skating, all Norwegians look forward to summer with impatient expectancy. For people of more southerly countries it may be difficult to understand the Norwegian excited anticipation of summer. Summer means light and the comfort of warmth and open air living, in Norway a bodily desire associated with the enjoyment of nature's beauties and an intense social life. Bad weather causes immense disappointment. A good summer, even if too dry for the farmers, is highly appreciated and long remembered.

Even if many Norwegians would prefer the mountains for their summer holiday, there are still more who stick to the seaside pleasures of bathing, sailing and fishing. And to an extent that probably has no parallel outside Norden, Norwegians are owners of summer huts.

Most of the huts are situated conveniently near the surroundings of towns, even away from the sea, if that is the only solution for getting there by cheap transport. Some of the huts are fine aesthetically, some are hideous, but nearly all are touching in their indications of happy family life and efforts to make something with your hands just for the fun of it, and to escape urban uniformity and monotonous civilized comforts. Huts and associated fenced property have become so common that other people thereby have been deprived of their old rights to go everywhere freely. A new open air law restores these amenities by prohibiting the erection of huts on shores and riversides that are declared common land.

Naturally cars and camping have also been introduced among Norwegians, and naturally some parts of their country are more attractive than others for a summer holiday. People living along the Oslofjord have become, in the travelling sense, the most provincial of all in Norway, because they have the warm, pleasant water of the fjord on their doorstep. Huts are everywhere, and the beaches and the littoral roches moutonnées swarm with bathers, whilst sails ornament the sea surface, and motorboats make their noisy ways on all fairways. Oslo-people have invaded Sørlandet, which has also become more and more popular with people from Vestlandet who can afford to come south and avoid the risk of a wet and cool summer.

Every Norwegian has a song in his heart:

In the dark days he well might be thinking:
"I could wish for a sunnier strand."
But the sun o'er the high mountains blinking
Would rekindle his love for his land.

(Ivar Aasen, translated by T. A. Robertson.)

NORWEGIAN ISLANDS IN THE ARCTIC
by Werner Werenskiold [1]

JAN MAYEN

Jan Mayen is a desolated island situated at about 71°N, 8°30′W. Its area is 380 km². The whole island is built of volcanic rocks, and the extinct volcano Beerenberg reaches a height of 2 277 m. The crater is snow-filled and many glaciers descend into the sea. Steam still issues from cracks in the rock, and earthquakes are frequent. The plant life is scanty, consisting mostly of mosses and lichens; 49 species of flowering plants have been found. The bird fauna is abundant, but of quadrupeds only foxes are found.

The island was possibly discovered in 1614 by the Dutchman Jan Jacobszoon May, and the waters around the island were much frequented by whalers. There are still ruins of Dutch oil cookeries. Austrian scientific expeditions wintered at Jan Mayen in 1882–83, and again in 1932–33. A Norwegian meteorological station was established in 1921, and, in 1958–62, a station for electronic navigation (Loran). Since 1929 the island has been under Norwegian sovereignty. Some hunters have wintered at intervals, catching foxes. There are no harbours, and landing is difficult.

[1] Professor Werenskiold died in 1961 and Tore Gjelsvik, Norsk Polarinstitutt, Oslo, has kindly revised this section.

SVALBARD

Svalbard is the name common to the Spitsbergen archipelago, Bjørnøya (Bear Island), Hopen, and some other islands. Spitsbergen is the main group, comprising four major islands and a great many small ones. The largest island is Vestspitsbergen, next come Nordaustlandet (North East Land), Barentsøya (Barents Island) and Edgeøya (Edge Island).

These islands are separated by narrow sounds; but a great bight, Storfjorden, separates Edgeøya from Vestspitsbergen. The western and northern coasts of Vestspitsbergen and Nordaustlandet are deeply intended by great fjords, but the eastern coasts are more regular.

The total area of the Spitsbergen group is 61 300 km². In 1194 the Icelandic annals mention 'Svalbard found'. The name means 'the cold coast'. Sailing directions prove that this coast must be Vestspitsbergen; but the discovery was soon forgotten. The group was rediscovered by a Dutchman, Willem Barendtsz, in 1596. Greenland whales were caught by expeditions from several nations, not without conflicts, but the disputes ceased because the whales were practically exterminated about

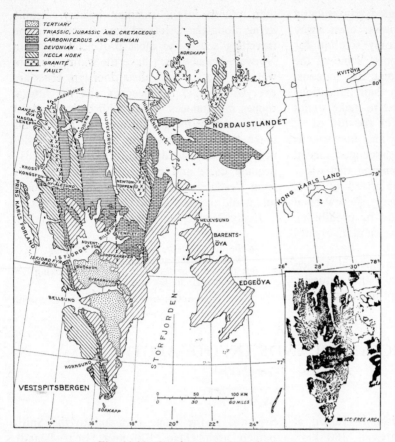

Fig. 11.22. Geology of Spitsbergen.

Geology

All geological formations are represented in Spitsbergen, from the Archaean to the Tertiary. However, the rocks formerly considered to be of Archaean age are now thought to be chiefly metamorphosed sediments of late Precambrian age — crystalline schists, banded gneisses etc., but true intrusive granites and gabbros also occur. A huge formation of sandstones, phyllites, limestones and dolomites is called the 'Hecla Hoek' complex: it is of Precambrian to Ordovician age; some fossils have been found. These rocks are separated from the Devonian by a great unconformity. All the later formations are shallow sea deposits, many exceedingly rich in fossils. Some sandstones were deposited on land and contain plant fossils and coal seams. Such are found in the Devonian (Bjørnøya), and, on Spitsbergen, in the Lower Carboniferous, in Cretaceous layers and even in Tertiary beds. The latter provide good steam coals. Basaltic sills have been intruded between the sedimentary layers at many places. At Bockfjorden, a branch of Woodfjorden, some small late Quaternary volcanoes have been discovered. Hot springs are found at many places, even as far away as Sørkapp. These springs seem to have some connection with north-south trending faults.

Up to the late Tertiary the climate was warm, apart from an ice age which occurred in the early Cambrian or Precambrian period.

The Hecla Hoek beds are strongly folded, upturned and overthrust in a belt along the west coast. A much later Tertiary folding occurred along the same zone; the various layers therefore appear in narrow strips, trending north-south. The dip of the beds diminishes towards the east, and in central Vestspitsbergen the sedimentary beds are nearly horizontal. The Hecla

1650. During the 18th century Russian trappers wintered in Spitsbergen, and ruins of their huts may be found in many places. This activity ceased about 1850. From about 1800 Norwegians began to catch fur-bearing animals.

Surveying and scientific exploration has been carried out mainly by Swedish and Norwegian expeditions, but many other nations have made contributions, e.g. Great Britain.

An international treaty of 1920 recognized Svalbard as part of Norway. The islands are under Norwegian domestic jurisdiction, but citizens of the contracting parties are granted certain rights. The Governor *(sysselmann)* resides in Longyearbyen. Norway operates four radio stations, Svalbard Radio in Longyearbyen, Isfjord Radio, Bjørnøya Radio, and Hopen Radio (on the lonely island of Hopen, to the southeast of Spitsbergen). Soviet Russia operates a radio station at Barentsburg (Grønfjord). Norway recently established two scientific stations at Ny-Ålesund, one for general scientific purposes, the other for receiving satellite data.

Hoek rocks are also widespread in the north of Vestspitsbergen and Nordaustlandet.

A huge block of Devonian sandstone and shale has sunk down between faults running north-south through Vestspitsbergen from the north coast to Isfjorden. The eastern islands, Barentsøya and Edgeøya, are built of flat Triassic beds which form large plateaux.

Landforms and glaciation

The present surface is a product of glacial erosion and frost action, and of marine abrasion along the coasts. The mountain shapes are largely dependent upon the underlying rock. The crystalline rocks form sharp peaks; the most conspicuous is Hornsundtind. The highest mountain is Newtontoppen, 1 717 m, in the northeast of Vestspitsbergen. The bedded rocks differ greatly in resistance to erosion, soft shales alternating with hard sandstones and limestone beds, and in many places, basaltic sheets. Along the folded zone, the hard beds form sharp ridges, steep towards the west, but gradually flattening towards the east, where the beds are almost horizontal. Here the hard rocks stand forth in precipitous walls, while the softer shales form slanting slopes, generally covered by talus.

The whole Spitsbergen group is intensely glaciated, but in the Quaternary period the snow-fields and glaciers were of course much larger. The valleys and fjords have the U-shaped cross-section typical of glacial erosion. The present glaciers and snow-fields cover 54 per cent of the area of Vestspitsbergen, and 77 per cent of Nordaustlandet.

Extensive snow-caps cover the eastern plateaux, but further west long rows of sharp peaks pierce the snow-fields. Glacier tongues stretch down the valleys; most of the fjords terminate against glacier fronts, some 30 to 50 m in height. At many places, especially along the eastern coasts, large glaciers enter the open sea. Most glaciers show marked signs of retreat, the lower tongues often being covered by heavy moraines.

The present snowline lies at an average height of some 300 m on the glaciers. The rivers issuing from the glaciers are overloaded with silt and gravel; they flow in many branches in the valley bottoms and build extensive deltas at their outlets.

Along the coast stretches a low platform which is continued along the shores of the fjords. This 'strandflat' may be from 200 m to 10 km broad, depending upon the hardness of the rocks. Smaller bays may have been cut off by gravel barriers, forming lagoons, but in general the coast proper is almost vertical and about 8 m in height; at low tide a narrow strip is laid bare along the foot of the cliff. The strandflat is dotted with lakes and mud flats, and is traversed by innumerable rivers.

Many strand-lines and wave-cut platforms, stages in the postglacial rise of the land, are found at higher levels. The most conspicuous is a broad platform at a height of 80 to 100 m above sea level. On the southwestern coast of Vestspitsbergen some platforms of marine abrasion reach heights as great as 225 and 334 m above sea level. Both are strewn with round stones. There are some signs of a quite recent elevation of the land towards the south, where lagoons have become fresh-water lakes. Farther north the lagoons are still at sea level.

Currents and climate

The currents off Spitsbergen run clockwise around the islands. A cold stream carrying much ice runs southwards along the eastern coasts, turning to the north past Sørkapp and running up the west coast. Outside this cold current, another warmer and more salt current —the last off-shoot of the Gulf Stream—runs northwards up along the west coast. This current disappears off the north coast, where it meets the arctic current from the east, carrying heavy pack ice. Navigation possibilities depend on the relative strength of these currents. The fjord ice grows to a thickness of about 1 metre.

The climate is of course arctic in character. At 80°N the sun is below the horizon from October 21st to February 20th, but the midnight sun shines from April 18th to August 28th. The winter temperature falls to 40°C below zero, but sometimes rain may pour down in January! The highest summer temperature is about 10–15°C. There is a marked difference between the west coast and the eastern areas, which are much colder. The weather is very unstable at the outer coasts with frequent gales, the worst blowing out through the fjords;

but in the interior areas the climate is more even. Precipitation is slight, about 300 mm annually; it is probably more on the west coast.

The site of the meteorological station has been shifted from Grønfjorden (Green Harbour) to 'Isfjord radio' further out on the coast, and there exists no continuous series of temperature measurements. But it is evident that the climate has become more temperate during the last 40 years, and the winters especially are now much milder than before. The Norwegian Meteorological Institute has kindly communicated the following average temperatures: Isfjord radio, Jan. 1912–16: –18°C, Jan. 1936–40: –6.9°C. The rapid rise in temperature started in 1917 and reached its maximum in 1940, and the above periods thus coincide with the greatest change. Since 1940 temperatures have been lower (1947–50: –10.6°C).

The rise is about 10°. The mean temperature of the whole year has also risen, but not so much. It may safely be said that the rise in temperature in Spitsbergen up to 1940 is greater than that observed anywhere in the world. The period of open water has become longer, and shipping has benefited.

Flora and fauna

About 130 species of vascular plants have been found in Spitsbergen. Most conspicuous is the yellow poppy *(Papaver dahlianum)*. In places sheltered from the wind, the vegetation may be quite rich, with many beautiful flowers, but as a whole the rocks and screes are naked, except below nesting places. In some of the inner valleys there are clusters of dwarf birch, a few inches high. There are no berry-bearing plants; mosses and lichens are common.

All along the coast millions of sea-birds nest during the summer—fulmars, gulls, auks, guillemots, rotchies and others—on ledges in steep hillsides; the eiderducks mostly nest on small low islands to avoid the foxes. Geese breed mostly in the green ground below the nesting places. There are no birds of prey, other than gulls. All these birds leave the Arctic in the autumn, some of them going beyond the equator in Africa. The only birds staying during the winter are ptarmigans and snow-buntings. The land animals are foxes and reindeer; they feed well in the summer, but in winter time food is

scarce. The reindeer are extremely fat in the autumn, but in early summer they are more like wandering skeletons. Polar bears roam along the coasts and on the drifting ice, hoping to kill some seal.

The sea around Spitsbergen formerly teamed with whales, walruses and seals; now only seals are found on the drifting ice. The Greenland whale was exterminated as early as 1650, and the walrus has become very scarce during the past century.

In some years great shoals of cod-fish appeared off the west coast, and there were great catches, but after some years the cod disappeared. One period of big catches began in 1875, and another in 1923. These fluctuations may be connected with variations in sea temperature. In some lakes red char is found, but the river water is generally too muddy for fish.

Some sturdy hunters and trappers still winter in Spitsbergen, two or three men living in small huts. Polar bears are killed by spring-guns, foxes are caught in primitive traps. In former days tragedies occurred, many men dying of scurvy, but now the winter rations are better balanced. Before wintering expeditions are allowed to depart their provisions have to be carefully scrutinized.

Coal mining

The most important activity is coal mining. Mining operations have been attempted at several places since 1900. An American establishment at Adventfjorden, a southern branch of Isfjorden, was bought by a Norwegian company, Store Norske Spitsbergen Kulkompani A/S in 1916. The main activity is centred in the Isfjord area. The mining 'city' is called Longyearbyen after the former American owner. During the war the German navy did much damage, burning all the buildings, but now everything has been rebuilt. There is a new church, hospital with two physicians, meeting house, library, school, etc. The number of winterers is about 700. The whole community is, of course, isolated during the winter. The first steamer comes in May, and the last one leaves in November. The annual export has been some 400 000 tons. The mining operations are favoured by two factors: the almost horizontal coal seam, about 1 m in thickness, is situated high up the hillside; the rock is frozen to a depth of about 300 m, and there is no water trouble.

Another Norwegian mining company, Kings Bay Kull Comp. A/S, operated at Ny-Ålesund, working coal seams situated in an isolated minor patch of Tertiary sandstones. Mine explosions have occurred at several occasions, and after the last one in 1962, the mining was exterminated. A Swedish coal mine has been bought by the 'Store Norske', but operations have been discontinued. The Russians work some coal mines in the Isfjord area, their export may be c. 400 000 tons, and the number of men wintering 2 000. Since the late 1950's oil prospecting by American, Russian and French geologists and a small Norwegian company has been going on, but only one deepboring has been made.

Bjørnøya

Bjørnøya is situated to the south of Spitsbergen, 120 nautical miles from Sørkapp, and 240 miles from Norway. The area is 178 km². The coast is precipitous except at some three or four places. The northern part is a desolate plain, 30 to 40 m above sea level, strewn with blocks, and studded with lakes, 700 in all. Towards the southeast Miseryfjellet reaches a height of 536 m. Mining of a coal seam in a Devonian sandstone has been attempted. The climate is rather mild for the latitude—the mean annual temperature is −4.3°C. The island is often fogbound. Vegetation is scanty: flowering plants are found only on a few Triassic outcrops. Polar foxes are the only quadrupeds, but bird life is abundant during the summer.

The island was discovered by Willem Barendtsz in 1596. A swimming polar bear was killed after a heroic fight—thence the name. Later the island was frequented by Dutch whalers, Russian trappers, and Norwegians. Bjørnøya became Norwegian in 1920. The island has been mapped in detail, and its geology examined by Norwegian expeditions.

CHAPTER 12

SWEDEN
by K. E. Bergsten[1]

INTRODUCTION

Geographical: the dual aspect

Southern Sweden has population densities which approximate to those of Central Europe. Northern Sweden was either settled late or includes areas beyond the limit of settlement. Gradation between denser, southern, and sparser, northern settlement is uneven.

An important physical boundary, that of the Norrland terrain (p. 295), divides Sweden into two roughly equal areas. South of it older surfaces predominate, notably the sub-Cambrian peneplane, and height differences are slight. North of the boundary are areas of newer relief which culminate in the northwestern mountains. The boundary of the Norrland terrain runs through Värmland, Närke, Dalarna and Gästrikland. Its role is not limited to morphological factors. It is an important climatological divide. There is a marked change in the boundary zone in winter temperature, number of days with frost and days with snow cover. It is therefore a phytogeographical boundary and the botanists' *Limes norrlandicus* approximately conforms with the boundary of the Norrland terrain.

North of the boundary the area of forest increases and the arable area diminishes. This is the result of both climate and relief. In Norrland large areas of high plateaux are covered with coarse moraines, and cultivation is limited to riverine sediments where it tends to form narrow strips. South of the boundary there are larger and more continuous arable areas, based on plains underlain by sedimentary rocks and on extensive areas of marine clay. The acreage of wheat, rye and oats decreases rapidly in and beyond the boundary zone, and grass is dominant in the north.

Within Norrland settlement is mainly restricted to valleys and coastal plains, and the average population density is low. Although Norrland and the mountain region cover more than half of Sweden, they have less than a fifth of its population. Industrialization has not proceeded far into the interior of northern Sweden, with the exception of Dalarna and Värmland on its southern fringe. But there are along the Bothnian coast large monocultural industries founded on the forest and mostly producing semi-manufactures for export, and Norrland has important iron mining. In the southern half of Sweden industry has developed much further than this and produces more finished products.

Because South and Central Sweden is an area of low relief which cannot produce much water power, it relies on imported fuels and on the surplus power of Norrland. Though very thinly peopled, Norrland therefore plays a decisive role with its export of forest products and ores for the world market and of power for South and Central Sweden.

Historical: the triple division

Sweden is divided into 24 *län* (counties). This division dates from the 13th century when royal castles in the län were supported by taxation of the surrounding countryside (for names and boundaries, see p. 6–7).

The older division into *landskap* (provinces) dates from prehistoric times when the part of Sweden then populated was divided into a number of small independent units. Later, groups of

---

[1] For valuable help the author thanks pol. mag. Lennart Améen (industry, especially its organization and distribution) and docent fil. dr. Olof Nordström (agriculture, industry, communications).

these were forged together and developed a common verbal law *(lagsagor)*. These lagsagor developed into provinces, and though they now have no administrative role they are important in the public consciousness. Their names are indicated on p. 7. The boundaries of the provinces and län often correspond over long distances. In South and Central Sweden the provinces may be divided into two or three län. Småland (the small countries) and the island of Öland have three, and Skåne has two. But in North Sweden, two provinces may in some cases be grouped in one län.

Prehistoric Sweden had two cores, i.e. the region around Lake Mälaren (Svealand) in the east, and Götaland in the southwest and south, where settlement was most dense on the plains of Östergötland and Västergötland. These areas of prehistoric settlement were surrounded by dense forests. Skåne, which became a part of Sweden at a late date, was a centre of considerable prehistoric settlement. It was isolated from the remainder of Sweden by dangerous forests and was linked with prehistoric Denmark.

In the early centuries of our era Svealand was consolidated as a kingdom centring on Uppsala and during the Viking period probably united with Götaland. It seems that there was a loose union about 1000 A.D. between these groups of provinces. Dalarna was colonized from the Mälaren region and their close relations are still evident in the strength of migration movement between them. Värmland, which had earlier turned to West Sweden and Norway, was also united with Svealand.

The third historical unit, Norrland, belonged to the Court of Justice of Uppland until the early 17th century, when the northern provinces were grouped as an administrative unit. Provinces were less significant in Norrland as the settled river valleys and coastal regions were often widely separated. The province of Norrbotten, for example, is a late creation and lacks long traditions.

In post-medieval times Sweden, like Denmark, was transformed from a sea-power to a land-power. Improvement of interior communications was partly responsible for this, as were several wars which took place beyond and within in the Norden countries and radically altered Sweden's frontiers. Sweden gradually lost large areas of the East Baltic region, finally losing

Finland in 1809, and turned westwards. In the mid-17th century Sweden conquered provinces which belonged to Denmark-Norway. In the south these were Skåneland (Skåne, Halland, Blekinge) and Bohuslän, which were added to Götaland; in the north Jämtland and Härjedalen were conquered.

When dividing Sweden into large geographical regions it is not always possible to follow the traditional tripartite division. The Norrland terrain includes large areas in Dalarna and Värmland, and in regard to forest resources, for example, Kopparbergs län (Dalarna) and Värmland must be grouped with Norrland. Industrially the Dalarna area is closely connected with the Mälaren region, as is Värmland with the Göteborg area. South Sweden is often identified with Götaland and Central Sweden with Svealand. But the densely populated plains of Östergötland and Västergötland belong to the Central Swedish plains, with Östergötland linked demographically with the Mälaren region and Västergötland with south and southwest Sweden. In this chapter, Central Sweden (with capital C) includes the province group of Svealand and Östergötland, Västergötland and Bohuslän. The map on p. 7 shows Central Sweden, thus defined, separated by heavy lines from South and North Sweden. In every-day Swedish, Göteborg, Bohuslän, Västergötland, Dalsland and Värmland are not included in Central Sweden, but are, together with Halland, called West Sweden, and this form also has been used below. Similarly, the counties of Kalmar and Blekinge and the eastern part of Kronoberg are termed Southeast Sweden.

Cultural trends

Sweden has a long coastline which faces the Baltic and eastwards. Before the 17th-century conquests her only western outlet was the mouth of the Göta river. Nevertheless, by far the strongest influences on post-medieval Sweden have come from Western Europe. They have affected agriculture, settlement and the Swedish constitution and, modified in Sweden, Western European traditions have been passed on to Finland and the Baltic states. Elements of folk culture have passed in the reverse direction, e.g. with the movement of Finns to Norrland.

Because of her remoteness from many of the new developments, there has been a timelag in their introduction to Sweden. This has sometimes been an advantage, and Sweden was thus able to avoid the worst evils of the Industrial Revolution as seen in Western Europe. Starting a century later, and lacking large coalfields, Sweden was able to avoid densely settled air-polluted conurbations. Her industrial equipment could also be of modern types and she is now highly industrialized, partly on the basis of hydro-electric power.

Innovations from Western Europe come first to the Mälaren region and to the western part of Skåne, and spread at varying rates to the remainder of the country. The two centres spread influences which seem to intermingle in a diagonal zone between Lake Vänern and northern Småland. Norrland is influenced from the Mälaren region.

The Swedish language arose out of the dialects of the different provinces. Olaus Petri, the major figure of the Swedish Reformation, was born in Örebro and worked in Strängnäs and Stockholm in the Mälaren region. He wrote several works in what became standard Swedish, and his translation of the New Testament in 1526 is important in this connection. He used the dialect of the Mälaren region and this became the accepted literary Swedish.

MORPHOLOGICAL FEATURES

Morphologically Sweden consists of the following main regions:

The area of Archaean rocks may be divided into two areas of elevation (A), and two areas of depression (B). See Fig. 12.1. These are:

A 1) A northern area which includes about half the surface of Sweden (the Norrland terrain);

A 2) A southern area (the South Swedish Highlands);

B 1) The Central Swedish Lowlands; and

B 2) The coastland of the Gulf of Bothnia and the extreme southeast of Sweden.

The following main areas of younger rocks adjoin the Archaean surfaces:

C 1) The Caledonian mountain range in the west;

C 2) The southeast: Gotland and Öland, which have Cambro-Silurian rocks; and

C 3) Skåne.

Areas of elevation

The Caledonian mountain range (C1). The great nappes of the Caledonian folding occupy large areas in western Sweden, where they may be as much as 140 km broad. The nappes must have reached considerably further east than they do today; the present mountain fringe is a denudation limit.

It would appear that the Caledonian mountain chain was largely destroyed and a relatively level land surface of uncertain post-Silurian age was formed. The whole area was elevated again and the relief was regenerated. The old surfaces emerge beautifully in some places as mountain plateaux cut up by very deep valleys hollowed out by glaciers. Three topographical zones may be distinguished.

a) The central zone with the highest mountain massif is found in the hard schists, granites, amphibolites and peridotites of the 'seve' nappe. Here are the highest mountains in the country, Kebnekaise (2 117 m, 67°55′N), Sarek (2 090 m, 67°25′N) and the somewhat lower and more southerly massifs such as Sylarna (1 796 m, 63°N) and Åreskutan (1 420 m, 63°25′N).

b) Within the western 'köli' zone of softer schists the mountain tops are lower; there are more lakes and the mountain plains are wider. The fact that this westerly low mountain region is not drained to the west, but eastwards through the harder schists by typically epigenetic valleys, suggests that the valley system is very old.

c) The third, eastern zone is well developed in South Lappland. It consists of Archaean and Proterozoic rocks and forms an eastern region of premontane high plains and low mountains which adjoins the undulating area of the Norrland terrain.

Between the northern and southern large nappes a lower terrain has been formed (the Jämtland Silurian plain). Further south, outside the nappes in Dalarna, is a large area of Proterozoic (Jotnian) sandstone forming plateau areas.

The Norrland terrain (A 1). The northern area of Archaean rocks falls away relatively smoothly from the premontane region to the southeast and south. The greater part of it is between 500 and 200 m high and it is bounded by the Bothnian coastal plain, and, to the south, by the Central Swedish Lowlands.

The important southern boundary of this so-called Norrland terrain is very faintly developed as a broader boundary zone north of Lake Vänern, but has more distinct features further east (cf. Colour Map 1 and Fig. 3.3, p. 41). Several morphological types can be distinguished, two occupying very large areas, viz. the monadnock plains and the undulating hilly country (cf. Figs. 3.5 and 3.6). The former type with well developed plains and isolated rounded hills is dominant above all in the extreme north. The other type with mountains and hills lying close together, and with well marked valleys, appears in a broad eastern zone in the south and stretches down to the area of the Vänern plain.

In the southern part of the Norrland terrain, in the Siljan district, is a circular fault area filled with Ordovician and Silurian limestones.

The South Swedish Highlands (A 2). The differences between the granite in the east and the gneiss in the west (cf. Colour Map 2) are rarely visible in the landscape. Region A 2 has, however, been divided into two large erosion surfaces, based on differences in relief which are probably cyclical: a) A northern area stretching in a broad band south of the Central Swedish Lowlands right across the country from the archipelago of Bohuslän to North Småland's much broken Baltic coast. The northern border has large relative relief and is dominated by tectonic blocks separated by numerous fissure valleys. The area around southern Lake Vättern has heights of up to 378 m and plateau-like formations. Cambrian sandstone appears as fissure fillings at all levels in the northern border zone. b) The plain of Southern Småland is Sweden's largest Archaean rock plain, an extremely level area with an average height of about 150 m. In the west this plain is bounded by a narrow, dissected zone leading down on to a small coastal plain in Halland, whilst in the east it is very

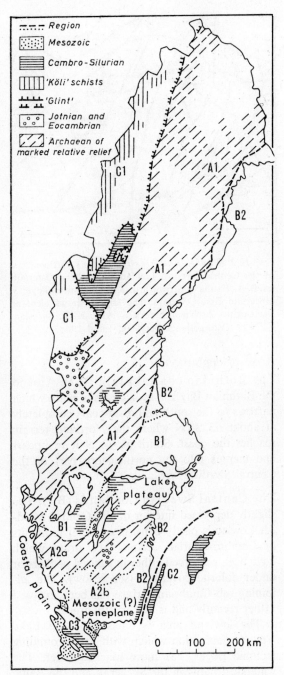

Fig. 12.1. Morphological regions of Sweden. The area of Archaean rocks is divided into two areas of elevation (A1 and A2) and two areas of depression (B1 and B2). C1 – C3 are areas with younger rocks (see Fig. 3.1, p. 32 and Colour Map 2). — After Atlas of Sweden 3–4 and Rudberg 1954.

gradually succeeded by another even surface, a sub-Cambrian peneplane, which disappears beneath Cambrian rocks and dips under the Baltic Sea.

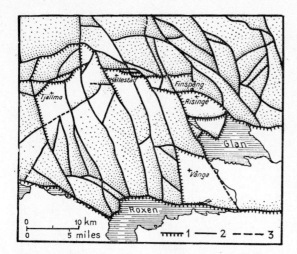

Fig. 12.2. Faults and fissure valleys in the east of the Central Swedish Lowlands (northern Östergötland). 1. Faults and overthrusts. 2. Fissure valleys. 3. Uncertain fissure valleys. The stipple shows elevated parts of the Archaean blocks. — After K. E. Bergsten: Östergötlands bergslag, Lund 1946.

Areas of depression

The Bothnian coastal plain (B 2). Around the Bothnian Bay is a broad coastal plain which narrows to the south and disappears completely at about 63°30′N where the Norrland terrain reaches the coast. South of 62°N it reappears and merges into the northeastern part of the Central Swedish Lowlands.

The Central Swedish Lowlands (B 1). The slightly depressed interior of the Central Swedish Lowlands partly consists of small remnants of Cambro-Silurian sedimentary strata which have been preserved either in faulted pockets or under dolerite coverings (see below). The adjoining sub-Cambrian surface has been exposed rather recently and is not greatly eroded.

The lowland area is crossed by the Lake Vättern depression which, with its surrounding tectonic ridges, has more marked relief. The watershed between the Skagerak and the Baltic Sea runs within this central zone of fractures which divides the Central Swedish Lowlands into two differing tectonic areas and two main plain areas.

In the east, W-E overthrust lines, bounded by tilted blocks, and fissure valleys running NW–SE, produce a broken block landscape (Fig. 12.2). The Sörmland lake plateau forms its central area. Remnants of Cambro-Silurian sediments in the Östergötland and Närke plains pro-vide good farmlands. Northern Uppland forms one of Sweden's largest areas of level plain. The boundary between areas B 1 and B 2 is not easy to define.

In the west, around Lake Vänern, is a large plain surrounded by areas of more marked relief. The land surface is extremely level south of Lake Vänern, but slightly more hilly further south and west.

South of Lake Vänern Cambro-Silurian remnants, preserved under a dolerite cover, produce the table mountains Halle- and Hunneberg (153 m), Kinnekulle (306 m) and the large Cambro-Silurian area of Billingen–Falbygden (up to 335 m). They are visible over long distances and give the plain its special character.

The southeast (C 2). Beyond the coast in the southeast is shallow water, probably wholly on Cambro-Silurian rocks, which stretches from about 55°30′N towards Estonia. From Öland it can be followed over Dagö to the Estonian *glint*. The islands of Öland and Gotland rise out of the sea and have cuestas on their western sides. Gotland has several cuestas of limestone facing northwest. Between the cuestas lie areas of slightly eroded calcareous marl and sandstone. Calcareous surfaces are widely exposed on both islands, and these, together with the low rainfall, create a sub-arid landscape (*alvar* on Öland, *hällmark* on Gotland).

Skåne (C 3). A series of faults running diagonally NW–SE divides Skåne into three large blocks of different type: a) In the northeast Archaean rocks continue the plain of southern Småland with a smaller Cretaceous area overlying them around Kristianstad. b) The centre of the middle block is covered with Silurian schists which dip southwards and produce an cuesta landscape. In the northwest the Silurian rocks are covered with thick Mesozoic deposits in which the Upper Trias brown coal seams are embedded. c) The southwestern block is covered with Cretaceous chalk and is linked with the chalk formations of Denmark.

The coast

At present the greatest land uplift is occurring in Västerbotten where the rate is about 100 cm a century. Uplift of land decreases southward; in Stockholm it is about 40 cm and in Göteborg 20 cm a century, while in Skåne uplift has ceased. Partly because of the land uplift most rivers lack deltas. Little solid debris is transported thus far, most of it is deposited in lake basins.

During uplift an archipelago *(skärgård)* is a transitional form, successively attached to the land, where Archaean plateaux, cut by fissure valleys, slope gently beneath the sea level.

In the Baltic the richest archipelago extends from northern Småland to northern Uppland and culminate in the Stockholm archipelago. The relief is more moderate, but the land upheaval more intense than in the archipelago of Bohuslän.

The low undulating coast plateau of Blekinge also ends in an archipelago. A fourth archipelago with very marked relative relief is that of Ångermanland, where the hilly Norrland terrain reaches the coast without an intermediate coastal plain.

Rivers and lakes

The valley system is largely a preglacial one, transformed by glacial erosion. Numerous rock basins have been formed in the valley bottoms and glacial deposits often force the rivers away from their preglacial furrows, so they have an irregular run over the Archaean plateaux. The lower courses of Dalälven and Klarälven are examples.

Land uplift has often altered the drainage pattern. Greater elevation in the north has caused lakes to drain southward. Lake Vättern, which originally had its outlet via the Närke plain, now flows out through the Östergötland plain. On the flat surface of the South Swedish Highlands former large lakes with more northerly outlets to the Kattegat now debouch further south and are much smaller.

Lakes cover 8.5 per cent of the total area of Sweden. The four largest (Vänern, Vättern, Mälaren and Hjälmaren) are situated within the Central Swedish Lowlands, which otherwise are poor in lakes. Skåne, the other clayey coastal plains of southern Sweden, Öland and Gotland and the monadnock plains of the far north also have few lakes. The most important lake regions are:

1) The South Swedish Archaean plain, where the lakes lie on an uneven moraine;

2) The northern margin of the South Swedish Highlands which has numerous dammed fissure-valley lakes;

3) The lake plateau of Södermanland, south of Mälaren and Hjälmaren;

4) The southern margin of the Norrland terrain, especially the area northwest of Lake Vänern, where long valley lakes have formed behind ice-eroded thresholds and glacifluvial dams; and

5) The lake chain within and outside the mountain region from 63°N to the Finnish boundary.

During the retreat of the ice margin some marginal zones of stagnation were formed. The most important of these occur in the Central Lowlands as systems of terminal moraines and deltas (Fig. 3.2 b, p. 37). They are continuations on a smaller scale of the Finnish Salpausselkä.

Drumlin topography is common throughout Sweden, e.g. in The South Swedish Highlands, where they appear in broad zones, often alternating with dead-ice topography. Drumlins and radial moraines (long ridges lying in the direction of the ice movement) are characteristic of the Norrland coastland, especially around Umeå. Drumlins also occur in the Central Lowlands.

In the southern part of interior Norrland the shrinking ice first freed the uplands, and the ice remnants in the valleys finally left a very rugged dead-ice terrain.

Glacifluvial material, especially in the form of eskers, is widely spread, but is notably lacking in central Skåne, in the area west of Lake Vänern and in the high mountains. In the world-famous esker region north of Lake Mälaren long eskers form the highest parts of the terrain.

The last ice remnants were left along the eastern border of the mountains. In the valleys between the ice and the watershed were lakes that drained westwards through what are now dry valleys. The largest lake, that of Central Jämtland, burst out eastward through the remaining ice at the end of the Late Glacial Period.

During the warmer postglacial periods there was probably no permanent ice in Sweden. Today there are some small ice fields (total area 329 km²), the southernmost being in Härjedalen (63°N). The glaciers are now retreating.

Postglacial and glacial deposits

The upper marine limit varies from 295 m above sea level on the coast of Ångermanland to c. 10 m in south Skåne. In the Central Lowlands it is at about 150 to 200 m. On heights well above the upper marine limit, the moraine is largely fine-grained ground moraine, but on slopes and in valley bottoms the material is coarser, often with a high boulder content. The morainic slopes are often furrowed by a pattern of melt-water gullies. On heights below the upper marine limit the moraine has been abraded by wave action. The fine-grained sediments found 20–30 m below the upper marine limit are of fundamental importance for agriculture and settlement. During submergence in brackish or in ice-lake water the melt-water deposits were stratified in 'varves'. Gerard De Geer formulated a time scale for the shrinkage of the ice in Late Glacial Time, based on the annual formation of alternating clay and silt layers. Postglacial changes in sea level are shown on Fig. 3.2 a, p. 37.

Many shallow lake basins have been infilled with organic sediments in postglacial times, creating peatland over large areas. In the wetter parts of western Sweden there are large areas of ombrogenous raised bogs. Some of these may be up to 50 km² in area. In western Dalarna bogs occupy 40–70 per cent of the surface.

POPULATION AND SETTLEMENT

Natural increase

The distribution and density of population and the distribution of certain types of economic activity in towns and countryside are discussed and illustrated in Chapter 6.

In Sweden regular censuses have been carried out since 1749 when the population was about 1.8 million. A century before this it was estimated at 1.2 million. Before 1749 the population can be estimated from parish registers, and, especially, from the lists of the parish catechetical meetings. Where such lists survive, e.g. in parts of Dalarna and Östergötland, accurate estimates from about 1680 are possible.

During the last 200 years the birth rate has fallen from an average of 35 per mille in about 1750 to 16 per mille in 1965. A very low point was reached in the 1930's, and after a rise during and immediately after the Second World War, the birthrate is now down again to the level of the 1930's.

At the end of the 18th century the death rate averaged 25–30 per mille, though this figure was greatly exceeded during famine, war, and epidemics. It has now fallen to 10 per mille.

During the 18th century, when the excess of births was about 5 per mille, the population grew slowly. In the 19th century the surplus of births increased, reaching 12 per mille in the seventies and eighties, and afterwards declining. During the Second World War it again increased to 10 per mille, but in 1966 the figure was about 6 per mille. In 1966 births exceeded deaths by 45 000, but this figure will decrease.

Emigration and immigration

The rapid increase of population between 1820 and 1860 caused great economic difficulties later in the 19th century. It resulted in frequent subdivision of farms, which was made easier by the widespread redistribution of land which resulted from the land reform of 1827. This created a large number of smallholdings, which were economically weak, and a considerable group of crofters and cottagers. The crofters held small rented holdings and did day work on larger farms. The cottagers were landless farm servants. Both groups grew considerably in the pre-industrial period and threatened the rural districts with overpopulation. Industrialism was still in its infancy and could not keep pace with the increase in population.

About 1840 the first small group of emigrants left Sweden for North America. After that the stream grew steadily, reaching its peak in the 1880's, when about 40 000 a year, or 8 per mille of the total population, emigrated. This emigration greatly slackened at the beginning of the 20th century, and, largely because of rapid industrialization, Sweden made a very small contribution to the large wave of emigration before 1914. Emigration practically ceased at the beginning of the 1930's. During the half century between 1865 and 1914 about 1.3 million Swedes emigrated, of whom 0.3 million returned. It was a considerable drain on the population, and emigration from Sweden was above the European average at that time.

Immigration into Sweden has largely consisted of returning emigrants. During and after the Second World War, there was a surplus of immigrants, mainly Finns, Estonians and Germans who were granted Swedish citizenship. The immigrants (47 000 in 1966) are now mostly Finns. In 1967 76 000 non-Norden aliens, many of them Germans and Yugoslavs, had residence and work permits.

Age-groups and distribution of sexes

Because of the sharp decline in the birthrate during the 20th century the age distribution of the Swedish population has greatly changed. Before 1910 every age-group was smaller in number than the one immediately preceding it. The population pyramid of 1965 shows, however, that the groups around 35–55 years of age are large, while the 25–35 group is under-represented. But the high birth-rate during and immediately after the Second World War produced a larger number in the 15–25 year age-group. The number of people in their twenties reached its peak in 1965. Since then these age groups have decreased. (Age pyramids for 1960, see Fig. 6.2, p. 73).

This means that for the next 10–15 years the age distribution of the population will be more and more unsatisfactory, as the over 65's will increase and form a larger part of the population than ever before, while the productive population will decline. The boys and girls who were born during the Second World War are still straining the educational resources or are in productive work, but they will be replaced by smaller groups of youngsters.

The age distribution differs between areas of dense urban population and rural districts. In the rural population the numbers in their thirties and forties have been greatly reduced through accelerated movement to the larger towns, where these age-groups have correspondingly increased.

The surplus of women is constantly diminishing, and now there are only 1 001 women to 1 000 men, because of the reduced infant mortality amongst males. Here also, however, migration to areas of dense population has given rise to a difference between town and country. Women move more than men from one area to another; they go particularly to the large towns. While in 1965 there were 1 041 women to 1 000 men in the towns (in Stockholm 1 141), the corresponding figure in rural districts was 930.

The rural communes

In 1951 Sweden had 2 365 rural and urban communes. They corresponded, allowing for the changes that have taken place during the centuries, to medieval parishes. Such units were very small in the plains, especially in the extreme south of Sweden and on the Västergötland plain in western Sweden. In the forest districts the units were much larger because in the later Middle Ages the common forests were divided up and added to them. In Norrland the units were very large (Sweden's largest parish, Jokkmokk, has an area of over 29 000 km^2). In 1952 a reorganization of communes was carried out, the small parishes being combined into units of from 2 000 to 4 000 inhabitants, thus reducing the number of communes to 995 *(storkommuner)*. In 1964/65 282 still stronger units were established *(kommunblock)*, each of them based on an administrative and economic centre.

Rural depopulation

Side by side with the great changes in age-groups in the 20th century there has been a revolution in the distribution of the urban and rural population, due to internal migration and a parallel change in occupational structure. In 1965 77 per cent of the population lived in densely populated areas.

Up to the 1880's the agricultural population was absolutely dominant. It then reached its apex and has since been continuously on the wane, while that in town industries and services has increased with the spread of industrialization. This very deep-reaching process in the whole body of society is proceeding at present at an accelerated rate.

The fall in the rural population has not been evenly distributed. It began about 1880 in South and Central Sweden, at a time when North

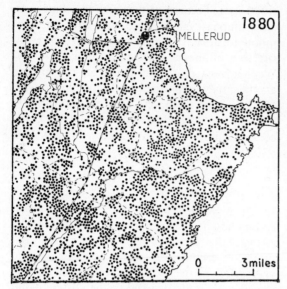

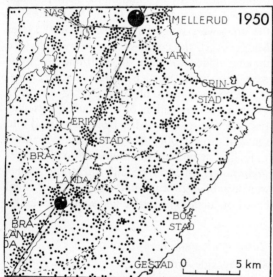

Fig. 12.3. *Depopulation of the countryside*. The Dalbo plain west of Lake Vänern in 1880 and 1950. Each dot represents 5 inhabitants. In 1950 Mellerud had 4 060 inhabitants. — After Anders Edestam: Dalslands folkmängd år 1880 och år 1950. Svensk Geografisk Årsbok 1955, plates between pp. 192–193.

Sweden could still be regarded as a pioneer area. Local migration caused urban centres to develop quickly, and good agricultural areas in South and Central Sweden lost population, while the forest districts in the extreme north showed an increase. In the 1920's the depopulation wave had reached Dalarna in Central Sweden and the boundary line of decreasing rural population moved northwards into Norrland. In 1940 the two northernmost districts still had an immigra-

tion surplus in rural districts because of the expanding mining in Lappland. Now the whole of rural Sweden has an immigration deficit. During 1960–65 the densely populated areas increased by 560 000 persons, i.e. by 10 per cent. Towns with more than 10 000 inhabitants have attracted a major part of the migrants.

Migration

The rural population is decreasing most sharply in the more densely populated rural areas around the larger towns. Internal migration is thus to a large extent over only short distances. About 70–80 per cent of the total migration is over distances of less than 50 km. Movement over 50 to 100 km accounts for about 10 per cent of migration.

In 1966 about 520 000 persons migrated to different communes, i.e. about 7 per cent of the Swedish population. Most rural districts show a loss by migration. Although migration movements over short distances between towns and surrounding rural districts are very important for the urbanization process, they have little effect on the population totals of the provinces. An important net migration between the provinces is only seen from rural regions with few towns to the great city regions of Stockholm, Göteborg and Malmö (West Skåne), and, to a smaller degree, to other cities in the Central Swedish Lowlands. Population changes between 1930 and 1963 can be closely related to urbanization (Fig. 12.4). Since 1963 the relationship has become more pronounced.

Between 1965 and 1966, when the total Swedish population increased by about 71 000, ten provinces showed population decrease; four were in Norrland and four in southeastern Sweden. The provinces of Jämtland and Västernorrland showed especially large losses.

In 1962 the net migration to the Stockholm region was 14 000, to Göteborg 2 800 and to Malmö 4 000 people. Stockholm was the great magnet for Norrland and southeastern Sweden, the flow from West Sweden was to Göteborg and Malmö. The boundary between the migration regions of Stockholm on one hand, and Göteborg and Malmö on the other, extend from southeastern Värmland in a southeasterly direction towards Blekinge. The province and city of Stockholm and the eight provinces of Uppsala, Västmanland, Södermanland, Östergötland, Jönköping, Älvsborg, Göteborg and Bohuslän (all in Central Sweden), together with the province of Malmöhus, in the south, have 17 per cent of the Swedish land area. In 1930 they had 45 per cent and in 1963 56 per cent of the Swedish population.

Intensity of migration

Regional differences in the intensity of migration can be observed. Previously two areas stood out in the demographic pattern: in the Mälaren region the number of births per rural family was low, whereas it was high in southwest Sweden, Southwest Skåne excluded. This difference, which was at first observed by Flodström during the first decades of the 20th century, comes out

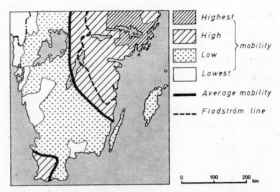

Fig. 12.5. Mobility of population in Southern Sweden. Size-groups (by area) have been used to calculate the average percentage of native-born in parishes of different size at the 1930 census. The map shows the difference between the actual percentage of native-born in the parishes and the average for parishes of the same size. — After K. E. Bergsten: Sydsvenska födelseortsfält. Lund 1951.

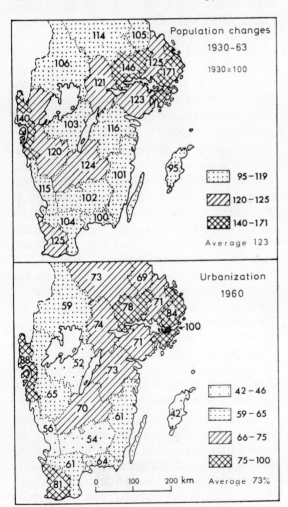

Fig. 12.4. Population changes 1930–63 and urbanization 1960 in South and Central Sweden. Urbanization is here defined as population living in agglomerations with more than 200 inhabitants.

more strongly the further back we go. Now it is being increasingly levelled out. This irregularity varied with the tendency to migrate: the population of the Mälaren region was considerably more mobile than the population of southwest Sweden except Southwest Skåne (Fig. 12.5). The difference can still be clearly observed. Variations in density of population have no influence on this demographic trend. The boundary zone between these two regions can be drawn more or less from Lake Vänern to the north end of Kalmar Sound ('Flodström's Line'). Thus in 1930 in the rural communes in the Mälaren districts 42 per cent were native born, while in southwest Sweden the corresponding figure was 60 per cent. In their towns the figures averaged 36 and 44 per cent respectively. These towns seem to show the same migration trends as their surrounding rural districts. The largest towns in the two regions, Stockholm and Göteborg, which are not included in the figures above, had percentages of 42 and 55 native-born respectively.

URBAN SETTLEMENTS

The most northerly Swedish town which dates from medieval times is Gävle. All the other medieval foundations are in South and Central Sweden. The town-building impetus came in several stages from more southerly lands. Medieval Sweden was orientated towards the Baltic.

Its present southern and western coastal districts belonged to Denmark and Norway. In the west there was only one port, Lödöse, situated as far up the Göta älv as the waterfalls would allow and with road connections inland to Västergötland. A number of market towns grew up on the better settled plains, and in certain cases

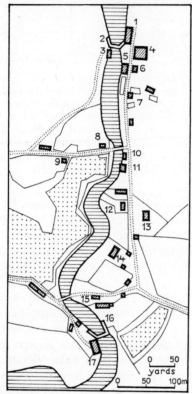

Fig. 12.6. The layout of a foundry. Grytgöl, Hällestads Bergslag, northern Östergötland (1775). 1. Toolshed. 2. Upper dam. 3. Sawmill. 4. Charcoal shed. 5. Bar-iron forge. 6. Bar-iron shed. 7. Dwelling-houses of smiths. 8. Miller's house. 9. Crofter's cottage. 10. Flour mill. 11. Foundry. 12. Inspector's house. 13. Man-servants' house. 14. Proprietor's house. 15. Cattle-sheds. 16. Lower dam. 17. Nail smithy. Arable land stippled; open rectangles indicate gardens. Today the sawmill (3) and nail smithy (17) have extended at the expense of the other works. — After K. E. Bergsten: Östergötlands bergslag. Lund 1946.

bishops' sees were afterwards located there. Such were Uppsala, Skara, Västerås and Linköping (Fig. 12.18).

Along the coast a line of seaports grew up, e.g. Stockholm, Visby, Norrköping, Söderköping (15 km south of Norrköping), and Kalmar. Of these Stockholm and Visby were organized as Hanseatic towns, and this influenced their architecture.

All Swedish medieval town centres have an irregular plan, in so far as they are known or have been preserved. The church and town hall are usually situated in the market-place. They were built of wood, except in Stockholm and Visby, and the burghers had large shares of the communally cultivated land. A similar organization is common throughout the lowlands of Western Europe.

In the southern districts, which belonged to Denmark, several medieval towns arose, but some have not been able to survive economic fluctuations. Such were Skanör–Falsterbo in Southwest Skåne with their famous 12th-century Hanseatic fishmarket. Others now form the hub of an important network of towns in western Skåne (Hälsingborg, Malmö, Landskrona and Lund). Buildings of brick and stone survive from the medieval centres of some of these towns. The old Swedish–Danish frontier is a zone between old towns north of it whose wood core was burnt, and those in the south whose old stone houses survive. On former Norwegian territory, Kungahälla (Kungälv), built to protect the estuary of Göta älv, should be noted.

The impetus for the next phase in the foundation of towns came in the 17th century and reached Sweden from continental Europe. Sweden was a century behind Central Europe in urban development and the regular, chessboard pattern of the Renaissance city began in Sweden only in 1623 with the foundation of Göteborg with the assistance of Dutchmen. A number of market fortress towns were founded along the coast or inland. Most of these 17th-century towns are in the Central Lowlands and on the Bothnian coast (Fig. 6.4, p. 79).

When the wooden buildings of medieval towns burnt down, they were replaced by Renaissance and Baroque buildings in a more regular lay-out. Between 1700 and 1900 very few new towns were founded.

The chessboard plan was well preserved until about 1900. Industrialism increasingly influenced the towns, but Sweden never had the densely populated industrial centres that were characteristic of Britain and Continental Europe. Much of the heavy industry was traditionally located in country districts, especially in the Bergslagen. The concept of the garden city won through in the 20th century, and from about 1920 the chessboard pattern has been abandoned. Newly laid-out areas have a street system more nearly following the lie of the land.

Owing to recent urbanization, the last few decades can be regarded as a third important period in the foundation of towns. The towns belonging to this group (e.g. Karlskoga, Kramfors) have usually only a very small civic and business centre, or none at all, while villas occupy very large areas. The location of these 20th-century towns has clearly been influenced by the railways, and they lie mostly in the interior of Central Sweden. In addition, the suburbs and 'new towns' of Stockholm form an important group and have many well-known innovations in town planning.

A special type of built-up area (Fig. 12.6) was that which grew up around old industrial sites, the so-called *bruk*. Near the forges and foundries there were lines of houses built by the owner of the works. These formed the *bruksgata* (foundry street) where the smiths and clerks lived, while other workers lived as crofters scattered over a wider area. Such settlements were characteristic of the Bergslagen and its neighbourhood, but may also be found spread over the whole country.

During the building of the railways, stations and houses for railway workers were placed at suitable points along the railway lines. These were often isolated originally, but they have been important in the formation of small and medium-sized centres of population. Around them have grown communities of a special type, the 'station town', which form a big group of Sweden's smaller built-up areas. Many of them have lost their main function because of railway closures.

The occupational structure and localization of the built-up areas is shown on Colour Map 10, and their number and types in Table 6.1, p. 80.

Three larger urban areas stand out, namely Greater Stockholm, Greater Göteborg and West Skåne (Malmö–Hälsingborg region). They are the nuclei of the most densely populated and most industrialized areas, and lie at the corners of a triangle in which the road and rail network is densest.

Greater Stockholm with about 1.4 million inhabitants is a developing metropolitan area. Within a circle with a radius of 150 km are several of the largest industrial and most rapid-

ly growing cities. From the north they are Gävle, Uppsala, Västerås, Eskilstuna, Örebro, Norrköping and Linköping, and with their rural areas they have (1966), together with the Stockholm area, about 36 per cent of the total population of the country.

Greater Göteborg has about 660 000 inhabitants. For topographical reasons population and industrial densities are greater than around Stockholm. The outer suburban zone spreads inland along relatively narrow valleys.

The third centre, highly industrialized West Skåne, with Malmö and Hälsingborg as the largest towns, lacks true suburban development. But the density of agrarian population in the adjacent rural districts is the highest in the country. The population of the urban area is estimated at about 620 000, with 280 000 in Malmö, and both in Denmark and in Sweden the opposing shores of Öresund are being transformed and may well become an 'Öresund city'.

Other developing urban areas include the Borås area with its textile industry in the Viskan valley, and the Sundsvall area with lumber and pulp industries on the Bothnian coast.

RURAL SETTLEMENTS

Swedish agriculture has undergone a radical modernization which has produced not only uniformity in farming methods, but also in farm types. But, in spite of extensive replacement of farmsteads and farm buildings, the regional differentiation of older farm types is still clear.

In Skåne, the coastal plain of Halland, in Öland, Gotland and on the inland plains west and east of Lake Vättern, the farms were usually grouped in villages. In the large northern area of dispersed farms, nucleated villages were also common round Lake Siljan in Dalarna and on the sediments of the lower parts of the Norrland valleys, i.e. the Lule älv valley. Most of these villages were split up during the 19th century redistributions. Fig. 12.9 shows the development of such a village.

Both distribution and types of rural settlement have thus completely changed, but remnants of the former pattern remain throughout Sweden. Fig. 12.7, a–c, shows the distribution of the main old types of farmstead with drawings of two of them.

The completely enclosed South Swedish

farmyard (1), associated with the former Danish region, is thought to be based on the cattle-yard of the castle which dates back to the feudal period. The North Swedish farmyard (2), again completely enclosed, is probably of similar derivation, but here there may also be farmbuildings outside the group which line the courtyard. Between regions 1 and 2 are areas where dwel- linghouses and farmbuildings are separated. The Central Swedish farmyard (3) has an enclosed, rectangular yard, but this is divided by a transverse shed with a central gateway. In the East Swedish farm (4) the buildings are more loosely grouped and the farmhouse is separated from the yard by a fence. Regions 5 and 6 have transitional or hybrid types of farms.

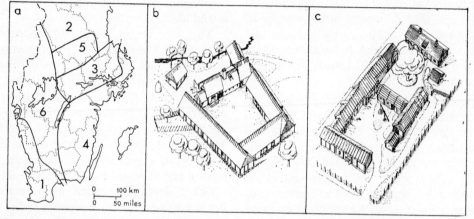

Fig. 12.7. a. *Distribution of farmstead types.* 1. South Swedish type. 2. North Swedish type. 3. Central Swedish type. 4. East Swedish type. 5. Mixed forms of 2–4 (Bergslagen). 6. Irregularly spaced farm buildings. —After Sigurd Erixon: Svenska kulturgränser och kulturprovinser. K. Gustav Adolfs Akademiens Småskrifter. 1. Stockholm 1945. — b. *South Swedish farmstead* from a village in Halland with dwelling-house (upper centre) and farm buildings on the three other sides of the enclosed farmyard. Similar farmsteads are found throughout Denmark. Cf. Pl. 8.5. — c. *Central Swedish farmstead,* a farm in Uppland with dwelling-house, servants' quarters and store-houses around the upper yard, separated by the stable from the lower yard, which is surrounded by the farm buildings proper. The position of the stable reflects the old peasant concept of the horse as a creature between man and beast.

AGRICULTURE

Reorganization of fields and farms

Large-scale maps of the arable land began to be made in the 1630's in Central and South Sweden. At first only holdings owned by the state or peasants were mapped (Fig. 12.8), but from the 1690's to the 1720's, a new series of maps were made. These were more accurate and also showed the large areas of land owned by noblemen. From these series of maps it is possible to study the open fields with their strips. It also seems possible to analyse these 17th century open fields and find traces of an older system, dating, according to Hannerberg, probably from Viking times. This earlier system was reorganized during the early medieval period. The first reorganization of the medieval open field system was made under the laws of 1749,

1757 and later *(storskifte),* in which the number of strips was reduced, but the village organization was left undisturbed.

The 17th and 18th century maps show that the arable land of the villages was laid out in one, two or three fields. They were sown with grain (rye, barley, oats). In the two- and three-field systems of the plains a half or a third, respectively, of the arable land was fallow each year and was used for grazing.

For the cattle the unenclosed forest and fallow were pasture areas in summer. The winter fodder was hay from meadows, partly from unenclosed boggy areas and partly from enclosed meadows. The leaves of trees such as oak, ash, and linden, and shrubs such as hazel were also used for fodder. These trees grew on a type of natural leafy meadow *(löväng)* which was an important element of the landscape, but during the late 19th century, with the modernization of agriculture, these natural meadows were transformed into high-yielding grasslands.

In 1803 the second redistribution of land began; it was based largely on the British model and was initiated by big landowners. The idea was that the farmsteads, then grouped together in the villages, should have their land in one piece *(enskifte)*. The old villages with their clusters of farmsteads were split up and the farms were dispersed. This redistribution of land was carried out only in Skåne and on parts of the plain south of Lake Vänern (Fig. 12.9), and was replaced in 1827 by a less rigorous law of redistribution *(laga skifte)*. This third redistribution of land has now been carried out over practically the whole country, and it hit especially the nucleated villages in the plains. In the woodland regions, with their dispersed settlement, its effect of course was less drastic. The last areas to adopt the third redistribution were Öland and the district round Lake Siljan.

The individual farmer now had better oppor-

tunities for using his own initiative than in the old village organization. In order to have their fields around their new farmsteads many farmers had to take land that had been cultivated very little or not at all. The first land to be brought under tillage was the old meadowland. This was made possible, *inter alia,* by improved drainage. The amount of new tillage that was achieved is not certainly known, but it would appear that the area of arable land increased in this way about 200 to 300 per cent during the 19th century. Actually the cropped area increased even more, because under the old system one third to one half of the fields lay fallow, and now the practice of fallowing declined sharply. Today fallowing is important only in and around the Mälaren district where it covers 8 per cent of the arable land.

Both on the arable land that had previously been in open fields and on the new arable areas an effective rotation of crops was slowly introduced. Rotation grasses and root-crops took their place beside cereals. These methods had been widely introduced by the end of the 19th century. The increase in the number and size of

Fig. 12.8. One of the oldest Swedish cadastral maps (1638). Original map left (scale 1 : 5 000), map redrawn by the author right. A single farm, Nygård, situated between two rivulets in the parish of Hällestad in the northern wooded region of Östergötland. On both maps: The farmyard (1), the arable land lying in two open fields (2, 3), meadows (4–7), woodland in the centre of the map with hillocks greatly exaggerated, (A) an iron furnace managed by a group of farmers. — Map by Johan De Rogier, Lantmäteristyrelsens Arkiv D 3:62.

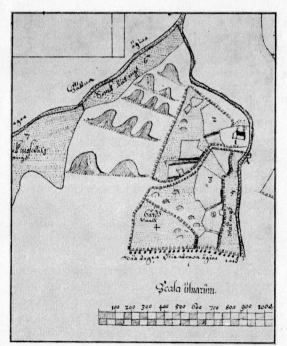

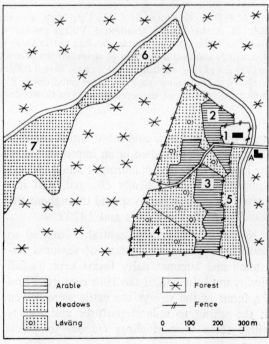

20

Fig. 12.9. Development of Lilla Uppåkra, a village south of Lund on the clayey moraine plain of western Skåne. 1. Arable land. 2. Meadow. 3. Village ground. 4. Road. 5. Open field boundary, shown only on the 1703 map. Until that date the arable was laid out in three open fields. In the 1703 map it has not been possible to give figures showing ownership of strips. At the *storskifte* in 1805–06 the number of strips was reduced, and in 1813 *(enskifte)* each farm got a consolidated holding. The former common village ground has become separately owned vegetable gardens. Later subdivision is shown on the 1912 map. This has been added by the author, the other three are reproduced from G. Nordholm: Studier i Skånes äldre ekonomiska geografi. Lund 1967.

cattle owing to larger and more varied supplies of winter fodder resulted in an improvement of the land by increased manuring. Farm tools and equipment were drastically changed, and improved ploughs began to spread throughout the country during the 1860's and 1870's.

North of a line from central Värmland to northern Uppland the system of seasonal migration and summer dairy farms kept its full vitality until the end of the 19th century. From the farms in the valleys the cattle were driven in the spring to upland pastures and forests where there were shielings *(fäbod)* in which

some members of the peasant family lived and guarded the cattle during the summer and made butter and cheese. This type of transhumance has disappeared because of new methods of modern dairying.

Size of farms

Table 12.1 shows recent changes in farm size, Colour Map 9 the distribution of small, medium-sized and large farms. Large farms (20–50 ha.) are found on the plains of the Central Lowlands, in Halland and in Skåne. In forest districts and in southwestern Småland farms are usually small, 15 ha. of arable is considered to be an average farm here.

The small farms in forest areas in southern and central Sweden are partly the result of an original settlement and cultivation by peasants, which can be widely traced from about the end of the Middle Ages to the beginning of the modern age. In Norrland it can be followed right down to the 20th century. Another reason for the occurrence of these small farms all over the country was that in former times the large farms obtained their labour from crofters, who received a small piece of land *(torp)* for cultivation and paid for it by day-work on the farm. During the first decades of the 20th century this social class disappeared and has been replaced by wage-earning agricultural workers. The croft has either been bought by the former crofter, encouraged by the agricultural policy, and has become one of the numerous smallholdings, or, on account of its having an unfavourable situation, it has ceased to function as a farm and its fields are now covered with woodland. The disappearance of so many crofts, which sharply changed the distribution of population in the countryside, took place particularly between 1890 and 1930.

This picture of the size of the farms is, however, misleading without consideration of the forest land that belongs to the farms. On a lowland farm in South Sweden there is a very small area of forest land, and the economy of the farm is almost entirely dependent on the yield of the arable land. In the forest regions a farm with a comparable acreage of arable land has a large area of forest, and its economy is to a large extent dependent on the production of timber and pulp-wood. Much of the work of the farm is devoted to the woodland.

The majority of Swedish farms are cultivated by the owners themselves. About 27 per cent of the arable land is cultivated by tenants. The largest percentage is to be found in the eastern parts of the Central Lowlands (Sörmland and Östergötland) and in Southwest Skåne where farms are large.

To prevent industrial capital competing for farmland, with consequent increases in land values and number of tenants, it was forbidden in 1947 for non-farmers to buy farms. Recently this law has been modified.

Changing trends

Swedish agricultural production has been largely directed towards supplying the needs of the country itself. During the 70's and 80's of last century, Russian and American competition in the domestic grain market dealt an extremely hard blow to agriculture, and the resulting depression suffered by the agricultural population is considered to have contributed to the sharp increase in emigration to North America. Industrialization had also begun in Sweden, accompanied by urban growth.

Import duties on grain were introduced in Sweden in 1888. But foreign competition could still be felt and helped to foster amongst farmers an interest in animal products. The worldwide economic depression at the beginning of the 1930's led to an increase in protection for Swedish agriculture. Amongst other regulations may be mentioned that of 1930, according to which a certain amount of Swedish grain had always to be used at the corn-mills. Minimum prices guaranteed by the state and import restrictions were introduced for grain, sugar beet and animal products such as butter, meat and bacon.

Development after the Second World War has been in sharp contrast to that of the first decades of the 20th century. In order to encourage mechanization and to create farms of an economic size, there has been a policy since 1947 whereby the smaller farms of less than 10 hectares (part-time farming) shall be reduced in number by being put together to make larger farms of 10 to 20 ha. or more (basic or family farms). These farms can be economically cultivated without paid help and they are large enough to give a family its livelihood.

This change of structure, which had already begun owing to the continued depopulation of the countryside, is to be actively hastened, but, nevertheless, it is a slow process. There is no constraint on the owners, but as soon as a small farm is put up for sale, it is decided whether it may continue as a self-sufficient unit or not. In 1965 204 000 Swedish farms were larger than 2 ha., that is 92 000 or 31 per cent fewer than in 1944. In the forties only crofts were abandoned, since then many small farms of about 5–10 ha. have been absorbed. Their share of the arable land has diminished; the larger farms (above 20 ha.) have increased their share from 45 to 57 per cent (Table 12.1).

Table 12.1. *Number and size of farms*

Size group		1944		1965	
		Number	Arable land	Number	Arable land
		%	%	%	%
2– 5 hectares		37	11.1	27	6.6
5–10	»	32	20.2	30	15
10–20	»	20	23.9	23	22
20–50	»	9.5	23.8	16	31
> 50	»	2.5	21	4.1	26
Total in 1 000		296	3567 ha.	204	3184 ha.

Labour and mechanization

The number of persons engaged in agriculture has decreased very rapidly during the last few decades, from 1950 to 1960 alone by 34 per cent. In 1960 only 11 per cent of the active population was engaged in agriculture. The number of salaried workers is particularly low and there is a severe shortage of female labour. Thus, for example, the number of unmarried women employed in agriculture between the ages of 15 and 45 is half the number of unmarried men between 20 and and 50.

This rapid fall in the agricultural labour force has not meant any reduction in agricultural production. On the contrary, this has increased somewhat. A normal harvest is in the 1960's calculated to provide about 112 per cent of the calorie requirements of the population; in the 1930's this figure was 90 per cent for a smaller population. The output per working hour has increased by 60 per cent since 1938/39.

This considerable increase in production is mainly due to mechanization. While in 1938 the number of tractors was still only 18 000 and the number of horses in agriculture 617 000, the corresponding numbers in 1966 were 163 000 and 92 000 respectively. The medium-sized farms have the largest number of tractors per km² of arable land. The greatest density of tractors was in the Mälaren district and in Skåne. Combine-harvesters are also widely distributed.

Plant breeding and co-operation

During the last decade of the 19th century scientific plant breeding began, and this has continued uninterruptedly. The pioneer centres of plant breeding have been Svalöv and Weibullsholm in Landskrona, both in West Skåne. Plant breeding and fertilizers have played as important a part in increasing the yield as all the other factors put together.

Side by side with these technical developments went a reorganization in the marketing of agricultural produce. When the peasants were self-sufficient they could to a large extent work up their products themselves and take the surplus to the market. Through improved communications and technical improvements in, amongst other things, dairying and slaughtering, this was replaced by trading by private businessmen, and later by the farmers' own co-operative buying and processing associations. The idea of co-operation originated largely in Germany and England. From these countries the idea spread, especially to Denmark, where it took a practical form and had the support of a large number of the farmers. From Denmark co-operation spread to Sweden.

Nearly all the co-operative undertakings developed first in Southwest Skåne and thence spread by way of the plains of Halland to Västergötland. Co-operative schemes also spread at an early stage to the Mälaren district and to Östergötland, and Southwest Skåne and the Mälaren region thus formed the most important innovation areas. Småland and Norrland, however, lagged behind.

The arable acreage

Sweden's agricultural population reached its highest figure in 1880; the acreage of arable land in 1920; and the number of holdings in 1932. The acreage of arable land has changed very little since the 1920's, though in the 1960's it has decreased by 2 per cent annually. Holdings which are small and remote from transport systems are being abandoned and their arable land becomes woodland or pastures.

In 1965 the arable acreage was 31 800 km² or 7.7 per cent of the land area. This means that, over the greater part of the country, forests form a nearly continuous cover broken by patches of arable land. Exceptional areas where the arable land is continuous include Southwest Skåne where two thirds of the land is arable (Colour Map 8). The plains of Central Sweden have 30–40 per cent in arable. The lower parts of the Norrland river valleys also have a similar percentage in arable. The South Swedish Highlands form an area with, on an average, 15 per cent arable land, and the interior of Norrland has less than 5 per cent.

Soils and climate

Archaean granites and gneisses with a large content of basic minerals give relatively good agricultural soils. The gneisses in the extreme north and in southwest Sweden are, however, poor, and certain southeast Swedish porphyries form extremely poor soils.

Except for the Jotnian and Cambrian sandstones, post-Archaean sedimentary rocks weather into good agricultural soils. When such rocks, rich in lime, occur, there are fertile moraine clays, e.g. in the Jämtland plain, in the Falbygden district in Västergötland, and, especially, in Southwest Skåne. All these areas lie above the upper marine limit.

The preponderant soil above the upper marine limit is, however, on moraine derived largely from Archaean rocks. On the South Swedish Highlands and in inner Norrland it is to some extent used for agriculture. In the Bergslagen area it has been shown that fine-grained sandy moraine occurs on the heights, while on the slopes and in the valleys there are coarser moraine types containing more boulders. It appears that this is usual and has favoured the cultivation of the uplands.

Moraine clays above the upper marine limit and marine clays below it are the most important superficial deposits for agriculture. The stiffer marine clays are most widely spread in the eastern part of the Central Lowlands, i.e. the Mälaren district and parts of Östergötland, and also on the plain around Lake Vänern. These clays also extend to the west coast, but here they become lighter and are often mixed with coarser elements. Below the upper marine limit on the coast of the Gulf of Bothnia and in the lower stretches of the North Swedish river valleys lie more sandy and silty sediments which here are the most important soils.

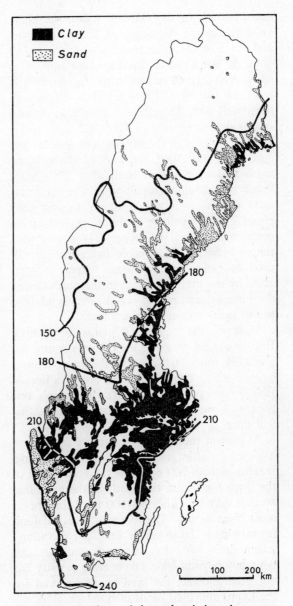

Fig. 12.10. Soils and length of farming year (number of days from the beginning of tillage in spring to the end of the autumn ploughing). — After Sveriges geologi 1963 and Atlas of Sweden 27–28.

Sweden extends for more than 1 500 km from south to north. The climatic conditions for agriculture vary greatly, offering possibilities for a Central European type of agriculture in the far south, while towards the limit of settlement along the whole mountain chain in the north, beyond the limit of the coniferous forests, agriculture is quite impossible. The long and severe winter in the extreme north means that the farther north one goes, the shorter the vege-

309

tative period. In the extreme south, the interval between the beginning of tillage in spring and the end of the autumn ploughing is 240 days, in the Central Swedish Lowlands it is about 190–210 days and in the far north it is less than 140 days. These intervals correspond fairly well with the period of growth as defined in Chapter 4 and used in Table 4.2, pp. 56–57. Thus cultivation in the far south of Sweden begins about 1st April, whereas in the extreme north it does not start until after 20th May. While the autumn ploughing in the southernmost regions does not come to an end until about 20th December, in the north it must be completed before 1st October. These very wide ranges between the possible dates for agricultural operations are to some extent counteracted by the longer daylight in the north during the summer season, and certain strains adapted to this light rhythm can ripen there.

Most of the cultivated plants of Central Europe can be grown in the extreme south, but gradually towards the north they reach limits beyond which their cultivation becomes impossible or uneconomic. The further north one goes, the smaller is the number of crops that will ripen.

At present the uppermost zone of settlement, a zone of cattle grazing and potato growing, reaches to 150–200 m below the upper limit of the birch forests; in the south of the mountain areas it may be within 50–100 m of the uppermost birch woods. The extreme practical limit for farming is the so-called 'limit of cultivation', which since 1867 has been an administrative boundary beyond which pioneering activity has not been allowed, the land being reserved for the Lapps and their herds of reindeer.

AGRICULTURAL REGIONS

On the basis of differences of climate and soil the country is divided in Swedish official statistics into 18 agricultural regions. They are here combined in three large groups:

A. Plains in South and Central Sweden,
B. Forest and valley districts in South and Central Sweden and
C. North Sweden.

The three southernmost plain districts are all near the coast, where the soil is marine clays below and moraine clays above the upper marine limit. The bedrock is mainly sedimentary.

Southwest Skåne consists of two fertile plains: one in the southwest, where Baltic moraine clay is deposited on Cretaceous limestone, and one in Central Skåne, where a more silty moraine, partly composed of Archaean material, is deposited on Ordovician clay schists. The Baltic moraine plain is more intensively used than any other region with 80 per cent of its land surface in arable land and gardens. It has, too, the highest yields in the country for most crops.

In the plains of the Central Swedish Lowlands the soil is mostly marine clays; but in large areas of the western parts of the Vänern district, in the northern part of the Mälaren and the northern Vättern districts are more silty marine sediments too. The bedrock is Archaean, except in some scattered areas with Cambro-Silurian rocks (cf. Colour Map 2). The Cambro-Silurian sediments on the bottom of the Gulf of Bothnia have given the morainic soils on the northern part of Uppland a high lime content.

The South Swedish Highlands region lies above the upper marine limit. It has cultivated areas on peatland, higher lying moraines, drumlins, and on glacial lake beds. The bedrock is Archaean, partly very infertile porphyries. The rainfall varies considerably between the west and east sides.

The forest districts surrounding the Central Swedish Lowlands are shown as two regions on Colour Map 8 (inset upper left). The northern limit is vague, but coincides approximately with the Norrland Terrain boundary. The clays are increasingly sandy. A large part of the area lies above the upper marine limit.

The river valleys below the upper marine limit along the coast of the Gulf of Bothnia have silty and sandy soils. The period of growth diminishes considerably in the north.

In the inland area of Norrland up to the limit of cultivation there are mostly silty and sandy soils in the river valleys, and these are cultivated, together with the moraine soils on hillsides with a southern aspect where there is less risk of frost by radiation in cold, clear nights. The Jämtland plain and the area around Lake Siljan have limestone bedrock.

AGRICULTURAL PRODUCTION

The important changes in the use of the arable land during the 20th century are apparent from Table 12.2. About three quarters of the arable acreage is now used for fodder crops. In the last few decades the tendency has been for vegetable and food crops to increase slightly in area at the expense of fodder crops. This is especially the case on the large farms.

As is also seen in Table 12.4, livestock play a dominating role in Swedish agriculture. Three quarters of the total agricultural income derives from livestock production. Most of this is from milk and dairying, which also needs most labour and gives most income on small farms, except those which specialize in vegetables and fruit. The total income from vegetable production is less than that from fat stock.

Cereal crops

The northern limit of widespread wheat cultivation is in the southernmost part of Norrland (about 61°N). Further north there are only scattered wheat fields. The areas where winter wheat is cultivated most intensively are the plains of Southwest Skåne, Östergötland, the Västergötland plain and the Mälaren area. The relative importance of winter wheat in the rotation is greatest on the plains of the Central Lowlands, especially Östergötland, because in Skåne competition with other crops is very intense. The yield per hectare is, however, largest in the extreme south of Sweden.

The most important area for the cultivation of spring wheat is the plains of Skåne and those

Table 12.3. *Value of agricultural production*[1]

	1950/51	1964/65
	%	%
Total vegetable production	20.6	23.5
Cereals	7.3	11.5
Potatoes, sugar beets	8.1	7.2
Other vegetables	5.2	4.8
Total animal production	79.4	76.5
Milk and dairying	43.7	34.1
Meat and pork	29.2	35.5
Other animal products	6.5	6.9
Total, million Sw. kr.	5051	5057

[1] At constant prices (averages 1960/61 — 1964/65).

of the Central Lowlands. Winter wheat formed about four fifths of the total Swedish harvest in 1965. The yield per ha. 1963–65 was 3 500 kg.

Rye is fast declining. Its northern limit is the same as that of wheat, and it is grown mostly in the drier areas in Southeast Sweden and in the Central Lowlands, where on more sandy soils it can replace wheat to a certain extent. Its yield per hectare is about 2 800 kg.

As a result of the increase in the acreage of wheat and the falling-off of rye, the total area in wheat and rye has remained more or less constant during the 20th century. About 1910 the per capita consumption of rye was three times as great as in 1950 (Fig. 12.11). Wheat consumption has steadily grown and has quintupled since the 1870's. From the 1920's onwards the consumption and production of wheat has exceeded that of rye.

The Central Lowlands and Southwest Skåne now have a wheat surplus, while the South Swedish Highlands and Norrland have a shortage. With regard to rye, practically the whole of South and Central Sweden up to the Norrland border is an area of surplus production.

Two-rowed barley, which demands good climatic and soil conditions, is intensively cultivated for cattle food especially in Skåne, on the calcareous soils of Öland–Gotland, in Östergötland and in the Mälaren region. Its area of cultivation has increased throughout southern Sweden.

Six-rowed barley, hardened to the climate, extends, as do potatoes, far up towards the limit of cultivation. It is most widely grown along the coastlands of the Gulf of Bothnia and on the Silurian plain of Jämtland. In North Sweden its

Table 12.2. *Use of arable land*

	1911–15	1941–45	1965
	%	%	%
Mainly for human consumption	21	21	18
Wheat and rye	14	13	11
Potatoes, sugar beet..	7	7	4
Oil-yielding plants ..	0	1	3
Mainly for fodder......	70	74	77
Cereals (oats, barley)	32	27	36
Grassland	38	47	41
Fallow	9	5	5
Total, per cent	100	100	100
» 1 000 hectares ..	3 692	3 738	3 211

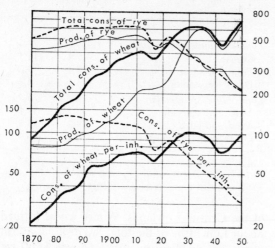

Fig. 12.11. Production and consumption of wheat and rye total and per capita, 1870–1950. Wheat consumption equals that of rye about 1924. Semi-logarithmic scale. — After Atlas of Sweden 73–74:4.

area exceeds that of all the other cereals put together.

During the latter part of the 19th century oats became very important especially in West Sweden, both on the plain of Västergötland and on the plain west of Lake Vänern. Oats are still very important throughout southern and central Sweden, being grown on more than 15 per cent of the arable land over large areas, but on the richest land unmixed oats have often been replaced by oats grown with barley or leguminous plants (mixed grain).

The total area under cereals is more than 45 per cent of the country's arable land. Cereal growing is particularly intensive in the Mälaren region, where it comprises more than half the farmed land. On the rich soils of Southwest Skåne sugar beet and oil-yielding plants appear as competitors; in the north grassland occupies larger areas, and in the farthest north, in the county of Norrbotten, about 12 per cent of the arable fields are occupied by grain which is cut green.

Rotation grass and pastures

In former times the arable fields were almost exclusively occupied by cereals. The winter hay was harvested on natural meadows. Livestock grazed the forests, scrubland and fallow land. The increase in livestock, which dates from the latter half of the 19th century, made it necessary to grow fodder on the arable land. The ploughing up of the meadows accentuated this need. As the open-field system gradually disappeared, rotation grass increased until it came to cover more arable land than any other crop. It now occupies about 40 per cent of Sweden's arable acreage. In the extreme south of Sweden, where agriculture is highly specialized and green fodder, e.g. grain cut green, vetches and lucerne, is available, rotation grass forms only 20 per cent of the arable area. In the extreme north it covers 80 to 90 per cent.

At the agricultural census of 1961 rotation grass covered an area of about 1.3 million hectares and was mainly used for hay. Natural meadows covered about 0.5 million ha. and had decreased during the previous 40 years by 60 per cent. These meadows are mainly grazed and are seldom cut for hay.

To these rather low-yielding pastures has recently been added about 0.2 million ha. of high-yielding permanent grasslands, mostly on land which has not previously been ploughed. Among the farmers in the forest regions it was always customary to let the cattle graze in the forest with its usual poor pasture. During the first decade of the 1900's enclosure and cultivation of natural pastures came in as an innovation from the Continent and Britain. They were subsidized by the state as a means of increasing fodder supplies and for protecting the young trees in the forests from grazing animals. Such high-yielding pastures are found on forest land that is cleared of trees, limed, manured and sown with grass. Arable fields, especially on bogland, may also be laid down as permanent grassland.

Other crops

Potatoes are grown mainly for the household needs for the Swedish population. The varieties that can be grown in the far north give high yields (more than 20 000 kg per hectare), mainly owing to the absence of diseases. Cultivation on a large scale for industrial purposes occurs on sandy soils on the plains in the extreme southeast and on the plain of Halland, with yields of 25–30 000 kg per hectare. Here is the greatest concentration of starch factories.

Sugar beet cultivation, which is state-subsidized, requires special soils and a favourable climate. From its Central European centre of cultivation it has spread to Skåne, Öland and Gotland, as well as to the plains of Östergötland and Västergötland. Profitable cultivation is possible only where the distance to the sugar refinery it not too great. Since the sugar industry was rationalized some years ago and limited to a few large refineries in Southwest Skåne and on Öland and Gotland, cultivation has been concentrated on these areas.

Oil-yielding crops were increasingly cultivated during the Second World War in order to ensure the country's oil requirements. As in the case of the sugar beet, these crops are subsidized by the state. Cultivation is concentrated on the better soils of the plains in southern Sweden. Rape is the most common crop, while linseed has diminished greatly. The latter crop is readily attacked by insects. Sweden is self-supporting as regards vegetable oils.

Fruit and vegetables

In certain well defined regions a considerable part of the available area is used for special types of cultivation. These mostly started many years ago on the initiative of private individuals and maintain their high standard of cultivation. The following may be mentioned:

Large firms in West Skåne have contracted with as many local growers as possible to ensure a local supply of vegetables, fruits, and berries for their freezing or canning plants. Skåne has about 12 000 hectares of such contract growing.

Fruit for domestic use is very evenly distributed throughout the country, but commercial fruit growing started on a large scale in northwest Skåne (Båstad), in the east coast districts of Skåne (Kivik), and in the extreme south of Småland, and is still largely concentrated there. Oddly enough, strawberries are grown *inter alia* in forest regions northwest of Lake Vättern (Finnerödja), in the skärgård of Stockholm and in Hälsingland.

The cultivation of such a small crop as horseradish began by chance on a small scale south of Göteborg in 1912. Onions are grown on the coastal plain of western Öland.

Glasshouse cultivation covered c. 400 hectares in 1965. It is concentrated on West Skåne and around Stockholm and Göteborg, but is also found as far north as the Torne älv valley. The main crops are tomatoes, cucumbers and cut flowers.

LIVESTOCK

Since the early 1930's there has been a general decline in the numbers of most livestock types, with the exception of pigs, as is seen in Table 12.4.

Table 12.4. *Livestock in thousands*

	1932	1958	1965
Cattle	2 920	2 542	2 250
Horses	612	244	109
Sheep	468	139	220
Goats	50	8	—
Pigs	1 495	2 031	1 884
Poultry	11 504	7 503	8 048

The decrease in numbers of cattle is connected with the change-over to farming without livestock on one fifth of the farms, and is also the result of rationalization. Even in the remaining herds the number of milch cows is often reduced, with a slight decrease in milk production.

The number of cattle is also closely bound up with the size of the farm. Small farms have, in proportion to their acreages, considerably more livestock than large ones. This is especially the case in the north of Sweden and in forest areas. The small farms concentrate more on milk production, while the larger farms have relatively more fat stock, and a higher percentage of young animals.

Milk production decreased in 1953–65 by 16 per cent. Of a total milk production of 3.7 mill. tons (1965) a third was consumed fresh, the rest was processed or made into butter and cheese. Milk still provides 38 per cent of the farmer's income and meat 35 per cent. As milk production is considered to be the least profitable, meat production increased both relatively and absolutely, but the livestock population has decreased during 1962–65.

The number of horses is rapidly decreasing. During 1961–65 there has been a loss of more than 15 per cent each year.

Pigs are numerous in Skåne and on the plains of Halland. Poultry rearing is also strongest in the extreme south of Sweden, where much of the product is frozen.

There are extremely few sheep on the plains. They flourish in North Sweden and especially on Gotland. Goats have practically disappeared.

FISHING

The number of fishermen is diminishing rapidly. In 1949 there were more than 14 000, in 1963 only 8 000. The same tendency holds good for smallholders who engage in fishing as a subsidiary means of livelihood (about 7 000). Similarly the number of fishing boats decreased. But the size of the boats has increased as has the catch. Of this catch four fifths came from Bohuslän and Göteborg, where 60 per cent of the fishermen live.

The main fishing district was previously in the central part of the Bohuslän coast, with Smögen as its centre. In recent decades the archipelago north of Göteborg has been completely dominant and the harbour of Hönö Klo-

va about 15 km from Göteborg has become Sweden's greatest fishing port. This is a result of the motorizing of the fishing fleet and of improvements in freezing methods. The fishermen sail directly with their catches from distant fishing grounds to the fish market of Göteborg, and from there express transport to other parts of the country is possible. Some of the fish landed at Göteborg, like most of that landed at Bohuslän ports with poorer communications, goes to the canning factories.

The system of communication along the coast of Bohuslän has been changed. The regular boat connections have mostly ceased and have been replaced by faster buses, which use an improved road system.

Herrings form about 60 per cent of the weight of the catch. Codfishing has decreased and now forms under 30 per cent. Trawlers have attained a completely dominating position, and more than three quarters of the catch is taken by them. The stockfish industry is unimportant in Sweden.

WOOD AND IRON

FORESTS

Forests are the most important source of raw material in Sweden and play an extremely important role in the economic life of the country. Two fifths of Sweden's exports are based on wood (Table 12.6).

In 1950 some 400 000 workers were employed in lumbering and transport at the height of the winter season. Their number has been rapidly decreasing owing to mechanization and in 1965 was estimated at 180 000. The number of workers wholly employed in forestry is, however, increasing, and they now do about two thirds of the work. This has produced great problems for the owners of small farms in Central and North Sweden which do not provide work throughout the year, and depend on forestry for a subsidiary income.

In 1965 the forest industries employed 143 000 persons or 14 per cent of the total employed in industry.

Forest area and tree species

The Swedish forests cover an area of 225 000 km² or 54 per cent of the land area, and 63 per cent if the bare mountains are excluded. There are 3.0 hectares of forest per inhabitant. By far the greater part of the forests are coniferous. Only in the southern coastal regions, and in the mountain birch belt, do deciduous trees predominate.

The area under forest varies greatly in different parts of the country. In the south a large part of the original forest land has been cleared. In the far north the forest area is interrupted by unproductive regions—mountains and bogland. Thus, proportionally, forests occupy the largest area in the interior of the southern parts of North Sweden (Fig. 12.12); in the provinces of Gävleborg and Västernorrland more than three quarters is forested. Rates of growth are three times larger in the south than in the north, and southern Norrland and the catchment areas of the Klarälv and the Dalälv have the largest production.

40 per cent of the forests are composed of pine, 45 per cent of spruce and 15 per cent of birch and other deciduous trees. Most of the birch is in the mountain region. In northern Norrland the pine is dominant below the moun-

tain zone. Pure spruce forests are limited to the eastern zone of lower mountains. The pine holds its own better on the flat, very boggy interior land. In central Norrland spruce predominates. Here, in the undulating hilly country, the drainage is much better, and the competitive possibilities for spruce seem to be greater. In the southernmost part of Norrland pure pine forests are very important, side by side with mixed forests.

In South and Central Sweden mixed coniferous forests predominate. In Skåne, Halland and Blekinge beech woods cover large areas; the area is being increased both relatively and absolutely by planting deciduous forest.

Ownership

Of Sweden's forest land, 25 per cent is owned by the state, the Church and local communes, 25 per cent is owned by companies and 50 per cent by farmers and landed proprietors.

The state formerly owned large areas of forest, especially in Norrland. Enormous areas were sold at low prices at the beginning of the 19th century, and state forest land in various parts of the country was transferred to farmers or to communes.

Ownership varies considerably in different parts of the country. In Norrland the state and the large forest companies have a large proportion, while the farmers' share is moderate (39 per cent). Towards the south the shares of the state and the private companies diminish, and in the extreme south of the country (Skåne, Halland and Blekinge) 88 per cent of the forest belongs to farmers and landed proprietors.

During the last part of the 19th century forestry companies were able to buy up large areas of forest in Norrland, and almost the whole of this extremely important group of owners has come into being during the past century. However, new laws, passed at the turn of the century, now prevent the private companies from increasing their forest holdings at the expense of the farmers. From the point of view of upkeep of the forests, this has not always had good results, as the forestry companies practise better methods of silviculture. The largest firm, Svenska Cellulosa AB, owns 1.6 million ha. forest; Korsnäs–Marma AB and Mo–

Domsjö AB each 0.5 mill. Their forest strips are, however, often long and narrow (cf. Fig. 12.22).

FORESTRY

During the second half of the 19th century the forests of Norrland were ruthlessly exploited. Later the slow-growing northern forests were neglected, and during the Second World War

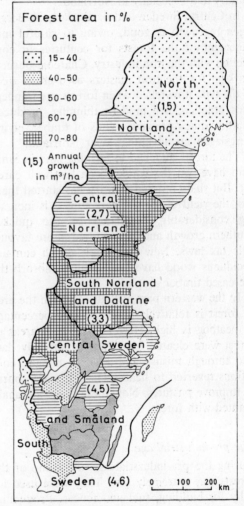

Fig. 12.12. *Swedish forests as a percentage of the land area* at the 1953–57 forest survey. 54% of Sweden's land surface is forest clad, the annual average growth 3.1 m³ per ha. incl. bark. The five main forest regions are shown. Colour Map 8, inset lower right, showing four forest regions, was based on figures from the 1938–1953 census. A more recent appraisal (1953–62) gives higher values of annual growth, particularly for Central and Southern Sweden, 1.8, 3.1, 3.5, 5.0 and 5.2 m³/ha. rspt. with 3.4 m³/ha. of annual growth for the whole of Sweden.

there was too much felling. The latest forest survey has revealed that only about 70 per cent of the annual growth has been felled during the 1950's. Now the northern forests are receiving more care. The former ruthless exploitation of the primeval forests has accelerated regrowth and produced younger and quicker growing stands. The ability of the wood-pulp industry to use timber of smaller dimensions has resulted in more rational thinning and has thus produced better forestry in all parts of the country and especially in Norrland.

In Central Sweden and particularly in Bergslagen regrowth is good, owing to careful management of the forests for centuries in connection with the iron industry. Charcoal-burners working for the iron masters used small trees of the type now felled when forests are thinned. This practice, like modern thinning, produced healthy, quick-growing stands of timber, giving Bergslagen an advantage over Norrland.

The forests attached to farming land in Småland have, on the whole, been less well cared for. But since rational forestry has started there too, the yield of the southern forests is increasing considerably, facilitated by the quicker southern growth and by modified, more favourable tax laws. New pulp mills which can use deciduous wood have been built to absorb the increased timber supply.

In the western part of South Sweden the area of forest is relatively small and the percentage of peatbog is high. Here considerable areas of forest were cleared for tillage at an early date and through misuse and adverse climatic conditions reverted to heath. The latter was burnt to improve pastures. Now these areas are again planted with forest.

The pre-industrial age

During the pre-industrial age the value of the forests was extremely low. They were used locally for building, fuel and fences. Production for sale was small. Nevertheless, the oak forests in South Sweden were very valuable for shipbuilding and were stringently controlled. Among coniferous forests those of the Bergslagen areas were the most valuable. In all the processes of iron production the need for fuel was enormous, both for ore-extraction and smelting. The possibility for producing large amounts of charcoal was an important condition for Sweden's predominance in the iron market until coke could be used in the industry. The need for charcoal was so great that complaints of a shortage of wood had already arisen in the 17th century in many parts of the central Bergslagen districts. Undoubtedly this shortage was in many places only apparent, and the complaints were basically due to longer transport that increased prices of forest products, but in certain limited areas charcoal-burners had not thinned, but had completely cleared the forests, and the shortage was real. Here tree-felling was afterwards strictly controlled and burnbeating for graingrowing prohibited.

Tar was a very important article of export and in the 17th century ranked next to iron. The Norrland forests, especially, were exploited for tar distillation, and its export from the ports of the Norrland coast was one of the main reasons for their development.

Modern developments

The mid-18th century saw changes in the exploitation of the forests. The export of timber began to increase, but during the early part of the century Norway had a larger export, because the Norwegian forests were more favourably placed from the point of view of export to Western Europe.

In Sweden the exports from Dalsland, via Göteborg, started early, but the fast developing timber demand of the 19th century could not be satisfied from the forest of southern Sweden. Its peasant-owned forest consisted of dispersed forest plots, unsuitable for large-scale exploitation, and the southern river systems offered poor possibilities for floating.

The exploitation of Norrland's enormous forest resources began at this time, and timber gradually replaced iron as the main industrial raw material of Sweden. From small catchment areas centering on water-driven sawmills in the interior of the country there was a change to steam-mills with larger catchment areas further downstream.

The big developments in saw-milling for export were mainly in northern and central Sweden, and the industrialization of Sweden in the modern sense began in the lower parts of the Norrland valleys, and especially in the Ångermanälv valley.

Timber transport

The floating-ways were developed mainly in the second half of the 19th century. Nine tenths of them are found in northern Sweden where the network of rivers is dense and the distance from the lumbering site to the floating-way is short. The gradient of the rivers is moderate and real falls are rare. The ice first breaks at the warmer coast and the spring thaw continues upstream. The melting snow causes high water for timber floating in spring and early summer. In South Sweden the low gradient of the rivers and the extent to which they are used for generating electric power makes their use for timber-floating difficult. The electric power stations want to keep back the water, while timber-floating requires high water to clear away all logs from the banks. In addition, through damming, long stretches of river have been converted into reservoirs.

The logs for floating are cut in winter and transported on sledges to the river and stored on the ice, after which they are separately carried down the river by the current when the ice breaks. During winter and spring a large part of the population of the interior is employed in lumbering and timber transportation.

The work of timber-floating occurs during the spring high water and consists partly of work on the rafts and partly of work at the places where the logs are sorted according to owners. On the rafts the greatest amount of labour is needed in the early summer, and at the sorting places in the late summer. In 1965 about 4 200 men were employed around 1st July in floating, and around 15th August about 2 300 in sorting. The 1955 figures were 12 000 and 5 000 respectively.

The greater part of the floated timber comes from the rivers of south and central Norrland. In 1964 the Ångermanälv delivered 1.54 million m³ of floated timber to the Kramfors district at its mouth, and the Indalsälv and the Ljungan together carried 1.79 million m³ to the Sundsvall district. This means that 34 per cent of all floated timber (130 million logs or 9.8 million m³) was concentrated on a short stretch of the Bothnian coast. A large amount of the wood from north Norrland (4 mill. m³, 1966) was transported from the river mouths southward by sea to the large wood-pulp districts in the neighbourhood of Örnsköldsvik and Sundsvall. The northern part of the Gulf of Bothnia is closed by ice for so long a period that local mills in the far north would be obliged to keep the pulp in stock too long before it could be exported.

Since World War II there has been a revolution in the transport of timber. Floating on the Indalsälv and the Ljungan will cease from 1968 and 1969 respectively. A forest road system of roughly the same length as the floating-ways has been developed there. This allows of quick transport by lorry all the year round, and the number of seasonal workers is gradually diminishing.

Forest work has also been greatly changed. It is now not necessary to strip the bark off the logs by hand in the forest. This is expensive but necessary in floating, as stripped logs float better than logs with bark. During the 1964/65 season the total timber production was 35 million m³ (without bark), of which 9.8 millions was delivered to saw mills, 23.6 to pulp mills and only 1.8 millions was used as fuel; 9.8 millions were floated. The total transport of timber in 1960 amounted to about 11 million ton-km or 30 per cent of all transport in Sweden that year.

FOREST INDUSTRIES

Sawmills

The first steam sawmills appeared in Sweden in the mid-19th century, and a timber exporting area began to develop in Dalsland and Värmland, near the port of Göteborg. Britain's abolition of import duties favoured this. At the same time the world demand for wood as building material developed with industrialization and the growth of cities, and the number of steam sawmills at the outlets of the main floating rivers and on nearby coasts in Norrland increased rapidly. Water-driven sawmills in the interior got into difficulties and were mostly closed down, with the exception of those that were important for the home market, more especially in South and Central Sweden. As the steam sawmills could be made larger than the water-mills, the total capacity increased considerably. A third period started, however, with the introduction of electric power. The electric saw-mills were often small and more widely distributed. Decentralization has also been facilitated by

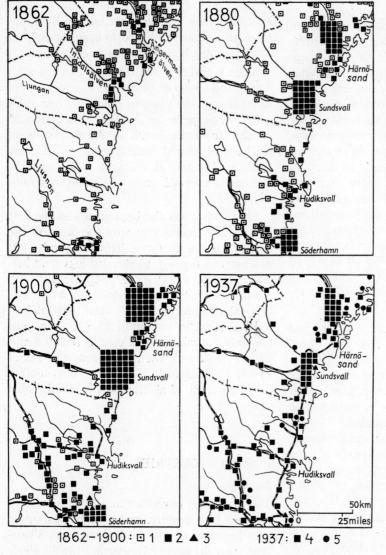

Fig. 12.13. The development and changing distribution of the sawmill industry in the Ångermanälven, Indalsälven, Ljungan and Ljusnan regions, 1862–1937. 1. Water-driven frame-saws, which reached their peak in the 1860's. 2. Steam-driven frame-saws, the first of which was set up in 1849. 3. Planing mills. 4. Frame-saws, 1937. 5. Circular saws, 1937. 4–5. Irrespective of source of power. — After Harald Wik: Norra Sveriges sågverks-industri. Geographica 21. Uppsala 1950, Pl. 2, 4, 6 and 12.

1862–1900 : ⊡ 1 ■ 2 ▲ 3   1937 : ■ 4 ● 5

the use of road haulage rather than floating (Fig. 12.13).

Saw-milling was Sweden's first large manufacturing industry. Labour, which had been local in the older industries, now flowed from all parts of the country to the estuaries of the Gulf of Bothnia, where the large sawmills were located. At the same time labour was needed for lumbering and timber transport in the interior of Norrland. This radically changed the attractions of an area of marginal agriculture by providing the farming population with increased opportunities for winter work, and new settlers arrived there too.

The sawmill industry reached its peak in 1900, when the stocks of large trees in Norr-land began to be exhausted and Finnish competition began to make itself felt. A rationalization and concentration of the industry in larger units has since occurred. The slump of the 1930's led to the closing down of a considerable number of the smaller sawmills. The production of sawn wood has since been maintained or slightly increased, while the production of wood-pulp has progressively increased (see below).

The greatest concentration of sawmills is now to be found on the estuaries of the Ljungan, the Indalsälv and the Ångermanälv, which have large catchment areas in the southern-most part of Norrland. Situated between the outlets of the Indalsälv and the Ljungan, the

Fig. 12.14. Wood manufac-turing, 1951. The distribution of sawmills has not notice-ably changed since 1951, but many small plants have been closed down. The sawmills produced 1.5 mill. std. in 1953 and 2 millions in 1964 (1 standard = 4 672 m³). The concentration of joinery (fur-niture, fixtures, and, more re-cently, prefabricated houses) on the South Swedish Uplands still exists, but since 1951 the industry has spread to the southern part of the Bothnian coast. Wood manufacturing employs more people than wood-processing (Fig. 12.15). In 1964 the three main groups (sawmills, fixtures and furni-ture) had 35, 33 and 22% rspt. of the total employment.—Af-ter Erik W. Höjer: Den sven-ska skogen. Svenska Turist-föreningens Årsskrift 1959. Stockholm 1959.

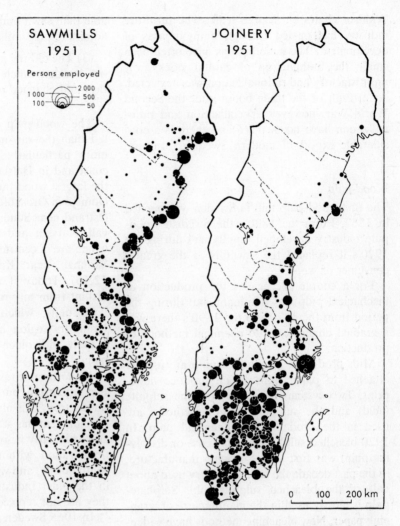

Sundsvall district alone controls 9 per cent of the Swedish forest areas. To this concentration comes a large amount of timber transported by sea from areas further north. The Sundsvall area has the largest concentration of wood-processing indus-tries in the world. 2 per cent of the world's sawn wood and 8 per cent of its wood-pulp come from this area.

Large sawmill enterprises can still be found throughout the coastlands of the Gulf of Bothnia from Karlsborg near Haparanda to Skutskär near the mouth of the Dalälv. This river differs from the other rivers of Norrland. It has two large falls just above its mouth, which is there-fore unsuitable for the location of a timber in-dustry. The wood is conducted by means of chutes to the Gävle–Skutskär district. Inland along the Dalälv there are large industrial undertakings. Here the old iron industry has largely changed over to wood-processing.

In West Sweden, the largest sawmill is that of Skoghall at the lake mouth of the Klarälv, the wood being sent to Göteborg for export.

Inland sawmills, producing largely for the home market, are found throughout the eastern part of South and Central Sweden. The plants are numerous but small or medium-sized (Fig. 12.14).

The sawmills in 1965 exported 51 per cent of their production, the rest being used in the fur-niture and joinery industries (a third in each) and for prefabricated houses (a quarter). The latter industry is mainly found in Värmland and Norrland and is highly export-orientated.

The furniture industry, with its high standard of manufacture and design, is mainly concen-trated in the northern part of the South Swed-ish Highlands with Nybro, Hultsfred and Tran-ås in Småland and Tibro west of Vättern as the main centres. There was a smaller and later de-velopment in Värmland and Norrland. The in-dustry is old-established and already in the 1890's some factories in Småland were making

Windsor chairs on a large scale. The furniture industry has passed through many phases of development. The undertakings have often been small, the building up of capital stocks was unsatisfactory and rationalization was neglected. As a result of the trade boom after the Second World War, however, specialization and rationalization have taken place and there is a considerable export of modern Swedish furniture.

Wood-pulp

The first wood-pulp mill in Sweden was opened in 1857. From the 1890's the Swedish wood-pulp industry developed rapidly and during the 1920's it replaced the sawmills as the greater consumer of wood.

For a couple of decades the production of mechanical pulp was dominant, but during the period from the 1870's to the 1890's there was a gradual change-over to chemical methods of production.

Mills producing mechanical pulp are usually attached to paper mills which produce newsprint. Two systems of production, the sulphite (acid) and the sulphate (basic) methods, are used in the production of chemical pulp. In 1920 bleached sulphite-pulp (viscose or dissolving pulp) was first used for rayon manufacture; in the past decade the rayon industry used about half of the bleached sulphite-pulp. Sulphate-pulp is mostly used in the manufacture of wrapping paper. New bleaching methods have widened the use of sulphate-pulp. Hitherto spruce wood has been principally used for sulphite-pulp, pine and waste from sawmills for sulphate-pulp. New techniques have led to a wider choice of raw materials; pine is now also used for sulphite-pulp. A new half-chemical (magnefite) method has been developed especially to use birch wood.

Three types of undertakings which initiated wood-pulp production can be singled out:

(1) Ironworks which owned forests. When the ironworks began to close down in the late 19th century, their sites and forest properties were used for sawmills and wood-pulp mills. More than 130 of the wood-pulp mills in Central Sweden started in this way. This was particularly the case in Värmland.

(2) Sawmills produce waste that can be used to make wood-pulp. As pulp was more profitable than sawn timber, the sawmills often set up adjoining pulp-mills.

(3) The old rag paper mills of South and Central Sweden which could no longer get enough rags and changed over to pulp production.

The wood-pulp industry is more concentrated than the saw-milling industry and is found more particularly on the southern Norrland coast and in Dalsland and Värmland. Some of the largest wood-pulp mills are those of Mo and Domsjö in Örnsköldsvik, Svartvik (Pl. 12.5) and Östrand near Sundsvall, Iggesund near Hudiksvall, Karskär and Skutskär near Gävle, all of which are in central and southern Norrland, and Skoghall near Karlstad in Värmland (Fig. 12.15). Today it is the Örnsköldsvik region, distant from any river mouth but with modern large units, which has developed, while the Kramfors region in the valley of the Ångermanälv with older and smaller units has stagnated.

A shortage of raw materials has impeded further expansion, but now, when wood from deciduous trees can also be used, a new phase of development has started, and in southern Sweden particularly new mills are being erected. Rationalization within the industry is going on continuously, and when old-fashioned pulp-mills in the older industrial areas cease production, they are not replaced.

In 1965 Sweden produced 6.7 million tons of pulp (dry weight), including mechanical pulp 20 per cent, sulphate-pulp 45 per cent, sulphite-pulp 25 per cent, viscose pulp 8 p.c. and half-chemical pulp 2 p.c.; 50 per cent of the pulp is exported. Sweden supplies 10 per cent of world production and about 30 per cent of the international trade in wood-pulp.

The by-products of the wood-pulp industry have increased in importance. For a long period the so-called waste solutions were not used, but now they form the basis of a considerable number of chemical products, e.g. sulphite alcohol, plastics, explosives, adhesives, pigments and medicines. The profitable sale of these new products has made it possible to keep the price of Swedish wood-pulp comparatively low in relation to quality.

An important industry connected with sawmills and wood-pulp mills is the making of plywood and wallboard, which began in the 1930's

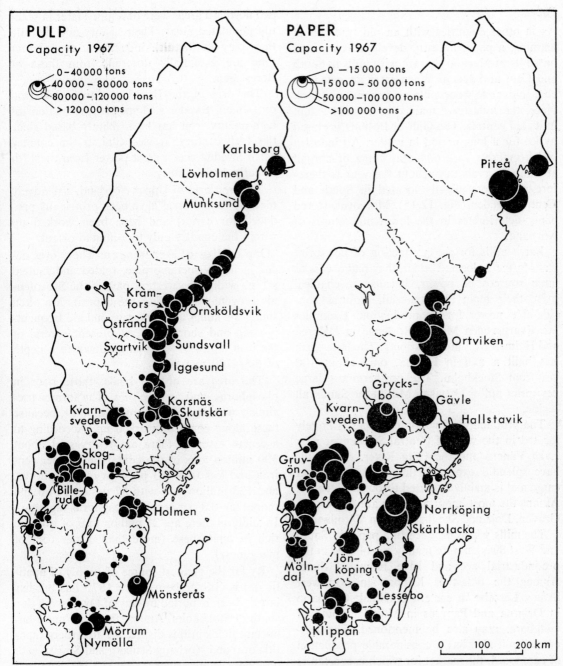

PULP
Capacity 1967

- 0 – 40 000 tons
- 40 000 – 80 000 tons
- 80 000 – 120 000 tons
- > 120 000 tons

Karlsborg
Lövholmen
Munksund
Kram-fors
Örnsköldsvik
Öströnd
Svartvik
Sundsvall
Iggesund
Korsnäs
Skutskär
Kvarn-sveden
Skog-hall
Bille-rud
Holmen
Mönsterås
Mörrum
Nymölla

PAPER
Capacity 1967

- 0 – 15 000 tons
- 15 000 – 50 000 tons
- 50 000 – 100 000 tons
- > 100 000 tons

Piteå
Ortviken
Grycks-bo
Gävle
Hallstavik
Kvarn-sveden
Gruv-ön
Norrköping
Skärblacka
Möln-dal
Jön-köping
Lessebo
Klippan

0   100   200 km

Fig. 12.15. Wood-processing, 1967. All symbols represent one unit only, though these units may be under the same ownership. From 1950 to 1965 pulp production increased from 2.8 to 6.2 mill. tons, that of paper and board from 1.2 to 3.1 mill. tons, of which one fifth was newsprint and one third sulphate-pulp (wrapping paper). Large new sulphate-pulp mills have been built in the southeast (Mörrum, Nymölla, Mönsterås) and in the far north (Karlsskoga, Lövholmen, Munksund). The newsprint mills increased their production of mechanical pulp at Hallstavik, Kvarnsveden, Ortviken and Norrköping (Holmen). The sulphite-pulp mills are still concentrated along the Bothnian coast between Örnsköldsvik and Gävle and in West Sweden; some minor mills have been closed down, other mills enlarged. — After Sveriges industri, Stockholm 1967.

and grew rapidly at the end of the 40's. It can be produced in smaller factories than pulp. The wallboard industry uses wood from forest thinnings and waste from sawmills. In 1965 production amounted to about 740 000 tons and half of this was exported.

Paper

As in other countries with an old tradition of learning, a paper industry developed early and based its production on rags with mills in South and Central Sweden. When later an extensive change-over to wood-pulp as raw material took place, the industry remained to a great extent in its old centres. The Gulf of Bothnia is closed by ice for a long period in winter. An industry which markets its produce at home or abroad at short intervals throughout the year is therefore more conveniently located in South and Central Sweden (Fig. 12.15). Moreover, stored paper deteriorates in the low temperatures of Norrland.

Large mills for the production of newsprint were formerly located where they had access to large sources of power, because mechanical pulp, their main raw material, requires considerable power for its production. Examples are Kvarnsveden Mill in Borlänge in Dalarna and Holmen Mill in Norrköping. The latter firm has built a mill in Hallsta, only about 100 km from Stockholm. The northernmost large newsprint mill is Ortviken Mill in the Sundsvall region.

The production of wrapping paper is largely located in the west of Central Sweden or near Lake Vänern and the Göta River. The mills have splendid export facilities. Paper is liner cargo and is mainly exported through Göteborg. Among the most important mills are Åmotsfors, Gruvön, Deje and Skoghall—all in Värmland.

The mills which produce fine paper in South and West Sweden were mainly established in the pre-industrial age and have remained there. Among the oldest is Klippan in northwest Skåne. Lessebo in eastern Småland, Grycksbo in Dalarna and Papyrus in Mölndal, south of Göteborg, may also be mentioned. The last-named mill also has a considerable production of cardboard, the market for which is constantly increasing with new packaging methods.

IRON AND METAL ORES

Iron ores

Iron and metal ores are found in three distinct areas in Sweden. These are the Bergslagen area, the Skellefte field and the Upper Norrland field (Figs. 12.16 and 12.17). In the southernmost area mining started in the Middle Ages. The two northern areas were developed later in scantily populated areas. Their history and the role they play in Swedish industry at the present time are essentially different from those of Bergslagen.

The ores of the Bergslagen area yield iron on which Sweden's domestic production of high-quality iron has been mainly based since the 14th century. It was vital to the country when Sweden was a great power from the 17th to early 18th century.

The iron ores of Upper Norrland, a relatively recently settled area, have been principally produced for export and have been worked up within the country only to a limited extent.

Ore bodies of Bergslagen. These ores occur in highly metamorphic, folded and faulted schists within the western part of the Svecofennic orogenic zone. Thus the deposits are often small, the mines are numerous and are frequently deep and short-lived. At present several of the iron mines in the area go down to a depth of 500–700 metres.

The ores are of two kinds: those poor in phosphorus, and apatitic ores. The former previously were the only deposits of value, because these alone could be worked up. According to a recent estimate there are reserves of about 500 million tons of ore containing 33 per cent iron and less than 0.3 per cent of phosphorus, and 123 million tons with 57 per cent iron and more than 0.3 per cent of phosphorus (apatitic). In addition there are 21 million tons of iron ore rich in manganese (more than 1 per cent of manganese).

By far the greatest source of supply of apatitic ore is Grängesberg. Since 1876 this ore has largely been exported by way of Oxelösund, due south of Stockholm. Among the other more important fields in this district are Idkerberg (apatitic ore) and Norberg, Striberg and Stråssa with ores poor in phosphorus (Fig. 12.16). The iron ores which are poor in phosphorus are mainly used within the country.

Outside the actual Bergslagen area lies the Dannemora field in north Uppland, whose extremely pure ore was important in the development of the Swedish iron industry, and the ore deposits of Taberg, south of Lake Vättern. These are titaniferous.

Ore bodies of Upper Norrland. These ores have quite a different character. They occur in large bodies within the Svecofennides. The deposits which are worth working lie superficially and are partly mined in open workings.

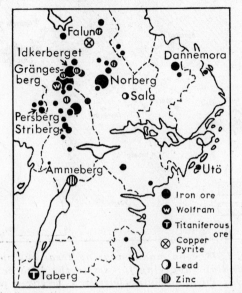

Fig. 12.16. *The more important ore resources* in the Bergslagen region. The deposits are represented by circles proportionate to the metal content of the known reserves. A vertical line has been added for lead mines which also produce zinc. The oldest field known to have been worked is the Norberg field. For scale, see Fig. 12.17. — After Sveriges industri. Stockholm 1961.

These ore deposits are the largest in the country. The ores have an iron content of 60–70 per cent and have a widely varying phosphorus content. The largest northwestern field, Kiruna, is said to contain over 1 000 million tons of ore and the southeastern field, Gällivare (Malmberget), to have about 400 million tons. Svappavaara, southeast of Kiruna, also has large ore deposits. Working is concentrated in a small number of large mines which include three open pits. The Pajala field is kept as a reserve.

These Norrland ores were not suitable for older methods of production and they first began to play an important part in the Swedish economy after the Thomas method was invented in 1878. The railway line between Luleå and Gällivare was opened in 1892 and was extended in 1902 through Kiruna to Narvik on the Norwegian coast. A railway to Svappavaara was built in 1964. Owing to ore transport, the Luleå–Narvik railway has the largest goods tonnage per kilometre of any railway in the country. Luleå is closed by ice half the year, but has a larger ore-loading capacity (1.5 million tons per month) than any other port in the world. As a result of this mining activity, centres of population totalling about 50 000 inhabitants have been founded north of the Arctic Circle. The opera-

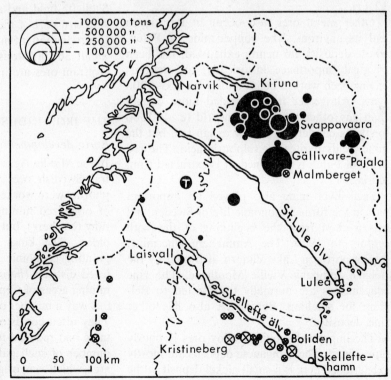

Fig. 12.17. *The iron ore field of Norrland.* The areas of the circles are proportionate to the metal content of the known ore reserves.—After Sveriges industri. Stockholm 1961.

tions are now managed by the state (Luossa-
vaara–Kiirunavaara AB, LKAB), as are the
railway and the ironworks established in Luleå
in 1940.

Whereas in the mid-18th century Sweden had
40 per cent of the world's iron-ore production,
it now has 5 per cent. The present production
is c. 29 million tons per annum (1965) of which
70 per cent comes from the Norrland field. Of
the whole ore production 90 per cent is exported, i.e. nearly all apatitic ore and some which
is poor in phosphorus. This export represents
about 7–8 per cent of Sweden's total export and
about 12 per cent of the iron ore in world trade.

Non-ferrous metals

The third largest ore province is the Skellefte
field, where a number of sulphide ores occur in
a limited area on both sides of the Skellefte
River. This field, which was discovered and
examined by modern prospecting methods, includes first and foremost Sweden's most important copper deposits (Boliden, Kristineberg),
but also lead deposits (Laisvall) and arsenic
(Boliden). Boliden is the main centre in the
mining area; a cableway goes through the mining area to the coastal smelting works of which
Rönnskär in Skelleftehamn is the largest (Fig.
12.17).

Other metal ores also occur in Bergslagen
and its environs. The copper-mine of Falun,
whose deposits are nearly exhausted, has been
of great importance historically, the deposits
having been worked continuously for about 900
years. Altogether it has yielded more copper
than any other mine in the world (c. 440 000
tons). Its copper ore is now exhausted, but the
mine yields pyrites for sulphuric acid. The red
ochre of Falun is renowned. It is extracted from
scoria.

Sala silver mine also played an important
part in the former economic life of Sweden and
was worked from the beginning of the 16th
century to 1920. The Åmmeberg zinc-mine,
east of northern Lake Vättern, is owned by the
Belgian company Vieille Montagne. The zinc
concentrates are normally transported to Belgium for smelting. Bergslagen also has other
zinc deposits.

The important group of alloy ores is poorly
represented. The manganese deposits are mostly
exhausted. There is a small nickel deposit in the

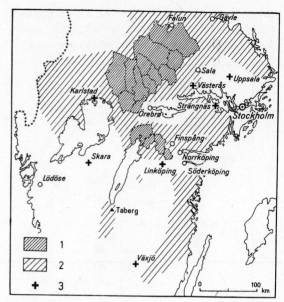

*Fig. 12.18. Iron manufacturing areas and sur-
rounding supplying forests in the 17th cen-
tury. 1. Privileged districts (bergslag s., bergslagen pl.)
with their administrative boundaries. In the north the
major grouping forming Bergslagen proper. A smaller
bergslag region lay north of Lake Vättern. 2. Areas
of bar-iron production and manufacturing which, for
relatively short periods, were administered as bergslag
districts. 3. Bishops sees. — After K. E. Bergsten:
Östergötlands bergslag. Lund 1946.*

Skellefte field and a small tungsten mine in the
southern part of the Bergslagen area. The yearly production of non-ferrous ores amounts to
about 360 000 tons (1966); all aluminium and
wolfram ores are imported.

THE IRON INDUSTRY

Early development

In the Middle Ages lake and bog ores, and Central Swedish ores which were poor in phosphorus, were worked. The first written evidence
of organized mining dates from the 14th cen-
tuhy (Norberg), but the works is no doubt much
older. The kings encouraged production by
granting economic and social privileges. Privileged districts (bergslag s.) grew up around the
mining areas of Central Sweden (Fig. 12.18). In
this way a number of mining districts developed.
They often consisted of parishes whose inhabitants had reduced taxes and military service. A
number of such parishes formed a loosely-knit
area which was originally, and is today, known

by the name Bergslagen (i.e. the mining teams). In addition to the main area so named, there were several southern bergslag districts which also dated from this period, all of which were fairly short-lived. During this early period miners from South Germany were active in the Bergslagen as instructors and entrepreneurs and their activities are commemorated in many place-names.

In the Middle Ages the miner-peasants made malleable iron from heated but not smelted iron (osmund iron). In the 15th and 16th centuries furnaces and forges were introduced: the furnaces for smelting the ore and making pig-iron, and the forges for working up the pig-iron into malleable iron bars.

Within the Bergslagen there were, consequently, ironmines, furnaces and forges. The ore-bearing rock was split by heating with wood fires, and then cooled rapidly with water. The state authorities exercised control over iron production, and from the 15th century the amount that might be produced and the area from which ore and wood (for use in the mines and for charcoal burning) might be taken, were precisely laid down. This was due to the desire to maintain prices by limiting the supply, and also to the belief that the forest resources were inadequate for uncontrolled iron production. Production units tended to be small because charcoal could not be transported over large distances. Limestone for flux was usually taken from adjacent deposits in the Archaean rocks. The furnaces and forges were often located on small streams which were able to operate their blast equipment and hammers only during periods of maximum flow in spring or autumn. Such works soon ran into difficulties and the undertakings which lay further downstream made greater progress.

About the end of the 16th and the beginning of the 17th century a gradual change occurred which altered the organization, and consequently the distribution of the industry. Whereas previously peasants who were miners and possessed furnaces, could also set up forges, the authorities now issued stringent regulations restricting the miners to the extraction and smelting of ore, while the forge (and foundry) work was to be transferred as far as possible to burghers and noblemen outside the bergslag areas on the pretext that a shortage of fuel was imminent in the

mining areas. In the long run this policy resulted in a wider distribution of forges. They were often placed in densely populated areas and on larger and more powerful streams. The present large iron and steel works and foundries of Sweden have, for the most part, developed from these small forges which were established in and outside the Bergslagen, and they have made its boundaries less definite.

A big development took place early in the 17th century when a number of Walloons introduced new methods. These Walloons first came to the foundries in Uppland and Östergötland which were managed by the Dutch financier Louis de Geer. They spread later through the Bergslagen area where their racial features and their names can still be traced in the population.

The Swedish iron industry mainly made semi-finished products (bar-iron) for export and Sweden was the leading nation in this field until the end of the 18th century. For more than 200 years malleable bar-iron was Sweden's most important commercial commodity.

Nineteenth-century development

From the middle of the 18th century to 1830 the production of pig-iron was between 60 000 and 85 000 tons a year. The export of pig-iron was prohibited until 1875 and almost the whole production was worked up into bar-iron. The annual production of bar-iron for the whole country up to 1830 was between 50 000 and 60 000 tons. In those days this represented a considerable part of world production.

Industrialization and the building of railways created a large home demand for iron, and from the middle of the 19th century production increased greatly. The furnaces became larger and it became possible to use a mixture of charcoal and coke for fuel. From the beginning of the 20th century pig-iron has been made mainly with coke.

During the second half of the 19th century iron-processing was revolutionized. 'German forging' was replaced by e.g. charcoal-saving 'Lancashire forging' and bar-iron disappeared. The acid Bessemer process was introduced into Sweden in 1858. The open-hearth process, which uses a mixture of scrap and pig-iron, has been used since 1868. The Thomas process (basic

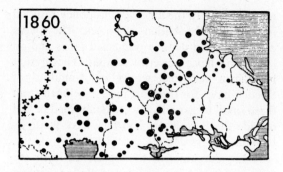

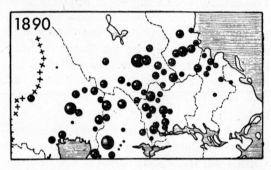

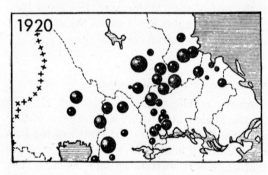

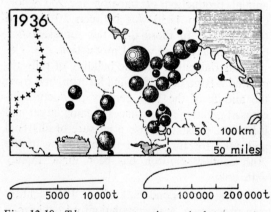

Fig. 12.19. The concentration of the iron industry of Central Sweden from the beginning of Sweden's industrial revolution to 1936. Note especially the decay of small plants in the west of the area. The size of the spheres indicates tonnage produced. For 1962, see Fig. 12.20. — After W. William–Olsson: Ekonomisk-geografisk karta över Sverige. Stockholm 1946.

Bessemer), which made it possible to use the apatitic ores from Grängesberg and Upper Norrland, was introduced into Sweden in the 1890's, but the open-hearth process became the one mainly used.

Electricity was applied to the Swedish steel industry after 1910. During the present decade production in electro-steel furnaces has surpassed other steel production methods in quantity. Sponge iron, steel produced directly from ore at rather low temperatures, is a Swedish development, as is the Kaldo-process for the production of oxygen steel, widely used in Sweden and abroad. The old forges *(hammare)* have long been replaced by modern rolling mills.

High quality iron dominated production in Swedish ironworks right up to the inter-war period. Ordinary structural steel could be imported at prices that were lower than those at which it could be produced at home. Therefore this sector of iron production stagnated in Sweden until the cutting-off of imports during the Second World War caused many steelworks to increase their output of structural and merchant steel.

Iron and steel works

Both sizes and sites of works changed with new methods of iron-processing. From a total of about 600 in 1830 the number of forges and foundries fell to 200 by about 1920 and to less than 35 about 1962 (Fig. 12.19). As a number of works came under the control of one owner, the majority were closed down and one of them was modernized and extended. Several large ironworks have arisen in this way, e.g. Fagersta. In other cases the old works were closed down and a new ironworks was built on a new and better placed site. This occurred at Sandviken, Domnarvet and Hagfors. They all arose during the period 1860–1880 when proximity to charcoal was still necessary. They were also located by small waterfalls to obtain power. Under modern conditions, when electric power can be transported over long distances and charcoal has lost its importance, it would have been better if they had been located in ore-shipping ports, where coal can be obtained at less cost, like the iron and steelworks completed at Luleå in 1940 and the new steel works built at Oxelösund from 1957. Two minor works, Kallinge (in Blekinge) and Halmstad are also at seaports. They mainly use scrap iron from southern Sweden.

The high reputation of Swedish iron was due to its quality, which depended on charcoal and ores with a low phosphorus content. This quality steel is partly consumed by Swedish engineering, partly exported. In structural steel goods, such as girders, heavy plates and reinforcement steel, Sweden's imports still exceed exports. In 1966, the trade in steel was:

Exports: 984 000 tons valued at 1 652 mill. Sw. crowns.

Imports: 1 242 000 tons valued at 894 mill. Sw. crowns.

At present the steel works specialize as follows: quality steel: Sandviken (the largest), Hofors, Surahammar, Avesta, Fagersta, Hällefors, Bofors and Hagfors; structural steel: Domnarvet (most important electro-steelworks), Oxelösund, Luleå, Nykroppa and Smedjebacken.

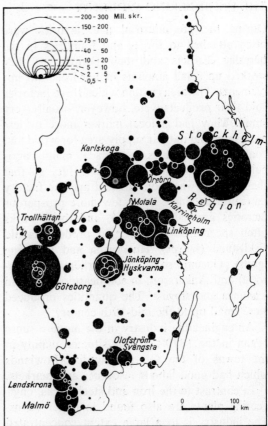

Fig. 12.21. Engineering 1954, excluding machinery, transport equipment and foundries. Circles indicate value added by manufacturing in cities and rural districts. Distribution has not changed noticeably since 1954. — After Atlas of Sweden 103.

Production has doubled since the last war and was in 1967:

	1 000 t.	%
Pig-iron	2 361	
Sponge iron	152	
Crude steel	4 768	100
electro furnaces	1 749	37
open hearth	1 361	28
Thomas (Kaldo) furnaces	1 658	35

The three largest works which refine other base metals are at Västerås (on the northern shore of Lake Mälaren), Finspång (near Norrköping) and Skelleftehamn in Västerbotten (Boliden company). In production value they can be equated with the largest iron and steel works. Aluminium is made in Avesta in southeast Dalarna and Sundsvall; production was started during the wartime blockade.

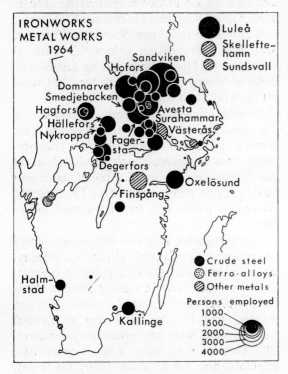

Fig. 12.20. Ironworks and works which refine other base metals, 1964. Outside the area shown are the Norrbotten Iron Works in Luleå and metal works in Skelleftehamn and Sundsvall, all at the Norrland coast. — After Sveriges industri. Stockholm 1967.

THE ENGINEERING INDUSTRY

During the pre-industrial age factories were often attached to forges and foundries in the bergslag districts and their peripheries; they worked up small amounts of bar-iron into implements. The areas within which these factories sold their products were, however, usually very small. They had a local market more or less corresponding to their supply area for wood and coal, and the articles they made, mainly agricultural implements, had a long life, so that their market was soon satisfied and the factory thereafter declined. But a few more prosperous factories gradually emerged, and these works often specialized in a certain product as did Eskilstuna (knives), Huskvarna and Finspång (guns), Gusum, south of Norrköping (brassware) and Ankarsrum in southeastern Småland (castings and stoves). The quantities produced were small up to the mid-19th century.

An engineering industry in the modern sense began in the 1870's. It was situated mainly in the towns of the Central Swedish Lowlands which had good labour resources and markets.

In contrast to the iron and steel works, engineering plants are also found in larger towns. The industry is to a large extent concentrated in a zone between Stockholm and Bofors (near Karlskoga in southeastern Värmland), the main concentration is in the Mälaren–Hjälmaren area. There are minor concentrations in the Östergötland plain, around Jönköping–Huskvarna, Göteborg and in West Skåne. In 1965 mining, base metal industries and the engineering industry had 510 000 workers, or more than 51 per cent of all workers included in Swedish industrial statistics. During the 1960's these industries contribute about 35 per cent of the total value of Sweden's exports. It includes manufacture and repair of vehicles, iron foundries, machine and engine factories, shipyards, electrotechnical plants and other engineering works. Many plants are involved in more than one of these manufactures.

There is often a close integration between engineering and related industries. For instance the Johnson group includes enterprises such as iron and steel (Avesta), shipyard (Lindholmen in Göteborg), shipping company (Johnson Line). The group also has tankers, oil refineries (Nynäshamn south of Stockholm) and Sweden's largest private bus system (Linjebuss). The Co-operative Federation is interested in many branches, notably wood-pulp (Fiskeby near Norrköping), china (Gustafsberg near Stockholm), rubber (Gislaved in Småland), refining of vegetable oils (Karlshamn in Blekinge), flour mills (Stockholm and Göteborg), soap and detergents, electrical goods and petrol import (Stockholm).

When the railway system began to be developed in the 1860's there was greatly increased activity in Bergslagen, where the production of rails was important. Domnarvet and the Norrbotten Iron Works at Luleå are now the only rail works. The rolling stock is made in Arlöv outside Malmö, Falun, Kalmar and Linköping (carriages), Motala Verkstad and Trollhättan (locomotives) and in Örnsköldsvik (tramcars). Of these the locomotive works in Trollhättan produces mainly for export.

The shipbuilding industry has developed greatly since the beginning of the century, and after the Second World War Sweden became one of the greatest shipbuilding nations with about a tenth of the world's annual launched tonnage. Half of this is exported. The largest undertakings are in Göteborg (Eriksbergs Shipyard, Götaverken and Lindholmen's Shipyard) and in Malmö (Kockums Shipyard). There are also large shipyards in Uddevalla, north of Göteborg, in Hälsingborg and in Landskrona north of Malmö. Thus the west coast has about 90 per cent of Sweden's shipbuilding.

Swedish production of arms and ammunition was concentrated between the 16th and 18th centuries in works in eastern Sweden. Thus products from Finspång, which developed under Dutch management, found a traditional export market in Europe via Amsterdam. The Finspång armaments works were later transferred to Bofors.

The distribution of plants making machinery and equipment for farming, mining and forestry, and machine tools, shows a partial concentration in a broad zone in Central Sweden. Agriculture machinery is mainly made in South Sweden, and forestry machinery in Central Sweden. Some large enterprises are internationally known, e.g. Atlas Copco (pneumatic machines) and AB Separator (dairy machines), both in Stockholm.

Manufacture of vehicles, a 20th-century development, meets keen foreign competition. In 1965 Sweden was able to pay for 60 per cent of its large import of cars by exporting cars to the Scandinavian countries and to U.S.A. The automobile industry is situated in Göteborg (Volvo), Södertälje south of Stockholm (Scania-Vabis) and in Trollhättan (SAAB). The latter firm makes planes in Linköping.

The largest motor-car works is Volvo, which has its assembly works in Göteborg, 15 other factories in Sweden and one in Canada. It employs 25 000 of whom 13 000 are in the main Göteborg works. The engines are made in Sköv-de in Västergötland, the gear boxes in Köping (the Mälaren region). Car bodies are manufactured in Olofström in Blekinge, tractors in Eskilstuna (Bolinder–Munktell) and jet motors in Trollhättan (Svenska Flygmotor AB). In 1963 Volvo sold 112 000 private cars and 32 000 lorries, of which a half were exported.

Works making electrical machinery and equipment are concentrated in a few places. The largest ones are in Stockholm where low voltage products such as telephones (L. M. Eriksson) and refrigerators and vacuum cleaners (Electrolux) are made. High voltage products (turbines, generators) are made in Väster-ås by ASEA (Allmänna Svenska Elektriska AB). These large firms have a world network of subsidiaries, and employ 44 000 and 34 000 respectively.

Other large engineering firms are AGA (AB Gasackumulator, lighthouses) and TALL (De Lavals Turbine Works), both in Stockholm; the latter firm also has works in Finspång. The Swedish Ball-bearing Works (SKF), Svenska Kullagerfabriken) has its main works in Göteborg with own ironworks in Hofors and Hälle-fors in Bergslagen where a very carefully tested ballbearing steel is made.

The latter firm is a good example of the vertical integration of the Swedish engineering industries. With its subsidiaries SKF is the largest industrial concern in Norden employing 68 000 at home and abroad and 7 500 in Göteborg alone (1966). Two thirds of its production is exported.

KINGDOMS OF IRON AND WOOD

Concerns of the type described above are found all over the world. Other big firms are peculiar to Sweden. They originate in old ironworks in Bergslagen which, to guarantee their charcoal supply, have acquired vast forest properties. When their ironworks had to be closed down, they had the alternative of changing to wood-processing on the same site. Thus big concerns working in both fields developed.

Uddeholms AB

An example of such a concern is Uddeholms AB in Värmland, north of Lake Vänern (Fig. 12.22). It was created by an ironworks proprie-tor buying up in 1720 a number of previously independent foundries and forges, all working with iron mined from the ore-field in the mining district of Filipstad in eastern Värmland. Even in 1860 furnaces were still to be found in the forests northwest of the ore-field, and forges along the valley of the Klarälv, which was the main transport route. In 1870 the under-taking was reorganized as a company in its pre-sent form, and in 1878 a new ironworks was started with blast-furnaces and a steelworks in Hagfors. This site was chosen because (1) there is a small, suitable waterfall there, (2) the char-coal supply, which was still important, was easi-ly obtainable, as Hagfors lies in the centre of the firm's own forests, (3) the transport facili-ties necessary for a large ironworks could be ar-ranged by the company itself completing a rail-way in 1877 between the ore-field and Hagfors.

At first the transport of finished steel was by way of the Klarälv to Karlstad, but this was too troublesome on account of the fall of the river, and was replaced in 1904 by a railway, also built by the company. By 1916 all the old foundries and ironworks except Munkfors had been closed down and replaced by Hagfors. Per-haps today the Hagfors works would have been more suitably situated on Lake Vänern, e.g. in Karlstad. Through buying up nearby ironworks belonging to other firms, Nykroppa (1918), Blombacka (1930) and Degerfors (1939), the Uddeholm company has undertaken a horizon-tal integration. The new works have specialized in different products. Two small hard-metal works which are located near Stockholm have later been added to the concern. In 1962 the Riddarhyttans AB in Västmanland, with iron mines and forests, were purchased.

In order to utilize the company's vast forests, sulphate and sulphite mills were established in 1890 and 1894 on the Klarälv near Hagfors,

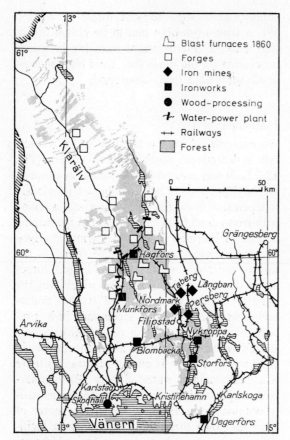

Fig. 12.22. Properties of the Uddeholm combine in eastern Värmland. — After Lennart Améen: Uddeholms Aktiebolag. Geografiska Notiser 10 (1952) Nr. 4 with later additions (1965).

lose products without trans-shipment to the different countries of Europe. In some ten of these countries the firm has its own sales organization.

The Uddeholm company employs some 15 000 persons.

Stora Kopparbergs Bergslags AB

Of the same type as Uddeholms AB is Stora Kopparbergs Bergslags AB in Dalarna (Fig. 12.23). The large forests belonging to the 650 year old company are grouped around the Dalälv and its most important wood industries are congregated in Skutskär near the mouth of the river. The iron industry had been concentrated on the Domnarvet ironworks, built in 1878 in the coal producing district. Now, however, the Domnarvet ironworks uses exclusively coke imported via Gävle. It was placed where the Dalälv was crossed by the railway right beside a waterfall. Now the river is merely a hindrance, as it inconveniently splits up the steel works. Today Gävle would have been a more suitable site.

Billeruds AB

Immediately to the west of Uddeholms AB another large company, Billeruds AB, is located. This enterprise has never been interested in the metal industry, but only in wood, and thus its

while a sawmill, started as far back as 1829 in Munkfors, was enlarged. From 1914–17 new pulp mills, a paper mill and sawmill, and a wood chemical works were erected at Skoghall, and all the old works were closed. In 1967 Uddeholm purchased the mills, forests and water rights of a Norwegian firm and thus increased its forest properties from 2 500 to 3 500 km². The intermingled forest plots of both companies can now be more rationally operated. The same applies to the water rights on the Klarälv and its tributaries, acquired in former days to safeguard the power needs of the furnaces and forges of both companies. They enlarged Uddeholm's power potentialities from 1.2 to 1.7 MkWh.

The Skoghall group of mills became the largest industrial establishment in Europe in the wood industry. Here the Uddeholm company has its own harbour, and by means of its own shipping companies carries both steel and cellu-

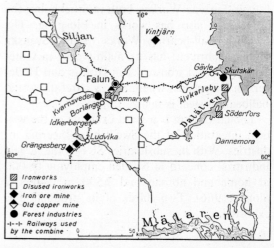

Fig. 12.23. Properties of Stora Kopparbergs combine about 1950; its headquarters are in Falun. 1. Old furnaces and foundries. 2. Forges. 3. Ironworks today. 4. Copper mine. 5. Wood industry today. 6. Iron ore mines. 7. Railways used by the combine. — After Jan-Erik Östberg: Järnet i Bergslagets historia. Bergslaget 3 (1948) Nr. 2.

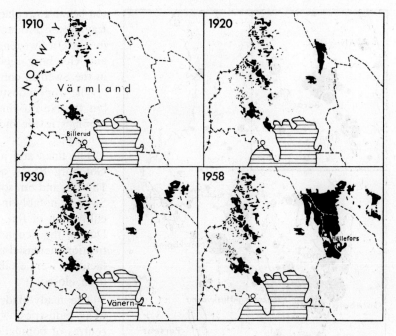

Fig. 12.24. *Forest properties of Billeruds combine,* 1910–1958. In 1958 the combine acquired Hellefors Bruks AB, on the boundaries between Dalarna, Värmland and Väst-manland.—After En bok om Billerud. Göteborg 1958.

history began as late as 1883, when a pulp mill was started at Säffle (Billerud) on Lake Vänern. At first Billeruds AB had no forests of its own, but at the beginning of the 20th century a number of ironworks which owned forests were bought up in western Värmland. Iron production was discontinued at once and the forests were utilized as sources of raw materials for new pulp- and sawmills built on the western shore of Lake Vänern. How its forest properties grew is shown in Fig. 12.24. In 1957 they covered 171 000 hectares of productive land, but a number of these forests lay rather far to the east, remote from the firm's works by Lake Vänern. In 1958 the possibility arose of acquiring Hellefors Bruks AB, situated at the boundary between Värmland and Västmanland, an under-

taking of the same kind as Uddeholms AB, viz. a combined iron and wood industry firm. As Billeruds AB was not interested in the iron industry, the ironworks were taken over by the Göteborg firm of Svenska Kullagerfabriken (SKF), which needed its own steelworks. Billeruds AB, on the other hand, could use the pulpmills and sawmill belonging to Hellefors Bruks AB, as they were conveniently located for the eastern Billerud forests. 113 000 hectares of forest land were included in the sale, and these are marked on the map for 1958 in Fig. 12.24. The intermediate section along the Klarälv is under the control of Uddeholms AB, whose industries and forest properties lie there. Billerud employed in 1966 7 200 people in sawmills, pulp and paper mills.

OTHER INDUSTRIES

In addition to the industries based on wood and iron, we will consider only food-processing and the extractive industries, which depend mainly on domestic raw materials and are very widely dispersed, and the textile industry, which is dependent on imported raw materials and is concentrated on large towns and on one specialized area. For other branches of industry, reference should be made to Fig. 7.5 and Table 7.11, p.

93, and to brief statements in the section on the industrial areas.

TEXTILES AND CLOTHING

These industries employ 9 per cent of the industrial labour force of Sweden (1965) and are relatively slightly developed in comparison with the textile industries of old industrial countries

331

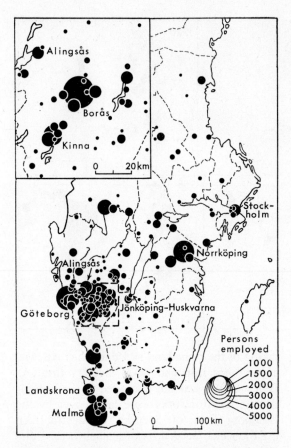

Fig. 12.25. *Textile industries,* 1964. The industry is centered on Borås and Göteborg. Circles indicate number of persons employed in each locality. The line of small localities through and beyond Borås lies in the Viskan valley. — After Sveriges industri. Stockholm 1967.

in Europe or Sweden's powerful wood and iron industries. They are largely based on the Borås district and on the Göteborg region. Towns which are noted for textiles include Norrköping and Malmö.

The clothing industry is found in the larger cities. In the Borås area and in the valley of the Viskan river there is an old handicraft tradition in linen and wool. Production was in the hands of middlemen, who provided the material, and there was also a selling agency, now obsolete, in the form of peripatic salesmen.

In Sweden the cotton industry was first introduced in the 1730's, at Alingsås, northeast of Göteborg. This was the only cotton mill for many years. During the Napoleonic blockade, Göteborg became an important free-port for cotton bought in Britain. In the Borås area cot-

ton began to replace linen and wool, and in this way cotton production became well established in western Sweden. Since about 1820 the Borås and Göteborg regions have been predominant in the Swedish cotton industry.

The wool industry is more widely distributed, but the Norrköping area has most of it. Norrköping's textile industry goes back to the 17th century.

The linen and jute industry is located in the Göteborg–Borås area, where it arose in the 1840's, and in some other places in western Sweden, notably in Oskarström in Halland. The cultivation of flax for linen has almost ceased. During the Second World War, domestic cultivation increased and a number of flax-dressing factories were established; all of them have since been closed.

The ready-made clothing, hosiery and knitwear industries, which need to be near large centres of population, are located in Göteborg, Stockholm and Malmö, but are also important in the Borås area. There is a smaller concentration in Jönköping-Huskvarna, where these industries, employing much female labour, have purposely been located in an area where the engineering industry is strongly developed.

FOOD-PROCESSING

The food-processing industries are largely localized in ports and in the plains, where the raw material is found. In numbers employed these industries rank third among Sweden's manufacturing industries.

The grain mills are modern and are concentrated in Stockholm, Göteborg, Malmö and Kalmar. Among the largest undertakings, which deliver over most of the country and abroad, are the crispbread (ryvita) factories at Filipstad in Värmland.

Dairies and slaughter-houses mainly belong to agricultural co-operative undertakings; they are concentrated in bigger units.

The sugar industry is very largely localized in Southwest Skåne. Svenska Sockerfabriks AB (SSA), centred on Arlöv near Malmö, has a monopoly of sugar production.

The highly organized canning and deep-freezing industry is based on special types of vegetable cultivation in West Skåne. The factories are at Bjuv (Findus) and Eslöv (Felix). The former were not originally connected with local cultivation. They were developed by a chocolate factory in Stockholm, which had to look for new outlets during the war and bought up a small liqueur-making works at Bjuv that had a coveted sugar ration. The Findus company, which has a large fish-freezing plant in Norway (Hammerfest), has amalgamated with the Swiss Nestlé company.

The production of margarine is now largely based on Swedish oilseed production and there are some 20 factories in South and Central Sweden, among which may be mentioned those at Norrköping and Kalmar. Production and prices are regulated by the state in order to prevent competition with butter production. The preparatory oil extraction is largely carried out at Karlshamn in Blekinge.

Starch works are concentrated on the Kristianstad plain in Skåne, where potato growing for industry occupies a large area. Most of the spirit made in the country both for industrial and human consumption is obtained by fermentation of the sugar in sulphite waste from paperpulp works in Norrland.

The tobacco industry, which has been state-owned since 1914, is now concentrated in Malmö. Tobacco growing, in the district of Åhus in eastern Skåne, has been discontinued.

EXTRACTIVE INDUSTRIES

Quarrying

By far the largest number of quarries lie in Central and South Sweden. The paving-stone industry is largely located among the fine-grained grey granites of north Bohuslän and the gneisses of the coastal district of Blekinge. In the 1920's the industry was very important and depended partly on a considerable export to England and Germany. The change-over to asphalt and cement as paving materials, together with the depression of the thirties, brought disaster to the industry. In Blekinge it has now largely ceased, but there is still some quarrying in Bohuslän.

Important quarries for granite, gneiss or quartzite for macadamized road metal and cast stone have developed in the Archaean horsts of southwestern Skåne. In other parts of the coun-try similar material for building and road-making is taken largely from eskers, which are widely exploited near large towns, important railway lines and roads. The eskers also play a vital role as water reservoirs for towns, and more and more attention is being paid to them in regional planning.

Cement

The first Portland cement-works were started in England. Germany followed in 1850 and Denmark in 1868. Another Danish cement-works was started in 1870 at Rødvig on the coast

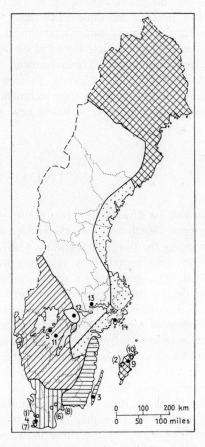

Fig. 12.26. Cement works and the areas which they supply. Black dots: present-day factories. Open rings: disused factories. 1. Lomma 1873–1905. 2. Visby 1883–1940. 3. Degerhamn 1886– . 4. Limhamn 1890– . 5. Hellekis 1892– . 6. Maltesholm 1898–1928. 7. Klagshamn 1900–39. 8. Bromölla 1907–40. 9. Slite 1918– . 10. Rute 1921–40. 11. Skövde 1924– . 12. Hidinge 1932– . 13. Köping 1941– . 14. Stora Vika 1949– . Skövde sells its cement throughout Sweden but the other works operate a sales cartel. The map shows how they divide the Swedish market between them. — After Lennart Améen.

about 50 km south of København. At Rødvig there was suitable limestone, while clay was imported by boat from Lomma in Sweden just north of Malmö. Lomma's contacts with cement manufacturers gave an impetus to the starting of the first Swedish works in 1873. Clay was found on the spot and lime was brought by boat fom Limhamn, southwest of Malmö and 14 km from Lomma. As lime forms three quarters of the raw material and clay only one quarter, it soon proved better to have the works in Limhamn, and the Lomma factory was closed down in 1905.

It can be seen from the map (Fig. 12.26) that of the ten works erected up to 1921, five were built in Skåne and three on Gotland, which means that the cement industry continued to be located on sites rich in limestone and where clay was also within reach. These factories were, however, distant from Central Sweden and especially Stockholm. Since then technical progress has made it possible to locate new works in Köping and Stora Vika, where the raw material resources are certainly inferior, but market conditions considerably better. At the same time several of the older works have closed down.

Coal mining in northwestern Skåne

Höganäs-Billesholms AB was founded in 1903 by an amalgamation of about ten firms which were started towards the end of the 19th century to exploit the coal of the southwest Skåne coalfield. These Upper Trias coals are of brown coal type. Mining and working of the clay beds between the coal seams is now more important than coal mining. They are used for refractory bricks of which the Swedish iron industry is an important consumer. This contact caused the firm to start experiments in sponge iron furnaces (p. 326). Though the original conditions for the activity of this great industrial concern have disappeared, it has survived by starting new lines of business.

INDUSTRIAL REGIONS

Sweden can be divided into two major industrial regions. South and Central Sweden up to and including the Bergslagen and the Gävle district forms one region. It is relatively thickly populated. The greater part of the industrial workers live in centres with varied industry and most of the industries produce finished products, often of high quality. The engineering and textile industries form the largest groups.

North Sweden—or Sweden north of the Gävle region—is sparsely populated, and the industrial population is concentrated in the coastal area. There are only a few inland industrial centres, mainly where mining is carried on. Industry is dominated by the wood industry and by mining and produces mainly semi-finished products or raw materials for export.

A number of industrial areas can be distinguished. In South and Central Sweden they are of two types.

Firstly there are those in and around the larger industrial towns. These regions often contain diversified industry and have a large absolute number of industrial workers. The main town, which also acts as a service centre for its area, if not included in the name of the region, is added in brackets below.

To this type belong the following 12 regions (Fig. 12.27), of which the three first mentioned are the largest ones in the country:

(1) The Stockholm region.

(2) West Skåne with diversified industry (Malmö–Hälsingborg).

(3) The Göteborg-Göta älv region.

(4) The Borås region and the Viskan valley, specializing in textiles.

(5) The Jönköping-Huskvarna region.

(6) The Östergötland region (Norrköping-Linköping-Motala).

(7) The Örebro-Kumla region, specializing in the shoe industry.

(8) Eskilstuna, with engineering.

(9) Västerås, with engineering.

(10) The Gävle-Sandviken region, closely connected with the Bergslagen district and dominated by iron and wood industries.

(11) The Bergslagen, with a traditional iron industry, which has partly changed to wood industry (Falun, Ludvika, Borlänge, Filipstad).

(12) The Värmland-Dalsland forest industry district (Karlstad).

There are, in addition, several large towns with a considerable number of industrial workers, e.g. Uppsala, Halmstad, Lidköping, Karlskrona and Kalmar, all with more than 5 000 industrial workers (initials on Fig. 12.27).

A second type of industrial region covers a larger area and is often highly specialized. In several cases enterprises within the same branch have been formed by ramifications from a few old-established businesses. These regions have no large industrial town as a centre, and the industries are often located in rather small communities. The total number of industrial workers is usually small and service centres are often weakly developed. These regions are:

(13) The East Småland glass-making district.

(14) The Anderstorp-Gnosjö district of small industries.

(15) The Småland joinery and cabinet-making industrial area.

(16) The Bohuslän stone industry district.

Two smaller rather specialized areas with a comparatively insignificant number of workers may also be mentioned. They are:

(17) The Southeast Sweden potato industrial area (Kristianstad) and

(18) The Öland-Gotland limestone industrial area.

North Sweden has three industrial regions.

(19) The wood industry area on the coast of Norrland north of the estuary of the Dalälv with wood and pulp industries.

(20) The Skellefte mining area.

(21) The Lappland mining area.

The regions not dealt with in the sections on wood and iron are described somewhat more extensively below.

South and Central Sweden

(1) The Stockholm region is the most important industrial centre in the country. A con-

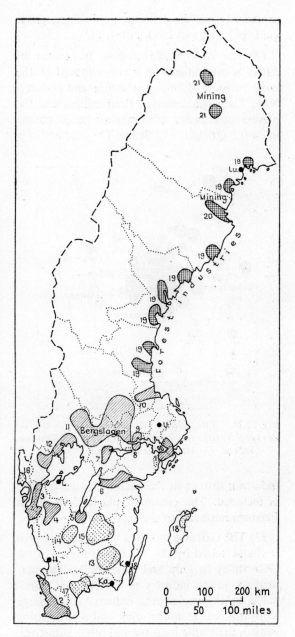

Fig. 12.27. Sweden's industrial areas. Areas with inclined shading have relatively large industrial centres; the stippled areas have only small centres; the cross-hatched areas are North Sweden's forest and mining industries. H = Halmstad. K = Kalmar. Ka = Karlskrona. L = Lidköping. Lu = Luleå. U = Uppsala. — Mainly after W. William-Olsson: Den svenska industriens geografi. Sverige som industriland. Stockholm 1950.

siderable number of the country's largest engineering firms are to be found here (see p. 328), but industry does not dominate the economic life of the capital itself. Industries typical of a

335

capital city are the printing, publishing, ready-made clothing and food industries.

(2) The West Skåne region. In general industry is diversified and is concentrated on the large towns of Malmö, Karlskrona and Hälsingborg. The sugar industry, flour-milling and the preserving industry are branches based on the intensive agriculture of Skåne. The coal and clay

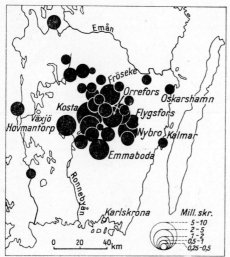

Fig. 12.28. *The glass manufacturing area of eastern Småland.* Production value in million Sw. kronor. — After Atlas of Sweden 103–104.

industrial district in the northwest (see p. 334) is included. The centre of plastic industry is Perstorp northeast of the region.

(3) The Göteborg-Göta älv industrial area is characterized by diversified industry. Up the Göta valley lie pulp and paper mills. The particularly varied industry of Göteborg is dominated by the engineering industry (three large shipyards, car manufacturing and a ballbearing works), the textile industry and other industries.

(4) The Borås region specializes in textiles (cotton-spinning and weaving, hosiery and knitwear). The industry has developed from old handicrafts in an area which has no special advantages for textiles nowadays.

(5) The Jönköping-Huskvarna region has old mining traditions. Jönköping is a service centre, but half its population is engaged in industry, including the pulp and paper industries and the main factory of the Swedish match combine. Founded in the 1840's it had an international market, and the industry had 38 enter-

prises in 1876, largely in southeast Sweden. Production reached its peak in the 1920's; then the industry began to lose valuable markets. This, together with technical developments caused a strong concentration of the enterprises. The combine employed in 1966 32 000 in Sweden and abroad. Huskvarna, with engineering, has the largest percentage of industrial workers of any Swedish town (80 per cent).

(6) In the Östergötland region is the textile industry of Norrköping, which can be considered the oldest industrial town in Sweden. It has wool, cotton and paper mills. Norrköping's paper mill started with textile waste as its most important raw material. There are also large electro-technical works. Linköping produces planes and data computers, and Motala has an important engineering industry, originally located there to provide equipment for the Göta Canal.

(7) The Örebro-Kumla region specializes in shoe manufacturing. The localization must be solely due to personal initiative, but the position is central as regards the market.

(8) Eskilstuna has a precision tool industry which started in the 17th century. No other Swedish town has so many workers employed in this branch (over 5 000).

(9) Västerås is Sweden's largest electro-technical centre making motors and plant (ASEA, see p. 329), and has also copper manufacturing (Svenska Metallverken). The town was an old port for the export of iron and copper, and because of its relationship to former mining development soon developed metal industries.

(10) The Gävle-Sandviken area is discussed on p. 326.

(11) The Bergslagen is discussed on p. 324.

(12) The Värmland-Dalsland forest industry region with Karlstad as its centre depends on its own raw material supplies. It is discussed on p. 329.

(13) East Småland's glass industry area. In 1742 the Kosta glassworks were founded, and managers and workers from Kosta started new glassworks in times of prosperity, and particularly in the mid-19th century, at a distance of about twenty miles from the parent company

(Fig. 12.28). Orrefors started in 1898. Some of the glassworks were small with little capital, and soon disappeared, but about a score of plants are still active. Rationalization has not proceeded further because the glassworks mostly produce household and artistic glassware, and can successfully cater for a variety of tastes at home or abroad.

(14) The Anderstorp-Gnosjö area. An iron industry, the most southerly in Sweden, was founded on ore mined at Taberg (Region 5). The blast-furnaces lay around this town. South of the actual mining areas a large number of small manufacturing industries were founded, mainly producing iron wire. These small works have developed into a large number of firms which each employ a small number of workers (2–10). Production first depended upon the traditional products of wire-works, but gradually developed an extremely varied assortment of metal products with a world market. Plastics are now important there. New firms have continuously been founded by workers setting up on their own. Nowhere in Sweden is the relative increase in the industrial population so large as here (Fig. 12.29).

(15) Småland's joinery region is discussed on p. 319.

(16) The Bohuslän stone industry region is discussed on p. 333.

(17) In Southeast Sweden there is an area with a large number of rural industries, although notably food and drink.

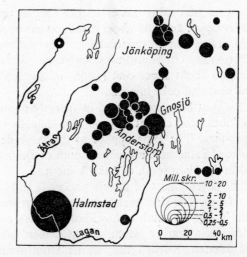

Fig. 12.29. The Anderstorp–Gnosjö region in western Småland. – After Atlas of Sweden 101–102.

POWER

Early development

Until the late 19th century, in addition to the home consumption of wood, production of charcoal was of enormous significance for satisfying Sweden's requirements of power.

Only small rivers could be used for water-power, and furnaces and forges were first located on them. As technical progress was made, the forges could be placed on larger rivers in lower lying and more thickly populated areas. The irregular fall of nearly all Swedish rivers also made possible water-driven flour- and saw-mills.

The latter half of the 19th century can be regarded as the age of steam power in Sweden. Steam-powered sawmills appeared in the lower reaches of the Swedish rivers and more diversified industry developed in the cities.

The first hydro-electric power station was erected in 1882 at Ryfors on the Viskan river

in West Sweden. Hofors Ironworks in Gästrikland set up an electric rolling plant for producing steel sheets in 1895. When high voltage transmission lines made possible the transfer of power economically over long distances, rivers lost their decisive role in the location of industry. In 1936 the first transmission line between Norrland's power plants and Central Sweden was completed from Krångede to Stockholm.

Production and consumption

Industry accounts for 42 per cent of the total Swedish power consumption (1960). The heating of dwelling-houses takes 34 per cent and motive power for means of communication 24 per cent. Of the energy thus consumed, almost three quarters is imported; two thirds of the imported fuel consists of oil and its derivatives, and one third of coal and coke. Only a third of Sweden's energy requirements is home-produced in the form of water power (15 per cent) and wood (15 per cent), despite of the building of large new hydro-electric power stations.

Oil import has increased rapidly; in 1965 it amounted to 19 million tons.

Fuel resources

Wood for fuel forms about 15 per cent of the timber hewn. In 1965 about 5 million m³ were used as fuel and for charcoal.

Brown coal from northwestern Skåne corresponds to about 2 per cent (1965) of Sweden's total coal and coke imports.

The peat bogs are situated in sparsely populated areas and cannot be used economically in peace-time. The same applies to the large deposits of Palaeozoic oil schists south of Örebro and in the plain south of Lake Vänern.

The development of atomic energy is still in its infancy. The first nuclear power station was built in Ågesta, south of Stockholm, others are being built further south, at Marviken and Oskarshamn. Sweden has, in its alum slate, large uranium resources, but the uranium content is small and expensive to concentrate.

Hydro-electric power

The long even slope of Norrland from the mountains to the Gulf of Bothnia produces a number of long rivers. Their catchment areas vary from 11 000 to 30 000 km². The most southerly, the Klarälv, debouches into Lake Vänern, which also receives tributaries from the Central Lowlands. The outlet of Vänern, Göta älv, has the largest catchment area, 50 000 km². South Swedish rivers have small catchment areas, between 2 000 and 6 000 km².

The run-off system depends on precipitation, evaporation and water storage in ice or snow, lakes and bogs. These factors give very varying types of run-off which include:

1. Mountain rivers: the flow is large; the great store of snow and ice, which causes low water in winter, melts first in the lowlands and then in the mountains, giving a powerful, prolonged spring flood. The most powerful, the Lule älv, has a mean high discharge of 1910 m³/sec. and a mean low discharge of 82 m³/sec. (Table 12.5).

2. The small rivers of the Central Lowlands flow mainly over clay plains and have rapid run-off. The spring flood is short.

3. On the South Swedish Highlands the smaller snow storage produces a less marked spring flood, and the water is higher in autumn, i.e. the wettest season. The western rivers, in an area with a higher rainfall, have about double the run-off to the square kilometre of those in the east.

Table 12.5. *Types of Swedish rivers*

	Catchment area	Run-off		
		mean high water	mean water	mean low water
	km²	m³/sec	m³/sec	m³/sec
1. *Mountain rivers*				
Lule älv	25 350	1 910	510	82
Dalälven	29 040	1 150	370	95
2. *Central Swedish rivers*				
Nyköpingsån	3 650	55	23	9
3. *South Swedish Highland rivers*				
Ätran (W-side) ..	3 350	165	50	12
Emmån (E-side)..	4 450	100	30	7
4. *Outlets of large lakes*				
Göta älv........	50 180	660	575	510

4. The outlets of the great Swedish lakes have a very even natural run-off. The huge water masses stored in Lake Vänern are used in periods of water shortage, and can even be stored for use in another year. The outflow of the Göta älv therefore exhibits a most unusual curve (Colour Map 7).

Power stations and transmission lines

Among the 46 milliards kWh, which are the developed hydro-electric power resources in Sweden in 1965, 11 milliards are produced in Upper Norrland, and 19 milliards in Central and South Norrland. The largest reserves are found in Upper Norrland, where as yet only 30 per cent of the resources is developed. In Central and South Norrland more than a half is developed.

Vertical falls are very rare in Norrland. Instead the water runs in long rapids, which necessitates complicated dams, tunnels and shafts in which the water drops vertically to subterranean power stations. Variations in flow are reduced by large dams on tributaries. In desolate areas dams create new lake systems; in Suorva, e.g., there is a difference of 18 m between the upper and the lower water level. The most heavily exploited river is the Indalsälv, which has been transformed into a staircase of reservoirs and high waterfalls. The largest reservoirs and power stations in 1960 are shown and named on Colour Map 7, which also shows the natural and regulated flow of the Indalsälv and the Göta älv. Because of the needs of nature conservation the additional building of hydro-electric stations are provisionally restricted on the Torne-, Kalix-, Pite- and Vindelälv.

The main problem of power development has been the distance between the power resources in Norrland and the regions of largest consumption in Central and South Sweden. The difficulties of transmitting electric power over long distances were to a large extent solved in 1921. Electrification of railways could thus begin without regard to the location of power stations. From 1936 it became possible to use the large hydro-electric resources of Central Norrland throughout Sweden.

The first 200 kW line was completed in 1936. Between 1952 and 1956 a new 380 kW transmission system was built from Harsprånget on the Lule älv in Upper Norrland and other power stations in Central Norrland to the south.

As reserves and regulators of supply there are large thermal stations, situated in the most densely populated areas.

The transmission lines and the largest power stations are shown and named on Fig. 7.4, p. 85. The largest hydro-electric power stations are:

Stornorrfors	(Ume älv)	385 000 kW
Harsprånget	(Lule älv)	330 000 kW
Kilforsen	(Ångermanälven)	270 000 kW
Messaure	(Lule älv)	240 000 kW
Trollhättan	(Göta älv)	235 000 kW
Krångede	(Indalsälven)	220 000 kW
Harrsele	(Ume älv)	200 000 kW
Trängslet	(Dalälven)	200 000 kW

The first five are state-owned. Krångede is the largest privately owned power station with several ironworks as part-proprietors. The state power stations produce 40 per cent of the hydro-electric power, private company-owned plants 55 per cent and plants owned by communes 5 per cent.

In 1965 thermal stations produced 5 per cent of Sweden's power. The three largest are (future output in brackets):

Stenungsund	300 000 kW	(830 000)
Malmö	230 000 kW	(400 000)
Västerås	240 000 kW	

Because the state started the first large enterprises in Central Sweden (Trollhättan on the Göta älv and Älvkarleby at the mouth of Dalälven) it controlled distribution in Central Sweden. The state also obtained control in Upper Norrland where the beginning was made when Porjus (Lule älv) was built in connection with the electrification of the Luleå-Narvik railway. Elsewhere distribution is under private or local government control, but through The Central Work Management (CDL) the whole system is linked together.

Costs per kWh of electric current are increasing, because more and more difficult building enterprises have become necessary. But hydro-electric power is still cheaper than electric power from thermal stations, in spite of their location near the centres of consumption with small losses in transmission.

COMMUNICATIONS AND TRADE

COMMUNICATIONS

Roads and canals

During the pre-industrial period there were local road networks between adjacent settlemens but few highways. These roads were not suited to heavy transport, but nevertheless the bar-iron had to be taken from the Bergslagen areas to the ports. Much of the transport had to be done during the winter, when the use of sledges across frozen lakes and swamps made conveyance easier. A winter with little snowfall always dislocated iron production and transport of both iron and charcoal. In summer heavy transport also largely used the lake system, which meant many trans-shipments.

The late 18th and the early 19th centuries, when the technique of building locks had been mastered, saw the beginning of the canal period in Sweden. The Trollhätte Canal was opened for traffic in 1800; along it bar-iron, and later timber, could be carried via Lake Vänern and the Göta älv to Göteborg. It brought about an immediate improvement in the economy of the whole Vänern area. In 1832 the Göta Canal was opened between the Baltic and Lake Vänern. It was never important commercially.

A number of lesser canals were also built between various lakes in Central Sweden, chiefly for the use of the iron industry. Apart from the Trollhätte Canal, whose locks were enlarged in 1844 and 1916, and the Södertälje Canal between the Baltic and Lake Mälaren, all these lesser canals have now been closed or are used only for tourist traffic.

Railways

The railway age began when the mines and foundries in the Bergslagen areas built railways for horse-drawn traffic (tramways) between the lakes in order to avoid transporting heavy materials by road. One example was the Yngen-Dalagränsen route in Värmland, which was composed of fifteen lakes and eleven sections of track. The iron goods had to be trans-shipped 25 times before they were finally loaded on to a large vessel in Kristinehamn on Lake Vänern.

After many years of discussion, parliamentary sanction for the construction of state railways was granted in 1853–54. The working principles then laid down explain much of what must now be regarded as an unsatisfactory rail network. Thus a main line was not allowed to follow an existing canal route, and could only cross it. Main lines were to pass through thinly populated regions, in order to assist their development, rather than through more thickly populated areas. In addition, the main lines might not be built too near the coast for military reasons. For example, the main line from Stockholm to Göteborg did not pass through the more densely populated lowlands south of Lake Vänern but took a more southeasterly upland route. The main line between Stockholm and Malmö was built through Småland in regions which are little cultivated. In this way a system of duplicated towns at some distance from one another was created. The older towns off the main railway stagnated, while the new

railway towns developed industries and grew rapidly. Among 'double towns' on the Southern main line are Eslöv–Hörby, Hässleholm–Kristianstad, Alvesta–Växjö, Sävsjö–Vetlanda and Nässjö–Eksjö, in which the firstnamed towns were new towns on the main line.

The main railway through Norrland was not taken through the line of towns on the coast, but some fifty kilometres inland, with short branch lines to the populated coastal regions.

Steam trains began to run in 1855 on a short industrial line serving an ironworks in Värmland. In 1856 parts of the main lines between Malmö and Stockholm, and Göteborg and Stockholm were opened to traffic. By 1900 the railway system had a length of 10 000 kilometres. A maximum length of 17 000 km was reached in 1937. In that year the last part of the Inland Railway was opened; it passes through very scantily populated areas in the inland part of north Sweden from Lake Vänern (Kristinehamn) to Gällivare, and was under construction for almost fifty years. Swedish capital was insufficient for railway building during the most intensive period, and large loans had to be raised, mainly in Britain.

The state railways had the standard gauge, while many of the private railway lines, which were mainly built between 1870 and 1890, had a narrower gauge. The latter were cheaper to construct, but they led to more expensive transport owing to trans-shipments, and gradually the private lines became uneconomic.

In 1880 only 33 per cent of the total length of railway lines belonged to the state. Since the 1930's, however, most of the private lines have been nationalized.

In the 1930's the railways began to feel severe competition from motor transport, but this was temporarily checked by World War II. A considerable part of the 13 200 km long railway system (1966) carries so little traffic that it is uneconomic and should be closed down as soon as a more adequate road system can be developed. Many railway stations are being closed.

The largest freights are at present carried on the main lines in South Sweden and on the Luleå–Narvik railway in the north (Fig. 12.30). The Lappland iron-ore traffic largely makes up for the losses on the rest of the railway system (25 million tons of a total goods traffic of 61 millions in 1965). In the Göteborg–Malmö–

Stockholm-triangle and on the main line from Central Sweden northwards (Mjölby–Hallsberg) there is also heavy freight traffic. From the Bergslagen areas and Värmland, and in winter from Norrland also, large quantities of timber and wood-pulp are transported to Göteborg.

A flourishing goods traffic by rail passes between Sweden and the continent by means of four train-ferries, viz. Hälsingborg–Helsingør, Malmö–København, Trelleborg–Travemünde and Trelleborg–Sassnitz. Several car-ferries ply between Sweden and Denmark (Fig. 8.30, p. 141). Sweden has rail communication with Norway through the frontier stations of Kornsjö, Charlottenberg, Storlien and Riksgränsen. Finland uses the Russian gauge, and no through traffic from Sweden is possible.

The most important goods brought into the hinterland by rail are different kinds of fuel (coal, coke and oil). The largest importing ports for such products are Stockholm, Göteborg, Malmö, Hälsingborg, Norrköping, Gävle, Sundsvall and Luleå. The greater part of the large imports to Stockholm remain in the city. Passenger traffic reaches its maximum in local traffic round Stockholm and on the main lines to Göteborg and Malmö. The Inland Line in the interior of Norrland is unimportant economically.

Since the problem of transmitting electric power over long distances was solved, the main railway lines have largely been electrified. At present 90 per cent of goods transport is on electrified lines, although not quite half the total length is electrified. Sweden ranks next after Switzerland in rail-electrification. On non-electrified lines diesel engines are increasingly used. The few Swedish lines which are double-tracked include the Stockholm–Göteborg and Malmö–Norrköping lines.

Road and rail transport

The period since the Second World War has seen a rapid increase in motoring. Private cars increased in 1953–66 from 0.4 to 1.9 millions, lorries from 103 000 to 134 000 and buses from 8 200 to 11 000. Food-processing, such as dairies, flour mills, sugar mills and slaughterhouses, have largely been centralized with a resultant increase in transport. In forestry the transport of timber by lorry is gradually re-

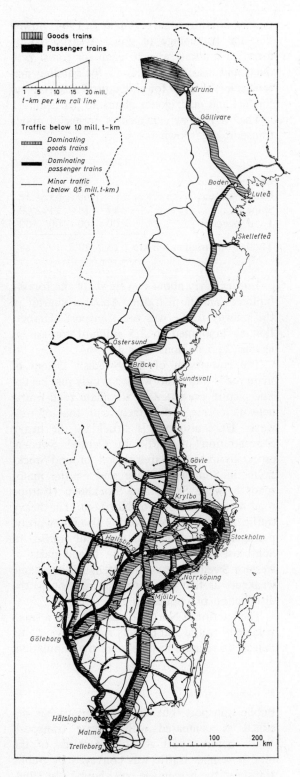

Fig. 12.30. Traffic on Sweden's railways, 1954. Brutto ton-km per km rail line, scale above. Broken lines for railways discontinued 1954–66. — After Sveriges Järnvägar hundra år. Stockholm 1956, plate between pp. 80–81.

placing floating. A survey made in 1964 showed that the percentage of goods transported by lorry (in ton-km) was 20 each for forest products and ores, more than 15 for building materials, less than 15 for agricultural material and for fuel and other goods about 30 per cent.

The varying percentages of forms of goods transport are shown below:[1]

	1950	1955	1960	1964
Lorries	20	26	34	39
Railways	63	60	55	51
Ships	17	14	11	10
Total, per cent	100	100	100	100
Total, 1 000 million ton-km	13.7	17.2	19.9	25.5

Lorries carry about two thirds of the forest-, building- and farm traffic. About a quarter of the railway traffic was ore transport. Timber-floating amounted to 1.5 milliard ton-km as against 25.5 millions by rail (1964).

The conversion of the Swedish system of main roads into motorways has only just begun. The picture presented by the main road-traffic network corresponds largely with that of railways. Here also one is struck by the heavy concentration of traffic in Central Sweden, especially in the Mälaren region, around Stockholm, in Southwest Skåne and on the major roads between Skåne and Stockholm (Europe road 4) and the coast of Norrland. The heavy traffic on the west coast road is also noteworthy, particularly as compared with rail traffic. In Southeast Sweden and in the inland parts of western Sweden the road system has the same weakness as that of railways in relation to the distribution of population.

The interior of Norrland naturally has a small volume of traffic and the bus routes have a long mileage in relation to the size of the population.

Passenger traffic

Public transport (bus, tram and train) has declined as compared with private transport. While before 1950 about two thirds of the total passenger traffic was conveyed by public transport, the percentage was about 17 in 1964. Thus the bus traffic system has been reduced, and the reduction has hit thinly populated areas

[1] Svensk ekonomi 1966—70 (Swedish long-term survey), appendix 5, Stockholm 1966.

badly. Bus traffic in the towns and their environs has, however, increased considerably.

The great increase in the use of private cars as a means of transport is accounted for by increased urbanization and longer distances travelled by commuters. Reorganization of schools has also made necessary longer journeys by school buses and private cars.

Bus communications are, however, beginning to influence the pattern of highly populated areas. Previously the city tended to grow outwards from the old market place in its most densely populated centre towards the railway station on its fringe. In many places there is now a corresponding outward growth of the city to and beyond the bus stations.

The increasing role of the private car in the conveyance of passengers is shown in the following estimates of passenger traffic[1]:

	1950	1955	1960	1964
Railways	6.6	6.2	5.2	5.3
Trams, subways	1.2	1.2	0.9	1.3
Buses	3.5	3.9	3.4	3.5
Private cars (incl. taxis)	5.6	16.4	33.2	50.5
Ships	0.2	0.1	0.1	0.1
Planes	0.02	0.04	0.2	0.3
Total	17.2	27.9	43.0	61.0

Air transport and tourist traffic

Internal air traffic is still relatively unimportant. The air network is incomplete and by far the largest number of scheduled services are concentrated on the airports of Bromma (and in international traffic) Arlanda (Stockholm), Torslanda (Göteborg), and Bulltofta (Malmö). A service along the Norrland coast, too, is much used as are the routes on Visby, Gotland. In 1964 2.9 million passengers left Swedish airports, among them 1.5 million on international routes, where a third went by charter planes.

Tourist traffic to Sweden from non-Scandinavian countries in 1964 was about 1.1 million passengers. It increased by 50 per cent in 1961–64. By far the largest number come from West Germany, followed by U.S.A. and Britain. The route generally preferred by American tourists follow the triangle København—Stockholm—Oslo. Another route followed by a smaller number runs through Norrland and ends in Narvik. In 1963 it was estimated that 17 per cent of all holiday journeys from the larger Swedish towns were to foreign countries.

TRADE

As regards national income per capita Sweden comes third after U.S.A. and Canada. It has 0.3 per cent of the population of the world but more than 2 per cent of its trade. In foreign trade per capita Sweden ranks fifth after New Zealand, Belgium, Canada and Switzerland.

Until the mid-19th century Swedish exports were limited to iron goods, tar and oats, and trade was with neighbouring European countries. Changes came with industrialization, cheaper transport for heavy goods and the breaking of trade barriers.

The economic policies of the importing countries have often obliged Sweden to export semi-finished and raw products. She has also been obliged to produce goods which could be bought more cheaply in foreign markets, in order to reduce imports. Many enterprises within the export group have formed subsidiary companies abroad, and set up plants there.

Figures for Swedish trade in 1963 are given in Tables 7.12 and 7.13, pp. 94–95 according to the ISIC classification for commodity groups (in value) and for the most important commodities (by weight). Another grouping has been used in Table 12.6, permitting a comparison between the iron- and wood industries. The former group contributes twice as much to Sweden's export trade as the latter group, but imports are important. Imports of machinery and transport equipment almost equal exports. Imports of electro-technical equipment surpass exports, whereas the import of wood products is insignificant.

The principal imports are types of fuel, particularly oil (1965: 19 million tons). In a year of normal harvest Swedish agriculture produces adequate food supplies, but the high standard of living accounts for large imports of fruit, vegetables, tobacco and wines. Some grain and animal produce are exported.

Trade by trade areas and principal countries are illustrated in Table 7.14, p. 97. About 80 per cent of Sweden's exports and 75 per cent of

its imports are with European countries. West Germany has long been Sweden's principal supplier and has recently surpassed Britain as a buyer. But Sweden's main export markets are now found in Norden. The other Norden countries absorb a quarter of Sweden's exports, the Norwegian imports of ships being particularly important.

Ores and semi-processed goods are sent mainly to European markets; more than 90 per cent of the sawn timber goes to Europe. Finished goods have a wider market.

Table 12.6. *Foreign trade in million Sw.kr. 1966*

	Exports	Imports	Balance
Food, beverages, tobacco	700	2 942	—2 242
Crude materials........	5 502	4 316	+1 186
Wood, lumber	1 422	68	
Pulp	2 332	5	
Ores	1 207	410	
Fuels	137	2 686	
Chemical products	831	1 872	—1 041
Manufactured goods ..	7 217	7 667	— 450
Paper	2 072	199	
Textiles	537	1 283	
Iron and metals	1 846	1 930	
Machinery and transport equipment	7 852	6 866	+ 986
Machinery, non-electr.	3 893	3 094	
Electrical machinery..	1 365	1 623	
Ships, cars	2 593	2 149	
Total	22 102	23 663	—1 561

If the ore-export ports of Luleå (and Narvik) and Oxelösund are excluded, the largest export port is Göteborg, which seems to be developing as the container harbour of the whole of Norden. Stockholm has the greatest total trade. The next largest ports are Malmö and Hälsingborg, Gävle and Norrköping, the two latter being overshadowed by Stockholm. Large inland ports are Västerås and Karlstad which are situated on lake routes navigable by ocean-going ships. In all these regional ports (with exception of Gävle where the scales are even) imports are dominant.

The merchant fleet includes about 4 500 000 gross tons (1966), and the largest shipping companies are based on Stockholm and Göteborg. A third of the tonnage is tankers.

SELECTED BIBLIOGRAPHY

In order not to increase the numbers listed, works included in the 1960-bibliography have been omitted if newer works cover the same field, as have part studies and preliminary reports if more syntetic works have been published since. Principally the bibliography contains publications in English, French and German, or studies in Scandinavian languages with substantial summaries in a foreign language. Some publications only in a Scandinavian language have however been included: a few handbooks and some studies about subjects not otherwise covered in the list. References are given in connection to maps and diagrams and are not included below.

NORDEN

AHLMANN, H. W:son: The present climatic fluctuation. — *Geogr. J.* 112 (1948): 165–195.

BAILEY, E. B. and O. HOLTEDAHL: Northwestern Europe Caledonides. — In K. Andrée, H. A. Brouwer & W. H. Bucher (edit.): Regionale Geologie der Erde 2 : II. Leipzig 1938.

BLÜTHGEN, J.: Der skandinavische Fjällbirkenwald als Landschaftsformation. — *Petermanns geogr. Mitt.* 104 (1960): 119–144.

CHABOT, G.: Finlande et les pays scandinaves. — In G. Chabot, A. Guilcher & J. Beaujeu-Garnier: L'Europe du Nord et du Nord-Ouest. Tome 2. — (Coll. Orbis.) Paris 1958.

DAHL, E.: Biogeographic and geologic indications of unglaciated areas in Scandinavia during the glacial ages. — *Bull. geol. Soc. Am.* 66 (1955): 1499–1520.

EKMAN, S.: Djurvärldens utbredningshistoria på Skandinaviska halvön. Stockholm 1922.

Geogr. Jb. 56 (1941). Basic bibliographies are given by J. BLÜTHGEN: Dänemark (1930–40), Finland (1929–41), Schweden (1929–40 mit Nachträgen) and by W. EVERS: Norwegen (1929–40).

HELLAND-HANSEN, B. & F. NANSEN: The Norwegian Sea, its physical oceanography, based upon the Norwegian Researches 1900–1904. — *Rep. Norw. Fishery mar. Invest.* II (1909) 2.

HULTÉN, E.: Atlas över växternas utbredning i Norden. Stockholm 1950. English summary. (Atlas of the distribution of vascular plants in NW. Europe.)

MANNERFELT, C.: Några glacialmorfologiska formelement och deras vittnesbörd om inlandsisens avsmältningsmekanik i svensk och norsk fjällterräng. — *Geogr. Annlr* 27 (1945): 2–239. English summary. (Some glaciomorphological forms and their evidence as to the downwasting of the inland ice in Swedish and Norwegian mountain terrain.)

MEAD, W. R.: An economic geography of the Scandinavian states and Finland. London 1958.

The Northern countries in world economy. Publ. by the Delegations for the promotion of economic cooperation between the northern countries. Finland 1937. Also published in French, German, Danish–Norwegian–Swedish, Finnish editions, and a revised English edition (1939).

On the forest-tundra and the northern tree-lines. Edit. by I. HUSTICH. — *Annls Univ. turku.* A II:36 (Rep. Kevo subarctic sta. 3), (1966): 7–47.

SJÖRS, H.: Nordisk växtgeografi. — Scandinavian University Books. Stockholm 1956.

SWEDBERG, S.: Våra grannländers näringsliv. Stockholm 1959.

TAMM, O. F.: Northern coniferous forest soils. Oxford 1950.

VORREN, Ø. & E. MANKER: Lapp life and customs, a survey. London 1962. Die Lappen. Braunschweig 1967.

DENMARK

General

Atlas of Denmark. Edit. by N. NIELSEN. Vol. I. The Landscapes. By A. SCHOU. København 1949. Vol. II. The Population. By A. AAGESEN. København 1961. Collected papers, Denmark. I.G.U. Congress 1964. Edit. by N. KINGO JACOBSEN.

Danmarks natur, Vol. 1–12. Vol. 1. Landskabernes opståen. København 1967.

Guide-Book Denmark. I.G.U. Congress 1960. Edit. by N. KINGO JACOBSEN. — *Geogr. Tidsskr.* 59 (1960).

HUMLUM, J. & K. NYGÅRD: Danmark-Atlas med Færøerne og Grønland. København 1961.

TRAP, J. P.: Danmark. Vol. 1–10. København 1958–67.

Physical geography

BORNEBUSCH, C. H. & K. MILTHERS: Jordbundskort over Danmark. Soil map of Denmark. — *Danm. geol. Unders.* III. Række, No. 24 (1935). Danish and English text.

HANSEN, V.: Sandflugten i Thy og dens indflydelse på kulturlandskabet. — *Geogr. Tidsskr.* 56 (1957) : 69–92. English summary. (The movement of sand dunes in Thy and its human consequences.)

JACOBSEN, N. KINGO: Mandø. En klitmarskø i Vadehavet. — *Geogr. Tidsskr.* 52 (1952–53) : 134–146. English summary. (An island in the Danish Waddensea.)

: Træk af Tøndermarskens naturgeografi med særlig henblik på morfogenesen. Bilag: Kortmappe med 29 plancher. København 1965. English summary.

JAKOBSEN, B.: The Tidal Area in south-western Jutland and the process of the salt marsh formation. — *Geogr. Tidsskr.* 53 (1954) : 49–61.

: Vadehavets morfologi. En geografisk analyse af Vadelandskabets formudvikling med særlig hensyn tagen til Juvre Dybs tidevandsområde. Summary in English and German. København 1964.

JENSEN, K. M.: An outline of the climate of Denmark. — *Geogr. Tidsskr.* 59 (1960).

KUHLMAN, H.: Sandflugt og klitdannelse. — *Geogr. Tidsskr.* 56 (1957) : 1–19.

LYSHEDE, J. M.: Hydrologic studies of Danish watercourses. — *Folia geogr. dan.* 6 (1955).

MILTHERS, K.: Ledeblokke og landskabsformer i Danmark. — *Danm. geol. Unders.* II. Række, No. 69 (1942). English summary. (Indicator boulders and morphology of the landscape in Denmark.)

MILTHERS, V.: Bornholms geologi. — *Danm. geol. Unders.* V. Række, No. 1 (1930).

: Det danske istidslandskabs terrænformer og deres opstaaen. — *Danm. geol. Unders.* III. Række, No. 28 (1948). English summary. (The morphology and genesis of the glacial landscape of Denmark.)

MØLLER, J. T.: Fladkystens og flodens morfologiske elementer i det tidevandsprægede landskab med dettes særlige vegetation og hydrologiske forhold. English summary. København 1964.

NIELSEN, N.: Eine Methode zur exakten Sedimentationsmessung. — *Biol. Meddr* XII, 4 (1935).

SCHOU, A.: Det marine forland. — *Folia geogr. dan.* 4 (1945). English summary. (The marine foreland. Geographical studies in the development of young coastal plains of Denmark, with an outline of their anthropogeography.)

: Die Naturlandschaften Dänemarks. — *Geogr. Rdsch.* 8 (1956) : 413–423.

: The coastline of Djursland. A study in East-Danish shoreline development. — *Geogr. Tidsskr.* 59 (1960) : 10–27.

: The Danish moraine archipelago as a research field for coastal morphology and dynamics. — *Proc. XVIIth Congress IGU.* Washington 1952.

Human geography

AAGESEN, A.: Die Bevölkerung Dänemarks. — *Geogr. Rdsch.* 8 (1956) : 424–431.

ANTONSEN, K.: Placeringen af Danmarks industri 1938 til 1960. English summary. København 1964.

BØCHER, S. B.: Træk af vejudviklingen i Danmark belyst gennem beliggenheden af vigtige vadesteder og broer. — *Geogr. Tidsskr.* 65 (1966) : 129–176. English summary. (Development of the Danish road pattern.)

Denmark. Published by the Royal Danish Ministry of Foreign Affairs and the Danish Statistical Dept. København 1960. This handbook is also published in German, French, Spanish and Italian.

HANSEN, V.: Vore landsbyers alder og struktur. — *Geogr. Tidsskr.* 58 (1959) : 66–102. English summary. (The Danish village: Its age and form.)

: Den rurale by. De bymæssige bebyggelsers opståen og geografiske udbredelse. — *Geogr. Tidsskr.* 64, 2 (1965) : 54–69. English summary.

: Landskab og bebyggelse i Vendsyssel. Studier over landbebyggelsens udvikling indtil slutningen af 1600-tallet. English summary. (Morphology and rural settlement in Vendsyssel.) København 1964.

HASTRUP, F.: Danske landsbytyper. En geografisk analyse. Med 10 kortbilag i farver. English and German summary. Århus 1964.

HUMLUM, J.: Landsplanlægningsproblemer. — *Skr. geogr. Inst. Århus univ.* 18 (1966). English summary.

ILLERIS, S.: The functions of Danish towns. — *Geogr. Tidsskr.* 63, 2 (1964) : 203–236.

: Funktionelle regioner i Danmark omkring 1960. — *Geogr. Tidsskr.* 66 (1967) : 225–251. English summary. (Hinterland delimitations of Danish towns.)

JENSEN, K. M.: A change in land-use in Central Jutland. — *Geogr. Tidsskr.* 63, 2 (1964) : 130–145.

KAMPP, A. H.: Landbrugsgeografiske studier over Danmark. — *Det Kgl. Geogr. Selskab's Kulturgeogr. Skr.* 6 (1959). English summary. (I. Agricultural regions in Denmark. II. The subdivision of agricultural land.)

: Some changes in structure of Danish farming, particularly from 1940–1960. — *Geogr. Tidsskr.* 62 (1963) : 80–101.

KAMPP, A. H. & K. E. FRANDSEN: En gård i landsbyen. — *Geogr. Tidsskr.* 66 (1967) : 198–224. English summary. (A farm in the village.)

MCLEISH, A. B.: A revised map of Danish fishing grounds. — *Geogr. Tidsskr.* 62 (1963) : 125–127.

SKRUBBELTRANG, F.: Agricultural development and rural reform in Denmark. — *FAO Agricultural studies* 22 (1953).

THE FAEROES

KAMPP, A. H.: Færøerne. København 1967.

The Faeroe Islands. Published by the Royal Danish Ministry of Foreign Affairs. København 1960.

GREENLAND

FRISTRUP, B.: The Greenland Ice Cap. London 1966.

Greenland. Published by the Commission for the Direction of the Geological and Geographical Investigation in Greenland. Chief editor: M. VAHL. London–Copenhagen 1928.

Greenland. Published by the Royal Danish Ministry of Foreign Affairs. København 1956.

A number of scientific papers dealing with Greenland are published in *Medd. Grønland.*

FINLAND

General

Atlas of the archipelago of southwestern Finland (Atlas över Skärgårdsfinland). Helsinki 1960.

Atlas of Finland 1960 with explanatory notes. Helsinki 1961. Previous editions 1899, 1910 and 1925.

Finland and its geography. New York 1955 = Suomi 1952 (see below).

GRANÖ, J. G.: Die geographischen Gebiete Finlands. — Fennia 52 (1931).

HUSTICH, I. (edit.): The recent climatic fluctuation in Finland and its consequences. A symposium. — Fennia 75 (1952).

MEAD, W. R. & H. SMEDS: Winter in Finland. London 1967.

Suomi. A general handbook on the geography of Finland. — Fennia 72 (1952).

Three faces of Finland. Guide-book I.G.U. Congress 1960. — Fennia 84 (1960).

Physical geography

AARTOLAHTI, T.: Oberflächenformen von Hochmooren und ihre Entwicklung in Südwest-Häme und Nord-Satakunta. — Fennia 93 (1965).

EUROLA, S.: Über die regionale Einteilung der südfinnischen Moore. — Annales botanici societatis zoologicae-botanicae fennicae Vanamo 33 (1962) 2.

GRANÖ, O.: Die Ufer der Südküste Finnlands. — Fennia 83 (1960).

HALONEN, R. & T. JUUSELA: Suomen peltojen maalajit, muokkauskerroksen syvyys ja maan happamuus. — Acta Agralia fennica 29 (1957). English summary. (The soil types of the fields in Finland, the depth of the tilled layer and the acidity of the soil.)

ILVESSALO, Y.: Suomen metsät vuosista 1921–24 vuosiin 1951–53. — Communicationes Instituti forestalis fenniae 47 (1958) No. 1. English summary. (The forests of Finland from 1921–24 to 1951–53.)

KLÖVEKORN, M.: Die finnlandschwedische Bevölkerung und die Sprachverthältnisse in Finnland. — Erdkunde 12 (1958) : 151–182.

KUKKAMÄKI, T. J. (edit.): Symposium on recent crustal movements in Finland with bibliography. — Fennia 89 (1964).

LISITZIN, E.: Contribution to the knowledge of land uplift along the Finnish coast. — Fennia 89 (1964).

RUUHIJÄRVI, R.: Über die regionale Einteilung der nordfinnischen Moore. — Annales botanici societatis zoologicae-botanicae fennicae Vanamo 31 (1960).

SAURAMO, M.: Die Geschichte der Ostsee. — Annales Academiae scientiarum fennicae A III, Geologica-Geographica 51 (1958).

SIRÉN, A.: On computing the land uplift from the lake water level. Records in Finland. — Fennia 73 (1950–51).

Symposium on man's influence on nature in Finland. Edit. by I. HUSTICH. — Fennia 85 (1961).

TANNER, V.: Die Oberflächengestaltung Finnlands. — Bidr. Känn. Finl. Nat. Folk 86 (1938).

VARJO, U.: Über finnische Küsten und ihre Entstehung. — Fennia 91 (1964).

Human geography

ALESTALO, J.: Die Anbaugebiete von Ackerpflanzen in Finnland. — Fennia 92 (1965).

Asutustoiminnan Aikakauskirja — Colonization activity yearbook 1950 –. English supplement. (Statistical data on state settlement activity.)

FOGELBERG, P.: Regionale Differenzierung in der finnischen Landwirtschaft. — Fennia 92 (1965).

JAATINEN, S.: The birthplace field of Helsinki, according to the census of 1950. — Fennia 86 (1962).

JAATINEN, S. & W. R. MEAD: The intensification of Finnish farming. — Econ. Geogr. 33 (1957) : 31–40.

LINDSTÅHL, S.: A survey of the geographical distribution of industry in Finland in 1952. — Fennia 79 (1955).

MEAD, W. R.: Farming in Finland. London 1953.

MIELONEN, M.: Die Vaara-Siedlung in Nord-Karelien und ihre Beziehung zur Landwirtschaft. — Fennia 93 (1965).

OKKO, V.: Die Tonvorkommnisse und die Ziegelindustrie in Finnland. — Fennia 81 (1958).

PALOMÄKI, M.: Post war pioneering in Finland, with special reference to the role of the settlement areas. — Fennia 84 (1960).

PALOMÄKI, M., J. GRANFELT & K. PALMGREN: Suomen keskus- ja vaikutusaluejärjestelmä. — Publications of the National Planning Office A 19 (1967). English summary. (The system of functional centers and areas in Finland.)

Report on the Floating committee on the improvement of transport facilities for timber produced in the main water-system areas of Saimaa and Pielinen. — Communicationes Instituti forestalis fenniae 1962. English summary.

SMEDS, H.: The distribution of urban and rural population in southern Finland 1950. — Fennia 81 (1957).

: Post war land clearance and pioneering activities in Finland. — Fennia 83 (1960).

: Recent changes in the agricultural geography of Finland. — Fennia 87 (1963).

SVENTO, I.: Vergleich zwischen dem Dichtort und seinem Einflussgebiet in Finnland. — Fennia 92 (1965).

TUOMINEN, O.: Zur Geographie der Erwerbe in Finnland. — Fennia 78 (1954).

VUORISTO, K.-V.: Die Wirkung der Veränderung von Verkehrsverhältnissen auf die Entwicklung einiger zentralen Küstenorte in Finnland. — Fennia 94 (1966).

ICELAND

General

Iceland. — Geographical Handbook Series B.R. 504. Cambridge 1942.

Iceland 1966. Handbook published by the Central Bank of Iceland. Reykjavík 1967.

MALMSTRÖM, V. H.: A regional geography of Iceland. — *National Academy of Sciences – National Research Council* Publ. 584. Washington D.C. 1958. (Mimeographed.)

THORARINSSON, S.: The thousand years struggle against ice and fire. Reykjavík 1956.

Physical geography

AHLMANN, H. W:son & S. THORARINSSON: Vatnajökull. Scientific results of the Swedish-Icelandic investigations 1936–37–38. — *Geogr. Annlr* 19 (1937) : 146––231, 20 (1938) : 171–233, 21 (1939) : 39–65, 171–242, 22 (1940) : 188–205, 25 (1943) : 1–54.

ÁSKELSSON, J., G. BODVARSSON, T. EINARSSON, G. KJARTANSSON & S. THORARINSSON: On the geology and geophysics of Iceland. Guide to excursion A 2. XXI Int. Geol. Congr. 1960.

BARTH, T. F. W.: Volcanic geology. Hot springs and geysers of Iceland. — *Publs Carnegie Instn* 587 (1950).

BEMMELEN, R. W. van & M. G. RUTTEN: Tablemountains of Northern Iceland. Leiden 1955.

EINARSSON, T.: Upper tertiary and pleistocene rocks in Iceland. — *Soc. Sci. Isl.* 36 (1962).

EINARSSON, Th.: Pollenanalytische Untersuchungen zur spät- und postglazialen Klimageschichte Islands. — *Sonderveröff. geol. Inst. Köln* 6 (1961).

HJULSTRÖM, F., J. JÓNSSON, L. ARNBORG & Å. SUNDBORG: The Hoffellssandur. I-II. — *Geogr. Annlr* 36 (1954) : 135–189, 37 (1955) : 170–245.

JÓHANNESSON, B.: The soils of Iceland. — *Univ. Res. Inst. Dept of Agric.* Ser. B, No. 13. Reykjavík 1960.

KJARTANSSON, G.: Sur la récession glaciaire et les types volcaniques sur le plateau central de l'Islande. — *Revue Géomorph. dynam.* 16 (1966) : 1–17.

NIELSEN, N.: Contributions to the physiography of Iceland. — *Mem. K. danske Vidensk. Selsk.* Ser. 9, t. 4, No. 5 (1933) : 183–288.

RIST, S.: Íslenzk vötn. Icelandic fresh waters. The State Electricity Authority. Hydrological survey. Reykjavík 1956.

SCHWARZBACH, M.: Geologenfahrten in Island. 2. Aufl. Ludwigsburg 1964.

STEINDÓRSSON, S.: Studies on the vegetation of the Central Highland of Iceland. The botany of Iceland. Vol. III, 4. Copenhagen 1945.

THORARINSSON, S.: Laxárgljúfur and Laxárhraun. — *Geogr. Annlr* 33 (1951) : 1–89.

: Notes on patterned ground in Iceland. — *Geogr. Annlr* 33 (1951) : 144–156.

: The Öræfajökull eruption of 1362. — *Acta nat. islandica* II, 2 (1958) : 1–99.

: L'érosion éolienne en Islande à la lumière des études téphrochronologiques. — *Revue Géomorph. dynam.* 13 (1963) : 107–124.

THORARINSSON, S., T. EINARSSON & G. KJARTANSSON: On the geology and geomorphology of Iceland. — *Geogr. Annlr* 41 (1959) : 135–169.

THORODDSEN, T.: Die Geschichte der isländischen Vulkane. — *K. danske Vidensk. Selsk. Skr. Nat. mathem. Afd.* 8, IX (1925).

WALKER, G. P. L.: Geology of the Reydafjörður area, eastern Iceland. — *Q. Jl geol. Soc. Lond.* 114 (1958) : 367–393.

Human geography

ASHWELL, I. Y.: Recent changes in the pattern of farming in Iceland. — *Can. Geogr.* 7 (1963) : 174–181.

PICARD, A.: L'essor récent des transports islandais. — *Norois* 42 (1964) : 205–212.

THORARINSSON, S.: Tefrokronologiska studier på Island. — *Geogr. Annlr* 26 (1944) : 1–217. English summary. (Tephrochronological studies in Iceland.)

: Iceland in the Saga period. Some geographical aspects. — *Third Viking Congress, Reykjavík* 1956: 13–24. Reykjavík 1959.

: Öræfajökull und die Landschaft Öræfi. — *Erdkunde* 13 (1959) : 124–138.

: Population changes in Iceland. — *Geogr. Rev.* 51 (1951) : 510–533.

NORWAY

General

Det Norske Geografiske Selskab 50 år. — *Norsk geogr. Tidsskr.* 7 (1938/39) : 257–694. In English, French and German.

Guidebook Norway. I.G.U. Congress 1960. — *Norsk geogr. Tidsskr.* 17 (1959/60).

HELVIG, M. & V. JOHANNESSEN: Norway. Land, people, industries. A brief geography. Oslo 1966.

MYKLEBOST, H. & S. STRØMME (edit.): Norge. Vol. I–IV. Oslo 1963.

SUND, T. & A. SØMME: Norway in maps. — *Geogr. Avh., Bergen* 1 (1947).
: La Norvège. Aspects géographiques. Rôle dans le Norden. Oslo 1962.

SØMME, A. (edit.): Vestlandet, geographical studies. — *Geogr. Avh., Bergen* 7 (1960).

VORREN, Ø. (edit.): Norway north of 65. — *Tromsø Mus. Skr.* 8 (1960).

Physical geography

ANDERSEN, B.: Sørlandet i sen- og postglacial tid. — *Norg. geol. Unders.* 210 (1960). English summary. (The late- and postglacial history of Southern Norway between Fevik and Åna-Sira.)

DONS, J. A. (edit.): Excursions in Norway. 17 guidebooks prepared for the XXI Int. Geol. Congress 1960. — *Norg. geol. Unders.* 212 (1960).

GJESSING, J.: Isavsmeltningstidens drenering, dens forløp og formdannende virkning i Nordre Atnedalen. — *Ad Novas* 3 (1960). English summary. (The drainage of the deglaciation period, its trends and morphogenetic activity in northern Atnedalen, with comparative studies from northern Gudbrandsdalen and northern Østerdalen.)

HOEL, A. & J. NORVIK: Glaciological bibliography of Norway. — *Norsk Polarinstitutt Skr.* 126 (1962).

HOEL, A. & W. WERENSKIOLD: Glaciers and snowfields in Norway. — *Norsk Polarinstitutt Skr.* 114 (1962).

HOLTEDAHL, O. (edit.): Geology of Norway. With 19 plates and a geological (bedrock) map of Norway and a glacial map of Norway. — *Norg. geol. Unders.* 208 (1960).

Human geography

ADAMSON, O. J. (edit.): Industries of Norway. Oslo 1952.

BARBE, M.: La pêche aux Îles Lofoten. — *Revue Géogr. Lyon* 41 (1966) : 29–60.

BJØRKVIK, H.: Norwegian seter-farming. — *Scandinavian Econ. Hist. Rev.* 11 (1963) : 156–166.

CABOURET, M.: L'évolution de la vie pastorale dans la vallée de l'Otta (Norvège orientale). — *Revue Géogr. alpine* 52 (1964) : 631–684.

HANSEN, J. C.: Industriell utvikling og tettstedsvekst. Norske eksempler. — *Norsk geogr. Tidsskr.* 20 (1965/66) : 181–265. English abstract. (Industrial development and urban growth. Norwegian examples.)

HELVIG, M. & K. J. JONES: Oslo, planning and development. Oslo 1960.

HOLT-JENSEN, A.: Hva er en fjellbygd? — *Norsk geogr. Tidsskr.* 19 (1963/64) : 113–141. English summary.

LÅG, J.: Fordelingen av jordbruksarealet i Sør-Norge. — *Norsk geogr. Tidsskr.* 17 (1959/60) : 264–270. English version. (Distribution of homefields in Southern Norway.)

MYKLEBOST, H.: Norges tettbygde steder 1875–1950. — *Ad Novas* 4 (1960). English summary. (Urban settlements in Norway 1875–1950.)

: Urbanization and rural depopulation in Norway. — *Proceedings Fourth New Zealand Geography Conference* 1965 : 167–176.

OUREN, T.: The port traffic of the Oslofjord region. — *Geogr. Avh., Bergen* 6 (1958).

PÖHLANDT, H.-J.: Stand und Probleme der norwegischen Stadtgeographie. — *Norsk geogr. Tidsskr.* 19 (1963/64) : 335–377.

RASMUSSEN, T. F.: Storbyutvikling og arbeidsreiser. En undersøkelse av pendling, befolkningsutvikling, næringsliv og urbanisering i Oslo-området. — *Samfunnsøkonomiske studier* 18 (1966). English summary. (Metropolitan growth, commuting and urbanization in the Oslo area.)

SKINNEMOEN, K. (edit.): An outline of Norwegian forestry. Det Norske Skogselskab. Oslo 1964.

Statistisk Sentralbyrå: Bosettingskart over Norge. (Population map of Norway.) Oslo 1955.

SØMME, A.: Jordbrukets geografi i Norge – Geography of Norwegian agriculture. — *Geogr. Avh., Bergen* 3 B. Atlas (1949). 3 A. Text vol. (1954).

: The physical background of Norwegian agriculture. — *Geography* 35 (1950) : 141–154.

SVALBARD

HEINTZ, A.: Russian opinion about the discovery of Spitsbergen. — *Norsk Polarinstitutt Årb.* 1964 : 93–118.

ORVIN, A. K.: Outline of the geological history of Spitsbergen. — *Skr. Svalb. og Ishavet* 78 (1940).

SWEDEN

General

AHLMANN, H. W:son a.o.: Sverige – Land och folk. I–III. Stockholm 1966.

Atlas of Sweden. Ed. by Svenska Sällskapet för Antropologi och geografi. Kartografiska Institutet. Generalstabens litografiska anstalt, Stockholm. National atlas published since 1953 in sheets with descriptions in Swedish and English.

BERGSTEN, K. E.: Svensk geografisk bibliografi. — *Svensk geogr. Årsbok.* Swedish geographical bibliography, annually since 1924.

Guidebook Sweden I.G.U. Congress 1960 — *Geogr. Annlr* 41 (1959), 42 (1960), *Gothenburg School of Economics Publications* 1960, *Svensk geogr. Årsbok* 36 (1960), *Ymer* 80 (1960), *Biul. peryglac.* 11 (1962) (The Abisko symposium 1960).

Physical geography

ÅNGSTRÖM, A.: Sveriges klimat. Stockholm 1958.

BERGDAHL, A.: Israndbildningar i östra Syd- och Mellansverige. Lund 1953. English summary. (Glacial marginal phenomena in eastern South and Central Sweden.)

HOPPE, G.: Glacial morphology and inland ice recession in northern Sweden. — *Geogr. Annlr* 41 (1959): 193–212.

JOHNSSON, G.: Glacialmorfologiska studier i södra Sverige. — *Meddn Lunds Univ. geogr. Instn* 31 (1956). English summary. (Glacial morphology in southern Sweden.)

LARSSON, I.: Structure and landscape. — *Lund Stud. Geogr.* Ser. A. No. 7 (1954).

LJUNGNER, E.: Spaltentektonik und Morphologie der schwedischen Skagerakküste. I–III. — *Bull. geol. Instn Univ. Ups.* 21 (1927–1930).

LUNDQVIST, G.: Description to accompany the map of the Quaternary deposits of Sweden. — *Sver. geol. Unders.* Ser. Ba, No. 17 (1959).

: Beskrivning till karta över landisens avsmältning och högsta kustlinjen i Sverige. — *Sver. geol. Unders.* Ser. Ba, No. 18 (1961). English summary. (Outline of the deglaciation in Sweden.)

LUNDQVIST, J.: Patterned ground and related frost phenomena in Sweden. — *Sver. geol. Unders.* Ser. C, No. 584 (1962).

: The Quaternary of Sweden. The Quaternary. Vol. I. Edit. K. Rankama. Bath 1965.

MAGNUSSON, N. H. et al.: Description to accompany the map of the prequaternary rocks of Sweden. — *Sver. geol. Unders.* Ser. Ba, No. 16 (1960).

MAGNUSSON, N. H., G. LUNDQVIST & G. REGNÉLL: Sveriges geologi. 4. ed. Stockholm 1963.

RAPP, A.: Recent development of mountain slopes in Karkkevagge and surroundings, Northern Sweden. — *Geogr. Annlr* 42 (1960) : 65–200.

RUDBERG, S.: Västerbottens berggrundsmorfologi. — *Geographica* 25 (1954). English summary. (The morphology of Västerbotten. An attempt at a reconstruction of cycles of preglacial erosion in Sweden.)

SCHYTT, V.: The glaciers of the Kebnekajse-Massif. — *Geogr. Annlr* 41 (1959) : 213–230.

Human geography

AMÉEN, L.: Stadsbebyggelse och domänstruktur. Lund 1964. English summary. (Urban settlement and domaine structure. Urban development in Sweden in relation to proprietary rights and administrative limits.)

ARPI, G.: Sveriges nutida näringsliv. 4 ed. Stockholm 1965.

DAHL, S.: Det svenska nätet av handelsorter. Göteborg 1965.

ENEQUIST, G.: Nedre Luledalens byar. — *Geographica* 4 (1937).

: Advance and retreat of rural settlement in northwestern Sweden. — *Geogr. Annlr* 42 (1960) : 211–220.

ERIKSSON, G. A.: Advance and retreat of charcoal iron industry and rural settlement in Bergslagen. — *Geogr. Annlr* 42 (1960) : 267–284.

GODLUND, S.: Population, regional hospitals, transport facilities and regions. — *Lund Stud. Geogr.* Ser. B No. 21 (1961).

: Den svenska urbaniseringen. Strukturförändringarna inom näringslivet – välståndsutvecklingen. English summary. (Swedish urbanization.) — *Ingenjörs-Vetenskaps-Akademien.* Medd. 139 (1963).

: Trafikutveckling och trafikinvesteringar. Statens offentliga utredningar 69. Stockholm 1966. English summary. (Traffic development and traffic investments in Sweden.)

GÖRANSSON, S.: Field and village of the island of Öland. A study of the genetic compound of an East Swedish rural landscape. — *Geogr. Annlr* 40 (1958) : 101–158.

HANNERBERG, D.: Die älteren skandinavischen Ackermasse. — *Lund Stud. Geogr.* Ser. B, No. 12 (1955).

HANNERBERG, D., T. HÄGERSTRAND & B. ODEVING (edit.): Migration in Sweden. A symposium. — *Lund Stud. Geogr.* Ser. B, No. 13 (1957).

HELMFRID, S.: Den interregionala migrationen i Sverige vid 1960-talets början. — *Ymer* 83 (1963) : 106–143. German summary. (Die interregionale Bevölkerungsbewegung in Schweden um 1960.)

: The storskifte, enskifte and laga skifte in Sweden – general features. — *Geogr. Annlr* 43 (1961) : 114–129.

JONASSON, O., E. HÖJER, R. TORSELL & S. HOLMSTRÖM: Jordbruksatlas över Sverige. 2. utg. Stockholm 1952.

KRISTIANSSON, A. L.: Kulturgeografiska studier i Stockholms norra skärgård. — *Geogr. Annlr* 29 (1947) : 48–127. English summary.

LEWAN, N.: Landsbebyggelse i förvandling. Lund 1967. English summary. (Rural settlement in transition.)

MORRILL, R. L.: Migration and the spread and growth of urban settlement. — *Lund Stud. Geogr.* Ser. B, No. 26 (1965).

NELSON, H.: Studier över svenskt näringsliv, säsongarbete och befolkningsrörelser under 1800- og 1900-talen. Lund 1963. English summary. (Studies on economic geography. Seasonal work, and population movements in Sweden during the nineteenth and twentieth centuries.)

NORDSTRÖM, O.: Svensk glasindustri 1550–1960. Lund 1962. German summary. (Die schwedische Glasindustrie 1550–1960.)

RASMUSSON, G.: Sverige ur social naturvårdssynpunkt. Ett försök till regional differentiering. — *Svensk Geogr. Årsbok* 41 (1965) : 96–110. English summary. (Sweden and social nature conservation. An attempt to regional differentiation.)

TÖRNQUIST, G.: Lokaliseringsförändringar inom svensk industri 1952–1960. Uppsala 1964.

WILLIAM-OLSSON, W.: Stockholm. Structure and development. I.G.U. Congress 1960. Uppsala 1960.

WINBERG, I. P.: Naturliga jordbruksområden i Sverige. — *K. Skogs. o. Lantbr. Akad. Tidskr.* 98 (1959) : 352–390. English summary. (Natural farming areas in Sweden.)

PLACE-NAME INDEX

On Colour Maps and text figures the national names have been used, e.g. Göta älv and Dalälven, the former in indefinite, the latter in definite form. In the text the definite article, which in the Scandinavian languages is placed at the end of the word, has usually been omitted and the English article added, e.g. the Dalälv, the Vestfjord (instead of Vestfjorden). Names of lakes are in their usual Scandinavian form, e.g. Storsjön. Common words which are parts of a geographical name have, as a rule, not been translated, but the English word, e.g. river, has sometimes been added. This has always been done for lakes, e.g. Lake Vänern, Lake Mjösa. All seas are named in English. In the text the Danish and Norwegian ø and æ have been used, on the maps the Swedish ö and ä. For Finland the Swedish names have, as a rule, been used only on pp. 6 and 7, and in the place-name index below.

Some nouns are the same in Danish, Norwegian and Swedish, e.g. dal (valley), fjell (mountain), nedre (lower), øvre (upper), sund (sound). Others are slightly different: bay = vik (N, S), vig (D); island = ø (D, S), øy (N); lake = sjø (N, S), sø (D); river = elv (D, N), älv (S); waterfall = foss (N), fors (S).

The corresponding Icelandic and Finnish names are: valley — dalur, laakso; mountain — fjall, tunturi; lower — neðri, ali; upper — efiri, yli; sound — sund, salmi; bay — vík, lahti; island — ey, saari; lake — vatn, järvi; river — á, joki; waterfall — foss, koski. In Icelandic names þ is pronounced as th in thousand, ð as th in mother.

For each place-name given below, the first figures indicate its location as shown on Plates, Text figures or Colour Maps. When location is not shown in any of these ways, the initial of the country and the county number (see pp. 6–7) have been added in brackets.

C.M. = Colour Map. The initial of the country is added in brackets. Pl = Plate. Tab = Table.

The letters peculiar to the Scandinavian alphabets have been systematized as follows: å as aa, ä and æ as ae, ö and ø as oe, ð as d and þ as th.

SCANDINAVIAN AND FINNISH TERMS[1]

aapa	164	gjá	211	landsby	76	sisu	156
alvar	296	glint	46	landskap	292	skärgård (S)	297
apalhraun	207	hällmark	296	lantalaiset	165	skifte	77
bolskifte	77	helluhraun	207	lapp	75	skjærgård (N)	212
botn	147	hytte	286	letto	164	solskifte	76
brisling	271	indmark (D)	147	lindá	213	storskifte	304
bruk	303	jätkä	190	ljesotundra	65	strandflat	46
by	76	jökulá	212	löväng	305	þúfa	210
dragá	213	jökulhlaup	212	mark	16	tind	47
eldborg	207	kambur	147	móberg	206	torp	167
enskifte	305	kirvesmän	156	moler	103	tún	232
fäbod	76	klint	113	neva	164	tunnland	167
fjäll (S)	45	klippfisk	271	nunatak	38	tunturi	64
fjell (N)	45	kog	113	nyskifte	169	turvekangas	164
fjellhei	64	kommunblock	299	palsa	165	udmark (D)	147
flá	210	korpi	164	ra	39	vaara	168
forte	77	laga skifte	305	räme	164	valkeajärvi	160
frälsejord	171	lagsagor	293	seter	76	vidde	238

----

[1]) Singularis

CONVERSION FACTORS

F°	C°
140	60
130	55
120	50
	45
110	40
100	35
90	30
80	25
70	20
60	15
50	10
40	5
30	0
20	5
10	10
0	15
10	20
20	25
30	30
	35
40	40

Length
1 millimetre (mm) . . . . = 0.039 inch
1 centimetre (cm) = 10 mm = 0.3937 inch
1 metre (m) = 100 cm . . . $\begin{cases} = 3.281 \text{ feet} \\ = 1.094 \text{ yards} \end{cases}$
1 kilometre (km) = 1000 m = 0.621 mile

Area
1 cm² . . . . = 0.155 square inch
1 m² . . . . $\begin{cases} = 10.76 \text{ square feet} \\ = 1.196 \text{ square yards} \end{cases}$
1 hectare (ha.) = 10 000 m² = 2.471 acres
1 km² = 100 ha. . . . . = 0.3861 square mile

Volume
1 cm³ . . . . = 0.061 cubic inch
1 m³ . . . . $\begin{cases} = 35.31 \text{ cubic feet} \\ = 1.308 \text{ cubic yards} \end{cases}$
1 litre (l) . . . . $\begin{cases} = 0.880 \text{ Imp. quart} \\ = 1.057 \text{ U.S. quarts} \end{cases}$
1 hectolitre (hl) = 100 l . . $\begin{cases} = 22.00 \text{ Imp. gallons} \\ = 26.42 \text{ U.S. gallons} \end{cases}$

Weight
1 kilogramme (kg) . . . . = 2.205 pounds
1 metric ton (1 000 kg) . . . $\begin{cases} = 1.102 \text{ short tons} \\ = 0.9842 \text{ long ton} \end{cases}$

Compound measures
1 m³/ha. . . . . = 14.29 cubic feet/acre
1 kg/ha. . . . . = 0.910 pounds/acre

Population density
1 inh./km² . . . . = 2.59 inh./square mile

Temperatures
$9/5 \, C° + 32$ . . . . = F°

Exchange rates 1965:
1 krone (Denmark) . . . . . . = 14.48 U.S. cents
1 new markka (Finland) . . = 31,25 —»—
1 króna (Iceland) . . . . . . = 2,33 —»—
1 krone (Norway) . . . . . . = 14.00 —»—
1 krona (Sweden) . . . . . . = 19.32 —»—

PHOTOGRAPHS

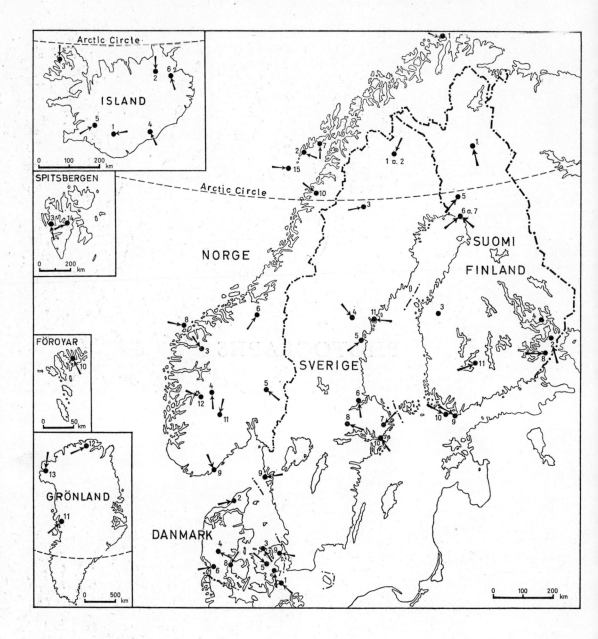

Photograph numbers correspond to chapter numbers, the arrows on the location map indicate the direction of photographing.

Plates 8.1 – 8.13 (Denmark)   Plates 11.1 – 11.15 (Norway)
   »   9.1 – 9.11 (Finland)   »   12.1 – 12.11 (Sweden)
   »   10.1 – 10.6 (Iceland)

Pl. 8.1: Limestone cliff in Møn. Senonian limestone and morainic deposits dislocated by ice pressure and modified by abrasion and weathering form the very varied cliff front. Beech forest covers the hummocky karst surface and the moraine which has slipped down gullies in the limestone cliff. The abrasion plain can be seen along the shoreline.

Pl. 8.2: The North Sea coast of North Jylland. The simplified shoreline is cut through morainic deposits, forming in the foreground the Lønstrup cliff. Cliff coast alternates with old heather-clad dunes in the background. Behind the dunes are scattered farms surrounded by heather moor. Near the coast is the fishing village of Lønstrup surrounded by holiday cottages and hotels. An inner and outer breaker zone reveal the presence of submerged sandbanks.

Pl. 8.3: Young hilly moraine landscape, North Sjælland. Marginal morainic hills with their longitudinal axis conforming to the line of the ice margin are typical of the young moraine landscape. The hummocky relief has been softened by more than 4000 years of cultivation. Depressions in the moraine contain lakes which are being infilled by vegetation. The steeper slopes are forested. In the foreground wheat, beyond it rotation grass.

Pl. 8.4: Outwash plain, West Jylland. In the foreground heather and oak-scrub, a remnant of the former forest; in the background reclaimed heath, characterized by shelter belts, conifer plantations and scattered farmsteads. In the upper right corner is a small recent agglomeration at a road crossing.

Pl. 8.5: Old village on moraine flat, Fjenneslev, Sjælland. The old village pattern with farmhouses grouped around the medieval church and the pond survives in spite of the enclosure movement. Farmsteads and farm buildings are set around courtyards. Some houses still have thatched roofs. The timber framing of the walls is concealed by whitewash.

Pl. 8.6: Ribe, the medieval western harbour of Denmark, formerly an estuarine port, is now 8 km inland because of salt marsh development. The cathedral is built of Rhineland tuff, the newer left-hand tower of locally made brick. As the old Danish town houses were timber-framed, with thatched roofs, Ribe has burned several times, but until recently the houses have been rebuilt in the old style. On the outskirts are small new factories.

Pl. 8.7: Landscape of the farmlands of South Sjælland. On the right the manor of Vemmetofte Kloster with extensive fields and forests surrounded by typical small farms. On the left Fakse limestone quarry where Danian coral limestone is worked. Most of the forest is deciduous, mainly beech, the darker patches are conifer plantations. Lower right, Fakse Bay and, left, the harbour village Fakse Ladeplads.

Pl. 8.8: The Lille Bælt bridge between Jylland (right) and Fyn carries rail, road and footways. It opened in 1935; the total length is 1178 m, the cantilever section 835 m and the head room under the middle span 33 m. The meandering Little Belt is a former river valley.

Pl. 8.9: København, the centre. In the foreground is Christiansborg Castle which contains the Parliament building and Royal Staterooms. On this island the first, 12th-century, fortress was built. Behind the channell which was København's first harbour, the site of the medieval city is indicated by the irregular street pattern. At the top right is the Cathedral in the 'quartier latin'. The City Hall lies at the top left, and beyond it is the urban development of the 19th century.

Pl. 8.10: Klakksvík, the most important fishing-centre and second largest town of the Faeroes, (3735 inhabitants, 1960) lies at the head of a fjord on Borðoy. In the background are table mountains with alternating basalt and tuff layers with, right, a glacially eroded cirque.

Pl. 8.11: Valley glacier, West Greenland (Kangerdluarssup Sermia, Umanak district). Ice masses flowing from the Greenland ice cap in a glacial trough with truncated spurs. Lateral and medial moraines are visible. The glacier-surface is split by crevasses and the steep gneiss-granitic valley walls by hanging valleys.

Pl. 8.12: Margin of a local ice cap, North Greenland. The edge of the ice cap in Etukussuks Valley, Peary Land, forms a steep wall in which horizontal lines indicate layers of dust and structure sheets. In the foreground is an outwash plain of coarse gravel. Note for scale the figure with rucksack.

Pl. 8.13: Plateau landscape, Inglefield Fjord, Thule district, North Greenland. The dog team is moving over an ice-covered fjord. Beyond is a table mountain composed of Eocambrian sandstone (Thule formation) and sculptured by normal erosion. Scree-cones lie at the base of the snow-filled gullies.

Pl. 9.1: Riesto village, Lappland, in the heart of the vast Poso-aapa bog (10 000 hectares) in the upper basin of the Kemi river. This pioneer settlement was started in the mid-19th century by settlers coming up the river. From 1969 it will be submerged as the Poso-aapa bog becomes covered by one of two large reservoirs for the upper Kemijoki hydro-electric scheme.

Pl. 9.2: Vaara (hill-top) settlement (Kesälahti) in the southeastern part of the Lake Region during the time of the hay harvest. Settlements and fields are situated on a morainic soil, rich in boulders and are surrounded by lower-lying forest.

Pl. 9.3: Flooded fields in southern Ostrobothnia where vast expanses along the rivers are regularly flooded in spring. Here, at the junction of Seinäjoki and Kyröjoki, up to 9000 hectares may be flooded. The fields are cut for hay which is stored in the numerous barns.

Pl. 9.4: Bundle-floating on Orivesi.

Pl. 9.5: Loose-floated timber is collected at a dam in the Kemi River (Petäjäskoski) and lowered by the log chute (bottom right) which takes 15 000 logs per hour. In 1959 nearly 5 million logs, corresponding to about 1 million m³ (solid) came down to the Petäjäskoski chute. The flow necessary for this is created by five electro-motors installed inside the multi-purpose booms. Loose-floating is being replaced by bundle-floating though hoisting of bundles over the dams slows down operations.

Pl. 9.6: Karihaara sawmill on an island at the mouth of the Kemi River, belonging to Kemi Oy. The company also owns pulp mills. The sawmill was originally founded in 1871 and has today, after several extensions and modernization an annual capacity of 50 000 to 60 000 standards. The timber stored in pounds in the foreground passes through the sorting plant in the middle distance to the timber intake of the sawmill to the right.

Pl. 9.7: Veitsiluoto sawmill at the mouth of the Kemi River. Boards ready for sale are stored in long rows (foreground) or in smaller blocks (behind the mill). In the sea the logs are stored behind booms.

Pl. 9.8: Kaukopää, Finland's largest pulp mill, on the southern shore of Lake Saimaa. In the foreground log-bundles which have been brought by tugs across the lake.

Pl. 9.9: Winter harbour of Hangö (Hanko), the second in importance after Turku in severe winters. A lane in the ice is kept open throughout the winter for shipping.

Pl. 9.10: Archipelago west of Hangö, with a village on a sandy island which is part of the second Salpausselkä. The villagers winter-fish off Gotland.

Pl. 9.11: Esker village (Kangasala) southeast of Tampere. One of the numerous medieval villages sited on eskers. The lake to the left of the church is in a kettle hole, formed by dead ice in the esker.

Pl. 10.1: After a period of quiescence since 1845 Iceland's most famous volcano, Hekla, began to erupt at 6 h 40 m on March 29 1947. Within 20 minutes the eruption column rose to 30 000 metres, but on the photo that was taken some hours later it rises to 10 000 metres, or to the tropopause. The finest ash was carried to Finland. The eruption lasted 13 months and the new lava covers 40 km². — In the Middle Ages Hekla enjoyed a legendary fame all over the Christian world as the Abode of the Condemned.

Pl. 10.2: The glacier river Jökulsá á Fjöllum has eroded a steep-walled canyon, guided by N-S running fault lines, through postglacial and interglacial basalt lava beds and intercalated sediment layers. The basalts are vertically jointed. The waterfall is Dettifoss, 44 m, the biggest in Iceland.

Pl. 10.3: The fishing village of Flateyri (550 inhab.), in the inner part of a fjord in the Vestfirðir area, is typically situated on a curved shingle spit. Its sheltered inner side forms a good natural harbour. The flat plateau-surface and the steep trap-featured walls rise to 700 m.

Pl. 10.4: Skeiðarársandur (1000 km²) is the biggest glacial outwash plain in Iceland. Over its eastern part flows Skeiðará, the prototype of a glacier river, which splits up into many braided streams. These constantly divide, rejoin and change their courses.

Pl. 10.5: þingvellir, site of Iceland's parliament 930—1800. Geologically þingvellir is a rift valley, part of the mid-Atlantic rift valley which crosses Iceland. In the background the Skjaldabreiður shield volcano.

Pl. 10.6: Burstarfell farm in Vopnafjörður, northeast Iceland, the homestead of a prosperous Icelandic peasant, was the typical dwelling of the 19th and the first decades of the 20th centuries — a symbol of the old Iceland.

Pl. 11.1: North Cape is one of several peninsulas on the exposed coast of Finnmark that protrude with precipitous cliffs into the Arctic Ocean. The plateau (about 300 m above sea level) is an extension of Finnmarksvidda. A tourist road connects the restaurant with Honningsvåg on the south side of Magerøy.

Pl. 11.2: Peaks, fjords, cirques and strandflat in Lofoten on Moskenesøy. The landforms result from local glaciation down to sea level. The peak on the left background is 850 m high. Reine fishing village is set on peninsulas and islands of the strandflat.

Pl. 11.3: Lake Loen is a continuation of Nordfjord. In the background is the plateau carrying Jostedals glacier, nearly 2000 m above sea level. Rock slides have caused disastrous floods especially in the flat valley bottom at the head of the lake. Small disused farms on sun-facing side appear as clearings in the birch woods.

Pl. 11.4: High fjell showing two levels near the Oslo—Bergen railway at Ustaoset. Frozen lake in foreground is c. 1000 m above sea level. Undulating surface in the centre is the northern part of Hardangervidda with regenerated surface of the sub-Cambrian peneplan. In the background upper plateau (about 1800 m above sea level) of Hallingskarvet, formed by overthrust igneous rocks, and resting upon soft Cambro-Silurian rocks, hence the precipitous front. — Village of huts (a hotel to the left) for skiing and summer vacations. Snow sheds protect station area.

Pl.11.5: Agriculture around Lake Mjøsa (124 m above sea level) is representative of Norway's best agricultural districts. Solid rocks are Cambro-Silurian; their schists and limestones contribute fertile soils to the ground-moraine. — Light cultivated land around Stange church is under grain, dark areas carry potatoes or fodder beet.

Pl. 11.6: Mountain farms in Sør-Trøndelag situated on sun-facing edge of plateau at about 450 m above sea level. Mountains in background c. 650 m. Mixtures of spruce and birch forest. Square courtyard between the farm buildings is typical of Trøndelag. In the foreground three farms.

Pl. 11.7 Sunday in Lofoten some decades ago. Line fishing boats in the harbour of Henningsvær, situated on small islands of strandflat off the 'Lofoten wall' of mountains.

Pl. 11.9: Brekkestø, a former ✝ port, now a popular holiday res the coast east of Kristiansand bare hills of southern Norway nate in creeks and coves, pro good sheltered harbours.

Pl. 11.8: Fishing for winter herring in rough seas off the coast of western Norway before the introduction of power block vessels. In foreground dories with catch made by purse seine.

Pl. 11.10: Glomfjord nitrate factory in Nordland is unusally sited on a shelf c. 100 m above sea level, and the hydro-electric plant is at the rocky fjord head. The transmission line is seen to the left behind the dwellings. — Liquid ammonia is stored in spherical tanks (on the right) and piped down to jetty (not visible) and shipped to Herøya, 828 nautical miles away.

Pl. 11.11: Power station and hydrogen plant at Vemork (Rjukan), where, during World War II, Norwegian commandos destroyed the heavy water plant. Right, the former water fall, 94 m high. The new power plant has a head of 300 m.

Pl. 11.12: Two valley generations. Owing to Tertiary uplift violent westward erosion has cut deeply into the old ('paleic') moderate relief. At the head of the young valley (Mabødalen) the river plunges down in a 163 m waterfall, Vøringfossen. The winding road, connecting Vestlandet and Østlandet across Hardangervidda since 1932, ascends 660 m in 12 km.

Pl.11.13: Kjerulfbreen, glacier calving in Trygghamna, a small fjord tributary to Isfjorden, Vest-Spitsbergen. Conic nunatak to the left is 325 m high, mountain in middle 525 m. Rocks are Carboniferous sandstones and schists. Photo from 1951.

Pl. 11.14: Tempelfjorden, Vest-Spitsbergen, an inner branch of Isfjorden. In the foreground horizontal Mesozoic rocks, at head of the fjord lies Postbreen (right) joining Tunabreen, in the background the ice-cap Negribreen (bre = glacier).

Pl. 11.15: The Røst archipelago at the southwestern tip of the Lofoten islands is a good example of the skerries which lie off the greater part of the Norwegian coast. The islands and skerries are part of the strandflat. The harbour (lower right), the main island, Heimlandet (left), and Stavøya (148 m) rising in the background. The surrounding rich fishing banks and an oceanic climate which makes possible outdoor grazing of sheep throughout the year, were formerly great assets.

Pl. 12.1: Kiruna mining town lies in the subalpine birch belt of Lake Luossa-järvi, 500 m above sea level. In the background, left, the Kirunavaara, the summit of which formerly reached 748 m. The Kiruna commune has an immense area (19 500 km²). Of its 29 600 inhabitants 21 500 live in the Kiruna mining town (1960).

Pl. 12.3: Forests and bogs of inner Nor west of Lake Hornavan in the southern of Norrbotten county. In the centre the älv, a tributary of the Ulme älv, in the ground Hornavan, Sweden's deepest 425 m above sea level. Open coniferous covers practically the whole area exce clearings where the best trees are le seeding.

Pl. 12.2: Kiirunavaara iron ore mine. The rich ore body of Kiirunavaara, north of the Arctic circle, is 3.5 km long and 100 m wide. Until 1959 it was an opencast mine, but underground workings are now more important, and Kiirunavaara is the world's largest iron mine with an annual production of over 12 million tons of ore.

Pl. 12.4: The Indalsälven valley near Sillre in Medelpad. In the background the undulating hill country so characteristic of southern and eastern Norrland. Settlements are mainly on the marine terraces of the left (sunny) side.

Pl. 12.5: Estuary of the Ljungan River in the Sundsvall wood-processing district with pulp mills on both shores, Svartvik in the foreground, and Essvik on the opposite (eastern) side. Between them is a deltaic island.

Pl. 12.6: An esker crossing Lake Hedesundafjärden on the Dalälv. In its lower course on the peneplane of the central Swedish Lowlands, the river forms such shallow lakes. Very long north-south trending eskers are characteristic of this part of Sweden.

Pl. 12.7: Vämblinge farm in Estuna parish in the eastern part of the Uppsala plain. Arable fields on marine clays cover most of the plain. The farm and the dispersed patches of forest, are situated on small mounds of outwash deposits and occasionally on rock outcrops.

Pl. 12.8 Surahammars Bruk on the Kolbäcksån river northwest of Västerås, an iron works in Bergslagen founded in the 17th century. From 1918 it is part of the ASEA-group, the leading Swedish enterprise in electro-technical engineering.

Pl. 12.9: Smögen on the central Bohuslän coast, once Sweden's most important fishing port and now a popular seaside resort. Erosion along joints in the granite produced a good natural harbour. The houses are massed near the shore on bare rock.

Pl. 12.10: The old nucleus of Stockholm is on an island between the two outlets of Lake Mälaren. In the foreground, covering the southern outlet, is "Slussen" (the lock) built in 1935 to carry the heavy north-south road traffic of Stockholm. In the background the tower of the Storkyrkan and the royal palace (right).

Pl. 12.11: Björnån, a hamlet in Nordingrå parish, Ångermanland near Härnösand where the undulating "Norrland terrain" reaches the coast. Between the hills arable fields on marine clays mainly in grass (not racks for hay drying). The farms and the small patches of barley and potatoes are on morainic deposits.

COLOUR MAPS

Colour Map 1. Relative relief, reduced from a scale of 1 : 2 000 000 (and greater scales for some parts). It shows height differences between peak, summit, crest or plateau edge and adjacent sea level, lake shore, valley bottom or plain. Within each contour the tints indicate the maximum slope. The map shows height differences of existing slopes, and not height differences within equally sized and spaced squares or circles, as is the case in different earlier published maps of relative relief.

For Denmark, Iceland, Norway, Sweden, and parts of Southern Finland the map is constructed from about 800 large-scale topographic sheets. Most of Finland (where modern maps are lacking) is based upon a map by V. Tanner (publ. in Oberflächengestaltung Finlands, Helsingfors 1938), a sketch map kindly drawn for this paper by H. Smeds and V. Okko, other maps and some observations by the present author. It has not been possible to give the Finnish part of the map the same accuracy as that of the other countries.

Colour Map 2. Solid rocks. The map is based on and generalized from the following maps:

DENMARK: Th. Sorgenfrei & O. Berthelsen: Rids af Danmarks historiske geologi. *Danm. geol. Unders.* III. Række, No. 31 (1954).

FINLAND: Kivilajikartta (Pre-Quaternary rocks), publ. in sheets, scale 1 : 400 000, 1900–58, by the Geological Survey of Finland. An unpublished map by A. Simonen (Geol. Survey of Finland), scale 1 : 2 000 000, has also been used.

ICELAND: A small-scale map for a school-atlas (Landabréfabók. Ríkisútgáfa námsbóka. Reykjavík 1962).

NORWAY: O. Holtedahl and J. A. Dons: Berggrunnskart over Norge (Pre-Quaternary rocks of Norway). *Norg. geol. Unders.* 164, Pl. 1 (1953), scale 1 : 1 000 000. Details have been added from S. Skjeseth: Contributions to the Geology of the Mjøsa Districts and the classical sparagmite area in Southern Norway. — *Norg. geol. Unders.* 220 (1963).

SWEDEN: Karta över Sveriges berggrund (Pre-Quaternary rocks of Sweden). *Sverig. geol. Unders.* Ser. Ba, No. 16 (1958), scale 1 : 1 000 000.

The geology of the Baltic sea-bed is based upon: A. Martinsson: The submarine morphology of the Baltic Cambro-Silurian area. *Bull. geol. Inst. Univ. Uppsala* 38 (1958). The small Cambro-Silurian remnants (fissures filled with Cambrian sandstones etc.) are taken from the last-mentioned paper and from a map by the present author (Rudberg 1954). The Cambro-Silurian of the Bothnian Sea are reproduced from V. Veltheim: On the pre-Quaternary geology of the bottom of the Bothnian Sea. — *Bull. Commn géol. Finl.* No. 200 (1962).

The map is more detailed than the text in order to provide more information for those interested in geology. To do justice to the geological survey of the great Archaean areas, a division into different rocktypes has been necessary; the Caledonian etc. have been similarly sub-divided.

Archaean rocks including Subjotnian and Jotnian are shown in pink, rspt. brown, with symbols for rocktypes, Proterozoic rocks in yellow, Caledonian rocks in blue and grey etc. In the sequence affected by the Caledonian orogeny, sediments of the geosyncline (non-metamorphic or metamorphic) are placed at the top, intrusive and volcanics in the middle, and rocks of partly unknown origin (but influenced by Caledonic tectonics) at the bottom.

Colour Map 3. Superficial deposits. The map is based on and generalized from the following maps:

DENMARK: Landskabskort over Danmark (Geomorphological map of Denmark), scale 1 : 750 000, in Atlas of Denmark, Vol. I, (1949).

ICELAND: Jarðvegskort af Íslandi (Soil map of Iceland), scale 1 : 750 000, adapted by University Research Institute, Reykjavík, from an unpublished paper by Dr. I. J. Nygard. Map prepared by Cartographic Division, Soil Conservation Service, U.S.D.A. Printed by U.S. Geological Survey 1959 and in Björn Johannesson: The soils of Iceland, Reykjavík 1960.

FINLAND: Superficial Deposits, scale 1 : 2 000 000, in Atlas of Finland 1960, 3–4.

NORWAY: O. Holtedahl and B. G. Andersen: Glacialgeologisk kart over Norge (Glacial geology of Norway). *Norg. geol. Unders.* 164, Pl. 16 (1953). Two unpublished maps have also been used: Oversiktskart over Norges jordarter (General map of the Quaternary deposits of Norway) by G. Holmsen 1949, and Quaternary deposits of Norway, compiled by R. W. Feyling-Hanssen 1959.

SWEDEN: Karta över Sveriges jordarter (Quaternary deposits of Sweden), publ. in *Sverig. geol. Unders.* Ser. Ba, No. 17 (1958), scale 1 : 1 000 000.

Limits of exposed bedrock and frost-shattered areas in Sweden by the present author.

Colour Maps 4 and 5. Winter, Summer. The data from Norway and Sweden are means for the period 1901–30, for Denmark and Finland as specified in the references below:

DENMARK: Det Danske Meteorologiske Institut: Danmarks Klima (1876–1925). København 1938.

FINLAND: Osmo Kolkki: Temperaturkarten und Tabellen von Finland für den Zeitraum 1921–50. Meteorolog. Zentralanstalt: Beilage z. Met. Jahrbuch für Finnland, Band. 50, Teil 1–1950. Helsinki 1959.

NORWAY: Det Norske Meteorologiske Institutt: Lufttemperaturen i Norge 1861–1955. Oslo 1957.

SWEDEN: Svenska Sällskapet för Antropologi och Geografi: Atlas över Sverige (27–28). Stockholm 1952. Sveriges Meteorologiska och Hydrologiska Institut: Meddelanden från Klimatavdelingen. Nr. 11.1 – 11.2 (1951).

Sea surface temperatures:

1. Wolfgang Krauss: Temperatur, Salzgehalt und Dichte an der Oberfläche des Atlantischen Ozeans. Berlin 1958.

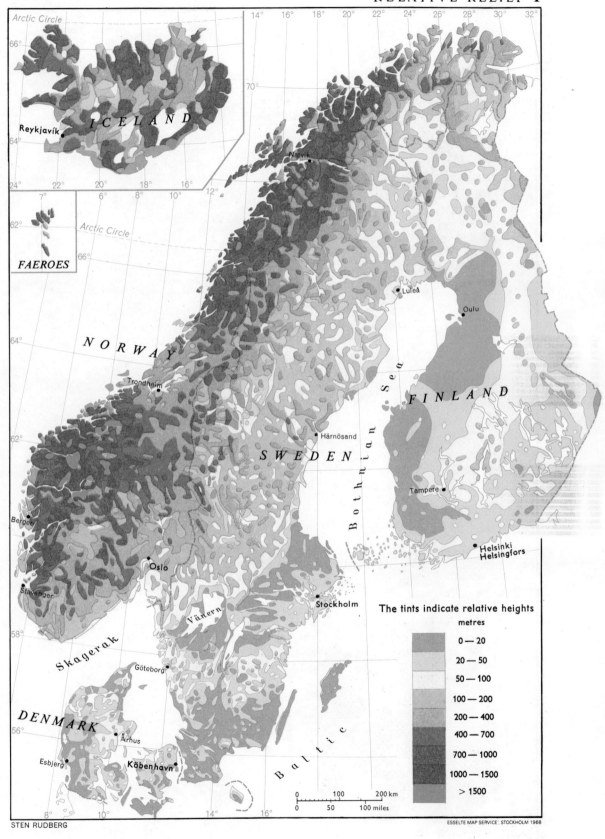

Arctic Circle
66°
64°
I C E L A N D
Reykjavík
24° 22° 20° 18° 16°

7°
62°
Arctic Circle
66°
FAEROES

Arctic Circle
66°
70°
Narvik
Luleå
Oulu
N O R W A Y
64°
Trondheim
F I N L A N D
62°
Härnösand
S W E D E N
Bergen
Tampere
Oslo
Stavanger
Vänern
Stockholm
Helsinki
Helsingfors
B o t h n i a n S e a

58°
Skagerak
Göteborg
B a l t i c
D E N M A R K
56°
Århus
Esbjerg
København

14° 16° 18° 20° 22° 24° 26° 28° 30° 32°

The tints indicate relative heights
metres

	0 — 20
	20 — 50
	50 — 100
	100 — 200
	200 — 400
	400 — 700
	700 — 1000
	1000 — 1500
	> 1500

0   100   200 km
0   50   100 miles

STEN RUDBERG

ESSELTE MAP SERVICE, STOCKHOLM 1968

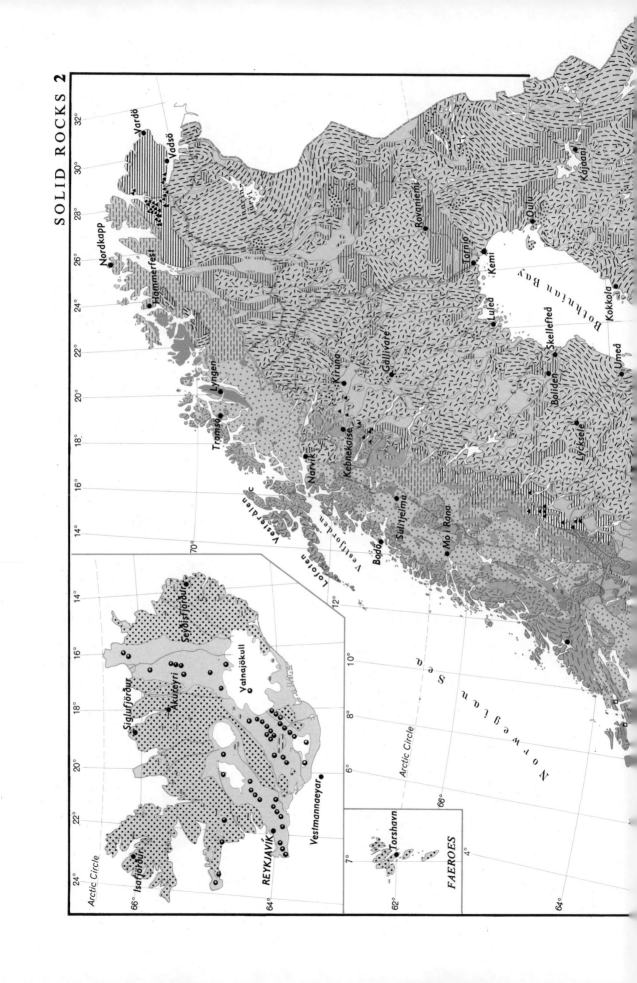

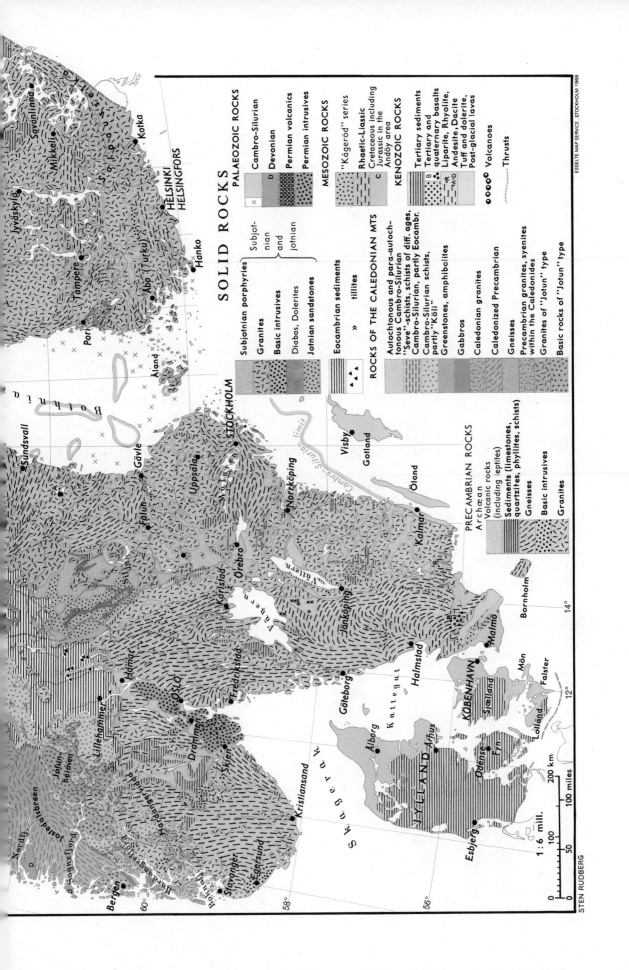

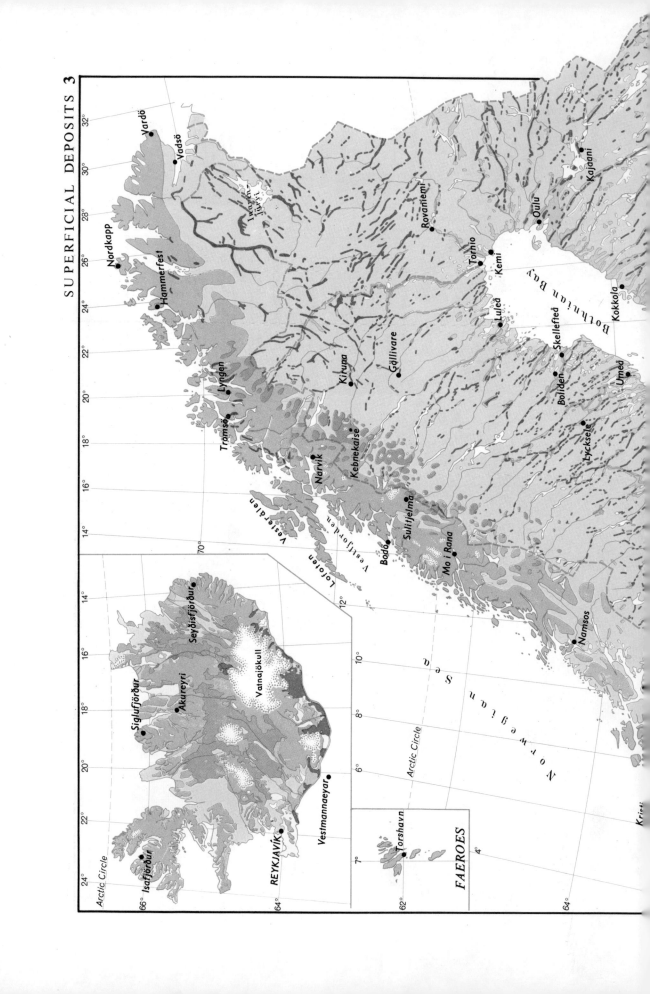

Vardö

Vadsö

Nordkapp

Hammerfest

Inqvén Jgvif

Rovaniemi

Kajaani

Oulu

Tornio

Kemi

Lyngen

Kiruna

Gällivare

Luleå

Bothnian Bay

Kokkola

Tromsö

Skellefteå

Umeå

Boliden

Narvik

Kebnekaise

Lycksele

Vesterålen

Bodö

Sulitjelma

Lofoten

Vestfjorden

Mo i Rana

Namsos

70°

Seyðisfjörður

Akureyri

Vatnajökull

Siglufjörður

N o r w e g i a n   S e a

Arctic Circle

Ísafjörður

REYKJAVÍK

Vestmannaeyar

Arctic Circle

Torshavn

FAEROES

Kristi

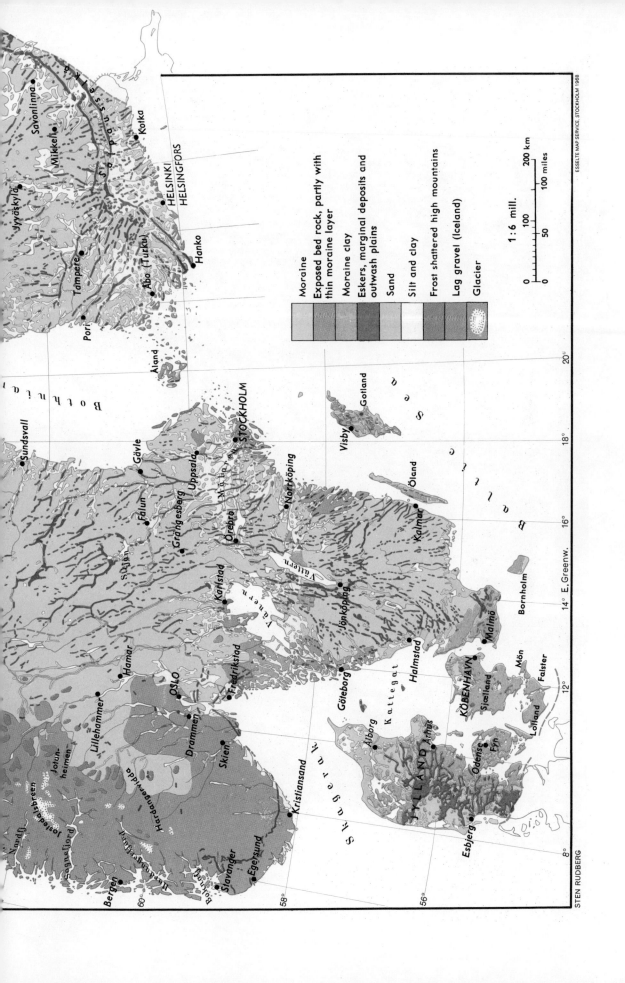

Moraine

Exposed bed rock, partly with
thin moraine layer

Moraine clay

Eskers, marginal deposits and
outwash plains

Sand

Silt and clay

Frost shattered high mountains

Lag gravel (Iceland)

Glacier

1 : 6 mill.

| 0 | | 100 | | 200 km |

| 0 | 50 | 100 miles | | |

ESSELTE MAP SERVICE, STOCKHOLM 1968

STEN RUDBERG

Savonlinna
Mikkeli
Jyväskylä
Kotka
Tampere
HELSINKI
HELSINGFORS
Pori
Åbo (Turku)
Hanko
Åland

Sundsvall
Gävle
Falun
Uppsala
Grängesberg
STOCKHOLM
Mälaren
Örebro
Norrköping
Visby
Gotland
Öland
Kalmar

Vättern
Vänern
Karlstad
Jönköping
Hamar
OSLO
Fredrikstad
Göteborg
Halmstad
Drammen
Skien
Malmö
Bornholm
Kristiansand
KØBENHAVN
Ålborg
Sjælland
Mön
Falster
Lolland
Fyn
Odense
Århus
JYLLAND
Esbjerg

Bergen
Jotunheimen
Lillehammer
Hardangervidda
Josedalsbreen
Sognefjord
Nordfj
Langfjellene
Hanko
Stavanger
Egersund

Bothnia

Baltic Sea

Kattegat

Skagerrak

60°
58°
56°

8°
12°
14° E. Greenw.
16°
18°
20°

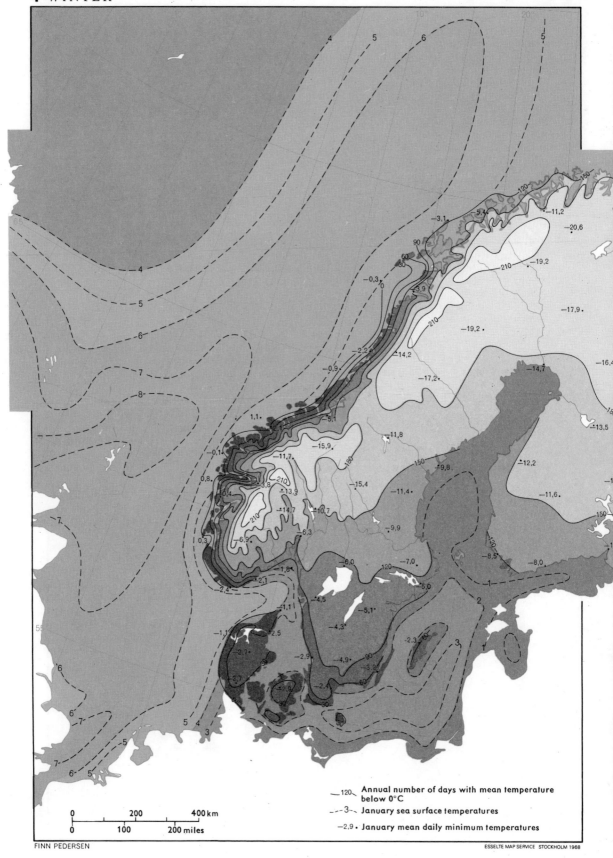

_120_ Annual number of days with mean temperature
below 0°C

--_3_-- January sea surface temperatures

-2,9• January mean daily minimum temperatures

0   200   400 km

0   100   200 miles

FINN PEDERSEN   ESSELTE MAP SERVICE STOCKHOLM 1968

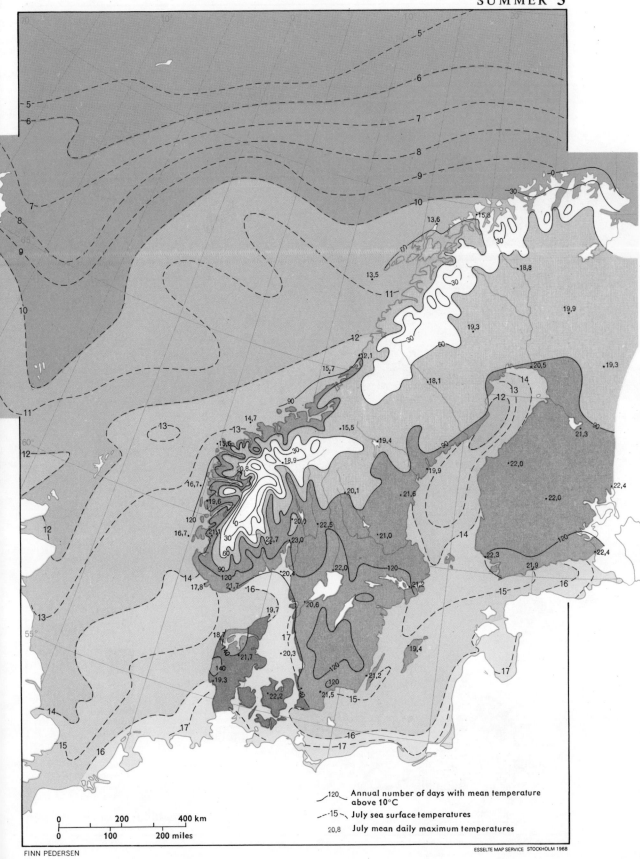

120   Annual number of days with mean temperature above 10°C

-15-   July sea surface temperatures

20,8   July mean daily maximum temperatures

0   200   400 km

0   100   200 miles

FINN PEDERSEN

ESSELTE MAP SERVICE STOCKHOLM 1968

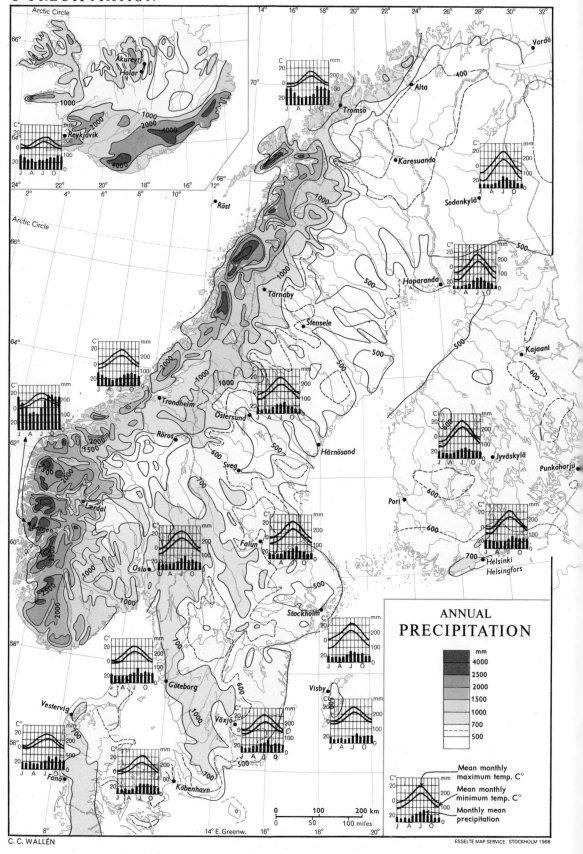

ANNUAL
PRECIPITATION

mm
4000
2500
2000
1500
1000
700
500

Mean monthly
maximum temp. C°

Mean monthly
minimum temp. C°

Monthly mean
precipitation

C. C. WALLÉN

ESSELTE MAP SERVICE . STOCKHOLM 1968

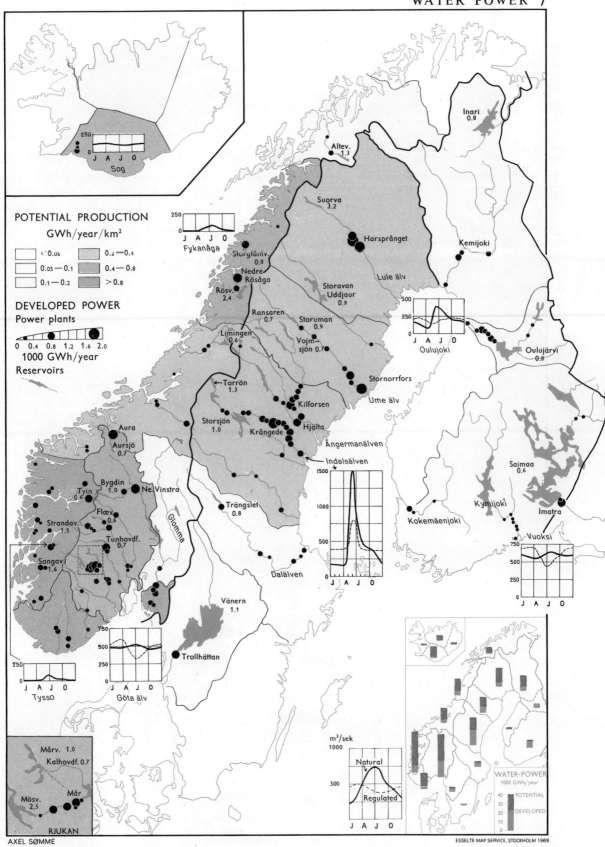

Sog

POTENTIAL PRODUCTION
GWh/year/km²

< 0.05	0.2—0.4
0.05—0.1	0.4—0.8
0.1—0.2	> 0.8

DEVELOPED POWER
Power plants

0 0.4 0.8 1.2 1.6 2.0
1000 GWh/year
Reservoirs

Inari
0.8

Altev.
1.3

Suorva
3.2

Harsprånget

Kemijoki

Fykanåga

Storglåmv.
0.8

Nedre
Rösåga

Rösv.
2.4

Storavan
Uddjaur
0.9

Lule älv

Ransaren
0.7

Storuman
0.9

Vojm-
sjön 0.7

Oulujoki

Oulujärvi
0.8

Limingen
0.6

Torrön
1.3

Stornorrfors

Ume älv

Kilforsen

Storsjön
1.0

Krångede

Hjälta

Ångermanälven

Indalsälven

Aura

Aursjö
0.7

Bygdin
1.0

Ne.Vinstra

Tyin
0.6

Flæv.
0.6

Trängslet
0.8

Saimaa
0.6

Kymijoki

Imatra

Kokemäenjoki

Strandav.
1.5

Tunhovdf.
0.7

Songav
1.6

Glomma

Dalälven

Vuoksi

Vänern
1.1

Trollhättan

Tysso

Göta älv

Mårv. 1.0
Kalhovdf. 0.7

Mår

Mösv.
2.5

RJUKAN

m³/sek
1000

Natural

500

Regulated

WATER-POWER
1000 GWh/year

40	POTENTIAL
30	
20	DEVELOPED
10	
0	

AXEL SØMME

ESSELTE MAP SERVICE, STOCKHOLM 1968

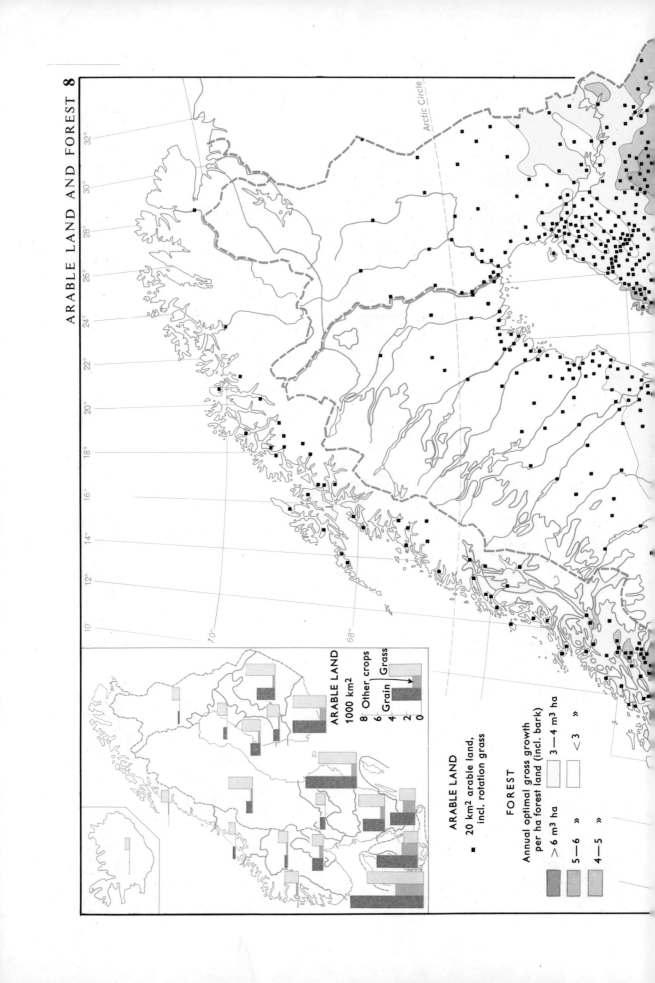

ARABLE LAND AND FOREST 8

Arctic Circle

ARABLE LAND
■ 20 km² arable land,
incl. rotation grass

ARABLE LAND
1000 km²

8
6
4
2
0

Other crops
Grain | Grass

FOREST
Annual optimal gross growth
per ha forest land (incl. bark)

>6 m³ ha   3—4 m³ ha
5—6 »   <3 »
4—5 »

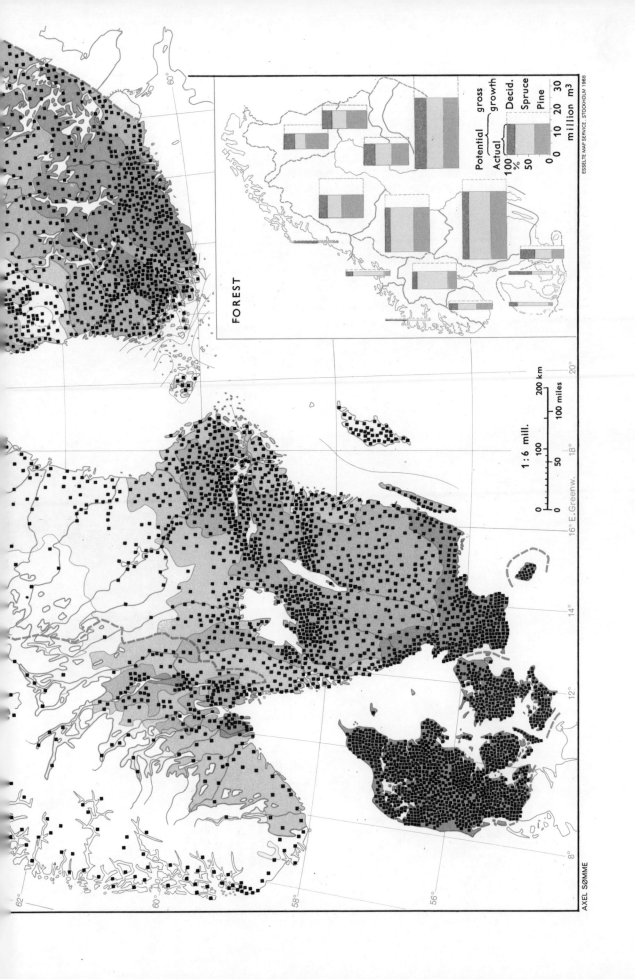

FOREST

1 : 6 mill.

0   100   200 km
0   50   100 miles

16° E. Greenw.

Potential } gross growth
Actual   }

Decid.
Spruce
Pine

100   50   0
%

0   10   20   30
million m³

ESSELTE MAP SERVICE. STOCKHOLM 1968

AXEL SØMME

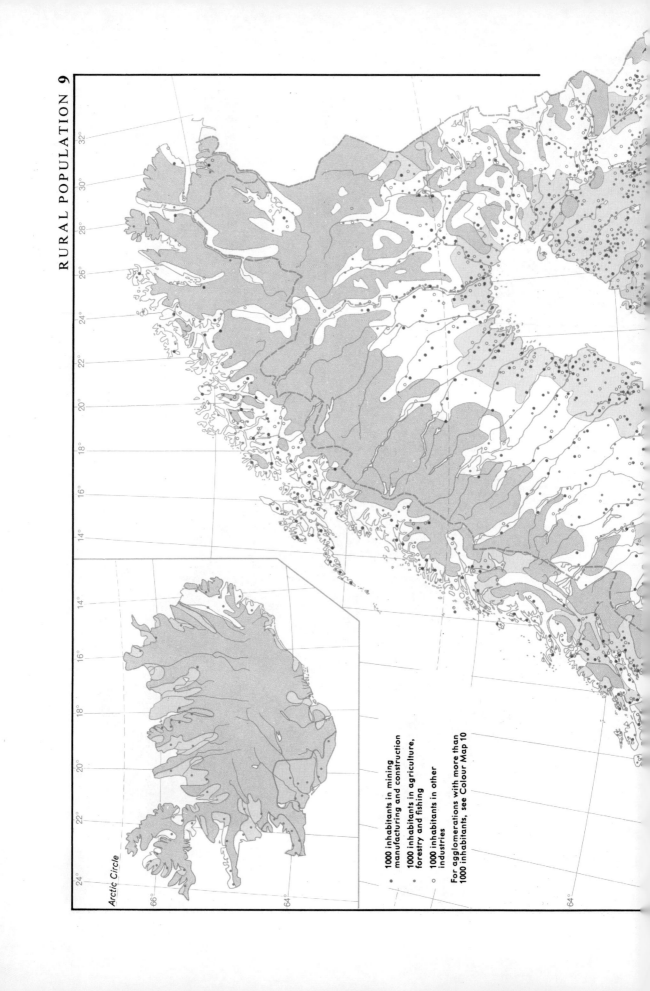

Arctic Circle

1000 inhabitants in mining
manufacturing and construction

1000 inhabitants in agriculture,
forestry and fishing

1000 inhabitants in other
industries

For agglomerations with more than
1000 inhabitants, see Colour Map 10

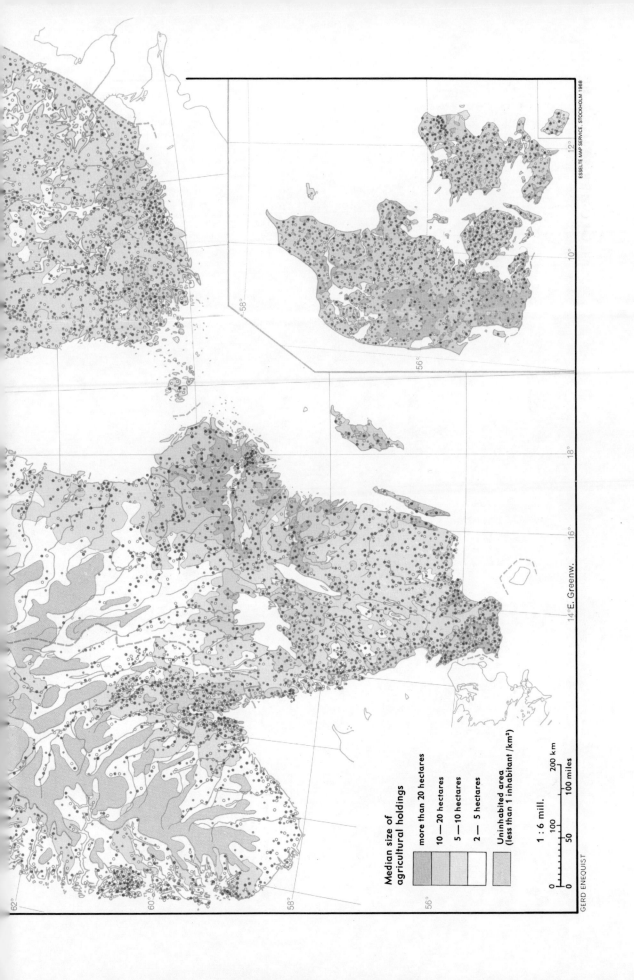

Median size of
agricultural holdings

more than 20 hectares

10 — 20 hectares

5 — 10 hectares

2 — 5 hectares

Uninhabited area
(less than 1 inhabitant /km²)

1 : 6 mill.

```
0        50      100
0                    100 miles
0                    200 km
```

GERD ENEQUIST

ESSELTE MAP SERVICE. STOCKHOLM 1968

14°E. Greenw.

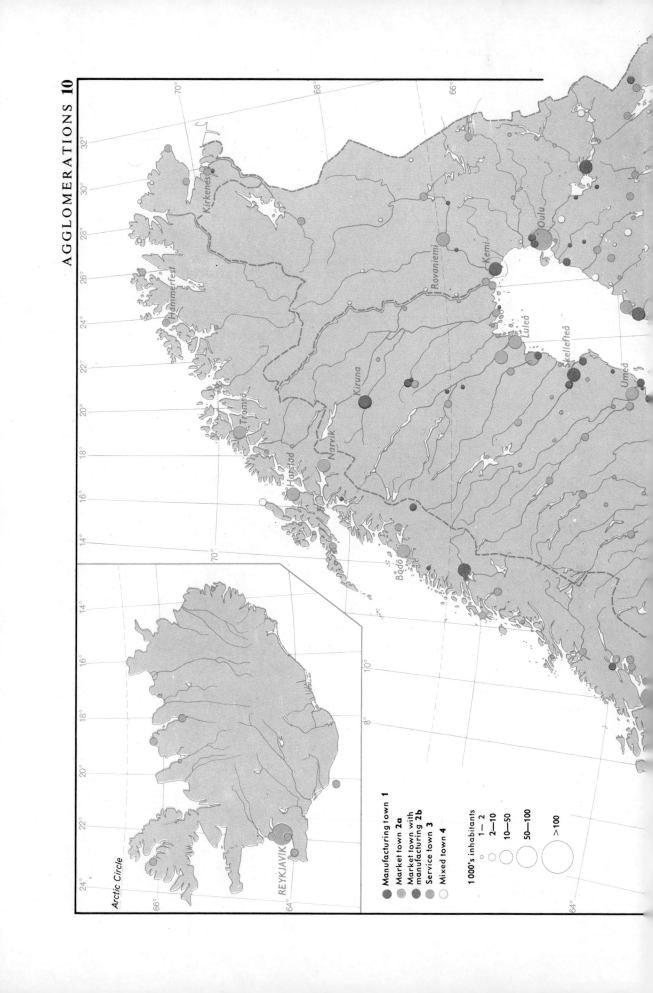

AGGLOMERATIONS 10

Arctic Circle

REYKJAVIK

Kirkenes
Hammerfest
Tromsø
Harstad
Narvik
Bodø
Kiruna
Rovaniemi
Kemi
Oulu
Luleå
Skellefteå
Umeå

Manufacturing town **1**
Market town **2a**
Market town with manufacturing **2b**
Service town **3**
Mixed town **4**

1000's inhabitants
1— 2
2—10
10—50
50—100
>100

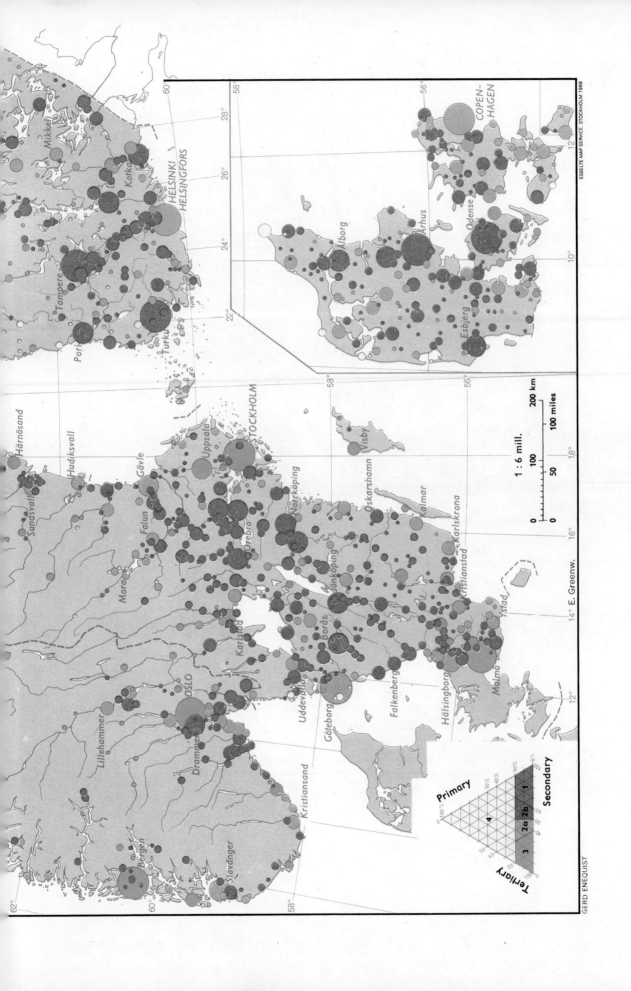

GERD ENEQUIST

ESSELTE MAP SERVICE, STOCKHOLM 1968

1 : 6 mill.

COPEN-
HAGEN

HELSINKI
HELSINGFORS

STOCKHOLM

OSLO

Mikkel
Kotka
Tampere
Pori
Turku

Härnösand
Hudiksvall
Sundsvall
Gävle
Falun
Mora
Uppsala
Örebro
Norrköping
Karlstad
Borås
Oskarshamn
Visby
Kalmar
Jönköping
Karlskrona
Kristianstad
Ystad
Malmö
Hälsingborg
Falkenberg
Göteborg
Uddevalla
Kristiansand
Drammen
Lillehammer
Bergen
Stavanger

Ålborg
Århus
Odense
Esbjerg

Primary

Secondary

Tertiary

100%
80%
60%
50%
40%
20%

3   2a 2b 1

4

0   50   100   200 km
0   50   100 miles

14° E. Greenw.

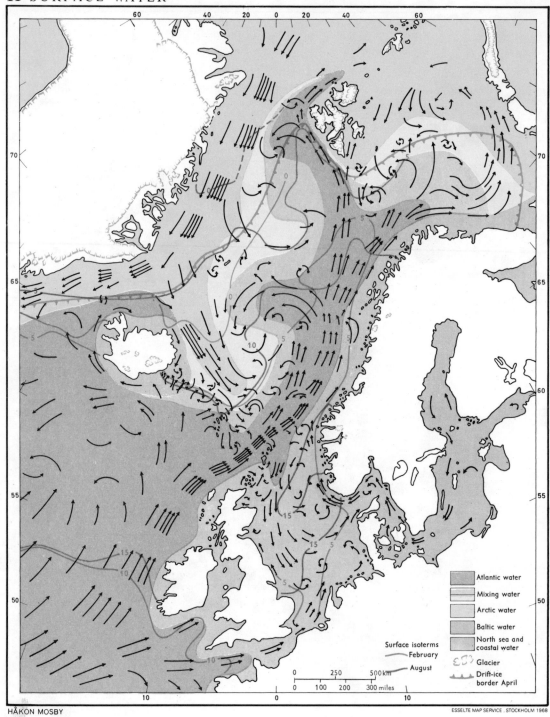

Atlantic water
Mixing water
Arctic water
Baltic water
North sea and coastal water

Surface isoterms
— February
— August

Glacier
Drift-ice border April

0   250   500km
0 100 200 300 miles

HÅKON MOSBY

ESSELTE MAP SERVICE . STOCKHOLM 1968

2. Günther Böhnecke und Günter Dietrich: Monats-
karten der Oberflächentemperatur für die Nord-
und Ostsee und die angrenzenden Gewässer. Ham-
burg 1951.

Colour Map 6. Mean annual precipitation.

Colour Map 7. Water-power resources. The
shading on the main map shows the yearly potential
production in 18 major regions at mean discharge expressed in GWh per km^2 (1 GWh $=$ 10^9 Wh $=$ 10^6
kWh). The black circles indicate the potential production of the power plants in operation in 1960 assuming
a mean discharge. In Finland and Iceland the regions
coincide with catchment areas, in Norway and Sweden,
with a few exceptions, with counties.

The power plants shown on the map represent about
80 per cent of the total production in the respective
countries. Power plants which produce 1 000 million
kWh or more are named on the map. All reservoirs
with a storage capacity equalling a yearly production
of 300 mill. kWh have been indicated, and those with
a production of 600 mill. kWh or more are named.
For convenience production from stored water has
been indicated as a multiple of storage capacity and
height above sea level. Harnessing of the river below
the dam, varying from intensive (Indalsälven) to
slight use (Glomma), has not been taken into account.

Natural and regulated flow is shown by diagrams
for selected rivers (for Fykanåga, Sog and Tysso natural flow only). Four of them represent special conditions: The prolonged summer flood of the Fykanåga comes from the Svartisen glacier; the even, natural
flow of the unharnessed Sog is derived from a catchment area of water-holding lavas, and the even flow of
the Göta river and Vuoksi are due to the storage capacity of Lake Vänern and Lake Saimaa. The Tysso,
Indalsälven and Oulujoki rivers are representative of
large areas.

The inset map shows potential and developed production by regions, their number being reduced from 9
to 6 for Norway. The potentialities of Lake Inari, used
in Norwegian and Russian power plants on the lower
Pasvik river, are not included in the Finnish water-
power resources. Totals are given below.

	Potential Developed 1960 at mean discharge		Actual production 1960 1966	
		1 000 GWh		
Finland	17	8	5.1	9.8
Iceland	21	0.7	0.5	0.6
Norway	149	34	31	48
Sweden	80	34	31	46

Colour Map 8. Arable land and forests. The
arable land in 1950 is shown by squares on the same
scale as the map. The optimal gross growth of timber
is approximately indicated in cubic metres including
bark per hectare of forest land, assuming normal
(fully stocked) tree density and age distribution (cf.
Fig. 7.3 p. 89). For Norway and Sweden the map is
based on averages for minor administrative areas, for
Finland on sampling plots. The forest survey data
used are summarized in Table 7.8, p. 89.

An inset map (upper left) shows the distribution of
the arable land on major regions in 1960. Another inset map (lower right) summarizes for major regions
the actual and estimated optimal gross growth. No
data are available for West and North Norway (left
in white on main map), but rough estimates for both
regions are given on this inset map. All values for
optimal gross growth are exclusive of production
from newly reclaimed forest area (bogs, barren land).

Colour Map 9. Rural population 1960. The
map shows, by dots representing 1 000 inhabitants,
population outside agglomerations with over 1 000
inhabitants (shown on C.M. 10), distributed by occupations. As the Norwegian and Swedish statistics give
only the occupational distribution of the active population, figures for the total population in these countries have been estimated.

The dots have been spaced according to large-scale
population maps (Statistisk Sentralbyrå: Bosettingskart over Norge, 1955, Atlas over Danmark II, be-
folkningen, 1961, Suomen kartasto, 1960, and various
maps of Sweden). In sparsely settled areas particularly,
1 000 inhabitant-dots cannot give a true picture of
population distribution.

Median values for the size of agricultural holdings
of over 2 ha. by rural districts are shown by shading.
Data are from the agricultural censuses of Finland
and Norway (1959) and Sweden (1961). As no figures
are available for Denmark, map no. 55 in Kampp:
Landbrugsgeografiske Studier over Danmark, 1959,
has been used. For Iceland the map is based on information supplied by Hagstofa Islands.

*Colour Map. 10. Size and economic type of ag-
glomerations, 1960.* All agglomerations with more
than 1 000 inhabitants, irrespective of legal status, are
represented on the map and classified according to
their economic type. Suburbs are included in the population of towns, and the occupational structure of
the suburb is taken into account as far as possible in
determining the economic type of the town. The
grouping into economic types is based on the system
shown in the triangle diagram, where three major economic types are considered: Primary (agriculture, forestry and fishing), Secondary (manufacturing, mining
and construction) and Tertiary (communications, trade
and services). Domestic work and unspecified occupations are excluded.

Five types of agglomerations have been defined:
1. Manufacturing town with over 60% of their population in manufacturing.
2. Market towns, divided into:
   a. where services predominate but do not reach
      60%,
   b. where manufacturing predominates but does not
      reach 60%.
3. Service towns with over 60% of their population
   in service industries.
4. Mixed towns (very few) with over 20% in agriculture, farming or fishing.

Colour Map 11. Surface waters.